M — 4 — 3 M/a

D1420620

VERTEBRATE PALEONTOLOGY

THE UNIVERSITY OF CHICAGO PRESS
CHICAGO, ILLINOIS

—

THE BAKER & TAYLOR COMPANY
NEW YORK

THE CAMBRIDGE UNIVERSITY PRESS
LONDON

THE MARUZEN-KABUSHIKI-KAISHA
TOKYO, OSAKA, KYOTO, FUKUOKA, SENDAI

THE COMMERCIAL PRESS, LIMITED
SHANGHAI

VERTEBRATE PALEONTOLOGY

By

ALFRED SHERWOOD ROMER

Professor of Vertebrate Paleontology in the
University of Chicago

THE UNIVERSITY OF CHICAGO PRESS
CHICAGO · ILLINOIS

COMPOSED AND PRINTED BY THE UNIVERSITY OF CHICAGO PRESS
CHICAGO, ILLINOIS, U.S.A.

PREFACE

The story of vertebrate evolution as revealed by the study of fossils is one of interest not only to the paleontologist but to those engaged in other branches of science—to the geologist and to the worker in many fields of biology. The present volume was undertaken because of the lack of any modern work in English dealing with the subject as a whole. Smith Woodward's excellent *Outlines of Vertebrate Paleontology* dates from the late nineties; and the English edition of Zittel's excellent reference work, *Grundzüge der Paläontologie*, is based on a German edition nearly as old.[1] During recent decades our knowledge of vertebrate fossils has increased greatly, but the new facts and the new concepts based on them have been but slowly taken up in general biological or geological literature.

The most general appeal of vertebrate paleontology lies in the evolutionary story it presents. In consequence the material is here arranged as a group-by-group treatment of the vertebrates, tracing out the various ramifications of the family tree.

Our knowledge of extinct vertebrates is based primarily upon their preserved skeletal remains; and the anatomical study of these remains is the solid foundation from which alone can arise any treatment of these forms from the point of view of taxonomy, stratigraphy, ecology, or evolution. No attempt has been made here to go into minutiae, but I have not hesitated to describe at some length the major structural features of the various groups encountered.

Although the relationships of many groups are quite uncertain or in dispute, it has been necessary to adopt, tentatively at least, some one theory in each case to establish an order of treatment and set up a usable classification. The phylogenetic framework and the taxonomic scheme here established upon it are, for the most part, conservative. In general I have adopted the theories of relationships now current among workers in the various fields, and have departed from common usages only where this has been necessitated by recent investigations.

To the worker in any field the history of his subject, the great figures in the science, and their individual accomplishments are matters of considerable interest. The writer feels, however, that for the beginner such a historical treatment is not particularly appropriate; it is with the history of animals, not scientists, that he is to deal. In consequence, personalities have been omitted from the text. For the more advanced student who wishes to delve into the original literature a knowledge of the workers and their achievements is of considerable interest and

[1] A revision of the volume dealing with the lower vertebrates appeared while the present work was in press.

importance. With this in mind, brief historical notes have been introduced into the bibliography.

The bibliography makes no pretense of comprehensiveness and includes only a restricted list of the more important or more useful works. Particular attention has been given to monographic works dealing adequately with entire groups, to recent papers giving the latest advances in the subject, to papers containing adequate bibliographies, and especially to works which contain adequate illustrations of a group or of representative forms.

As regards illustrations, a complete skeleton and skull of a representative member of each group is shown whenever possible, and in addition other significant or diagnostic skeletal details, such as the limbs or teeth. In order to facilitate comparison of forms, original figures have been reversed in numerous cases, so that all skulls and skeletons are viewed from the right, and all limb bones are of the right side; in the mammals upper dentitions are of the right side, while the lower dentitions are from the left jaw ramus, to afford easier understanding of occlusional relations. The skeletons are almost all direct copies of well-known figures. The other illustrations are, for the most part, new drawings, although the majority are adapted from pre-existing figures. In contrast to the illustrations in an original scientific paper, which are generally dedicated to the faithful portrayal of often imperfect material, those in this volume aim to give the reader as complete a picture as possible of the structure of the forms portrayed. With this in mind, missing portions of skulls have been freely restored and composite restorations attempted in many cases, although the writer thereby lays himself open to possible criticism.

I am greatly indebted to many friends for assistance in the preparation of this volume. Dr. W. K. Gregory, of the American Museum of Natural History, has read nearly the entire work and has offered many helpful and stimulating criticisms. Dr. F. B. Loomis, of Amherst College, and Dr. G. G. Simpson, of the American Museum, have read the chapters dealing with mammals and have saved me from numerous sins both of commission and of omission. My colleagues Drs. R. T. Chamberlin, J Harlen Bretz, and Carey Croneis have read portions of the manuscript; and Mr. Bryan Patterson, of the Field Museum of Natural History, has aided in the chapters on South American ungulates and edentates.

The greater part of the original illustrations, particularly the skull figures, are the work of Mr. L. I. Price, to whom I am indebted for much painstaking work as a collaborator rather than merely as an illustrator. Mr. Brandon Grove has assisted greatly with photographic work.

Finally, and most greatly, I am indebted to my wife, Ruth Hibbard Romer, for her unfailing aid throughout the course of preparation of this book.

ALFRED SHERWOOD ROMER

CONTENTS

CHAPTER   PAGE

I. INTRODUCTORY 1

II. PRIMITIVE JAWLESS VERTEBRATES 22

III. SHARK-LIKE FISHES 35

IV. BONY FISHES 62

V. AMPHIBIANS 93

VI. PRIMITIVE REPTILES 120

VII. VARIED REPTILIAN TYPES 141

VIII. RULING REPTILES 163

IX. DINOSAURS 179

X. BIRDS 206

XI. MAMMAL-LIKE REPTILES 220

XII. THE STRUCTURE OF MAMMALS 239

XIII. PRIMITIVE MAMMALS 255

XIV. PLACENTAL ORIGINS; INSECTIVORES; BATS 268

XV. CARNIVORES 279

XVI. ARCHAIC UNGULATE GROUPS 297

XVII. PERISSODACTYLS 319

XVIII. ARTIODACTYLS 339

XIX. SUBUNGULATES 366

XX. EDENTATES 381

XXI. WHALES 392

XXII. RODENTS 400

XXIII. PRIMATES 411

A SYNOPTIC CLASSIFICATION OF VERTEBRATES 433

BIBLIOGRAPHY 451

INDEX 475

vii

CHAPTER I
INTRODUCTORY

The present work gives a brief account of the history of vertebrates as revealed in the fossil record. We shall find it difficult, however, to confine ourselves strictly to fossil animals, for our subject is intimately related to many other scientific fields.

Vertebrate paleontology is essentially a biological science. To the paleontologist the animals of the present constitute but a brief cross-section of the vertebrate story. To him a separation of fossils from the modern forms which have descended from extinct types and are destined to become the fossils of the future would seem extremely artificial. Paleontology has much to learn from many other biological fields and much to give in return. With anatomy and evolutionary studies the connections are particularly close, while not only the taxonomist and ecologist but even workers in such seemingly remote fields as physiology and medicine may benefit from the possession of a historical background.

Paleontology is also intimately connected with the history of the earth itself, the field of historical geology. In the study of fossil human types the field of the vertebrate paleontologist overlaps that of the anthropologist. And, finally, the study of vertebrate evolution is history of a sort—but a history written in terms of millions of years rather than decades or centuries.

Since it is probable that this book will fall into the hands of readers with varied backgrounds, this opening chapter is devoted to a number of topics which may well be omitted by those grounded in the fundamentals of biology or geology.

Vertebrate fossils.—But few of the countless individual animals of the past have been preserved to us as fossils. When a land animal dies today, its remains are usually scattered and destroyed by flesh-eaters or disintegrated by plant roots, soil acids, and bacterial action. Similar conditions no doubt were present in the past.

More exceptionally and more fortunately, a dead animal may be buried deep in a deposit of mud or sand, where the soft parts will usually quickly rot away but where the skeleton will be left surrounded by a gradually hardening matrix. The bony matter may persist and become gradually altered into a complex type of mineral in which much of the original constituents of the bone remain. Meanwhile the cavities are in the course of time filled by minerals brought in in solution, so that the originally porous bone becomes a heavy solid structure. But since the mineral matter filling the cavities is usually of a different nature from that into which the substance of the bone has been transformed, fossil bones, when sectioned and studied microscopically, usually show in perfect fashion the structural details of the original.

The softer portions of the body are sometimes, although much more rarely, preserved. Certain forms recently extinct, such as the dodo or the giant moas of New Zealand, may be considered as fossils of a sort, although their bones are usually but little altered chemically; in these cases feathers, ligaments, and other soft parts have been preserved. In America gigantic ground sloths are entirely extinct, and many of their remains are perfectly orthodox fossils; but in several instances skeletons have been found with patches of skin and hair still adherent. Extinct mammoths have been completely preserved in natural "cold storage" in the Siberian tundras, while two woolly rhinoceroses have been found pickled in entirety in a Galician oil seep.

But even among much more ancient forms traces of soft parts are occasionally found. Specimens crushed flat in shales have in many cases preserved the outline of the skin. Certain dinosaurs appear to have been mummified before burial, so that the surrounding material, hardening before the disintegration of the skin, has left a cast of the mummy. In Bavarian lithographic limestone deposits impressions are sometimes preserved of such delicate structures as feathers. In some small ancient amphibians the outlines of the stomach and intestine are visible; while in specimens of a Devonian shark, remains of the muscles and kidneys are so perfectly preserved that individual cells and striations in the muscle are seen under the microscope.

We may gain much information concerning fossil forms in other ways. Footprints are often found in the now solidified mud flats of former periods. Egg shells pertaining to various groups—birds, turtles, skates, dinosaurs—have been discovered; and series of growth stages are known in some forms. Much information can be gathered concerning the food habits of fossil types, aside from the knowledge afforded by the teeth and skeleton. Remains of the bones of devoured animals have been found in the position of the stomach; "gizzard stones" have been discovered lying within the skeletons of several reptilian types. Tooth marks tell us of the fate of the animal whose bones bear them. Faeces, the remains of digestion, known as "coprolites" in the fossil state, are frequently encountered. Wounds and diseased conditions may be discerned on the bones of fossil types. Even though actual remains of such structures as blood vessels, nerves, brains, and muscles are almost never found, a study of the skeleton often gives us much information concerning them.

The geologic time scale.—The history of the earth is divided by geologists into a number of major units—eras. The life of the earliest of these is not well known, and we shall have to do here only with the last three—the Paleozoic Era, during which vertebrates underwent their early development; the Mesozoic Era, or age of reptiles; and the Cenozoic Era, the age of mammals and finally of man. The

eras are somewhat arbitrarily divided into periods usually bearing a name suggestive of a region in which rocks formed during the period are abundant. These
periods will be constantly referred to in our discussions of vertebrate occurrences
and are listed in the accompanying table. The estimates of duration of periods in
years are, of course, only rough approximates, based on the rate of disintegration
of radioactive materials in the rocks. The list of periods given here is one which is,

TABLE OF GEOLOGIC PERIODS

(The older eras, in which vertebrates are unknown, are not included.)

Era	Period		Approximate Time (In Millions of Years)	
			Duration	Since beginning
Cenozoic (Age of mammals and man)	Recent		0	0
	Pleistocene		1	1
	Tertiary		54	55
Mesozoic (Age of reptiles)	Cretaceous		65	120
	Jurassic		35	155
	Triassic		35	190
Palaeozoic (Age of invertebrates and primitive vertebrates)	Permian		25	215
	Pennsylvanian	Carboniferous	35	250
	Mississippian		50	300
	Devonian		50	350
	Silurian		40	390
	Ordovician		90	480
	Cambrian		70	550

for the most part, generally accepted. In certain cases, however, there are variations in usage; the Pennsylvanian and Mississippian are usually considered as a
single period (Carboniferous) by European geologists, while by many the Tertiary
is often divided into a number of short periods.

Evolutionary theories and phenomena.—In passing over many curious and widely
divergent types adapted to a great variety of modes of life, it is impossible to avoid
speculation as to the processes through which their evolutionary development was
accomplished. This subject cannot be adequately discussed here, but we shall
mention a few of the chief problems involved and the theories brought forward
for their solution.

All animals are well fitted for the lives they lead (although sometimes, it is true, the fit does not seem to be a perfect one). We also find, in almost every case where fossil ancestors are known, that these animals have descended with many modifications in structure from forms seemingly less well adapted to their present modes of life. How have these changes come about?

Occasionally we find a statement of this type: "The giraffe, descended from short-necked ancestors, has acquired a long neck because it is useful to him in browsing off the higher branches of the trees." It is true that the long neck is of use to the giraffe, but the citation of a useful result does not in itself explain the nature of the process by which the result was obtained. The statement given would suggest either that some power outside the giraffe brought about the change with a useful end in view or that the giraffe had thought the matter over and brought about the change through his own volition. The first suggestion immediately takes us outside the realm of scientific thought; the second seems obviously absurd, although certain theorists have suggested the existence of some vague "vital force," a mysterious inner "urge," which has driven animals on toward an evolutionary goal.

A much more plausible suggestion is that which may be applied under the theory of the inheritance of acquired characters, of the effect of the use and disuse of parts, advocated more than a century ago by the French naturalist Lamarck. It might be that the individual giraffe, by constantly stretching after the foliage on the higher branches, tended to increase the length of his neck during life, and that this increase was transmitted to his offspring; a cumulation of such individual lengthenings was supposed to have resulted in the development of a long-necked from a short-necked form. This type of theory is plausible at first sight; but there is no evidence, despite repeated experiments, that changes taking place in the body of an individual during his lifetime have any effect upon his offspring.

A much sounder theory to explain evolutionary changes, and one which first brought about general belief in evolution, was that advocated by Darwin three quarters of a century ago. The Darwinian theory points out that no two animals are exactly alike and that, to cite the giraffe again, a form with a neck slightly longer than the average would, especially in times of famine, have a better chance of survival than a shorter-necked form. This selective process would tend, Darwin believed, to the gradual development of the long neck.

Darwin assumed the presence in nature of individual variations which were inherited. Modern experimental work has done much to clear up this situation. It is now known that many individual differences are due to the influence of the environment and are not passed on to descendents, and that most other individual characteristics do not mark the appearance of new features but merely the result of varied combinations of characters already present in the species. Under such circumstances, all selection could do would be to sort out the best assortment of existing factors. Beyond this the evolutionary process could not go were it not that occasionally there occur mutations, definite changes in the germ cells which give rise to the next generation, produced seemingly without relation to the needs of the animal, and making definite, although usually small, changes in the structure of the descendents. Mainly injurious, and hence quickly weeded out, an occasional favorable mutation would offer new material for the selective process to work upon; a "chance" mutation increasing the length of a giraffe's neck without other unfavorable accompanying features might tend to be bred into the race. Such an evolutionary process would obviously be slow in action. But even such a comparatively modern animal as a giraffe has had millions of years at its disposal.

In many groups of fossils it would seem that there has been no such "indecision" as the theory just outlined would suggest; groups once started along an evolutionary line have seemingly kept straight on toward a "goal" without deviation. Because of this, there has been built up a theory of orthogenesis, or "straight-line" evolution. But the seeming absence of side branches may be due to the fact that they were nipped in the bud; selection alone might have resulted in an advance in the single direction of greatest adaptive value. Much seeming orthogenesis may thus be explained through mutation and selection. There are still, however, many puzzling facts; and we are far from a complete and satisfactory solution to all of our problems of vertebrate evolution.

Both living and extinct vertebrates show many cases of wide evolutionary divergence within a group, parallel evolutionary tendencies in related forms, and close convergence in adaptive features in quite unrelated types. Competition within an animal group encourages divergent adaptations toward varied modes of life and produces an adaptive radiation. A striking example is the radiation of the Australian marsupials, which presumably began at the dawn of the Tertiary. The kangaroo and the Tasmanian wolf are quite unlike in all adaptive characters; but basically both are clearly derivable from a primitive type not unlike the opossum and are members of the same order.

The adaptive radiation of a number of groups tends to result in convergence in evolution, the attainment of similar adaptations by two or more unrelated types. The Tasmanian wolf is similar in many features to the true wolves of other continents; the pouched Australian wombat is quite similar to a woodchuck. But these resemblances do not at all imply relationships; they are merely the taking-on of similar structural features necessary for survival in similar modes of life.

Quite a different phenomenon is that of parallelism, the tendency for two or more closely related types to undergo similar structural changes. Several types of extinct South African mammal-like reptiles had a secondary palate like that of mammals. We are sure that this feature was not present in their common ancestor but that, with a similar ancestry and similar build, there has been a tendency for related forms to acquire similar structures— to "drift" in the same evolutionary direction.

Taxonomy and classification.—Zoölogists have found it necessary, in referring to living animals, to use a system of scientific names formed mainly from Greek and Latin roots, rather than variable popular terms. This necessity is even greater in the case of extinct forms for which no popular names can well exist. Every animal bears two names: the first, that of a genus, usually including a number of related forms; the second, that of the particular species of that group to which reference is made. Thus the domestic dog, together with the wolves and jackals, constitute the genus *Canis*. When referring to the dog, the specific name is added—*Canis familiaris;* the wolf, a close relative, is *Canis lupus*. This system is not unlike our human usage of proper and surnames, only the order is reversed.

Upon the genus and species as a base has been erected a system of classification originally designed as a method of "pigeonholing" animals in larger and smaller groups according to the degree of resemblance between them. Thus, for example, the dogs are obviously fairly closely related to the foxes and to other dog-like tropical forms; and these are all united in a family, the Canidae. This group, in turn, is somewhat more distantly related to the cats, bears, and other flesh-eaters; and all these forms are united in an order, the Carnivora. This great group, again, has many features (such as the nursing of young and the presence of hair) which tend to bind it with an array of forms ranging from men to bats and whales; all these are considered members of a common class, the Mammalia. These mammals have a number of characters (such as the possession of an internal skeleton) also present in birds, reptiles, amphibians, and fishes; and in consequence all are grouped together in a phylum, the Chordata, one of the primary subdivisions of the animal kingdom. The complete list of major terms used in such a classification is thus: phylum, class, order, family, genus, and species. Further flexibility is often obtained by using prefixes to give such terms as subclass and superorder.

Originally adopted merely as a convenient method of "sorting out" animals, the recognition of the evolutionary theory put the matter of classification in a new light. Obviously these various taxonomic divisions represented, in a general way, the branches of the family tree. There has been a continual attempt to make classifications "natural," to see that each group established—whether genus, family, or higher division—should contain only forms descended from a common ancestor.

With living types alone to consider, groups may be fairly easily established and defined. But with the continued discovery of intermediate fossil types, classification becomes increasingly difficult. The living Equidae (horses, asses, and zebras) can be easily told from the related rhinoceroses by such characters as the presence of but a single toe on each foot and the absence of horns. But some of the earliest horses had three toes, as do the rhinoceroses; and many of the early rhinoceroses were hornless. We cannot always give definitions which will hold true of all members of a group; we can merely cite the characters of typical members and build the groups about them. Tendencies, rather than the arrival at specific conditions, must be our criteria. Only a few late horses are actually one-toed, but a trend in that direction was early evident; the ancestral rhinoceroses were hornless, but a tendency for the development of horns soon appeared in several independent lines.

Two types of classification are possible—"vertical" and "horizontal" (Fig. 1). Under the first system each family or other unit comprises all members of a known line from its first beginnings to its end or to modern times; the cleavage between lines is carried down to the very base of the evolutionary tree. But when, for example, forms are discovered seemingly ancestral to two distinct families or closely related to both, their inclusion in one or the other seems improper. Under such circumstances the best solution seems to be a "horizontal" cleavage, the erection of a stem group including the base from which the long-lived later families have been derived.

The large number of taxonomic terms with which one must become familiar in the study of fossil vertebrates tends to dishearten the beginner. But it will soon be recognized that (except in cases where names of persons or localities have been utilized) these terms are mainly compounded from but a few score simple and easily recognizable Greek and Latin roots and are based on some real or fancied characteristic of the form described.

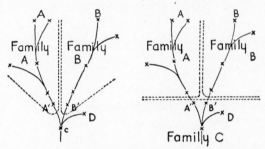

FIG. 1.—Diagram to show the contrast between "vertical" and "horizontal" classifications. A hypothetical family tree showing the descent of two living forms, *A* and *B* (horses and rhinoceroses, for example) from a common ancestral form, *C;* known forms are indicated by crosses. At the left, a vertical classification; the divisions between groups are carried as far down to the roots as possible. This makes clear the relation of early ancestors *A'; B'*) to their descendants, but separates them sharply from *C*, the common ancestor, and other side branches, such as *D*, to which they are closely related. At the right, a "horizontal" classification, which unites all the similar early forms into a common ancestral group *C*.

It is to be noted that, while considerable variation occurs in the formation of names of various larger groups, those of superfamilies invariably end in *-oidea*, those of families in *-idae*, of subfamilies in *-inae*, all suffixed to the root of the name of a typical included genus, as: Equoidea, horse-like forms; Equidae, horses; Equinae, modern horses.

Vertebrate structure.—Before we can adequately discuss the history of the varied vertebrate types, a basic knowledge of their anatomy is a necessity. We shall here briefly review some of the more essential structures of the primitive water-living vertebrates, the fishes, especially as regards the skeletal system. (The morphological features of higher vertebrates will be discussed later.)

All vertebrates are bilaterally symmetrical animals, with the long axis of the body usually in a horizontal position and with a tendency for the concentration of organs related to the environment at the anterior end. This type of symmetry appears to be an expression of the usually active life of vertebrates, as contrasted with that of the comparatively motionless invertebrates possessing radial symmetry. In land animals the development of large limbs tends somewhat to mask the primitively simple arrangement, while a radical change in the position of the body axis occurs in man and other bipeds.

Body form in fishes.—The ideal shape for a swimming vertebrate is that which engineers have approached in torpedoes and ship hulls as offering least resistance to the water—streamlined, with the maximum width somewhat anterior to the middle. Active swimming fish usually have this shape. Locomotion in such forms is principally accomplished by lateral undulations of the trunk and tail, a series of curves traveling backward and pushing the fish forward through the water; paired fins are usually steering organs only. Sinuosity is sometimes exaggerated, giving eel-like forms, usually degenerate end-products of evolutionary lines; while bottom-living types are usually depressed, with broad flat bodies.

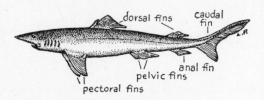

FIG. 2.—Diagram to show the position of the median and paired fins of fishes.

Lying dorsally and ventrally along the main axis of the fish body are unpaired median fins consisting of a dorsal fin or fins projecting from the upper side of the body; a caudal fin, in the tail region; and an anal fin, lying behind the anus (Fig. 2). Dorsal fins are usually one or two in number in primitive types; a single anal fin is common. There may be great variation in the way of fusion or subdivision of the dorsal fins and fusion of either anal or dorsals with the caudal.

Two types of caudal fin are common in more primitive fish—the diphycercal and the heterocercal (Fig. 3). In the former the fleshy termination of the body containing the backbone runs straight out to the tip of the tail, and the fin is arranged symmetrically above and below it. In the heterocercal tail the body, containing the backbone, tips up posteriorly, and nearly all the development of the fin takes place beneath. In a few primitive fishes we find a reversal of this symmetry, the tip of the body tilting down and the fin erected above it—a reversed heterocercal type. The symmetrical diphycercal fin would seem logically to be the primitive type; the heterocercal, a specialized derivative. However, as we shall see, the latter is almost universal in the earliest members of most fish groups; and it is not improbable that the diphycercal type is in reality derived from this.

Notochord.—Vertebrates and their close relatives differ from the common invertebrate types in the possession of an internal skeleton for support and the facilitation of muscular movement. Among invertebrate types the skeleton, when developed, is an external one, covering the surface of the body. Such a skeleton was early developed by vertebrates and is present in many forms today, but some internal skeletal structures are always present in addition. Most primitive and earliest of such internal structures, we believe, was the notochord, a long slim rod usually extending from the base of the skull down the back to the tail. Composed of a soft jelly-like material surrounded by a tough sheath, it forms in primitive vertebrates a firm but flexible supporting structure. In some water-living vertebrates it may persist throughout life; in higher types it is supplanted by the backbone, but is always present in the embryo. Containing no hard parts, it is never preserved as a fossil.

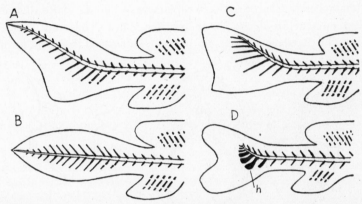

FIG. 3.—Diagram of caudal fin types. *A*, Heterocercal type, found in most sharks, primitive lungfish and actinopterygians, and some early crossopterygians. *B*, Diphycercal type, found in pleuracanth sharks and later lungfish and crossopterygians. *C*, Abbreviated heterocercal, and *D*, the derived homocercal type, found in later actinopterygians. In *D* the enlarged haemal arches (*h*) are termed "hypurals." *C* and *D* are undoubtedly derived from *A*, and so probably is *B* as well. (Modified from Goodrich, *Vertebrata craniata*.)

Cartilage and bone.—In addition to the notochord, all vertebrates have a skeletal system composed of cartilage or bone. The former is a comparatively soft and translucent material, containing rounded cells and capable of growth by expansion. Although common in lower vertebrates, ordinary cartilage is seldom preserved in fossil specimens, for it shrivels up and disintegrates easily upon exposure. In many fishes, however, calcium salts are laid down in the cartilage; and in this calcified condition it is a much firmer substance, capable of preservation.

Bone is the predominating skeletal material in higher vertebrates. In microscopic section it is easily distinguishable from cartilage by the presence of irregularly branching cell spaces. Bone consists of a fibrous matrix heavily impregnated with calcium salts, and forming a much stronger supporting material than cartilage. Unlike that substance bone is incapable of expansion and can grow only by the addition of layers on its surface. In large bones the interior often contains a large marrow cavity as well as numerous smaller canals containing blood vessels and nerves.

In bony types much of the skeleton is first formed in the embryo as cartilage. Later these cartilages are destroyed, and bony tissue takes their place. These facts have suggested that historically cartilage was the older substance and that bone has gradually replaced the poorer material. But while this may be true in the long run, we find that bone was already present in many of the oldest known vertebrates. We know that some living vertebrates have much less bone and more cartilage in their skeletons than did their ancestors; considerable degeneration appears to have occurred in many groups.

Bone found deep within the body and replacing cartilaginous skeletal structures is called "endochondral" or "cartilage-replacement" bone. Quite different in origin and development are dermal or membrane bones. These are never preceded in the embryo by cartilage and are, in contrast, superficial in origin, formed in the

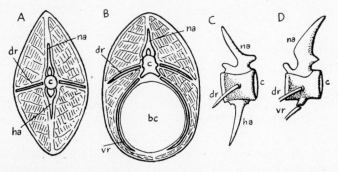

FIG. 4.—*A*, Diagrammatic section through the tail of a fish; *B*, through the trunk, to show the relation of the vertebrae and ribs to the musculature and body cavity. *C*, Diagrammatic caudal vertebrae of a teleostean fish; *D*, trunk vertebrae. *bc*, body cavity; *c*, centrum; *dr*, dorsal ribs lying between dorsal and ventral muscle groups; *ha*, haemal arch and spine; *na*, neural arch and spine; *vr*, ventral ribs surrounding the body cavity.

deeper layers of the skin. In fossil lower vertebrates dermal bones often covered the body completely, commonly as large plates over the head and shoulder region and smaller scales over the trunk and tail. The dermal plates often tend to unite with replacement bones, especially in the head region; the human skull, for example, is a composite of bones having these different origins.

The internal skeletal structures of fishes may be grouped under four heads: the axial skeleton of the trunk and tail; the braincase; the branchial arch system; the skeleton of the paired appendages.

Axial skeleton.—The main elements of the axial system are the vertebrae constituting the backbone. During embryonic development the notochord becomes more or less surrounded by a series of cartilaginous elements. For each segment of the body there are often four such cartilages, which in many forms unite to form a disk or ring-shaped body, known as a "centrum" (Fig. 4). In some primitive forms the notochord remains large, but in most cases its growth is restricted, and in advanced types it disappears altogether in the adult. The nerve cord lies directly above the notochord; a Y-shaped protecting element usually develops above the centrum in each segment. The two branches, the neural arch, meet above the nerve cord and project upward as a neural spine. Important blood vessels lie just below the notochord in the tail, and these are usually surrounded by haemal arches analogous to the neural arches above.

Ribs extending out from the sides of the vertebrae and lying between dorsal and ventral groups of muscles are usually present in the trunk region; primitively they are present in every segment from the neck to the base of the tail. In addition to these intermuscular dorsal ribs which alone are present in land forms, fish usually possess a second series, ventral ribs, which lie deeper and partially surround the body cavity. In the tail the ventral ribs are continued by the haemal arches.

Accessory skeletal structures are often found in the trunk. Additional bones are sometimes placed between various muscles (the shad is all too good an example), and in most land forms there is a breastbone or sternum to which many of the ribs attach ventrally. The median fins are supported by a series of parallel rod-like cartilages or bones, the radials; while below them, in the fish's body, basal elements connect them with the vertebral column. (In addition they are covered superficially and stiffened distally by scales or elongated rays derived from scales or from the skin itself.)

Braincase.—We are accustomed to think of a skull as a complex solid structure which includes the braincase and upper jaws. But in the most primitive of living and fossil vertebrates many of the elements which make up the skull in higher forms are absent. There were originally no jaws, and even in many fishes possessing these structures they are but loosely attached to the braincase. The primitive "skull" consists mainly of a box of cartilage inclosing the brain and articulating with the vertebral column at its posterior end (Figs. 5, 26). Anteriorly nasal capsules protect the nostrils; hollows in the sides receive the eyes; and extensions from the sides of the posterior part (otic capsules) inclose the primitive ear.

Branchial arch system.—A series of cartilaginous or bony bars found between the gill openings in typical vertebrates serves to stiffen the gill (or branchial) region and affords support for the muscles opening and closing the slits (Fig. 6). Each arch is normally divided into upper and lower halves, bent somewhat on each other; and further subdivision usually occurs. Jaws are absent in the most primitive vertebrates; and it is believed that they have been derived from an anterior pair of gill arches, the upper jaw corresponding to the upper half of an arch, the lower jaw to the main ventral segment. In land types (with the loss of gill breathing) there is great reduction in this originally important skeletal system.

Appendicular skeleton.—Paired appendages, the paired fins of fishes, and the homologous legs of land forms are present in most vertebrates. There are normally two pairs (Fig. 2)—pectoral appendages just behind the gill region or neck, and pelvic limbs typically situated at the posterior end of the trunk in front of the anal opening. Support for the limbs is afforded by girdles contained in the body of the animal. They are composed primarily of cartilage or of replacement bone, but the pectoral girdle often has membrane bones attached to its outer and anterior margins. Running out from the side of the girdle region is the appendage proper, the skeleton of which usually consists of a complicated series of jointed cartilages or bones (cf. Figs. 27, 56). The appendages are primitively small steering and balancing organs in fishes but become of paramount importance in locomotion in

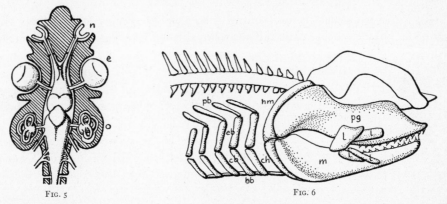

FIG. 5   FIG. 6

FIG. 5.—Diagram to show relation of braincase to nervous system and sense organs in fishes. The braincase is represented as sectioned in a horizontal plane. The braincase forms paired capsules inclosing the nasal sacs (*n*), protects the eyeballs (*e*), and incloses the canals and sacs of the ear (*o*).

FIG. 6.—The jaws and branchial arch system of a shark, essentially the Mesozoic *Hybodus*. The braincase and spinal column are indicated in outline. *bb*, basibranchial elements of the branchial arches; *cb*, ceratobranchials, the main ventral elements; *eb*, epibranchials, the principal dorsal elements; *pb*, pharyngobranchials; *ch*, ceratohyal and *hm*, hyomandibular, elements of the hyoid arch immediately behind the jaws; *pq*, primary upper jaw (palatoquadrate); *m*, lower jaw or mandible; *l*, labial cartilages in the corner of the mouth, perhaps remnants of preoral branchial arches. (After Smith Woodward.)

land vertebrates. The great variations in structure in these organs will be one of the central themes in our study of vertebrate evolution.

Paired fins are poorly developed or absent in some of the lowest vertebrates. Their origin has been much debated. It seems probable, however, that they were at first merely flaps which had grown out from the sides of the body just as the median fins appear to have grown out in the mid-line of the back and tail regions; the two types of fins often have a similar structure and similar steering functions and may well have had similar origins.

Skull.—We have noted that the primary skeletal structure of the head region was the braincase, while a second set of cranial structures appears with the development of jaws formed by an enlargement of an anterior pair of gill arches. In sharks these are not closely attached to the braincase. Early in vertebrate history, however, the story was complicated by the appearance of dermal bones covering the head region. These came into contact with the underlying braincase and in many cases have replaced that structure to a considerable degree (Fig. 7). Covering the sides of the cheek and mouth region and even appearing in the skin lining the mouth, the dermal bones became attached to the primary jaws and tended to replace them. Thus in most vertebrates the development of membrane bones has resulted in a unified cranial structure, the skull, composed of three primitively distinct elements: (a) the braincase, of cartilage or replacement bone; (b) the primitive upper jaw, formed from the same materials; (c) membrane bones, investing and partially replacing both of the former.

Nervous system.—The central nervous system of vertebrates consists of the brain, the spinal cord running down the body from this, and nerves passing out

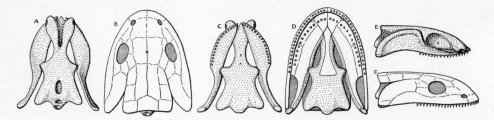

FIG. 7.—Diagrams to show comparison of the skull in forms with and without dermal bones. Cartilage or cartilage replacement bones stippled, dermal bones white. *A*, dorsal, *C*, ventral, and *E*, lateral views of a shark-like form, with separate braincase and primary jaws (cf. Fig. 26, etc.). *B, D, F*, dorsal, ventral, and lateral views of the skull type found in bony fishes and higher forms. Dorsally and laterally the dermal bones cover the original structures and unite them into a single mass. Ventrally a dermal element underlies the anterior end of the braincase, other dermal bones cover most of the primary upper jaws, and the lower margins of the roofing elements form a new outer margin to the jaws (cf. Figs. 53, 54, 85, etc.).

from these structures to sensory and motor end-organs. The spinal cord differs radically in position from the main nerve trunk of most invertebrates in that it lies in a dorsal position, passing down the back above the notochord and vertebral centra and protected by the neural arches between which the nerves emerge (a pair to each segment). The brain possesses an exceedingly complicated structure, of which we may note the superficial features often revealed by casts of the inside of the braincase (Fig. 8). A rough division may be made into three portions— forebrain, midbrain, and hindbrain. The first has paired swellings above—the cerebral hemispheres—which, primitively associated with the sense of smell, in higher forms tend to enlarge greatly and become the seat of the highest functions of the brain. Extending up behind the hemispheres is the stalked pineal body, usually a well-developed eye in early types; while a ventral projection from the forebrain is the infundibulum, in most vertebrates associated with a pocket-like growth from the roof of the mouth, the hypophysis, to form the pituitary body, an important gland of internal secretion. Above the midbrain are paired optic lobes, associated with sight. The main portion of the elongate hindbrain is the medulla oblongata, which has mainly to do with touch, taste, balance, and hearing; while above it lies the cerebellum, the "tree of life," which has control over body posture and muscular co-ordination.

The cranial nerves are of interest to the paleontologist since the openings (foramina) through which they emerge are usually visible in good fossil skulls. There are always at least ten, sometimes twelve, pairs of nerves. Three go to major sense organs: I, to the nostrils; II, to the eye; VIII, to the ear. Three (III, IV, VI) are small nerves which move the muscles of the eyeball. The others (V, VII, IX, X) mainly receive sensory impressions from the skin of the head and neck and lining of the mouth and move the muscles of the jaws and throat.

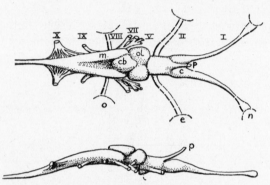

FIG. 8.—Dorsal and lateral views of restored brain and cranial nerves of *Macropetalichthys*, a Devonian armored shark-like fish. The cranial nerves are numbered (see text); the three small nerves to the eye muscles omitted. *c*, cerebral hemispheres; *cb*, cerebellum; *e*, eye; *i*, infundibulum; *m*, medulla oblongata; *n*, nostril; *o*, ear; *ol*, optic lobes of midbrain; *p*, pineal organ. (After Stensiö.)

Sense organs.—All vertebrates have the three major sense organs found in ourselves—nostrils, eyes, and ears. The nostrils in primitive forms do not usually connect with the interior of the mouth but are simply a pair of pockets into which water can pass and in which the sensory cells of smell are located. In some very primitive vertebrates there is but a single nostril. In addition to the universal paired eyes the median pineal eye often reaches the surface (especially in older fossil forms) through an opening in the top of the skull. The primitive ear possesses no drum or earbones, as it does in higher forms, but consists merely of a series of liquid-filled sacs and canals lying entirely inside the braincase; a fish can hear only vibrations which have passed into its body and set up vibrations in its braincase. The ear seems to have been primitively a balancing organ, and that function is still important today. This sense is located in a series of semicircular canals, usually three in number, although only two (or even one) may be present in some low types.

Primitive water vertebrates seem to possess a sixth sense in the lateral line organs, situated in canals or pores extending in a line along the sides of the body and forming a complicated pattern on the head. It is believed that these organs are sensitive to water currents or pressure as an aid in swimming; and from the fact that the inner ear may communicate by a tube with the surface of the top of the head in sharks, it has been suggested that our ears (really pressure organs) may be but deeply sunken and specialized portions of this same system.

Circulatory system.—We shall not be greatly concerned with the blood system in a study of fossil forms. We may merely note that primitively the blood is carried to the heart from the body by a series of veins; from there it is carried forward along the throat in a ventral aorta from which branches arch up between the gill slits. After passing through capillaries on the surface of the gills, these arches reunite above, and the main current of blood passes backward to the body in the dorsal aorta. With the introduction of lungs and the reduction of gills the system becomes, of course, highly modified.

Respiratory system.—The lower vertebrates and their relatives possess a unique breathing system of internal gills. Water passes (usually through the mouth) into the throat, thence through a series of gill chambers, where respiration occurs, to the surface of the body. In most fishes five typical pairs of gills are present; originally the number may have been much higher (cf. *Cephalaspis*, Fig. 17). The spiracle, an additional anterior opening high up on the side of the head, is sometimes enlarged and may function as an inlet for water; in many higher fish it is reduced or absent. With the development of lungs and air breathing, the gills atrophy; the spiracle becomes the tube of the ear; other pouches form glands of internal secretion.

Digestive and urino-genital systems.—We shall have little to do directly with these organ systems (jaws and teeth are discussed elsewhere), although many skeletal features are directly related to food habits and reproduction. Primitive vertebrates are, of course, egg-laying types, although even among some sharks the egg may undergo development within the mother's body. Usually the eggs are unprotected in water-living forms, although in some cases (skates and chimaeras, for example) a hard egg case capable of preservation is present.

Muscular system.—Although muscles are practically never preserved, these organs are of importance to us since they are so intimately associated with the skeleton. Somewhat comparably with the skeleton, the muscle system may be divided into axial, branchial arch, and appendicular series. The axial muscles constitute the main means of locomotion and the greater part of the bulk of water-living vertebrates. They are arranged segmentally in a series of layers down the back and flanks of the fish. Between each successive segment lies a rib; opposite each segment lies a vertebra. It is probable that the segmentation of the skeleton took place primarily in relation to that of the muscles. The small muscles which move the eyeball are probably highly modified portions of this axial group. A special group of muscles is that associated with the branchial arches; the muscles of the jaws, when these structures are formed, were derived from this group. With the development of limbs, strong sets of muscles form above and below the skeletons of these appendages.

Skin derivatives.—Not only membrane bones, previously discussed, but other structures may arise in the outer layers of the body. From the most superficial portion of the skin are formed in various groups of higher vertebrates horny scales, claws, true horns, or feathers; these are usually incapable of fossilization. From deeper layers in the skin of many fishes are formed denticles, typically hollow cone-shaped structures mainly composed of compact dentine and covered with a film of very hard, shiny, enamel-like material (Fig. 9). In typical sharks such denticles are scattered over the surface of the skin, giving it a rough, sandpaper-like texture; while in many early and primitive fishes they form a surface covering for underly-

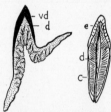

Fig. 9.—Denticle of shark (left) and mammalian incisor (right). *c*, cement; *d*, dentine; *e*, enamel; *vd*, vitrodentine (analogous to enamel).

ing dermal bones or scales. Teeth are identical in composition with denticles and are thought to have originated from them.

Primitive chordates.—The vertebrates, although a large and important group of animals, do not in themselves constitute a major division of the animal kingdom but are grouped together with a small number of other living forms of more primitive character to form the phylum Chordata, animals with a notochord. These other types are almost entirely unknown as fossils but must be considered briefly because of their bearing on the origin and early history of the vertebrates.

Amphioxus.—The Cephalochorda comprise but a few small marine forms, such as *Amphioxus* (Fig. 10). This little marine animal has the appearance of a small translucent fish; but structurally it is far inferior to any of the true vertebrates. There are no bones or cartilages, no paired fins or limbs, no jaws or teeth but simply a circular opening for a mouth, and there is little indication of a brain and only rudiments of sense organs. There are, however, a number of features which tend to show that *Amphioxus* is related to the vertebrates. Although hard skeletal parts are absent, there is a well-developed notochord; a dorsally situated nerve cord runs the length of the body; and breathing is accomplished by means of numerous internal gills.

Such characters strongly suggest that this form lies near the stem of the vertebrates; and it is of interest that the larva of the lampreys, lowest of living vertebrates, is very similar to *Amphioxus* in many structural details. *Amphioxus*, itself, however, is debarred from any ancestral position because of such specializations as the forward extension of the notochord to the tip of the snout (hence the name of the group) and the development of a pouch covering the gills—features seemingly connected with burrowing habits.

Tunicates.—The Urochorda include a considerable number of marine animals known as the tunicates or sea squirts; the central types are perhaps the solitary, sessile forms found as adults attached to rocky surfaces in shallow waters.

They are motionless, shapeless masses covered with a leathery tunic. Water is drawn in through an opening at the top and passed out through a second orifice at the side of the body. Superficially they are quite unlike vertebrates or even *Amphioxus*, and internally the resemblances are at first sight not much greater. There is no notochord, no nerve cord. The water drawn in is strained through a barrel-like structure which occupies the greater part of the interior of the creature. Food

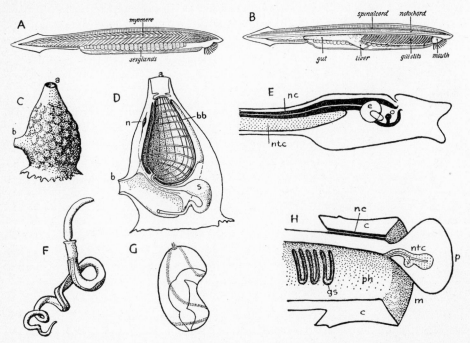

FIG. 10.—Lower chordates. *A, Amphioxus* superficial view; *B*, median section. *C*, External view of a simple tunicate; *a*, incurrent opening; *b*, excurrent opening. *D*, Section of simple tunicate; *bb*, branchial basket; *n*, nervous system; *s*, stomach. *E*, Section of trunk and part of tail of larval tunicate (simplified); *e*, rudiment of eye; *nc*, nerve cord; *ntc*, notochord; *o*, otocyst (rudimentary ear). *F*, Adult acorn worm. *G*, Larval acorn worm; the stippled areas are ciliated bands comparable to those of echinoderm larvae. *H*, Diagrammatic sagittal section through anterior part of body of acorn worm; *c*, collar; *gs*, gill slits; *m*, mouth; *nc*, nerve cord; *ntc*, notochord; *p*, proboscis; *ph*, pharynx. (*A, B* from Gregory after Delage and Herouard; *C-H* mainly after Delage and Herouard.)

particles collected here pass through an opening at the bottom of the barrel to the stomach and intestine and out through an anus to join the water leaving the body through the lateral opening.

But this barrel which strains the food is also the breathing organ of the animal, and consists of a much elaborated set of internal gills. Confirmation of this suggestion of chordate nature is furnished by the study of the embryo, which, unlike the adult, is a free-swimming tadpole-like form with a long tail; in this tail are found both a dorsal nerve cord and a well-developed notochord. Later in life the tunicate becomes attached to a rock, and the tail (and with it the notochord and most of the nerve cord) disappears. It seems probable that the tunicates are degenerate descendents of forms similar to *Amphioxus*.

The acorn worms.—Most characteristic of the Hemichorda are the acorn worms, so called because at the anterior end of the elongate body is a tough proboscis-like digging organ with a collar in back of it, the two together somewhat resembling an acorn in its cup. The body, although worm-like in appearance, is in structure radically different from that of the common worms; and its true chordate nature is shown by the presence of numerous gill slits similar in structure to those of *Amphioxus*. Much of the nervous system is rather diffuse, but there is a dorsal nerve cord in the collar region; and a rudimentary structure in the head may be homologous with the notochord. Altogether it would seem that the acorn worms and their relatives are a specialized offshoot from the base of the chordate stock.

The tiny larva of the acorn worm is in appearance and structure very similar to the larvae of certain echinoderms, and for a long time was thought to pertain to that group.

These living lower chordates are obviously types which are related to the vertebrates but which differ in being more primitive, specialized, or degenerate. Fossil lower chordates are unknown, since there are almost never hard parts capable of preservation.

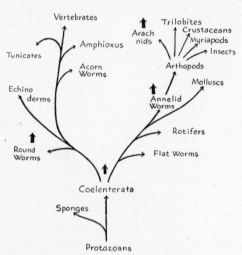

FIG. 11.—Simplified family tree of invertebrates and lower chordates. The heavy arrows indicate groups which have been advocated as ancestors of the vertebrates by various authors.

Vertebrate ancestry.—At one time or another the ancestry of the vertebrates has been sought in almost every invertebrate group (Fig. 11). Some have suggested that vertebrates have been derived directly from the coelenterates, the base of the metazoan stock. Obviously these forms must have been the original ancestors; but they lack so many structures which are found both in vertebrates and many other invertebrates that it seems much more reasonable to believe that the splitting-off of the group lay somewhat higher in the scale.

The descent of the vertebrates from the annelid worms has been advocated. These forms are bilaterally symmetrical, as are vertebrates; they are segmented (as are vertebrates in backbone, nerves, and muscles); and they have a well-developed nerve cord. The nerve cord lies on the ventral side of the worm; but if the form be supposed to have turned over, the nerve cord is on the dorsal side.

But such diagnostic vertebrate structures as gill slits and notochord are not found
in annelid worms; and since the mouth of the annelid was on the under side of the
head, we should expect that the mouth of vertebrates would lie on the back of the
head unless we suppose that the old mouth has closed and a new one formed.

The arthropods, most highly organized of invertebrates, have also been strongly
advocated as vertebrate ancestors, especially the arachnids, a group including not
only the spiders but the scorpions and a number of water-living types such as the
horseshoe crab and the extinct water scorpions, the eurypterids. Arachnids have
an external, not an internal, skeleton; but some of the earliest fossil vertebrates
had a highly developed armor which in some cases greatly resembled that of aquatic arachnids. It has been suggested that this resemblance denotes a real relationship. According to this theory, however, it should be the under surface of one
group which should resemble the dorsal side of the other (for the nerve cord, as in
annelids, lies ventrally in arachnids). Unfortunately this is not the case; and just
as in the case of the worms, there are great difficulties involved in assuming a reversal of the top and bottom sides of the animal. In addition it is necessary to do
away with the jointed limbs and other complicated structures of the arthropod
and remake the entire animal. There is no positive evidence of such a radical re-
building. Further, the theory implies that the lower chordates are quite unrelated to the vertebrates, despite the many similarities in structure.

The most reasonable theory of vertebrate origin seems to be that which uses
the evidence derived from the primitive chordates. While *Amphioxus*, tunicates,
and acorn worms are obviously not in themselves actual vertebrate ancestors, it is
highly probable that they are specialized or degenerate relatives of these ancestors.
And we have noted a suggestive point, that the larva of the acorn worms, simplest
of chordates, is quite similar to that of the echinoderms.

No group, at first sight, would seem to be farther removed from the vertebrates
than the starfish and sea urchins, with their radial symmetry and various peculiar
and complicated organs. No one would derive the vertebrates from echinoderms
as such. But it is not impossible that both may have been derived from a form
similar to the echinoderm and acorn-worm larva, a form advanced above the
coelenterate level of organization but still a rather generalized bilaterally symmetrical animal. From it, with the development of sessile life and of radial symmetry
might have arisen the first echinoderms; on the other hand, forms tending to become increasingly active swimming types would presumably have retained bi-
lateral symmetry and developed locomotor organs in the way of muscles, notochord, and, finally, the vertebrate skeleton.

Under this theory the early ancestors of the vertebrates would have been small,
soft-bodied animals, practically incapable of preservation as fossils. Hence it is
almost hopeless to expect paleontology ever to give us any record of the earliest
vertebrate ancestors.

Classification of vertebrates (Fig. 12).—Most of the classes into which vertebrates should be divided are obvious. The higher types include the mammals
(class Mammalia), birds (class Aves), reptiles (class Reptilia), and amphibians
(class Amphibia). The lower, water-living types are often regarded as forming a
single class—the fish, or Pisces. But some subdivision of this last group seems
necessary. Superficially, the various kinds of "fish" seem quite similar in nature;

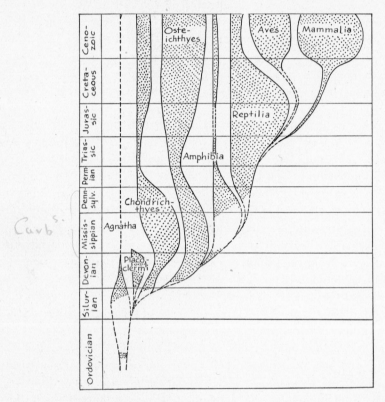

Fig. 12.—A family tree of the vertebrate classes. A rough indication of the comparative abundance
of the various groups is furnished by the thickness of the various branches.

they are all water-living types and in that connection have many common features.
But in structure there is a vast amount of variation. A lamprey and a codfish, for
example, are in many respects as different as a frog and a man; and it is not reasonable to "lump" them in a single class. The lampreys and hagfishes, together
with related fossil forms, may constitute the class Agnatha, primitive vertebrates
without typical limbs or jaws. Certain armored fossil fishes in which jaws and
paired appendages are present but peculiarly constructed may be considered as
constituting a class Placodermi. The sharks and their relatives comprise the class
Chondrichthyes (although, as will be seen, the term is not altogether appropriate);

the higher bony fish, the class Osteichthyes. For convenience, the term Pisces ("fish") may be used to include all the primitive water-living groups; and Tetrapoda ("four-footed") is a term descriptive of the land forms. Our classification is thus as follows:

Superclass Pisces
{
Class Agnatha
Class Placodermi
Class Chondrichthyes
Class Osteichthyes
}

Superclass Tetrapoda
{
Class Amphibia
Class Reptilia
Class Aves
Class Mammalia
}

CHAPTER II
PRIMITIVE JAWLESS VERTEBRATES

The lampreys and hagfishes, usually termed the "cyclostomes," are outstanding among living vertebrates in the presence of seemingly primitive characters. These peculiar forms of eel-like appearance are quite devoid of jaws such as characterize all other living vertebrates and are limbless, whereas all other living groups of fishes have well-developed paired fins. Turning to fossil types, we find that the most ancient of known vertebrates were forms usually grouped as the ostraco-derms. These fishes were almost always incased in a heavy armor of bone or other hard material and thus seem quite unlike the soft-skinned modern cyclostomes in which the skeleton is entirely cartilagenous. But there, too, jaws appear to have been totally absent and limbs at the most poorly developed. It is probable that the living cyclostomes and the fossil ostracoderms are members of a common stock of primitive ancestral vertebrates which we may term the class Agnatha, jawless vertebrates.

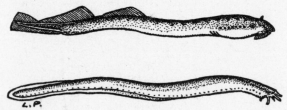

FIG. 13.—Living cyclostomes. Above, the lamprey *Petromyzon;* below, the hagfish *Myxine.* (After Dean.)

Cyclostomes.—The living agnathous forms include the lampreys, such as *Petro-myzon,* and the hagfishes (*Myxine, Bdellostoma*) (Fig. 13). They are semiparasitic in habit, attaching themselves to fish and living on their flesh. The body is elon-gate, eel-shaped; there are no scales or denticles in the tough and slimy skin. Paired fins are absent, although median fins are developed. From six to fourteen pairs of gills are present; these differ from the slit-like structures of other living vertebrates in being spherical pockets connected with the inside and the surface by small tubes. In the lampreys the margins of the round jawless mouth form a sucking disk for attachment to the prey; in the hagfishes the mouth is surrounded by tentacles. Jaws are functionally replaced by a long protusible "tongue" armed with a patch of horny structures resembling teeth; this forms an efficient organ for rasping away the flesh of the lamprey's prey. There are paired eyes and a median pineal eye (well developed in lampreys, rudimentary in hagfishes). In-stead of the three semicircular ear canals of most vertebrates, lampreys have but two and hagfishes one. The olfactory organs are still more peculiar, for, instead of the double nostril found in all other living vertebrates, there is but a single median nasal sac.

The skeleton consists of uncalcified cartilage. The braincase is of a rather specialized and complicated structure. An elaborate system of branchial arches is present in the lamprey; but these arches, instead of being separate elements, are fused into a peculiar basket inclosing the gills, while part of the branchial skeleton is modified into a support for the "tongue." The notochord is large and unrestricted. All forms have cartilaginous supports for the median fins, while *Petromyzon*, although lacking vertebral centra, has a row of small neural arches.

A striking difference between the lampreys and hagfishes is shown in the position of the single nostril. In most vertebrates the nasal openings are near the front of the head, or even slightly on the under side. In the hagfishes the nostril opens at the tip of the "snout," but in the lampreys a large "upper lip" grows out

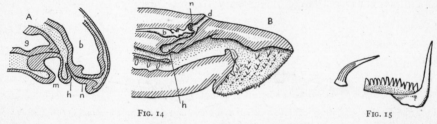

FIG. 14.

FIG. 15.

FIG. 14.—Diagrams to show the development of the dorsal nostril of lampreys. *A*, longitudinal section through the head of a larval lamprey, showing the ventral position of the nostril and hypophysis. *B*, a later stage, in which hypophysis and nostril have migrated dorsally. *b*, brain; *d*, dorsal common opening of hypophysis (*h*) and nostril (*n*); *g*, gut; *m*, mouth. (After Goodrich, simplified.)

FIG. 15.—Ordovician conodonts. Left, *Scolopodus*, right, *Prioniodus*, much enlarged. (After Pander.)

from the front of the roof of the mouth to form the tip of the body; the originally ventral nostril (together with a second pocket-shaped structure, the hypophysis) is forced around forward and upward until in the adult it is found opening downward high on the top of the head just in front of the eyes—a situation unparalleled in other living vertebrates (Fig. 14).

Possessing no bones, true teeth, or other hard parts capable of preservation, the cyclostomes are unknown as fossils. Certain small paleozoic tooth-like structures, conodonts (Fig. 15), have been thought to be cyclostome "teeth"; but this is uncertain, and the conodonts may be of invertebrate origin.

The lampreys and hagfishes are obviously lower in their plane of organization than any other living vertebrates. But before concluding that they are really primitive types, we must take into account the fact that these forms are semi-parasitic and that parasites are generally specialized and degenerate rather than truly primitive forms. Specialized they undoubtedly are in such respects as the peculiar "tongue." Can it not be that many of the features of simplicity in their structure are really due to losses associated with parasitism, rather than to true primitiveness? We may seek an answer in the study of related fossil types. As will be seen, many cyclostome features were present in the oldest known fishes.

Ostracoderms.—The oldest certain remains of vertebrates are fragments contained in Ordovician rocks from Russia and from Colorado and other western states. The nature of the sediments in America suggests that these remains are the débris of forms living in inland waters which, after death, were washed out into a shallow bay. This supports the theory that the vertebrates were of freshwater origin and helps to explain the almost utter absence of vertebrate remains in the dominantly marine sediments of the early Paleozoic. The fragments are too small to allow us to gain any idea of the appearance of these early types, but their microscopic structure shows that we have to do mainly with pieces of armor such as are found covering the bodies of vertebrates in the following periods. It is of particular interest that some of these specimens show that bone had already developed in this earliest stage of known vertebrate history.

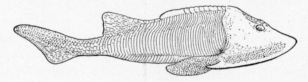

Fig. 16.—*Cephalaspis*, a typical late Silurian and Devonian osteostracan ostracoderm. (After Goodrich, *Vertebrata craniata.*)

It is not until late Silurian and early Devonian times that we gain any adequate idea of these forms, or rather their successors. Then, as the Silurian draws to an end, we find increasingly numerous remains of vertebrates quite unlike any existing forms in appearance. Almost all are covered with varied types of armor, a feature to which the name "ostracoderms" ("shell skinned") is due. In bodily outlines and the presence of hard skeletal parts they seem remote from the cyclostomes; but we find that all these forms, like living lampreys and hagfishes, are characterized by the absence of jaws and by the absence or poor development of paired fins; and that, further, those which are best known show striking resemblances to the cyclostomes in many structural features. When we first see them, these ostracoderms have already had a long history behind them and are divided into several distinct groups.

Osteostraci.—*Cephalaspis* and its relatives constituting the order Osteostraci are known in more detail than any other ostracoderms, and hence merit first consideration. These types are abundant in late Silurian and Lower Devonian rocks, while a few forms lingered until the close of Devonian times.

Few were of great size, the length ranging generally from a few inches to a foot or two. They were completely incased in an armor of plates and scales. When sectioned, it is seen that these plates, unlike those of other ostracoderms, were composed of true bone, while on the surface was a tuberculated layer of dentine comparable to fused dermal denticles. The body (Fig. 16) was rather fish-like in appearance, somewhat broad and flattened ventrally, with one or two dorsal fins and a heterocercal caudal. There were no pelvic fins, but behind the head were two scale-covered flaps which may represent a primitive type of pectoral fin; their internal structure is unknown. The body scales were arranged in a series of vertical rows each containing but a few elongate members.

The head region (Fig. 17) was covered dorsally with a nearly solid shield of bone with marginal "horns" of variable length lying in front of the supposed pectoral fins. The eyes, directed upward as in many bottom-living types, were situated close together near the center of the shield; between them lay a median plate with an opening for the pineal eye. Anterior to this plate was a slit which lodged a nostril exactly comparable in position to that of the lamprey. In the center of the skull, behind the eyes, was an area filled by a series of small polygonal plates, and there were similar areas near each margin.

The shield folded under onto the margins of the flattened ventral surface. Behind its front edge was a small and obviously jawless mouth, while posterior to this a series of movable plates covered the throat region. At the edge of these plates were round external openings for the numerous gill pouches.

Recent work has disclosed much of the internal structure. It was long supposed that while ostracoderms had superficial armor plates, the internal skeleton was purely cartilaginous. But in *Cephalaspis* an ossified cranial skeleton was present. Its composition was in contrast to that of most vertebrates, for, instead of a separate braincase and jointed branchial arches, there was a single unified structure underlying the entire dermal shield. This seems at first sight a highly specialized feature; but it is possible that it is really a primitive undifferentiated condition and that the establishment of independent units was a later development.

From the internal cavities most of the structure of the soft parts of the head can be made out. The brain and nerves and blood vessels are found to have been quite similar to those of lampreys and seem to show a very primitive vertebrate pattern. In the ear there were two semicircular canals, as in the lampreys. The numerous gills extended much farther forward than those of any existing vertebrate; for, whereas in living types the most anterior one (the spiracle) is about opposite the ear region, there were here in front of this position several which apparently have been forced back or lost in higher types through the growth of the mouth and jaws.

Besides the ordinary nerves of the head, very stout nerve trunks, apparently motor in nature, are found running to the polygonal plate areas mentioned previously. It is suggested that these areas were powerful electric protective organs such as are present in certain skates, eels, and catfish today. It is surprising to

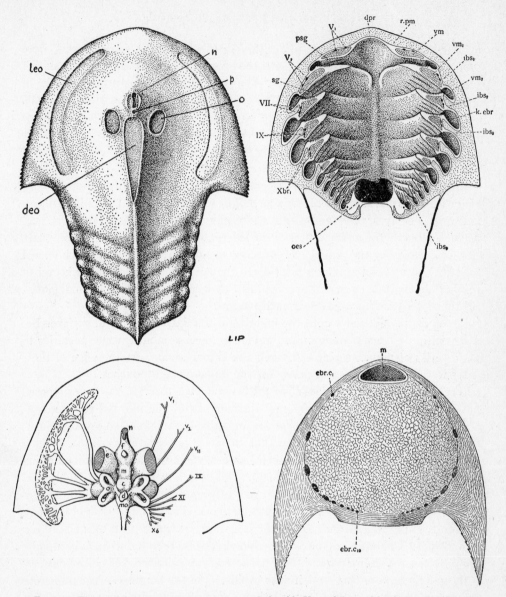

FIG. 17.—The cranial anatomy of *Kiaeraspis*, a cephalaspid. Upper left, top view of head and anterior part of trunk region. *deo*, supposed dorsal electric organ, *leo*, supposed lateral electric organ; *n*, opening of single dorsal nostril; *o*, orbit; *p*, pineal opening: Lower left, diagrammatic dissection of top of head, to show brain, nerves, and sense organs. Nerves to supposed electric organ shown on the left; other major nerves (numbered) on right, arranged in a series corresponding to the gill slits. *c*, cerebellum; *d*, nerve to dorsal electric field; *e*, orbit; *f*, forebrain; *m*, midbrain; *mo*, medulla oblongata; *n*, nostril; *o*, ear region showing two semi-circular canals. Upper right, restoration of ventral surface of head, with the plates covering the throat removed, showing the ten gill sacs and the small, anteriorly placed mouth. Roman numerals indicate cranial nerves. *ibs*, partitions between gill sacs; *kebr*, ducts from gill pouches to surface; *oes*, oesophagus; *psg*, a prespiracular gill pouch lost in higher vertebrates; *rpm*, rostral region in front of gills; *sg*, gill pouch corresponding to the spiracle of higher fishes; *vm*, muscles of gill pouches. Lower right, restoration of ventral surface of head, covered by small plates. *ebrc*, opening of the gills; *m*, mouth. (After Stensiö.)

find such highly specialized structures in such an early form; but we must remember that by late Silurian times the vertebrates must already have had a long, even if unknown, evolutionary history behind them, and these small forms had large predaceous invertebrates as contemporaries.

The Osteostraci were a homogeneous group, with few variations. The "horns" varied considerably in size; there was sometimes a spike projecting from the front of the head; and more or less of the body armor tended to fuse onto the back of the skull. *Cephalaspis* and its relatives were obviously, from their depressed shape and dorsally situated eyes, bottom-living forms. The slit-like mouth suggests that, like the modern sturgeons, they were stream-bottom scavengers.

It is obvious that these ancient types were fundamentally quite close to the modern lampreys in structure. Can the lampreys have descended from them?

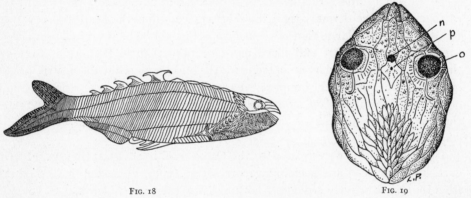

FIG. 18   FIG. 19

FIG. 18.—*Birkenia*, an anaspid from the late Silurian of Scotland. Original about 12 inches long. (From Stetson.)

FIG. 19.—Dorsal view of the head plates of *Pharyngolepis*, a late Silurian anaspid from Norway, showing the lateral (*o*) and pineal (*p*) eyes and the single nostril (*n*). (After Kiaer.)

Many of the differences may be correlated with a change from a bottom-dwelling to a semi-parasitic mode of existence. The most striking contrast lies between the well-ossified skeletal system of the ancient types and the purely cartilagenous skeleton of the lampreys. But similar degeneration is known to have occurred in other groups; and despite their superficial dissimilarity, the osteostracans may quite possibly have been ancestral to the lampreys.

Anaspida.—The order Anaspida includes a number of forms such as *Birkenia* (Fig. 18), *Lasanius*, *Pharyngolepis*, and *Rhyncholepis* from the Upper Silurian of Europe (there is a possible late survivor in the Devonian of Canada). None was more than 3 or 4 inches in length. They were in most cases completely covered with an armor composed of scales arranged in regular rows on the body and a complicated pattern of small plates in the head region. The nature of the material composing this armor is unknown. Unlike any normal vertebrate of later times, the

tail tilted downward, rather than upward, to give a "reversed heterocercal" type
of caudal fin, found among living animals only in the larval lamprey. So unexpected was this find that for many years these forms were restored bottom side
up! The tilt of the normal heterocercal tail tends to turn the front of the animal
upward; this reversed type would tend to keep the anaspid close to the bottom.

A series of spines, presumably defensive in nature, lay along the dorsal side of
the body. An anal fin was present. Of typical paired fins there were none; but
there were large dermal plates at the point where pectoral and pelvic girdles are
developed in higher types, and a small movable spine in the shoulder region may
have represented the beginnings of a pectoral fin. Behind the head a row of small
circular openings slanting back and down were the exits from a series of gill
pouches.

No trace of internal structure has been discovered; the skeleton was presumably
cartilaginous. The dermal armor, however, reveals that the head structure was
fundamentally similar to that of *Cephalaspis* (Fig. 19). The two large orbits were
somewhat farther apart and faced more laterally than in that form. Between
them lay a plate pierced by an opening for the pineal eye; while the nostril, just as
in the last order and in the lampreys, reached the surface through an opening high
on the top of the head. The mouth was shaped more like that of higher vertebrates
than in other agnathous types, but it is improbable that true jaw structures were
connected with it.

That these forms were related to the Osteostraci is obvious; they were, however, less depressed and seemingly more active types, suggesting a trend away
from the comparatively sedentary bottom-living existence which may have characterized the earliest jawless vertebrates. They may well have been even more
closely related to the lampreys than *Cephalaspis*. One type, *Lasanius*, was only
partially armored; if the remainder of the dermal covering were lost, there would
be, as far as our knowledge goes, little to distinguish anaspid from lamprey.

Palaeospondylus.—From a single quarry in Scotland containing shales of Middle
Devonian age have come numerous examples of *Palaeospondylus* (Fig. 20), a tiny
animal with a long name, which may be considered as the sole member of the
order Palaeospondyloidea. In structure it is far removed from any other early
fossil types. There is no trace of dermal armor of any sort, but a considerable series
of internal structures has been preserved. No microscopic details are to be seen in
sectioned fossils, so that we cannot say whether the material was calcified cartilage
or bone. There are no traces of paired fins, but supports for a caudal fin were
present. While the backbone in most early vertebrates appears to have consisted
largely of ordinary cartilage and is hence inadequately known, this tiny form had
well-preserved ring-shaped centra and neural arches. There was a well-developed
braincase (Fig. 21) with otic capsules at the posterior corners and other structures of uncertain nature at the sides, while a central longitudinal trough con-

tained the brain. Anteriorly this trough continued into a large circular terminal opening surrounded by a series of projections, the whole resembling a crown in shape; this may have lodged a single nostril having the position that it occupies in the hagfishes. Beneath the braincase and extending backward from it we find a series of rods and bars which represent some sort of modified branchial arches. They obviously did not include typical jaws, and it may be that they represent supports for a tongue-like organ such as is found in the cyclostomes.

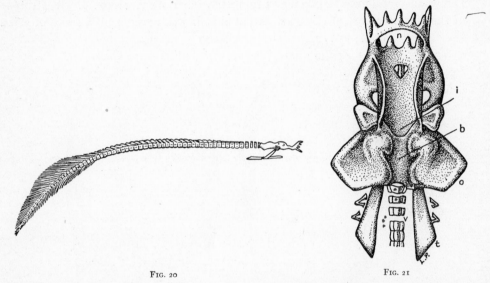

FIG. 20   FIG. 21

FIG. 20.—Restoration of *Palaeospondylus*, a Middle Devonian form possibly ancestral to the hag-fishes. Lateral view, length of actual specimen about 1½ inches. (After Traquair and Bullman.)

FIG. 21.—Dorsal view of the cranial region of *Palaeospondylus*. *b*, central trough containing the brain; *i*, pit presumably containing the infundibulum; *n*, anterior opening presumably for the nostril; *o*, ear region of braincase; *t*, part of ventral bar system perhaps associated with a tongue-like structure; *v*, vertebrae. Length of original about ¼ inch. (After Bullman.)

The relationships of this little form have been the subject of endless argument. One suggestion is that it was the larval form of some contemporary fish. But usually the vertebrae of small embryos are cartilaginous, and the vertebrae of *Palaeospondylus* are better preserved than those of any of its large contemporaries. Others have suggested that the form is a fossil hagfish, and there are no structural features known which rule out this interpretation. It is quite possible that this form was intermediate between an early armored ancestor and the modern degenerate types. Higher bony fish which form the prey of hagfishes first appear at this time (Middle Devonian); only then was a trend toward parasitism possible.

Heterostraci.—Varied in appearance and structure (as the name would indicate) were the members of the order Heterostraci which (like the Osteostraci) were abundant in the late Silurian and early Devonian but had disappeared completely by the end of the latter period. Usually there was a complex armor comparable to that of *Cephalaspis* but lacking bone cells. In contrast with the cephalaspids and anaspids the paired eyes were far apart on the sides of the head, the pineal eye often failed to pierce the top of the skull, and a striking difference lies in the fact that there was no opening for a dorsal nostril. The tail is usually poorly known but may have been generally of the reversed heterocercal type.

Pteraspis, which with related types was common in late Silurian and early Devonian times, may be taken as a typical member of this group. Little is known of the posterior part of the body except that it was covered by a series of thick

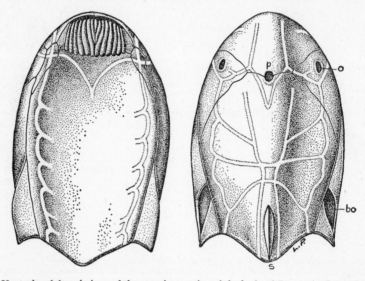

FIG. 22.—Ventral and dorsal views of the anterior portion of the body of *Pteraspis*. Lateral line canals are indicated. The mouth lay in front of the slender series of plates near the anterior end of the ventral surface. *bo*, common opening of the gill pouches; *o*, orbits; *p*, pineal opening; *s*, median dorsal spine. About twice the size of the original. (After Kiaer.)

diamond-shaped scales and was presumably rather normally fish-like in contours. The anterior half of the body was protected by armor which consisted essentially of two large oval plates, one covering the dorsal surface, the other the ventral side (Fig. 22). The former appears to have been primitively a single element, but in some types is broken up into a number of lateral elements surrounding the eyes and connecting with the ventral plate. A spine projected backward from the end of the dorsal shield. Small circular orbits were present at the sides of the head; and in *Pteraspis*, at least, the pineal eye was functional.

A single lateral opening indicates a common outlet for the gills; the position of the gill pouches is indicated by a series of six or seven paired impressions on the inside of the dorsal shield. A small "horn" projects laterally behind the gill opening.

On the under side of the rostrum a transverse slit, bounded behind by a series of small parallel movable plates, indicates the position of the mouth. The nasal apparatus must also have been situated in this slit, and one specimen shows markings suggesting that there were two nostrils as in higher vertebrates.

Although *Pteraspis* and its close relatives must have been, like other jawless types, mainly bottom-living foragers, the body was only slightly flattened. In contrast is *Drepanaspis* (Fig. 23) from the Lower Devonian of Germany, in which the whole head and much of the trunk formed a broad flat structure, covered

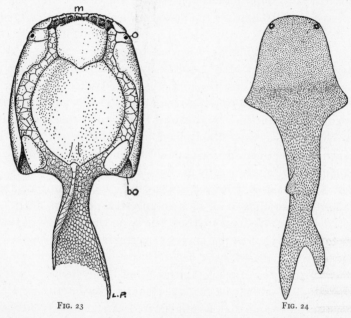

FIG. 23   FIG. 24

FIG. 23.—Dorsal view of *Drepanaspis*, a Lower Devonian heterostracan, original about 1 foot long. *bo*, branchial opening; *m*, dorsally situated mouth; *o*, orbits. (After Traquair, Kiaer, and Heinz.)

FIG. 24.—*Thelodus*, a late Silurian and Devonian heterostracan covered with dermal denticles, length of original specimens about 3–8 inches. (From Traquair.)

above and below by a series of larger and smaller plates generally comparable with those of *Pteraspis*. The eyes were quite small; the mouth apparently was similar to that of *Pteraspis* but in the fossils appears at the front end of the upper rather than the under surface. Obviously this form must have been a sluggish bottom-dweller. *Phyllolepis*, from the end of the Devonian, appears to have been somewhat similar and is of interest in that it is the only ostracoderm, apart from *Palaeospondylus*, where remains of the vertebral column have been observed. Plates apparently pertaining to similar forms have been found in various Devonian deposits.

Thelodus (Fig. 24) and *Lanarkia* of the late Silurian are the only well-known members of a third group of heterostracans. In these small creatures we see a body form quite similar to that of *Drepanaspis*, with a fish-like tail, a broad flattened anterior region with flaps at the corners, and eyes far apart. Structurally they probably were similar to the preceding forms, but their external skeleton consisted merely of small loosely united dermal denticles instead of thick plates. Scattered denticles of this type have been found in many late Silurian and Devonian deposits; these forms seem to have been widespread but usually had disintegrated before burial. It was once generally believed that this type of covering represented a stage in the initiation of armor; that dermal denticles, originally isolated, have fused at their bases to form dermal bony plates and scales. But well-developed armor was present in vertebrates a full period earlier than this, and it seems more probable that we have here a degenerative process; the denticles are the last remains, rather than the beginnings, of dermal armor.

The Heterostraci are obviously not closely related to the living and fossil groups with a single dorsal nostril—lampreys, Osteostraci, Anaspida. Are they ancestral to the hagfishes and to *Palaeospondylus?* This is not impossible, as far as our knowledge goes. But there is no strong reason to assume a close association here, for the heterostracan nostril may have been a double structure. It may be that the known Heterostraci are remnants of a generalized primitive vertebrate group which might have given rise, by modification and specialization, to the other jawless types. Known forms, however, appear to be too late in time and too specialized on their own account to fill such an ancestral position.

Primitive vertebrates.—We have touched briefly on the problem of the nature of the skeleton to be expected in the ancestral vertebrates. The lowest of existing forms, cyclostomes and sharks, have a purely cartilaginous skeleton; in the embryo of higher vertebrates cartilage appears long before bone. Consequently it has been generally held in the past that the primitive vertebrates were forms with a cartilaginous skeleton and that bone appeared at a relatively late time. That armored ostracoderms appeared at an early date has long been known, but it was assumed that these forms were merely aberrant side branches from a presumed main evolutionary line of soft-bodied forms supposed to have been contemporaneous with them.

It has, however, become increasingly difficult to maintain such a position. Bone or bone-like material was present not only in the ostracoderms but also in the earliest shark-like forms, and we shall see that the earlier members of many fish groups tended to be better armored, better ossified, than their descendants. We find it almost impossible to escape the conclusion that armor, probably bony in nature, and some ossification of the internal skeleton were developed at a very early stage in vertebrate history, and that the cartilaginous skeleton of the lower existing types represents a degenerate, rather than a primitive, condition. The late Silurian and Devonian ostracoderms described above are, of course, too late in time to be the most primitive ancestral forms, since we possess fragments of armored vertebrates a full period earlier. However, the Heterostraci may represent comparatively late survivors of the primitive stock which, while still in a jawless stage, gave rise to single-nostril forms leading not only to *Palaeospondylus* and the hagfishes but also to the varied types with a dorsal nostril, of which the lampreys alone survive. Further, *Thelodus* and *Lanarkia* appear to demonstrate the degenerative process by which the shagreen skin of sharks may have arisen from a primitively armored condition.

These ancient armored types indicate that the absence of jaws is a really primitive vertebrate character. We have seen, however, that some indication at least of pectoral fins is often present, and it may be that the development of paired appendages was inaugurated at an early stage in vertebrate development. Five gills are generally present in later fish types; cyclostomes and ostracoderms agree in suggesting the presence of a higher count in early vertebrates. The ostracoderm body is almost always depressed; and this may well have been a truly primitive character since, in the absence of jaws, the ancestral types must almost inevitably have been feeders on small bottom-dwelling forms of life.

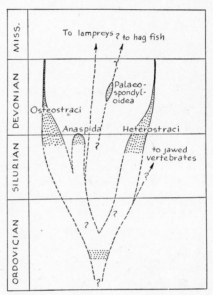

FIG. 25.—Diagram to show distribution of jawless vertebrates.

Since living lower chordates and lower vertebrates are mainly marine types, it was formerly assumed that the sea was the home of primitive vertebrates. But it has been suggested that the high motility of vertebrates points to the fresh waters as the place of the development of the group. With this conclusion the fossil record is in accord, for until the middle of the Devonian fossil vertebrate remains are almost never found associated with marine invertebrate faunas.

Why should primitive vertebrates have been universally armored? Later armored types are usually protected against their own carnivorous relatives; but we believe that the earliest vertebrates were without biting jaws and incapable of ingesting other vertebrates as food. Obviously the enemies must have lain among invertebrate types. The inland-dwelling vertebrate would not have come in contact with cephalopods or other marine forms which one might at first think of as possible enemies. We do, however, find that one group of predaceous invertebrates was present in the same beds with the early vertebrates—the eurypterids, aquatic scorpion-like Paleozoic creatures of large size, with well-developed claws and biting mouth parts. It is probable that the early vertebrates furnished a food supply for the "water scorpions" and that vertebrate armor (and the electric organs of the cephalaspids) served as a defense against these carnivorous enemies. When, in the Devonian, faster-swimming fishes supplanted the comparatively sluggish ostracoderms, the eurypterids dwindled into insignificance and presently disappeared. The activity which characterizes the vertebrates may be related not merely to the taking-up of life in running stream but also to the necessity of escaping early eurypterid enemies.

CHAPTER III

SHARK-LIKE FISHES

The numerous fish types remaining for consideration possess many common characteristics indicative of a higher degree of organization than that of the agnathous forms already discussed. All possess jaws, structures indicating so great and significant an advance that these forms, together with the land vertebrates, are often spoken of as gnathostomes ("jaw-mouthed"), in contrast with the more primitive Agnatha. Paired limbs are usually present in the form of pectoral and pelvic fins. The nostrils are always paired; the gill openings have the form of slits, rather than the rounded shape found in the Agnatha, and seldom number more than five in addition to a spiracle.

Within this array of fishes, there exists such a great diversity of structure that we are hardly justified in including all of them in a single class. Instead we shall treat of them as constituting three groups: (1) the class Placodermi, including two Paleozoic orders of primitive but highly aberrant fishes—the arthrodires and anti-archs; (2) the class Chondrichthyes, an exceedingly varied series of offshoots from the early gnathostome stock, some highly specialized but all essentially primitive in their fundamental features, numerous in the Paleozoic but represented today only by the sharks and related types; and (3) the class Osteichthyes, a very important group of highly organized bony fishes, an offshoot of the primitive stock which rapidly rose to a position of dominance and has long included the vast majority of the world's fish population.

The first two of these three classes will be considered in the present chapter. Before proceeding to a detailed consideration of their history and deployment, some structural features (briefly touched upon previously) to which constant reference will be made may be discussed.

Jaws.—The jaws of a shark (Figs. 6, 26) consist of a pair of cartilages on either side of the mouth. The upper one runs fore and aft below and a bit to one side of the braincase, to which it appears primitively to have been attached by a joint back of the orbit. At its posterior end it articulates with the cartilage forming the lower jaw, which runs forward beneath the upper and is more or less loosely united to its fellow of the opposite side. Just back of the jaws lies the hyoid arch, first of the branchial arches, and in succession behind this other arches (usually five in modern types). The main element of the upper portion of the hyoid arch usually takes the form of a stout bar, the hyomandibular, articulating above with the otic (ear) region of the braincase and ventrally bracing the jaw articulation; it thus acts as a prop for the jaws.

35

The jaws are similar in essential structure to the branchial arches behind them; the muscles and nerves with which they come into relation are similar to those of the branchial arches; and it is exceedingly probable that when the early vertebrates first began to feed on large and hard objects, the jaws originated by the enlargement of a pair of branchial arches lying behind the expanding mouth.

The relations of the upper jaw with the braincase may be variously modified. The supporting function of the hyomandibular may be eliminated either by a fusion of the upper jaw with the braincase or through the formation of a compact

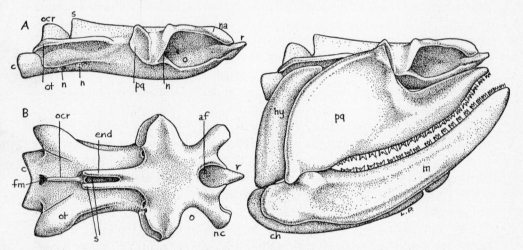

FIG. 26.—The cranial anatomy of a Paleozoic "shark," *Pleuracanthus. A*, lateral view of braincase, *B*, dorsal view, *C*, lateral view with jaw and hyoid arch articulated. One-third size of a large specimen. *af*, anterior opening (fontanelle) in roof of braincase; *c*, occipital condyle; *ch*, ceratohyal; *end*, common opening for endolymphatic ducts from internal ear; *fm*, foramen magnum; *hy*, hyomandibular; *m*, mandible; *n*, exits for certain cranial nerves, *na, nc*, nasal capsule; *o*, orbit; *oc*, occipital condyle; *ocr*, occipital crest for attachment of body muscles; *ot*, otic region; *pq*, upper jaw (palatoquadrate bar) and its point of attachment to postorbital process of braincase; *r*, rostrum; *s*, paired processes to which a large spine (peculiar to pleuracanths) is attached.

set of dermal bones connecting these two elements. On the other hand, direct contact between skull and jaw may disappear and the hyomandibular become the sole means of jaw support.

The teeth, presumably derived from dermal denticles, show many variations related to feeding habits. Usually there is a prominent row along the jaw margins, but teeth may develop anywhere within the lining of the mouth and may even extend into the throat region. Methods of tooth attachment and replacement are varied. Teeth may be firmly attached to dermal plates developed along the jaws or in the mouth. In the higher groups they are often implanted in sockets in dermal bone; in modern sharks they are but loosely attached to the jaws. In most groups an indefinite number of teeth may be produced in succession to those worn out or broken off from the jaws. Often this replacement is from a tooth which grows up from the socket left empty; in most sharks rows of teeth are formed within the jaws, ready to move up into position on the margin as the functioning member of a series drops out.

Gills.—While in lower chordates gills are very numerous and eight, ten, or more are not uncommonly met with in the Agnatha, higher fishes seldom have more than five typically developed slit-like gill passages. In modern sharks these open separately on the surface of the body. But it is probable that a gill covering, an operculum, was primitively present, since it is found not only in the higher bony fishes but in the living shark-like chimaeras, the placoderms, and even some ostracoderms.

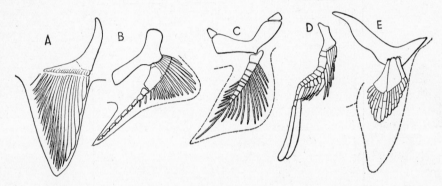

FIG. 27.—The paired fins and girdles of shark-like fishes. All except *D* are pectoral fins. *A, Cladoselache*, of the late Devonian, with parallel radials extending out from the girdle. *B, "Cladodus" neilsoni* (Carboniferous), with a posterior axis developed, transitional between *A* and *C* or *E*. *C*, a pleuracanth shark, with archipterygial structure. *D*, pelvic fin of male of the same, with clasping organ. *E, Hybodus*, a Mesozoic heterodont elasmobranch. (*A*, after Dean, *B* after Traquair and Goodrich, *C* and *D* after Fritsch, *E* after Smith Woodward.)

In addition to the normal gills there appears to have early developed a specialized small anterior gill opening, the spiracle, lying just behind the upper jaw. It is reduced or absent in many of the more active fish types but large in the skates and rays, where (with the mouth buried in the mud) it serves as a dorsal intake for water to the gills. Possibly it originated in primitive fish types which may have been bottom-dwellers.

Fins.—Paired fins are almost universally present, although they are peculiarly developed or rudimentary in some primitive or aberrant types. Of these steering and balancing organs there are usually two pairs, of which the anterior (pectoral) pair is in general more highly developed than the pelvic. In living Chondrichthyes there are large eggs which often develop within the female's body or are surrounded by a heavy shell; here internal fertilization is necessary, and a clasping organ used in copulation is present on the pelvic fins of the male (Fig. 27*d*).

Two principal types are represented in the skeletal structure of paired fins. In one (Fig. 27a) the fin supports consist of a number of parallel rods of cartilage or bone extending out from a broad base, all articulating independently with the girdle. A second type (Fig. 27c) has a narrow base and leaf-like shape with a central jointed axis and side branches running out from it; only the proximal segment of the main axis articulates with the girdle. The first resembles structurally the median fins of many fishes and may well be the primitive type. An intermediate condition (Fig. 27e) is that found in many modern sharks in which some of the

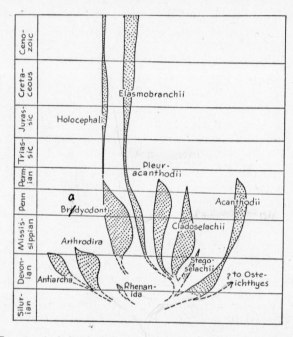

FIG. 28.—A phylogenetic tree of placoderms (at left) and "sharks."

cartilages articulate with an axis running out toward the back edge of the fin, but others have a direct connection with the girdle.

The basal fleshy parts of both median and paired fins are protected by scales or denticles similar to those on the trunk. Distally the fin membrane is stiffened by dermal rays which in sharks are of a horny material but which in bony fishes have been formed from highly modified scales. The anterior edge of the fins, which bear the brunt of pressure from the water in locomotion, are often reinforced by spines of hard dermal skeletal material, by a row of special ("fulcral") scales, or by enlarged rays.

Scales.—Almost all fishes are protected by hard dermal structures placed in the skin of the trunk and tail. Two types of these dermal defenses are found: (1) true scales, consisting principally of bone or similar materials, arranged in regular

rows often overlapping shingle-fashion and usually forming a complete body covering; such structures have been noted in many ostracoderms and are nearly universal in bony fishes as well as in some shark-like forms; (2) tooth-like dermal
denticles which, in sharks, lie isolated in the skin, giving it the texture of sand-
paper (shagreen). In forms which possess true scales denticles may be present as
well, either fused to the surface of these structures and forming an ornamental
pattern or lying free in the skin outside the scales. It was once thought that the
denticles were the original covering and that true scales have evolved by a fusion
of the bases of a group of denticles. But it now seems more probable that the
primitive dermal covering consisted of bony scales or plates with a superficial
pattern of denticles as an integral portion of their structure, and that with the reduction of scales the denticles may persist as isolated remnants of a once con-
solidated armor.

Arthrodires.—The Placodermi include but two orders of Devonian armored
fishes—the arthrodires and antiarchs—so peculiar in structure that their proper

Fig. 29.—*Coccosteus*, a small arthrodire of the Middle and late Devonian with reduced pectoral spines,
original about 16 inches long. (From Heinz.)

position has been much debated; even the question of their possession of jaws or
limbs has been disputed. The more important of the two groups is the order
Arthrodira, whose members may be characterized by the presence of a bony armor
composed of two parts, one covering the head and gill region and the second inclosing much at least of the trunk, the two connected by a pair of joints. Peculiar
bony jaws were present, as well as bone-covered structures seemingly representing
the pectoral fins. These features are well shown in such typical Arthrodires as
Coccosteus (Fig. 29) and *Dinichthys* (Fig. 30). The former was a Middle and Upper
Devonian fish of modest size, reaching perhaps 2 feet in length, the latter, a giant
late Devonian type; but except for some features suggesting reduction in the
dermal armor in the latter type, the two were essentially similar in known structures.

The body appears to have been of fairly normal fish shape, although rather
broad and flat. The posterior region of the body is adequately known only in
Coccosteus. Scales or denticles have been found in but a few instances, and the
skin may have been smooth and naked in most arthrodires. No trace of vertebral
centra has been discovered, but there were well-calcified neural and haemal arches.
The column tilted up at the posterior end, suggesting the presence of a heterocercal
tail. A series of cartilages above the backbone indicates the presence of a dorsal

fin, while a ventral plate presumably supported an anal. In front of this last structure was a paired plow-shaped element in the position of a pelvic girdle, and in a
few specimens there are indications of pelvic fins.

The armor plates were of bone, often ornamented superficially by dermal denticles, and comprised a complex series of median and paired elements, which were
in general uniform in number and position throughout the group. Grooves in the

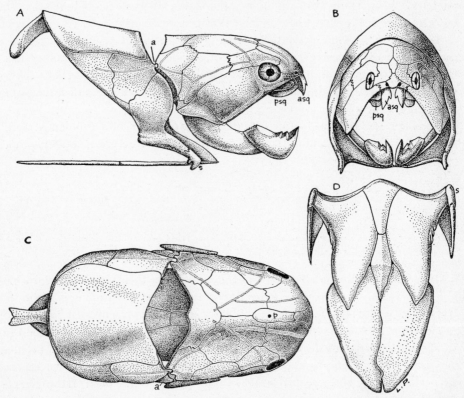

FIG. 30.—*Dinichthys*. *A*, lateral, *B*, anterior and *C*, dorsal view of armor; *D*, ventral shield. Mainly
based on the large *D. terrelli* in which the armored region is about $10\frac{1}{2}$ feet long. Lateral line canals are
indicated. *a*, joint between head and thoracic shields; *asg*, anterior upper jaw element; *psg*, posterior
upper jaw element; *p*, pineal opening; *s*, plate including the rudimentary pectoral spine. (After Heinz.)

surface of the plates indicate the presence of a well-developed lateral line system.
The head shield consisted of a series of plates covering the top and sides of the
cranial and gill regions. Large paired orbits were present and a pineal eye as well,
although this often failed to pierce the armor and reach the surface. A sclerotic
ring of thin bony plates was present in the eyeballs. This protective structure,
found in many higher bony fish and tetrapods, consisted in arthrodires of four
elements. In some cases notches at the anterior end of the shield mark the position
of paired nostrils. Most of the head plates were firmly united, but the plates be-

neath and behind the eyes and over the gill region were but loosely attached to the roofing bones.

The jaws were very peculiar in structure. Above the mouth there was a small median element and a pair of bony plates on either side, the front ones usually having a sharp tusk-like projection, the posterior one bearing a long shearing edge. Below, a single long element bearing a "tusk" in front and a shearing edge farther back was present on either side. It is obvious that these structures were very different from the jaws of normal fishes. The projections seen in the adult were not teeth but simply hard bony surfaces; in some cases young forms possessed pointed tooth-like structures, but these were merely outgrowths from the bone itself. There was no bony connection between the different parts of the jaw apparatus or between upper jaw bones and the head plates; but presumably there were in life cartilaginous jaws lying beneath the bony plates, and the lower jaw had a weak connection with the head shield. The two halves of the lower jaw were quite separate and in some cases bore small tooth-like structures on their opposed edges; there seems to have been a side-to-side motion of the lower jaws as well as the usual vertical movement.

The thoracic armor entirely surrounded the body. Dorsally on either side it articulated with the head shield by complicated peg-and-socket joints, indicating that there was a habitual movement of the head on the trunk. It is probable that in arthrodires (in contrast with other vertebrates in which the head remains fixed and the lower jaws move) the lower jaws remained stationary in feeding and the head moved up and down on them. Laterally a slit between the two sets of armor probably was an opening for a gill chamber situated beneath the back corners of the cranial shield. The thoracic armor both above and below extended far back over the trunk region, and below it also extended some way forward to protect much of the throat. The somewhat arched dorsal shield and the flattened ventral plate were composed of a number of closely connected elements with a nearly uniform arrangement in all typical members of the order. The lateral bony elements connecting the dorsal and ventral shields were situated in what is obviously the shoulder region and have been compared with the dermal bones in the same situation covering the pectoral girdle in the Osteichthyes. From the sides of the shoulder region projected a fixed bony spine, fairly long in *Coccosteus*, rudimentary to absent in later and larger types. This spine was in the position of the pectoral fin in more normal fishes; its nature has long been a subject of debate.

The internal skeleton of the head of the typical arthrodires is almost entirely unknown. Rugose surfaces and projections on the under side of the cranial bones indicate that there was a well-developed braincase, but it presumably consisted entirely of cartilage.

Coccosteus was fairly common in the Middle Devonian and probably ranged from fresh to brackish waters, showing a tendency, exemplified in many other chondrichthyian groups, toward a marine existence. A number of related but highly varied forms, all comparatively small and well-armored types, have been found in the lower part of the marine Upper Devonian of Germany. In the late Devonian arthrodires, then seemingly inhabiting brackish to salt waters, reached a climax in size and numbers. A great assemblage of types has been recovered from the black shales of the Cleveland region. Most common is *Dinichthys*, which reached a length estimated at 30 feet. In this giant type, in contrast with *Coccosteus*, the armor was shortened, both on the head and trunk; the shoulder spine was tiny or absent; an unprotected gap developed between the two shields; and the bones tended to be proportionately thinner and more loosely attached to one another. These changes were also present in great measure in a number of other contemporary forms. Some were smaller than *Dinichthys*, but *Titanichthys* was even larger, and the average size had greatly increased since Middle Devonian days. The jaw apparatus varied considerably; *Mylostoma* had even developed crushing plates for mollusk-eating. In all, however, a reduction of armor seems to have occurred with increase in size and tendency toward a marine life. This climax practically marks the end of the group, for no typical arthrodires survived into the Mississippian.

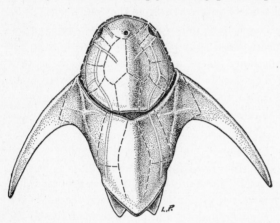

FIG. 31.—Dorsal view of *Jaekelaspis*, an acanthaspid arthrodire with enormous pectoral appendages. The jaw and lateral elements are unknown; their position is indicated by dotted lines. (After Heinz.)

Early arthrodires.—*Acanthaspis* and *Jaekelaspis* (Fig. 31) are representatives of a group of small and early arthrodires which appeared in Lower Devonian times and thus constitutes one of the oldest gnathostome types known; a few survived into the Middle Devonian. These forms had a head shield much like that of later arthrodires but with the eyes far forward; plates bordering the mouth have never been discovered. The stout thoracic shield was elongated and rather flat, and only in seemingly advanced forms are there indications of a division into separate elements. The trunk armor extended nearly as far back at the sides as it did above and below, whereas in forms from the late Devonian upper and lower shields were almost separate. A conspicuous difference from later types was that, instead of small spines at the side of the shoulder region, there were long hollow curved cone-shaped projections of the armor. These fixed structures would have been a hindrance rather than a help in swimming; the rather flat build of these fishes suggests that they were bottom-living forms, and these wing-like projections may have been of use in wriggling upstream against a current.

That these curious little forms were actual ancestors of the types found later in the period seems probable. In the highly developed thoracic armor and huge lateral spines we see structures not only reduced in size or stoutness in *Coccosteus* but further reduced in the still later *Dinichthys*. It is obvious that the history of arthrodires must extend back into the Silurian, but of the ancestral types we know nothing whatever.

Other arthrodires.—The name *Ptyctodus* has been applied to small bony plates, often no larger than a date pit, found in late Devonian and early Mississippian deposits. Usually a hardened area is to be found on one surface, suggesting that they were grinding jaw plates of a small fish of some sort. It was once thought that they pertained to chimaeras, shark-like types with somewhat similar tooth plates; but these forms appear much later in geologic history. Some Devonian ptyctodont plates were much larger and more like those of arthrodires, and in one instance remains of a set of shoulder plates of arthrodire type have been found in association. It is probable that these forms were late surviving arthrodires so degenerate that dermal armor had been lost.

Another side branch of the arthrodires is that represented by *Homosteus* and one or two other types found chiefly in the Middle Devonian of Europe. The armored region was very broad and flat, showing them to have been obviously inactive bottom-dwellers. One possessed a head shield probably as much as 4 feet in length. These forms soon disappeared and seemingly left no descendants.

The presence of bone and apparently of jaws has been argued as showing a relationship of arthrodires to the highest of fish groups, the Osteichthyes, and especially to the lungfish. But comparisons have been made not between primitive forms of the two groups but between late and specialized types, and it seems certain that the arthrodires were not on as high a plane of organization as the true bony fish. On the other hand, it has been held that they were related to the ostracoderms. But the arthrodires possessed jaw structures, although these are of a highly peculiar character; and we are thus forced to conclude that they represent a specialized side branch of the primitive jawed vertebrate stock of which the sharks are the closest living representatives. Quite probably the sharks themselves are descendants of once armored ancestors; and the arthrodires (and antiarchs) form, as placoderms, an odd and sterile side branch of this primitive gnathostome stock.

Antiarchs.—Related to the arthrodires but even more specialized were the members of the order Antiarchi, small but abundant Devonian fresh-water forms. The first representatives of the group are found in Middle Devonian strata where

Pterichthys (Figs. 32, 34) and *Asterolepis* are the common types, while in Upper Devonian deposits *Bothriolepis* (Fig. 33) is very numerous; the group then disappeared without leaving any descendants in rocks of later times.

The posterior portion of the trunk and tail was rather normally fish-like in appearance, scaled in *Pterichthys* but naked in *Bothriolepis*, with a heterocercal caudal and a single dorsal fin. The anterior portion of the body was covered with an armor structurally similar to that of arthrodires and similarly divided into head and trunk portions. The under side of the solid box formed by the armor was flattened, but the thorax was arched, with a decided peak at the top. The head shield was quite short and composed of a number of plates not readily homologized with those of arthrodires. The two orbits, with the pineal eye between them, were

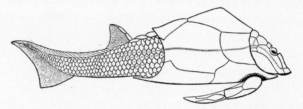

FIG. 32.—*Pterichthys*, a scale-covered Middle Devonian antiarch, original about 6 inches long. (After Traquair.)

FIG. 33.—Lateral view of the Upper Devonian antiarch *Bothriolepis*, a form with a scaleless trunk and tail. (After Patten and Goodrich.)

situated close together on the top of the head and directed upward. This gave an appearance somewhat like that of *Cephalaspis* but only indicates that we are again dealing with bottom-living forms. The preserved jaw parts consist of small transversely placed plates of bone even more aberrant in appearance than those of arthrodires. The gills were located under somewhat movable plates at the back corners of the head shield. The arrangement of the elements of the trunk shield was quite similar to that found in primitive arthrodires and suggests a close relationship to those forms.

Folds of skin found in *Bothriolepis* at the back end of the trunk shield may possibly represent pelvic fins. In the shoulder region, instead of a small spine or a fixed hollow cone as in arthrodires, there was a peculiar jointed flipper of considerable length covered with a series of bony plates and articulated by a complex joint with the body armor. This structure, with an external skeleton, seems more like an arthropod limb than a vertebrate appendage in which the skeleton lies within the fin. But in *Bothriolepis* it has been found that there are traces of an internal as well as an external skeleton.

These small fishes appear to have been bottom-living forms perhaps crawling about with their peculiar flippers more than swimming. With their small mouths and weak jaw apparatus they presumably fed either on small invertebrates or on soft vegetation.

Chondrichthyes.—The sharks and related living fishes form the basis upon which the class Chondrichthyes has been established. If one takes only existing forms into account, it is easy to distinguish them from the fish types which constitute the Osteichthyes, for in modern sharks bone is absent and skeletal materials consist only of cartilages internally and isolated denticles and fin spines in the dermal skeleton. Unfortunately this distinc-

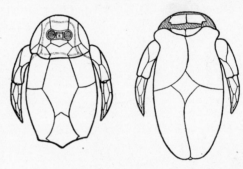

tion (to which the very name of the group itself refers) breaks down when fossil forms are considered; we know of fossil relatives of the sharks, including some of the most ancient members of the class, in which dermal plates and scales of bone or bone-like material were present, and in which there was sometimes bone in the internal skeleton as well. These facts suggest that in this group, as in the cyclostomes, the lack of hard skeletal parts is a degenerate rather than a primitive condition.

FIG. 34.—Dorsal and ventral views of the armor of *Pterichthys*. The elements of the thoracic armor are comparable to those of arthrodires (cf. Fig. 30). (After Traquair.)

In consequence of these findings a common definition of the group as a whole is difficult to give. We can merely say that the structure of the forms which we shall here include in the Chondrichthyes is in general a primitive and shark-like one, and that (even though bone may be present) the skeletal organization, while varying widely, never assumes the ground plan which we shall later find among the Osteichthyes and all the higher vertebrates derived from them.

The Chondrichthyes are without doubt a very ancient group. Few remains attributable to them have been found in Silurian rocks; but, since several orders were present in early Devonian times and almost every other shark type had become established by the beginning of the following period, their evolution must have begun well back in Silurian days. The early types seem to have been inhabitants of fresh waters, but during the Devonian there was a strong tendency toward marine life, and the surviving groups are almost exclusively sea-dwellers. The oldest known forms had well-developed dermal defenses, but armor tended rapidly to disappear within the group. The Chondrichthyes, previously abundant, declined rapidly in numbers toward the end of the Paleozoic and constitute but a small proportion of living fishes.

We shall for the most part discuss the widely varied forms ranged within the Chondrichthyes in the chronological order of their appearance. In so doing, it will be seen that we begin with forms which differ greatly from typical sharks and only later come upon the living groups and fossil forms resembling them.

Acanthodians.—The spiny sharks of the order Acanthodii were small fishes common in many fresh-water deposits from Devonian to Permian times; most averaged but a few inches to a foot or so in length. An obvious and significant difference from later shark types lies in the considerable development of dermal armor. Instead of isolated dermal denticles, these forms were covered by a series of scales and plates which resembled closely the true bony ganoid scales of many Osteichthyes (Fig. 52). A peculiar structural feature is that all the fins (except the caudal) were armed in front with a large stout spine.

FIG. 35.—*Climatius*, a Lower Devonian acanthodian with accessory paired fins, about 3 inches in length. (From Traquair.)

The body was of a normal fusiform shape in many acanthodians; but some early types, such as *Parexus*, exhibit a considerably flattened body, possibly a primitive character. One or two dorsal fins and an anal were present; the tail was heterocercal. The paired fins were attached to the body by a very broad base, a presumably primitive character seen also in the later cladoselachians; the internal structure of the fins is little known. Traces of the primary limb girdles are sometimes seen, but in addition superficial dermal plates were present in both shoulder and pelvic regions. In many Lower Devonian forms such as *Climatius* (Fig. 35) there were additional spines or fins between the two sets of paired appendages normally present in vertebrates; in one case there were as many as six pairs of fins. The earliest vertebrates in which limbs were developed may have shown considerable variation in the number of fins and only later settled down to the normal two pairs.

A series of plates similar in nature to the body scales appears to have covered the head of the earlier types, but little is known of their detailed arrangement. These early sharks were thus truly armored types, as were the ostracoderms, arthrodires and antiarchs, and the primitive Osteichthyes.

In the late (Permian) form *Acanthodes* (Fig. 36) much of the internal skeleton appears to have consisted of ordinary cartilage, but a number of cranial structures have been preserved. The braincase, as far as known, was of the generalized type to be expected in the ancestors of higher fish groups, and there was a series of jointed branchial arches. The jaws seem to have been essentially similar in nature to the branchial arches but of course considerably larger; the upper jaw articulates with the braincase behind the eye region.

Teeth were often weak or absent. When present they were pointed structures with a principal central cusp and smaller lateral ones, a tooth type which we shall see repeated in the cladoselachians. In some cases they were fused to the edges of

the jaws; in others tooth replacement appears to have taken place as in sharks through rows of successional teeth placed within the jaws. The members of such a row may be fused at their bases to form a whorl of teeth, as between the two jaw halves of *Ischnacanthus*. A similar fusion of teeth is found in some later shark types.

No complete examples of these fishes are known from the Silurian; but specimens which appear to be acanthodian jaws, scales, and fin spines have been reported from rocks of that period. In the Lower Devonian fresh-water deposits they are very abundant and already varied in structure; possibly they had developed in the upper reaches of river systems in earlier times and only migrated down-stream into regions where deposition was tak-

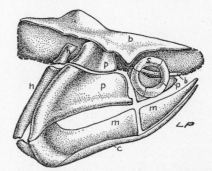

FIG. 36.—Lateral view of the cranial region of *Acanthodes*, Permian acanthodian. *b*, calcified (or ossified?) dorsal and ventral regions of braincase (approximate outlines of the cartilaginous portions are indicated by dashed lines and shading); *c*, an ossified (?) bar lying below the mandible; *h*, hyomandibular; *m*, mandible; *p*, upper jaw (the last three elements subdivided); *s*, sclerotic plates in orbit. (After Reis.)

ing place at the end of the Silurian. Numerous in the early part of the Devonian, they became rarer with the appearance of more advanced fish groups in Middle Devonian times, but *Acanthodes* survived until the Permian.

Apart from the typical acanthodians described above (mainly fresh-water fishes), there were more aberrant members of the group. Some of the early depressed forms with large spines may have been the ancestors of *Gyracanthus* and other Carboniferous types (known almost entirely from spines) which appear to have been large bottom-living members of the group. In the Middle Devonian lived *Onychodus*, known mainly from large bony jaw plates containing pointed marginal teeth and with a whorl of large teeth between the two halves of the jaw. The relations of this form are problematical, but it may have been a specialized acanthodian. These two types appear to have migrated into salt waters as did many other Devonian shark-like fishes.

At first glance, acanthodians appear to have been a specialized group, without relation to the evolution of later types. The presence of dermal plates and scales and highly developed spines was once thought to debar them from any ancestral connection with later sharks. True scales and dermal plates, however, were present in ostracoderms, arthrodires, and antiarchs and again in higher fish types; and it is hence but reasonable to assume that they were present in the ancestors of later sharks. Spines are found, on the dorsal fins at least, in many later sharks and may well represent the retention of a primitive character. Except for the first of the arthrodires and a peculiar form (*Gemundina*) to be considered later, the

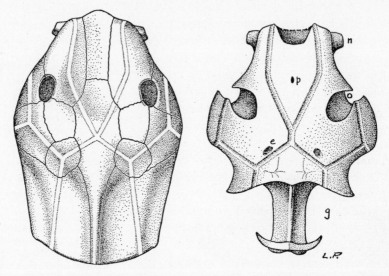

Fig. 37.—*Macropetalichthys*, a Devonian armored shark-like fish. Left, dorsal view of dermal armor of cephalic region; right, braincase lying beneath dermal plates. The position of the lateral line canals is indicated. *e*, opening of endolymphatic duct from inner ear; *g*, position of gill chamber beneath lateral back corners of shield; *n*, nostril; *o*, orbit, *p*, pineal. Original about 9 inches long. (After Stensiö.)

spiny sharks are the oldest of known jawed fishes. It is probable that the primitive gnathostomes were forms covered with a dermal armor of scales and head plates and may have been close to the acanthodians, if not actually members of this group. From a type such as these, with an overdevelopment of armor, may have come the arthrodires on the one hand, and on the other, through forms in which the dermal skeleton was reduced, later shark types.

Armored sharks.—If the sharks and shark-like fishes of later times have descended from armored forms, intermediate, partially armored forms should be expected. A few types seemingly of this nature have been described, but they are none too common. Best known is *Macropetalichthys* (Figs. 8, 37), a Middle Devonian marine fish the known parts of which consist mainly of a bony head shield; no other dermal remains have ever been certainly associated with it. The shield is an elongated structure, with the eyes well forward, and with an arrangement of bony elements somewhat comparable to that of the arthrodires.

There have been found beneath the head shield in a few specimens remains of the partially ossified braincase, from which much of the structure of the head, including brain, nerves, and blood vessels, has been made out. This structure lay below the anterior two thirds of the bony head shield; posteriorly an extension ran back to connect with the front end of the vertebral column, while cavities containing blood vessels show that the gills were located under the back part of the shield on either side. The cast of the brain cavity indicates that the brain was about on the level of organization of that of the sharks, and the braincase was shark-like in many other respects. It is not at all improbable that *Macropetalichthys* is a representative of an ancient armored stock which, through degeneration of its bony

spine found in some

FIG. 38   FIG. 39

FIG. 38.—Above, *Cladodus* teeth from the late Devonian and Carboniferous; below, pleuracanth teeth from the Permian. Somewhat reduced.

FIG. 39.—*Cladoselache*, a late Devonian shark-like fish. Original specimens range from about $1\frac{1}{2}$–4 feet in length. In addition to the normal paired fins, a pair of horizontal "rudders" may be noted at the base of the tail fin. (After Dean.)

covering, was on the way to becoming a soft-bodied shark. The term Stegoselachii ("armored sharks") seems appropriate as a provisional ordinal term for such intermediate types. Two other braincases essentially similar to that of *Macropetalichthys* have been discovered in Middle and Upper Devonian rocks which apparently pertain to forms more degenerate, lacking bone and covered only with dermal denticles; shark teeth are associated in one case. In the early Mississippian has been found a single specimen of a small shark (*Cratoselache*) which had fins and jaws similar to those of the members of the following order but which preserved a few small remnants of roofing plates on the top of the skull.

Cladoselachians.—The loss of armor had occurred in most sharks before the close of the Devonian, for we find in the late Devonian shark-like types covered only by dermal denticles and with an internal skeleton consisting only of cartilage.

Our knowledge of members of the order Cladoselachii is in most cases confined to teeth to which the name *Cladodus* is applied. These teeth (Fig. 38), first appearing in Middle Devonian deposits, are found in considerable numbers in Carboniferous rocks and finally disappear in the early Permian. They consist of a tall central cusp with a broad base on which are found one or more pairs of smaller lateral tubercles. In the Cleveland shales of the late Devonian an exceptional type of preservation has given us numerous specimens of *Cladoselache*, a shark possessing this tooth type in which much of the body structure can be made out (Fig. 39). This form is found in nodules in which are preserved, not only the remains of the teeth and calcified cartilages of the skeleton, but also impressions of the skin and body outline, and even traces of such soft tissues as muscle and kidney. There were two dorsal fins, each with basals and radials consisting of parallel rods of cartilage. The tail fin was very markedly heterocercal, the posterior end of the vertebral column tipping sharply upward. Well-developed pectoral and pelvic fins were present, the former much the larger, while far back at the base of the tail fin and just in front of the supposed position of the anus was a pair of outgrowths from the side of the body, seemingly a third pair of fins absent in later sharks. Like the median fins the pectorals (Fig. 27a) and pelvics had a skeleton of parallel bars of cartilage, the portions within the body partially fused into shoulder and pelvic girdles; the base of the fins was very broad, in contrast with those of most other fish. It is probable, as we have previously noted, that this is a very primitive type of fin structure from which may have arisen, by a constriction of the base, the fan-shaped fin of most later sharks and even the leaf-shaped appendage of a number of paleozoic fish types.

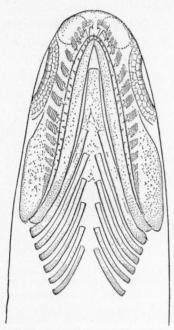

FIG. 40.—Ventral view of head and throat region of *Cladoselache* to show the ventral segments of the branchial arches and the jaws seemingly homologous with them. The position of the nasal capsules is indicated by dotted outlines; the orbits, seen laterally, are surrounded by enlarged scale-like denticles. (After Dean.)

The crushed condition and imperfect calcification of the cartilages render our knowledge of the head structures somewhat incomplete (Fig. 40). There were large paired eyes with concentric rows of denticles about them (no pineal has been observed) and definite indications of paired nostrils. The mouth seems to have been nearly terminal (it is usually fairly well back on the under side in modern sharks). There were typical shark jaws partially propped by the hyomandibular and lined with a well-developed row of teeth beneath which were numerous successional ones ready to replace them. Behind the jaws lay the hyoid and five successive branchial arches. As in acanthodians the jaws, except for their larger size, were quite similar to the other arches.

This shark seems to have been an active marine carnivore. Small fish, however, are not numerous in the deposits in which it is found, and it may have lived chiefly on invertebrates.

Cladoselache, however, was not the only type of fish to bear the *Cladodus* type of tooth. In the same shales are a few specimens of *Ctenacanthus*, a shark with similar teeth and similar fin structure but with large ornamented spines in front of its dorsal fins. Such spines occur as late as the early Permian, and it is probable that many teeth of the *Cladodus* type found in the Carboniferous may have belonged to this form. Similarly placed spines of varied patterns are found in many members of the modern shark group (elasmobranchs), while the fin spines in *Ctenacanthus* may possibly be a heritage, in turn, from a primitive acanthodian ancestor.

Both *Cladoselache* and *Ctenacanthus* have paired fins in which no axis was developed, but forms are found in the Carboniferous in both America and Europe

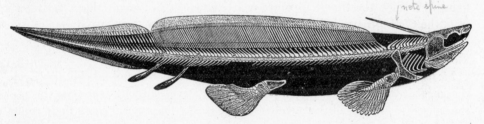

note spine

FIG. 41.—*Pleuracanthus*, a Carboniferous and Permian shark-like form. An average specimen perhaps 2½ feet long. (After Fritsch, from Smith Woodward.)

which had the *Cladodus* tooth type but in which an axial series of cartilages extended backward along the base of the fins (Fig. 27b). Such fins foreshadow the elasmobranch type and tend to show the derivation of these more modern forms from cladoselachian ancestors.

Pleuracanth sharks.—The order Pleuracanthodii includes a small number of predaceous types not uncommon in fresh waters in late Paleozoic times. The body of *Pleuracanthus* (Fig. 41) was long and slim, with an elongated dorsal fin stretching far down the back. The tail, unlike that of most early fishes, was diphycercal; but the tip tilted slightly upward, suggesting derivation from a heterocercal ancestor. The anal was a peculiar double structure. The paired fins (Fig. 27c, d) were leaf-shaped and contained a main skeletal axis with numerous side branches. Such a fin structure has been thought by some to have been present in primitive vertebrates. Here, however, we are dealing with a group seemingly specialized and not particularly early in appearance. This type of fin may have been derived by the gradual development of a posterior axis from one of cladoselachian type; the branches were not fully developed on the back side of the axis, suggesting a transitional condition. A clasper is attached to the pelvic fin in the males. This

structure is present in living sharks and chimaeras but unknown in forms previously considered.

There were no dermal plates on the skull; the braincase, jaws, and branchial arches are sometimes preserved in calcified cartilage (Fig. 26). A long movable spine bordered by two rows of small denticles projected from the back of the head. The teeth, loosely attached to the jaws, consisted of two divergent prongs and a central cusp (usually small), set on a button-like base (Fig. 38).

Pleuracanths are rare in late Devonian deposits but were quite common forms in Carboniferous and Lower Permian fresh-water pools, where they presumably preyed on small ray-finned bony fishes. They disappeared completely, however, before the close of the Paleozoic; with the extinction of these forms and of the acanthodians, sharks disappear from the fresh waters of the world, thereafter populated almost exclusively by bony fishes.

Little is known of the ancestry of the pleuracanths. In some cases teeth are known in which the three cusps are nearly equal in size, suggesting a derivation from the *Cladodus* type of tooth by a reduction of the central cusp and emphasis of the lateral ones. The presence of claspers suggests a fairly close relationship to the modern sharks and the chimaeras.

Elasmobranchs.—We shall designate as the order Elasmobranchii the living sharks, skates, and rays and their close fossil relatives, although the term is sometimes used to include all the members of the class. The typical shark body is of a fusiform shape with a heterocercal caudal fin, while the bottom-living skates and rays develop flattened bodies and a whiplash tail. The skin is covered with denticles; there are no dermal plates or true scales of any sort, although spines are present in front of the fins in the most primitive types and in a few living genera. There are one or two dorsals, an anal, and paired fins with constricted bases somewhat intermediate in structure between the presumably primitive broad-based type of the acanthodians and cladoselachians and the leaf-shaped fin of the pleuracanths.

The internal skeleton is composed only of cartilage, although this is often well calcified. There is a well-developed braincase to which the jaws were primitively attached both directly and through the medium of the hyomandibular. The hyomandibular, however, is the sole means of support in most living elasmobranchs. Usually there are five normal gill slits which open separately onto the surface of the body and lack the covering of skin or bone found in a majority of fish types. All except a few of the most active modern types have a spiracle. Its presence suggests that the primitive elasmobranchs were somewhat flattened forms, as is the most archaic of living types, *Heterodontus*, for this structure is seemingly an adaptation for water intake in bottom-dwellers.

The teeth are typically pointed structures, variously modified, often with low accessory cusps, and might well have been derived from the *Cladodus* type of tooth seen in both acanthodians and cladoselachians. But even in many early forms we find flattened teeth suitable for coping with hard invertebrates as food, and the development of a solid pavement is characteristic of the skates and rays. The teeth of sharks are usually loosely attached to the jaw margins, with replacing rows lying internal to the functional member of each series.

From many of the early types previously mentioned the elasmobranchs are easily distinguished by such characters as the absence of dermal plates or true scales and the presence of a clasping organ. The cladoselachians, however, resembled the more primitive elasmobranchs in many features; they differed essentially only in fin construction, and even in this feature intermediate types are known. It seems highly probable that the true sharks have been derived from some cladoselachian type, and (in view of the frequent presence of fin spines in primitive elasmobranchs) from such a member of that group as *Ctenacanthus*. The elasmobranchs were already marine forms when they first appeared in the early Mississippian.

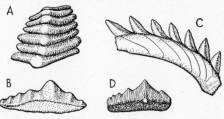

Heterodont sharks.—Most of the Carboniferous elasmobranchs exhibited a peculiar modification of the "*Cladodus*" dentition in which the front teeth were sharply pointed but the posterior ones were flattened and adapted for a molluscan diet. Curving series of replacing

FIG. 42.—Dentition of heterodont sharks. *A*, *Orodus* (Carboniferous), crown view of a tooth series ($\times \frac{3}{4}$). *B*, Same, lateral view. *C*, *Edestus* (Carboniferous) tooth whorl, reduced. *D*, *Hybodus* (Triassic) natural size. (*C*, after Dean.)

teeth lay within the jaws, often with a fusion of the bases of the component teeth. In some forms, as *Edestus* (Fig. 42c), a whorl of enlarged pointed teeth appears to have been situated in the front of the mouth between the two jaw halves. Posteriorly, in such forms as *Orodus* (Fig. 42a, b), several flattened teeth of each series appear to have functioned simultaneously instead of there being but a single marginal tooth in use. This mixed type of dentition is still found in a living shark, *Heterodontus* (or *Cestracion*), the Port Jackson shark of the Pacific, seemingly a survivor of this most primitive elasmobranch type.

While cladoselachian and possibly other types of carnivorous sharks were present in the Carboniferous seas, none survived through the Permian, for the seas of that time were almost barren of other fish types which might have served as prey. But the heterodont forms with a seemingly mixed type of diet struggled through into Mesozoic days. Marine invertebrate life, depleted in the Permian, increased greatly in the Triassic and offered a plentiful molluscan diet, while an invasion of the sea by bony fishes gave an opportunity for the redevelopment of a carnivorous mode of life. The heterodonts seem to have made the most of these possibilities; and a considerable number of types, such as *Hybodus* (Figs. 42d, 43) and *Acrodus*, are present in Triassic and Jurassic deposits. In later strata remains of these forms become rare, and we have noted that but a single representative of this most ancient line survives.

Modern sharks.—The decline of these primitive elasmobranchs appears to have been due to the fact that from them there developed two diverging types of special-

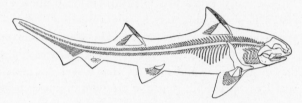

Fig. 43.—*Hybodus hauffianus*, a Mesozoic heterodont shark. Original about $7\frac{1}{2}$ feet long. (From Smith Woodward.)

ization. One comprises varied predaceous forms in which the entire dentition came to be the sharp-pointed flesh-seizing type found in the front part of the mouth in the heterodonts and in which a fast-swimming fusiform body was developed.

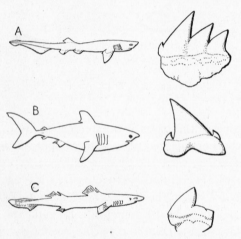

Fig. 44.—Representative shark types (left) and their fossil teeth (right). A, *Notidanus;* B, *Lamna;* C, *Squalus.*

In other types, leading to the skates and rays, the dentition became entirely flat-toothed and pavement-like, highly specialized for mollusk-feeding, and there occurred a marked further flattening of the body and a spreading of the pectoral fins. Much of the radiation of these groups of still living sharks and rays took place during Jurassic times, and by the beginning of the Tertiary all of the living families of elasmobranchs appear to have come into existence.

Among the predaceous sharks, three main groups may be distinguished:

1. The notidanoid sharks, such as *Notidanus* (Fig. 44a) and *Chlamydose-lachus,* known from Jurassic times onward, although far from common. Their sharply pointed teeth are in most cases easily derivable from the type found in *Hybodus,* and these forms seem to be comparatively little modified carnivorous descendants of the primitive heterodont stem. A seemingly primitive feature is the presence in these types of six or seven gill slits rather than the five normally found in living fishes. Fin spines are absent, and the spiracle is small.

2. The lamnoid sharks, numerous from the late Jurassic on, and including the

great majority of the active carnivorous types of late Mesozoic and later times. They are all active, fast-swimming sharks; the spiracle is small and sometimes lost entirely. There are several families; *Scyllium*, *Lamna* (Fig. 44*b*), *Odontaspis*, *Oxyrhina*, and *Carcharias*, are representative types known from both fossil and existing species. Some of the living forms are of considerable size, but a maximum seems to have been reached in a Tertiary *Carcharodon*, which may have had a jaw gape of 6 or 7 feet.

3. The squaloid sharks, of which the spiny dogfish *Squalus* (Fig. 44*c*) is an example. These forms are fairly active types, with fusiform bodies. But it is to be noted that the spiracle is large and there is no anal fin—features found in the skates and rays, where the spiracle is very important in the intake of water and where the anal fin, lying on the side of the body pressed to the bottom, would be a hindrance. These facts suggest that the spiny dogfish and related types may be close to the ancestry of the rays and that they may exhibit in their body form a late reversion from a bottom-living existence. Members of this group are none too common as fossils but had come into existence by the end of the Jurassic; *Protospinax* of that period was a primitive member of this group which still retained an anal fin.

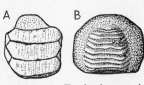

FIG. 45.—Teeth of rays. *A*, Part of a fossil dental battery of *Myliobatis*, with three complete plates and fragments of others. *B*, A single tooth of the large Cretaceous skate *Ptychodus*. (One-half natural size.)

Skates and rays.—All remaining elasmobranchs may be included in a suborder which we may term the Batoidea, comprising a series of forms which have become bottom-living types, often very depressed in shape and with enormously expended pectoral fins extending out from the sides of the body. Swimming is accomplished by an up-and-down motion of these large fins; the tail tends to be reduced and is often a mere whiplash; caudal and anal fins and often the dorsals are reduced or absent, and the spiracle is much enlarged. Skates and rays are mostly mollusk-eaters, and in relation to this the teeth (Fig. 45) are usually flattened and often form a solid crushing pavement.

Within this group many varied types have been developed. The most primitive members, and among the oldest in their geological appearance, are types intermediate in structure between sharks and rays, forms in which the pectoral fins are enlarged but in which the body is still somewhat rounded, and well-developed dorsal and caudal fins are still present. These include living types, the angel fish *Squatina* (Fig. 46*a*) with wing-shaped pectorals and the banjo fish *Rhinobatis*, both represented in the Jurassic, while a side branch, developing in the Cretaceous (Fig. 47), includes the peculiar sawfish *Pristis* with a long projecting snout armed with teeth on either side. Jurassic types had, however, developed further by the close of the period to produce typical rays of the existing *Raja* type (Fig. 46*b*), in which we find a flattened body with huge pectorals attached along the sides, a whip tail, and median fins reduced almost to the vanishing-point.

Two further groups are still more specialized. The Tertiary and recent torpedoes (such as *Torpedo* itself) are types in which the large pectoral fins have fused with the head to produce a rounded outline to the front of the body, while certain muscles have become modified into electric organs capable of severely shocking any enemy coming in contact with them. (We have noted the probable development of a similar organ in another, but vastly older, bottom-dweller, *Cephalaspis*.) The sting rays, such as *Trygon* (Fig. 46c) and *Myliobatis* (Fig. 46d), have so enormously developed the pectoral fins that the two meet in a point in front of the head as well as expanding into great flaps at the sides. These forms have in many cases developed a poisonous "stinger" from a modified fin spine situated on the

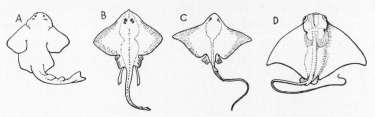

FIG. 46.—Various skates and rays. *A, Squatina; B, Raja; C, Trygon; D, Myliobatis.* The forms are known both from living representatives and Tertiary fossil types. (*A–C* after Goodrich; *D*, after Bridge.)

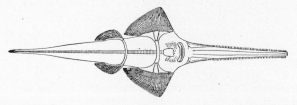

FIG. 47.—*Sclerorhynchus,* a Cretaceous sawfish. About 3 feet in length. (From Smith Woodward, *Outlines of Vertebrate Paleontology.*)

tail. These two groups are the last developed and perhaps at the present time the most successful of the Chondrichthyes.

The elasmobranchs have had a varied and checkered career. They seem to have been originally derivatives of the cladoselachian stock which had taken up life as mixed feeders with a dentition partly of a predaceous type, partly adapted for mollusk-crushing and a somewhat depressed body. It may have been their versatility in feeding habits which enabled them to survive the seemingly difficult times at the close of the Paleozoic, when the seas were swept clean of almost all other forms of vertebrates. With an increase in marine molluscan life and the ingress of a copious supply of possible food for carnivores in the shape of bony fishes, there took place during the Mesozoic the expansion of the modest ancestral forms into the varied shark and ray types which are still important factors in marine vertebrate life.

Gemundina.—We shall now retrace our steps, geologically speaking, to consider briefly a single fish, *Gemundina* (Fig. 48), from the marine Lower Devonian of Germany, a type of such peculiar structure and problematical relationships that we may consider it as constituting the sole representative of an order Rhenanida. The body was much flattened and similar in general appearance to that of the modern bottom-living skates and rays. Extending out at the sides were expanded paired fins, the pectorals being especially enlarged. The tail was slim with a spine representing the dorsal fin. The skin was covered with dermal denticles and with scales arranged in rows on the tail. Beneath the denticles, on the upper surface

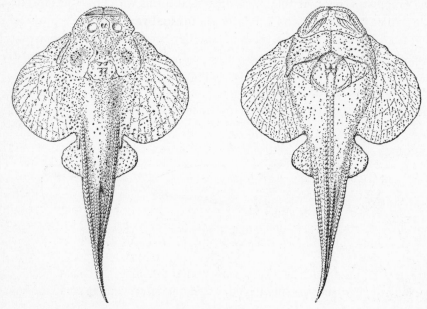

FIG. 48.—*Gemundina*, problematical fish from the Lower Devonian of Germany, dorsal and ventral views. (From Broili.) Original about 9 inches long.

of the broad head and below the shoulder region, were broad plates; their structure is unknown, although their position suggests that they were dermal bones, and possibly this form is still another example of a type descended from well-armored ancestors. The large eyes were directed straight upward, and almost between them were structures which seem to be paired nostrils. The mouth was a broad slit at the front end of the head, bordered by transverse jaws behind which are traces of a series of branchial arches. A number of neck vertebrae were fused into a solid bar behind the skull, while farther back were well-preserved centra of normal construction.

There are no other well-known forms which are at all close to this extraordinary fish. It is superficially similar to the skates and rays, but the resemblances are merely a parallelism due to similar bottom-living habits, for these latter forms appear only in the Jurassic. Possibly *Gemundina* was ancestral to the bottom-living bradyodont sharks of the following period; but this is purely a guess, in the absence of connecting forms.

Bradyodonts.—We have noted the presence in the Paleozoic of mollusk-eating fishes which appear to have been true elasmobranchs. Far more abundant, however, in carboniferous rocks are teeth of mollusk-eating forms more aberrant in structure and difficult to include in that group. Only from two or three specimens have we any clue as to the general appearance of these ancient mollusk-eaters. These examples show that they were depressed forms with large pectoral fins, as in the earlier *Gemundina* and the later skates and rays. We may provisionally unite these aberrant Paleozoic types in an order Bradyodonti, the name referring to the peculiar slow type of tooth succession. Their remains consist mostly of teeth, among which three common types may be distinguished:

1. Petalodonts (*Petalodus, Dactylodus*, Fig. 49a). The teeth of these forms have broad lozenge-shaped crowns which appear to have been applied closely to those

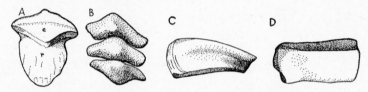

FIG. 49.—Teeth of pavement-toothed sharks. *A, Petalodus* ($\times\frac{1}{2}$), *c*, crown; *r*, root. *B, Helodus*, three teeth, crown view ($\times\frac{2}{3}$). *C, Deltodus*, crown view $\times\frac{1}{4}$). *D, Psammodus* ($\times\frac{1}{2}$).

adjacent, a group of such teeth forming a solid crushing pavement. Each tooth had a long root, sometimes subdivided, extending downward at an angle from the surface of the crown.

2. Cochliodonts. Although there appear to have been small anterior teeth, the main tooth structure in *Cochliodus, Deltodus*, and related types (Fig. 49b, c) consisted of a long spirally curved tooth plate in each half of each jaw. In adult forms this plate was a single mass, but there were often crosslines which suggest that it arose through the fusion of an entire successional series of teeth.

3. Psammodonts. In *Psammodus* (Fig. 49d) the dentition consisted of a few large quadrilateral plates arranged above and below in two rows which met in the mid-line. The origin of these plates is obscure; and while they were probably formed by a fusion of teeth, there is no indication of this in the specimens.

These bradyodonts were exclusively late Paleozoic marine forms. They appeared at the end of the Devonian and were very numerous in the Mississippian. Still plentiful in the Pennsylvanian, they became reduced in numbers as the invertebrate life tended to become less abundant. The psammodonts are not found after the Carboniferous; a few of the others persisted into the Permian, but none survived beyond that time.

With our limited knowledge, the origin of these bradyodonts is none too sure. The cochliodont spiral might have been derived from the fusion of teeth like those of the heterodont sharks; the simple petalodont tooth might also have had such an origin; the evolution of the psammodont plates is more puzzling. A derivation from very primitive elasmobranchs is not unreasonable. Another suggestion, however, is that the depressed bradyodont body may have been an inheritance from a type like *Gemundina* and that the bradyodonts were a very ancient and independent gnathostome stock.

In the Upper Paleozoic are found numerous isolated fish fin spines of various types. Some of these are known to belong to members of groups previously discussed, but many certainly pertain to sharks of the present order. In most cases,

Fig. 50.—Skull and shoulder region of a Jurassic chimaera, *Acanthorhina*. (After Fraas.) About ⅓ natural size. Upper right, mandibular dental plate of the Jurassic chimaera *Myriacanthus*. (After Dean.)

however, we cannot surely associate such spines with any particular tooth type. In this state of uncertainty, such spines are usually grouped as Ichthyodorulites and have been given generic and specific names as a provisional matter until the day when we can certainly assign them to forms already known from teeth or other skeletal parts.

Chimaeras.—In the deep seas today are found a few genera of comparatively rare cartilagenous fish, the chimaeras or ratfish, such as *Chimaera*, which constitute the living members of the order Holocephali. They are fairly active swimming types but often with the tail fin reduced to a whiplash with little indication of its true heterocercal nature. In many features (such as the construction of the paired fins and the presence of a clasper) they resemble the elasmobranchs. But there are some striking differences (Fig. 50). There is often a large rostrum, and the males have an odd clasping organ on the "forehead." The gills are covered with a flap of skin, an operculum, contrasting with the open slits of the sharks; and there is no spiracle. The dentition consists merely of a large tooth plate on each jaw ramus and an additional pair or two of smaller plates. This construction appears to be related to the mollusk-eating habits of chimaeras. The upper jaws are firmly united with the braincase, giving a firmer leverage for the bite.

Chimaeras have never been numerous, as far as our records show, and have been found only as far back as the Triassic. The most reasonable suggestion as to their ancestry is that they may represent modified survivors of the older mollusk-eating bradyodonts; the spirally curved tooth plates of some of the chimaeras are quite similar in appearance to those of the cochliodonts, while the large pectoral fins and reduced tail fin suggest an origin from flat-bodied bottom-dwellers.

Evolution of the lower fishes.—The foregoing account of the primitive gnathostome fishes has laid before us a great diversity of creatures. While our knowledge of their history is far from complete, we have seen that in many cases a plausible evolutionary story can be made out. But we are still confronted with the fact that at the earliest appearance of jawed fishes in the Lower Devonian at least three widely divergent types had already developed: acanthodians, arthrodires, and *Gemundina*. The ancestral gnathostome is still unknown.

Perhaps we may be permitted to try to gain some conception of the nature of this hypothetical creature which must have existed in some, as yet unknown, Silurian inland waters, basing the discussion on our knowledge of the evolutionary tendencies in the groups descended from it. It would seem highly probable that an external armor, and one containing true bone, was present as a series of plates over the head, gills, and shoulder region and as scales covering the body, and that some bone was present internally as well. That the body was rather flat and broad is suggested by the arthrodires, *Gemundina*, bradyodonts, and primitive elasmobranchs, as well as by the fact that a flattened body is common among the earlier jawless types. Conditions in the arthrodires and antiarchs make it seem probable that at this stage the jaws were still in a rudimentary state and that the paired limbs also must have been in a primitive stage of development, the pectorals probably the more advanced.

From such a hypothetical ancestor may have been derived on the one hand the arthrodires and antiarchs, through an evolutionary process accompanied by an over-exaggeration of bony structures, a loss of scales, and the development of peculiar types of jaws and limbs. And on the other hand, such a form might have given rise, with the more normal development of jaws and limbs and a rounding-up of body shape, to the acanthodians and later fish types.

Leaving this speculative territory, we may note three salient facts in the known history of the Chondrichthyes: (1) There was a tendency toward the loss of bone and dermal armor. Seemingly universal in the oldest known Devonian fishes, bone is practically unknown in the Chondrichthyes after the close of that period, and dermal defenses have been reduced to comparatively rare spines and small denticles. (2) There was a rapid trend toward a marine mode of life. Although the stem forms may have been inhabitants of fresh water, the great majority of the class had entered the seas by Carboniferous days, and fresh-water types are almost entirely unknown after the close of the Paleozoic. (This contrasts with the history of the Osteichthyes, which were comparatively late invaders of the oceans.) (3) Finally, the shark-like types have been, in the long run, a comparatively unsuccessful class of vertebrates. The greater number of chondrichthian groups failed to survive beyond the Paleozoic; only two of the eight orders into which we have here divided them are in existence today. This is in great contrast to the Osteichthyes, a group which rapidly rose to the assumption of the leading rôle in the story of aquatic life.

CHAPTER IV

BONY FISHES

The groups thus far considered, although prominent in the older geologic periods, have in later times become much reduced in numbers; the higher bony fish constituting the class Osteichthyes have, on the other hand, continually increased in importance. Appearing in the Middle Devonian fresh waters they flourished greatly and by the end of the Paleozoic had sole possession of the lakes and streams. By that time they also had invaded the seas, and at the present time the group includes not only all fresh-water fishes but also the vast majority of marine forms as well.

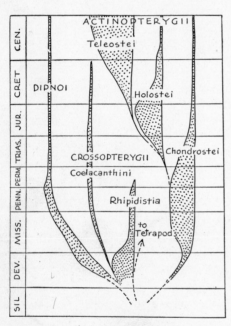

FIG. 51.—A family tree of the Osteichthyes.

There are three main subdivisions of the Osteichthyes, to which we shall constantly refer (Fig. 51); when the class first appears in the fossil record, these groups were already distinct, although much closer to each other than at present. They comprise: (1) the subclass Actinopterygii, the ray-finned fishes, rare at first but destined to become the dominant types; (2) the subclass Crossopterygii, or tassel-finned fish, extinct forms which lie close to the line of descent of land vertebrates; and (3) the subclass Dipnoi, the lungfish, a side branch of the last, abundant at first but now represented only by three genera.

As the name suggests, the possession of bone, not only in the internal skeleton but also superficially in the form of scales and of plates arranged in definite pattern, is characteristic, of the group. Some sort of air sac or lung appears to have been present in all primitive forms (in contrast to groups previously discussed); and there are advanced characters in the brain and other organ systems.

The primitive members of all three subclasses appear to have been active swimming types with a fusiform body and a heterocercal caudal fin. This last structure may be variously modified, and in almost all later members of the class the tail tends to become a symmetrical structure. In lungfish and crossopterygians this symmetry is attained by the evolution of a diphycercal tail; in the ray-finned types superficial symmetry was reached by a different process. One dorsal fin was present in the earlier actinopterygians, two in the other groups; a single anal is found in all.

Skeleton.—Bone is, of course, no unique possession of the Osteichthyes. We have seen that it was present in jawless types and in early shark-like forms; probably some sort of bony skeleton was present in the main line of vertebrate evolution throughout the early history of the group. In the lower fishes replacement bone seems to have been comparatively rare and was lost early in their history, whereas in the older true bony fishes the replacement of internal cartilagenous structures by bone had taken place to a very considerable degree. Many ancient forms among the Agnatha and Placodermi and even the Chondrichthyes had a dermal armor of body scales and of plates over the head and shoulder region. But while the armored members of these more primitive groups early became extinct or degenerated to an unarmored condition, the Osteichthyes have tended to preserve these scales and plates to a very considerable degree. We have noted that the arrangement of head plates in the earlier types was a variable one. In contrast we find throughout the members of the present class a common ground plan in the arrangement of the bony plates covering the head and shoulder region which, with variations, can be identified in all members of the group. This consistency in pattern indicates the common ancestry of the bony fish as a whole. In many cases the history of individual bony elements can be traced through into land types; for example, almost every bone in the human skull can be fairly accurately compared with its homologue in fishes.

There is generally considerable ossification in the internal skeleton of the body and tail in bony fishes. Often among early forms the centra of the vertebrae fail to ossify; but usually the neural and haemal arches and ribs are bony elements, as well as many of the median fin supports. The degree of ossification of the paired fins and the girdles supporting them is somewhat variable, but primitively all the main elements appear to have been bony structures.

Scales.—In the older bony fishes the trunk and tail were completely incased in an armor consisting of continuous and usually overlapping rows of bony scales, presumably rhomboidal in shape in the most primitive stage. These afforded considerable protection without interfering with the necessary motility of the body. Dermal denticles were often present in addition, as ornaments on the surface of the scales. Scales were present in many ostracoderms and some placoderms and early Chondrichthyes, but in the last group have disappeared, leaving only denticles as a protection to the skin.

Two main types of scale are found in early bony fishes—the cosmoid and the ganoid (Fig. 52). The former type was present in primitive crossopterygians and lungfish. Its base consisted of bone arranged in parallel layers. Above was a layer of spongy bone filled with spaces for blood vessels, while the surface consisted of a layer of dentine (termed "cosmine") with numerous pulp cavities and with a thin layer of shiny enamel on the surface. The whole suggests a series of fused denticles united with a basal plate of dermal bone.

A second ancient type, found in the older actinopterygians, was the ganoid scale. As in the last case, there was a layered bony base, a central vascular layer, and a layer of cosmine. But instead of a thin layer of enamel there was a thick series of concentric layers of enamel-like material, here called "ganoine." It is of significance that almost exactly the same type of scale was present in the spiny sharks; possibly the ganoid scale is the primitive type, and the cosmoid scale has resulted from a reduction of the superficial ganoid layers.

The term "ganoid" is often used to designate certain ancient bony fish. Properly such a term may be applied to primitive actinopterygians which have scales

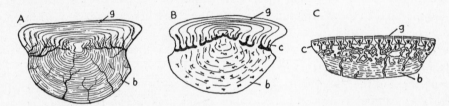

FIG. 52.—Vertical sections through the scales of: *A, Acanthodes*, an acanthodian shark; *B, Cheirolepis*, a Devonian actinopterygian; *C*, Megalichthys, a Carboniferous crossopterygian. All highly magnified. *b*, basal layers of bone or bonelike material; *c*, cosmine layer; *g*, superficial region—enamel or layers of enamel-like material (ganoine). (After Goodrich.)

of the ganoid type. But frequently (and unfortunately) it is applied to any primitive-looking fish with thick shiny scales and to forms with cosmoid, as well as ganoid, scales.

Both types of scale have undergone great modification and reduction; no living fish has a cosmoid scale; few have the ganoid type.

Skeleton of the head.—In the posterior part of the body the internal skeleton and the scaly dermal covering form two distinct units. But in the head and shoulder region a different situation exists, for, instead of scales, this portion of the body is covered by a series of bony plates similar in structure to the scales of the body. These come into contact with the internal skeletal elements and in great measure replace them. The braincase and upper jaws of a shark are usually separate elements; in bony fish the presence of dermal elements welds them together into a composite structure, a true skull. The lower jaw is also a composite, and even the shoulder girdle is of a dual nature, dermal bones being fused to the underlying primary girdle. We have thus in bony fishes (and in all higher types) a complicated series of cranial structures consisting partly of cartilages or replacement bones and partly of superficial dermal elements (cf. Fig. 7).

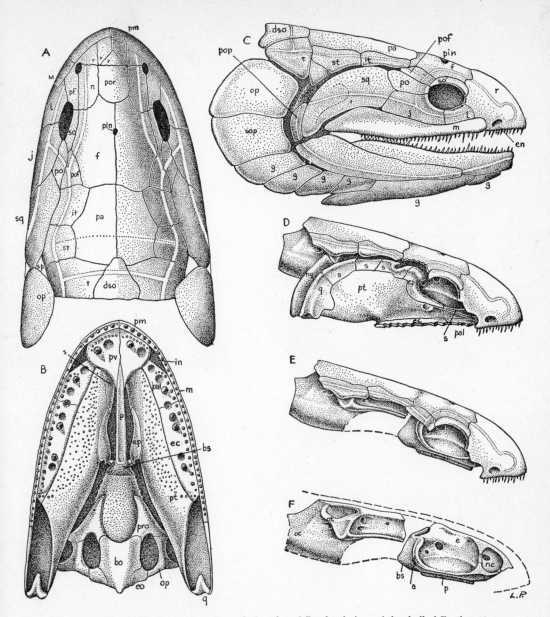

FIG. 53.—The skull in crossopterygians. *A*, dorsal, and *B* palatal views of the skull of *Eusthenopteron* of the Upper Devonian of North America. *C*, Lateral view of the skull and opercular region of *Osteolepis* of the Middle Devonian. *D, E, F* a diagrammatic "dissection" of the skull of *Osteolepis* to show internal structure. In *D* the opercular plates and the bones of the cheek region removed to exhibit the primary upper jaw. In *E* the primary jaw and hyomandibular removed to show the braincase in relation to the dermal skull roof. In *F*, the braincase isolated. The upper jaw and palatal region of *Osteolepis* are not well known; these structures have been restored from a later crossopterygian. *a*, articular facet on brain-case for upper jaw; *bo*, basioccipital; *br*, branchiostegal bones of throat region; *bs*, basisphenoid region of braincase, partly unossified in crossopterygians but stippled in *B; cl*, clavicle; *co*, circumorbitals; *cth*, cleithrum; *dso*, dermal supraoccipital; *e*, ethmoidal region of braincase; *ec*, ectopterygoid; *en*, external nares; *eo*, exoccipital; *ep*, epiterygoid (or metapterygoid); *f*, frontal; *g*, gulars; *hy*, hyomandibular; *in*, internal nares; *iop*, interopercular; *it*, intertemporal; *j*, jugal; *l*, lacrimal; *m*, maxilla; *nc*, nasal capsule; *o*, operculum; *op*, opisthotic; *ot*, otic region of braincase with articular facet for hyomandibular; *p*, parasphenoid; *pa*, parietal; *pal*, palatine; *pf*, prefrontal; *pof*, postfrontal; *pi*, pineal; *pm*, premaxilla; *po*, postorbital; *pop*, preopercular; *por*, postrostrals; *pot*, posttemporal; *pro*, proötic; *pt*, pterygoid; *pv*, prevomer; *r*, rostral(s); *s*, suprapterygoid(s); *sct*, supracleithrum; *sm*, supramaxilla; *so*, supraorbital; *sop*, subopercular; *sp*, spiracular opening; *sq*, squamosal; *st*, supratemporal; *t*, tabular. (*A, B* after Bryant, Watson, and Stensiö; *C*, after Goodrich.)

Our account of the arrangement of these bones will not be based upon any single fish skull, for we find considerable variation in pattern in different types. Instead, we shall describe an idealized primitive bony fish and lay down the fundamental pattern which, with modifications, can be traced not only through the varied fish groups but up through all terrestrial types as well. The arrangement of cranial elements in either a primitive actinopterygian such as *Cheirolepis* (Fig. 54) or the crossopterygians *Osteolepis* and *Eusthenopteron* (Fig. 53) approaches this pre-

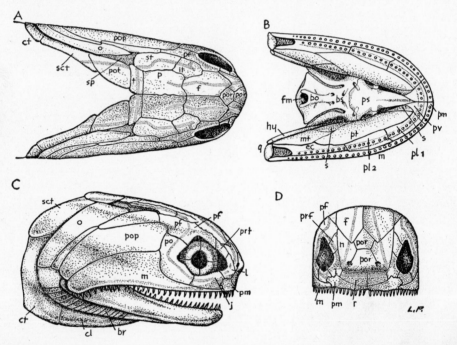

Fig. 54.—*A*, dorsal, *C*, lateral, and *D*, front views of the skull and shoulder region of *Cheirolepis*, a Middle Devonian paleoniscid. About natural size. (After Watson.) *B*, restoration of the palate of a palaeoniscid, based mainly upon *Eurylepis*, as described by Watson. For abbreviations see Figure 53.

sumably primitive pattern. The names used for the elements are drawn, wherever possible, from those used in the skull of man or other higher types.

Dermal bones.—The largest and most conspicuous group of dermal bones is that which forms a shield protecting the top and sides of the head. The braincase is fused to the middle of the under surface of this shield; to the lateral posterior margins are often attached the hinder ends of the old primary jaws, which are thus connected with the other cranial structures. The main tooth row of most bony fishes is carried by the outer members of this roofing series.

For convenience the elements of this set of roofing bones may be divided into a number of groups:

1. A paired series extending along the mid-line of the head. The most prominent members of the series are the frontals, situated between the eyes, and, farther back, the parietals (both still important elements in the human skull). Anterior to the frontals a pair of nasals are often present; but this region is quite variable in fishes and may be occupied, for example, by a solid rostral plate or a series of rostral bones. The pineal opening, if present, is usually between the frontals in fish; in land forms, between the parietals.

2. Marginal tooth-bearing elements, the premaxilla and maxilla, the latter usually much the larger.

3. A circumorbital ring of bones somewhat variable in number and arrangement. There may often be distinguished a prefrontal, lacrimal, jugal, postorbital and postfrontal.

4. Bones covering the cheek region between the orbit and the jaw articulation. Often little developed in fish, this region may have a squamosal as its main element and in addition smaller and more variable bones such as a quadratojugal. In actinopterygians the cheek region is little developed and much of it covered by an element associated with the gill cover, a preopercular.

5. The slit for the spiracle, when present, lies above this last series; above it at the side of the median series lie small elements sometimes identifiable as homologous with the intertemporal and supratemporal of early tetrapods.

6. A posterior marginal row of bones, usually including a dermal supraoccipital (single or paired) in the mid-line and laterally a tabular.

Dermal bones also develop in the skin lining the roof of the mouth. An elongate parasphenoid lies below the front of the braincase in the mid-line. On either side there is a series of dermal bones beneath the position of the old shark jaw, concealing and in great measure replacing that structure. These bones include the prevomer, palatine, ectopterygoid, and pterygoid, the last extending back toward the jaw articulation.

The lower jaw (Fig. 55) consists of dermal bones except for the articular region. The main tooth-bearing element is the dentary; below and back of this on the outside is a series often including a presplenial, splenial, angular, and surangular; on the inside are small coronoid bones and a prearticular.

The gill region is covered over in bony fish (in contrast to the usual shark condition). The gill covering, or operculum, is supported by a series of bones, normally consisting of a large opercular and smaller pre- and suboperculars, while a series of gular plates extends down under the throat region between the lower jaws.

The primary shoulder girdle is retained, but a series of dermal bones has been added to this region; typically there is a clavicle (the human collar bone) below and above it a larger cleithrum, while one or more bones connect the shoulder region firmly with the tabular region of the skull (Fig. 94a).

Replacement bones.—The dermal bones have taken over many of the functions originally assumed by the internal skeletal structures, but these latter are still present. The braincase (cf. also Fig. 86) is often incomplete above, since protection to the top of the head is afforded by the roofing series of dermal bones. A number of ossifications are always present, although considerable cartilage persists in many forms. In the posterior (occipital) region around the opening through which the spinal cord passes (foramen magnum) there usually develop a basioccipital below, a supraoccipital above, and a pair of exoccipitals at the sides. In front of the occipital region lies a ventral basisphenoid, above which there may be lateral elements somewhat variable in nature. Still farther forward there may be

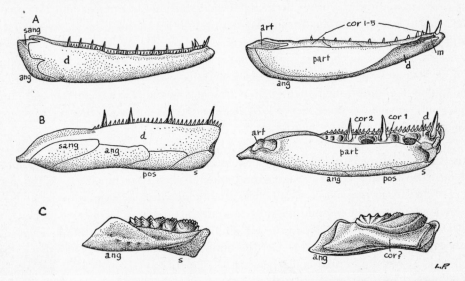

Fig. 55.—The lower jaw in bony fish. Outer view at the left, inner view at the right. A, *Nematoptychius*, a primitive actinopterygian. B, *Megalichthys*, a Carboniferous crossopterygian. C, *Sagenodus*, a Carboniferous lungfish (the articular unossified). *ang*, angular; *art*, articular; *cor*, coronoid; *d*, dentary; *part*, prearticular; *pos*, postsplenial; *s*, splenial; *sang*, surangular. (After Watson.)

an ossification in the front portion of the braincase, an ethmoid bone of one sort or another. At the posterior lateral corners of the braincase, the area in which the inner ear lies concealed, there are usually two ossifications, a proötic in front of the ear cavity and an opisthotic (paroccipital) behind this region and at the side of the exoccipitals.

The primary jaws of the shark type have been almost entirely replaced by the dermal bones of the palate, especially the pterygoid. In primitive bony fishes, however, a series of replacement bones lying in the roof of the mouth may be present inside and above the pterygoid and represent the original upper jaw. Two members of this series are especially persistent—a quadrate bone at the back outer corner articulating with the lower jaw, and an epipterygoid (metapterygoid) bone farther forward articulating with the braincase. The hyomandibular bar, as in sharks, usually functions as a prop from the jaw joint to the braincase region; and one or even two ossifications may occur in this element. The original lower jaw has been almost entirely replaced by dermal bones and is usually represented only by a small posterior element, the articular, which forms the joint with the quadrate.

The branchial arches are well developed and often well ossified.

Paired fins (Fig. 56).—The most primitive type of paired fins in bony fishes is probably that found in many of the actinopterygians. In early forms of this group the fins appear to have had a comparatively broad base with a skeleton consisting of a number of parallel bars of bone or cartilage. This is essentially the structure seen in the cladoselachians. In the actinopterygians the internal skeletal elements are usually short, and there is consequently only a comparatively small scale-covered fleshy lobe; the greater part of the fin consists of a web of skin stiffened by dermal fin rays. It is to this feature that the group owes its name.

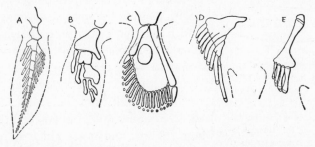

FIG. 56.—The paired fins of bony fishes. Pectoral fins of: *A, Ceratodus*, a modern lungfish, *B, Eusthenopteron*, an Upper Devonian crossopterygian, *C, Polypterus*, a modern relative of the palaeoniscids. Pelvic fins of: *D*, the sturgeon *Scaphyrhynchus*, *E, Polypterus*. (Mainly after Goodrich.)

In contrast a large lobe is developed in the fins of crossopterygians and lungfish, and the dermal rays merely form a fringe about its margins. In this lobate type there has been a great change in the skeleton of the fin. Only one stout element articulates with the limb girdle. Beyond this the crossopterygians usually exhibit an irregular branching arrangement. The dipnoans and some crossopterygians, however, have developed a leaf-shaped fin the skeleton of which consists of a long jointed central axis with symmetrically placed side branches. This is a parallel development to that in the pleuracanth sharks.

The fins of sharks are stiffened by long slim horny rays. In bony fishes these structures may be present but are much reduced. The fleshy lobe of the fin is covered with scales, and in addition the remainder of the fin is stiffened by fin rays composed of long slim modified scales arranged in rows. Such rays are present both in paired and in median fins.

Lungs.—Gills, never more than five in number, are always present, covered by an operculum and opening by a common slit just in front of the shoulder region.

In addition a spiracle appears to have been present in primitive types but is lost in most recent bony fishes. However, lung breathing, which we naturally associate only with land forms, had its beginning early in the history of bony fishes (Fig. 57).

Probably the most generalized condition of the lung is that found in the primitive living actinopterygian, *Polypterus*, in which there is a simple bilobed sac opening out of the bottom of the throat and situated on the under side of the chest in the position of lungs in land animals. It is probable that a similar type of lung existed in the extinct crossopterygians, and a functional lung is present in all the three living lungfish.

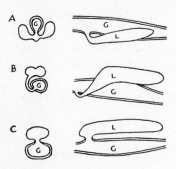

FIG. 57.—Diagram to show the development of lungs in fish and tetrapods. Left, cross-sections of gut and lungs, right, longitudinal sections. *g*, gut; *l*, lung; *A*, paired ventral lungs, found in tetrapods, African and South American lungfish and *Polypterus*. *B*, lung dorsal but duct ventral, as in Australian lungfish. *C*, single dorsal lung—air bladder—with dorsal duct, as in most actinopterygians.

The explanation of this unexpected development of lungs in water-living forms is suggested by the habits of the living types mentioned above. These live in regions (such as the upper reaches of the Nile) where there are alternate periods of rain and drought. During the wet season lungs are useless, but with the drying-up of streams, with water present only in stagnant pools, ordinary fish die by the myriad, while those which have lungs may survive until the next rains. Devonian bony fish, as far as we can tell from the sediments, appear to have lived under quite similar conditions, in freshwater streams and lakes which were subject to periodical droughts. Lungs were a considerable asset to them under these circumstances.

But lungs had obvious disadvantages. They seem to have lain originally in the under part of the chest and would have tended to make the fish top-heavy. In relation to this fact we find that in the lungfish the lung has shifted around to the top side of the body, although its duct may still be attached to the bottom of the throat. And in all the remaining living fishes we find that the lung, or air bladder, is present as a single sac which grows out from the upper side of the throat.

But while a lung is a useful adjunct under the peculiar conditions which we assume to have been present generally in the Devonian and which still exist in a few regions today, it is of little use under more normal climatic conditions. In most living fishes (actinopterygians) the lung has almost entirely lost its original function. But the structure is not lost; it has merely been changed to serve its possessor in another and highly useful way. It is present in most living fishes as the air bladder, a hydrostatic organ. By filling or emptying this sac, the specific gravity of the fish is altered and it is enabled to float higher or sink lower in the water.

In lower vertebrates, the nostrils are simply sacs opening to the outer surface of the head. In land types there is, as well, an internal opening of the nostrils into the roof of the mouth. Such internal openings are not present in any known actinopterygians, but in both the lungfishes and crossopterygians internal nostrils were early developed and permitted the intake of air into the lungs without the necessity of opening of the mouth and running the risk of "shipping water."

Bony-fish ancestry.—The appearance of the bony fishes in the geologic record is a dramatically sudden one. There are no traces of the group in the Silurian and only a few fragments which may be of Lower Devonian age. In the Middle Devonian they appear full-fledged and diversified and at once dominate the scene. The initial stages in their development must have taken place long before, quite probably in the upper reaches of river systems from which no deposits have been preserved.

The common ancestor of the bony fish groups is unknown. But we can deduce many features to be expected in such a form from those present in primitive crossopterygians and actinopterygians. The body must have been fusiform, with a heterocercal caudal fin, one or two dorsals, and an anal. The paired fins presumably had a broad base and but a moderate fleshy lobe and a skeleton of parallel bars with little, if any, development of an axis. The body and tail were covered with rhomboidal scales, quite possibly of the ganoid type, while a well-developed series of bony plates of the general pattern described above covered the head, gill region, and shoulder. The internal skeleton of the head region was presumably well ossified, that of the body probably less completely so. A pair of ventral lungs may have been present as a supplement to gill breathing, but internal openings for the nostrils had presumably not yet developed.

In most respects the earliest actinopterygians, the forms shortly to be described, were very close to this hypothetical ancestor, although even they had become somewhat specialized. It will be noted that in many features, such as fins, scales, and the presence of head plates, the acanthodian sharks of the Lower Devonian show resemblances to this hypothetical form. They are seemingly somewhat degenerate as regards the development of the skeleton and differ in the presence of spiny fin supports. Even so, they may be close to the ancestry of the present group. The bony fish may perhaps be regarded as merely one line among many which diverged from a primitive stock of armored sharks, but one which has advanced so far and so successfully that we are fully warranted in regarding them as constituting a separate class of higher fishes.

Ray-finned fishes.—Of the three types of bony fishes, the actinopterygians perhaps merit first consideration because the early members of the group appear to have been, on the whole, somewhat closer to the probable common ancestor of the bony fishes and because the ray-finned fishes, although comparatively rare at the first, have been destined to play the chief rôle in fish history. Today, except for three genera of lungfish, all fresh-water fishes are ray-finned types and so also are all marine forms except a small percentage of sharks and skates.

The ray-finned fishes may be conservatively divided into three orders: (1) Chondrostei, containing primitive Paleozoic types and rare or degenerate survivors; (2) Holostei, mainly Mesozoic fishes descended from the Chondrostei and leading to (3) Teleostei, the dominant Cretaceous and Tertiary forms.

The tail was heterocercal in the oldest known actinopterygians, as was also the case in early lungfish and many crossopterygians; but it differed in that there was practically no development of fin membrane above the backbone. In consequence, almost never has a member of the present group been able to develop a diphycercal tail, an evolutionary process in which an upper lobe (here generally non-existent) must be greatly developed to equalize the lower one. A similar end, however, has been attained by the development of a homocercal tail (Fig. 3d), a superficially symmetrical type found in the teleosts in which the lower lobe only is concerned but in which the scaly tip of the tail is reduced and no longer projects outside the rounded posterior termination of the body. The end result is a tail fin externally somewhat like the diphycercal one but constructed in a very different way.

In contrast with other bony fishes, there is usually little extention of the flesh and internal skeleton into the paired fins (Fig. 56d, e), which are mainly supported by long dermal rays. The internal skeleton of the fins consists generally of a number of short parallel bars of bone which may articulate directly with the girdle, although there may be some development of an axis. There is but a single dorsal fin, in contrast to the two other groups. Above the front edge of the dorsals and caudal in earlier actinopterygians are frequently found rows of large V-shaped fulcral scales forming a protective cutwater for the fins. These are not found in other fish groups and are lost in most later ray-finned types.

The scales primitively had the typical ganoid structure; in early forms they were usually rhomboidal in outline. In later types, holosteans and teleosts especially, the scales may become rounded, tend to become thin, lose the ganoine, and have been lost in some cases.

In the earliest actinopterygians the general arrangement of the bony plates of the head was quite similar to the generalized pattern described above (Figs. 54, 55a). An enormous amount of variation, however, is found in the group (cf. Fig. 71). In some the bones in various regions tend to increase in number; on the other hand, there is quite commonly a reduction in the number of elements; this is particularly true in the cheek region. The primary upper jaws are often not closely connected with the dermal elements of the skull roof, and the hyomandibular is usually large and well ossified and performs an important supporting function; usually there is an additional element (the symplectic) in association with it. The braincase appears to have been well ossified primitively, but in some forms there has been a tendency to reduce the degree of ossification. Typically there are sharp conical teeth in a series on the margins of the jaws and numerous smaller teeth within the mouth. There are many variations in the teeth; sometimes they extend into the throat; and in various groups blunt crushing teeth are developed.

The originally large gular plates covering the throat tend to be reduced to a series of small thin rods, the branchiostegal rays. The dermal part of the shoulder girdle primitively contained both clavicle and cleithrum, but the former tends to be lost.

There is no sure indication of an internal opening of the nostrils in any living or fossil form; the spiracle is present only in the more primitive types; and there is never an opening for a pineal eye. The lung is well developed only in the Polypterini; in all other living forms it is a single dorsal sac with little or no breathing function, and in many teleosts it has even lost its connection with the gut.

Like the other bony fish groups, the Actinopterygii appear to have been originally fresh-water forms. They are found almost entirely in this type of surroundings until near the close of the Paleozoic. But at the beginning of the Mesozoic the group tended to migrate into the seas, and from the Jurassic onward the ray-finned fishes have been equally at home in both inland and salt waters.

The Chondrostei.—The oldest known ray-finned forms and their modern descendants may be placed in the order Chondrostei, a group ancestral to the remaining actinopterygians and probably not far from the ancestral bony fish stock. Primitive chondrosteans were distinguished from other later actinopterygians by the presence of a fully developed heterocercal tail, a clavicle, fulcra on the dorsal and caudal fins, thick shiny ganoid scales, and by the absence (as is usual in older fish types) of ossification in the central region of the vertebral column. Most later members of the group have lost many of these features.

Cheirolepis (Figs. 54, 58) of the Middle Devonian is the oldest known ray-finned fish and had an exceedingly primitive structure. There was a well-developed heterocercal tail; the paired fins, especially the pelvics, had a much broader base than is usually the case in actinopterygians; and the fleshy lobe was not as small as in most later actinopterygian types. The fins were well reinforced by fulcral scales. The body scales were small rhombic structures similar in appearance to those of the acanthodian sharks. The cheek region was completely covered by bones in close contact with the large maxilla, which was the major tooth-bearing element. A spiracle appears to have been present, and not improbably (as deduced from living relatives) there were functioning lungs not yet transformed into an air bladder, situated on the under side of the chest.

Cheirolepis was comparatively rare and was far outnumbered by the contemporary crossopterygians and lungfish. But by the beginning of the Mississippian, conditions were reversed; and during the remainder of the Paleozoic the primitive actinopterygians, of which *Palaeoniscus* (Fig. 58) of the Permian is the most familiar, are the commonest fresh-water types. Most of them are closely related to and descended from *Cheirolepis*. These palaeoniscids were generally small active predaceous types with pointed teeth; they probably preyed chiefly on invertebrates, and in turn may have afforded a food supply for their larger contem-

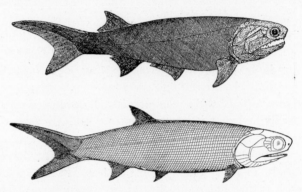

FIG. 58.—Paleozoic palaeoniscids. Above, *Cheirolepis trailli*, a primitive Devonian form. Below, *Palaeoniscus* of the Permian. Both about 9 inches long. (From Traquair.)

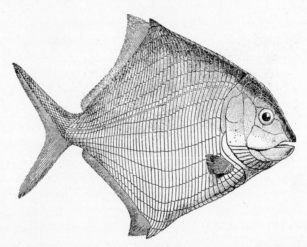

FIG. 59.—*Cheirodus*, a Carboniferous platysomid. About ½ natural size. (From Traquair.)

poraries, the crossopterygians, pleuracanth sharks, and the bigger amphibians. During the Triassic they were largely replaced by more advanced actinopterygians but survived in diminishing numbers until late Jurassic times.

It was not long before varied branches of the palaeoniscid stock began to make their appearance. Conspicuous is a group found in the Carboniferous and Permian of which *Platysomus* and *Cheirods* (Fig. 59) are typical; these had a deeper, shorter body with long dorsal and anal fins and blunt teeth. These adaptive characters have been developed over and over again in the actinopterygian groups;

they appear to denote a life in still waters and a food supply of small inactive shelled invertebrates. Another derived group, common in the Triassic, was that of *Catopterus* (Fig. 60) and its allies, differing from the palaeoniscids in having the heterocercal tail fin somewhat abbreviated, the tip of the backbone not extending to the end of the fin. In this they simulated the holosteans, although they were probably not their actual ancestors.

Derived from the palaeoniscids but differing greatly from them in many respects are several Mesozoic and Tertiary families which include degenerate surviving members of the order. *Chondrosteus* (Fig. 61) of the Jurassic and early Cretaceous

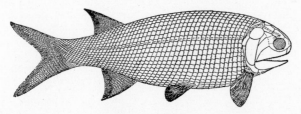

FIG. 60.—*Catopterus*, an advanced Triassic chondrostean with an abbreviated heterocercal tail. Original about 5½ inches long. (From Brough.)

FIG. 61.—*Chondrosteus*, a Jurassic fish intermediate between palaeoniscids and sturgeons. About 3 feet long. (From Smith Woodward.)

was a marine form in which there was considerable reduction of the bony elements of the skull and of the body covering, normal ganoid scales being found only on the tail. The teeth were much reduced, the jaws weak and short, while a rostrum projected above the mouth. A further stage in degeneration is that found in the Tertiary and recent sturgeons, such as *Acipenser*. The skull is well ossified superficially, but internally the skeleton has mostly reverted to a cartilagenous condition, and instead of a body covering of ganoid scales there are only a few rows of large bony scutes. The jaws are feeble and toothless, and a long rostrum projects forward beyond them. The food consists of small invertebrates stirred up along the bottom by the long snout. The paddle fishes (*Polyodon*, etc.) of the Mississippi and Chinese rivers, fossil relatives of which run back to the Cretaceous, are similar in habits and general structure to the sturgeons but are distinguished by the huge spoon-shaped rostrum and the almost entire absence of dermal bones and scales.

Of uncertain position are the peculiar Triassic marine types *Belonorhynchus* (Fig. 62) and *Saurichthys*. These were fairly large elongate fishes, obviously fast-swimming carnivores with a long beak armed with sharp teeth; the scales were reduced to a number of rows down the sides of the body as in sturgeons. In most respects they appear to have been chondrosteans; but the tail was apparently diphycercal in nature, not heterocercal. These forms are difficult to place but may perhaps be considered as widely divergent offshoots of the palaeoniscid stock.

Although the typical palaeoniscids are extinct, primitive forms apparently derived from them survive in tropical Africa—*Polypterus* and a rather eel-like relative, *Calamoichthys*. The position of these fishes has been much disputed, and (except for a few scales from the Tertiary of that continent) nothing is known of them as fossils. They were long thought to be living members of the Crossopterygii. But it appears upon study that they are probably comparatively little-modified descendants of the palaeoniscids and are in many features the most primitive of living bony fishes.

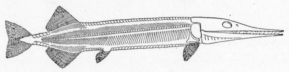

FIG. 62.—*Belonorhynchus*, a specialized Triassic chondrostean. About 20 inches long. (From Smith Woodward, *Outlines of Vertebrate Paleontology.*)

Polypterus is obviously specialized in such respects as the subdivision of the dorsal fin into a number of finlets (a feature to which the name is due) and in the development of a diphycercal tail which presumably has had a history parallel to that of the later crossopterygians and lungfish. But there are many primitive features, such as the retention of thick shiny scales and head plates, the persistence of the spiracle, and especially the presence of well-developed paired lungs in the seemingly primitive ventral position (Fig. 57a). These forms live in regions liable to seasonal drought (as do the surviving lungfish), and it would seem that they have persisted unchanged in the type of environment which may have surrounded all the bony fishes in Devonian days.

In studying these forms, most workers have usually focused their attention on the paired fins, especially the pectoral (Fig. 56c), which has a large fleshy lobe fringed about by dermal rays. This lobe is much more developed than in the usual ray-finned types and has been considered as strong evidence for crossopterygian affinities. But in *Polypterus* there is no internal opening for the nostril as there was in all known crossopterygians, no pineal opening (again in contrast to their supposed relatives), and the skull pattern, although somewhat specialized, appears to be more like that of the actinopterygians. The scales, too, when sectioned are seen to be of true ganoid structure, rather than of the crossopterygian cosmoid type. And while the lobe of the pectoral fin is well developed, its skeletal pattern does not resemble that of crossopterygians. Not only are there three proximal elements, but beyond them a series of short parallel bars comparable to those of the primitive ray-finned forms.

Altogether these characters show us that we are in reality dealing with an actinopterygian but one markedly different from any other living member of that group. Except for some evolutionary changes in the fins, *Polpyterus* seems to be a primitive survivor from the earliest days of actinopterygian history, a relic of the ancient palaeoniscid stock.

The chondrosteans were mainly a late Paleozoic group. By the end of the Triassic they had been in great measure supplanted by the holosteans descended from them, and beyond the Jurassic only the few rare or degenerate forms mentioned above survive.

Holosteans.—The order Holostei, an intermediate group in the main evolutionary story of the ray-finned fishes, comprises a great series of forms descended from the chondrosteans and replacing them in importance in Middle Mesozoic days, only to dwindle in turn after having given rise to the modern teleosts. In holosteans the caudal fin is usually of an abbreviated heterocercal type, the scale-covered tip of the body extending but a short way along the top of the fin; the clavicle has been lost, leaving the cleithrum alone as a cover to the shoulder girdle; ganoid scales are usually present, although tending to thin out in higher families; and fulcral scales are usually present. Living forms include only the gar pike, *Lepidosteus*, of American fresh waters, and *Amia*, the so-called dogfish or bowfin of American lakes.

The single dorsal air bladder still functions slightly as a lung in living forms, although its chief use is hydrostatic. The spiracle has been lost. Ossifications are often developed in the central region of the vertebral column. The skull tends to drift away structurally from the primitive type, especially in the cheek region, which is no longer covered by bone. The gape of the mouth becomes shorter; and the maxilla, originally a very large bone, is reduced in size and no longer comes in contact with other elements posteriorly, leaving the cheek region bare of dermal bones. This skull structure leads readily to the teleost condition (Fig. 71).

Although the first holostean, *Acentrophorus*, appeared in the late Permian, it was only toward the end of the Triassic that members of the order became abundant. The Jurassic witnessed the maximum development of holostean types, and during that period they were by far the most important of fishes. In the Cretaceous they were already being crowded out by their descendants, the teleosts, and were well on the way toward their present insignificant position. A feature of note is the fact that these forms tended strongly to break away from the fresh-water habitat in which bony fishes had their origin and became dominantly a marine group. This seaward migration seems to have taken place mainly in the Triassic and was accompanied by a similar movement on the part of the surviving chondrosteans and the coelacanths. It may have been stimulated by the renewal at the beginning of the Mesozoic of abundant marine invertebrate life suitable for food and was, as has been seen, followed by a recrudescence of carnivorous shark life.

The most common of Triassic forms were *Semionotus* (Fig. 63) and its relatives, types which resembled, superficially at least, the palaeoniscids but differed in the loss of the clavicle and in the abbreviated heterocercal tail. But although these early forms were seemingly close to the stem of the order, most semionotids, such as *Lepidotus* of the Jurassic (Fig. 63), tended to become deep-bodied fishes,

FIG. 63.—Above, *Semionotus agassizii*, a primitive Triassic holostean. Original about 1 foot long. Below, *Lepidotus minor*, a deep-bodied Jurassic semionotid, original about 1 foot long. (*Semionotus* from Eastman, *Lepidotus* from Smith Woodward.)

a tendency culminating in the Jurassic *Dapedius* (Fig. 64). This body form, together with the fact that the teeth became flat and pebble-like, suggests that the later semionotids were inhabitants of still waters such as those of coral reefs. These forms are a close parallel to the earlier platysomids.

A further development of coral-reef adaptations is seen in *Pycnodus* and its allies such as *Mesodon* and *Microdon* (Fig. 65), types which appeared in the Triassic and persisted, unlike most of the holosteans, until the Eocene. In these peculiar but abundant forms the body was almost circular in outline; and instead of the complete covering of thick ganoid scales present in the semionotids, many of the scales were lost or transformed into a latticework of jointed rods. There was a tiny mouth filled with pebble teeth for coral nibbling, a peculiar beak, and cheek and throat regions broken up into a mosaic of tiny bony plates.

Remains of the gar pike, *Lepidosteus*, are known only from Eocene and later rocks. This living form is a rather primitive holostean in such respects as its retention of primitive thick ganoid scales, and seems obviously an offshoot of the semionotid stock. But in other features, such as its long rapaceous jaws, the gar is highly specialized. In this type and the remaining families to be mentioned, the tail is much abbreviated and superficially is nearly symmetrical, although the development does not quite reach the homocercal condition.

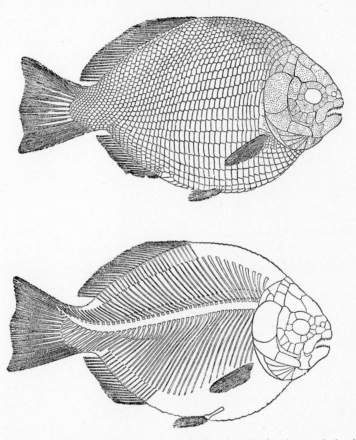

Fig. 64.—*Dapedius*, a deep-bodied Jurassic holostean (Semionotidae). About 14 inches long. (From Smith Woodward, *Outlines of Vertebrate Paleontology*.)

The holosteans so far considered are either rather primitive members of the order or forms which diverged early from the main line of holostean evolution. More typical members are to be found in a group of families abundant in the Jurassic and represented by such types as the extinct *Caturus* (Fig. 66), *Pachycormus* and *Amiopsis* (Fig. 67), and the living bowfin *Amia*. These fishes are primitive and generalized in body shape, but the backbone is shortened in the tail region to a condition approaching that of the teleosts. *Caturus* and closely related types retained the thick rhombic ganoid scales of their ancestors, but

Pachycormus and *Amia* and their relatives tend to reduce the scales to thin wafers of bone with rounded margins. Fulcral scales had degenerated. The caturids and

Fig. 65.—*Microdon*, a Jurassic pycnodont fish. About 5 inches long. (From Smith Woodward.)

Fig. 66.—*Caturus*, a Jurassic holostean (Eugnathidae). (From Smith Woodward.)

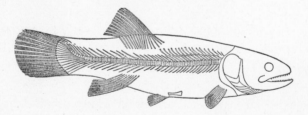

Fig. 67.—*Amiopsis*, a Jurassic relative of the living holostean *Amia*. (From Smith Woodward.)

pachycormids (the latter group tending to develop a long rostrum like that of a swordfish) did not survive the end of the Mesozoic; *Amia*, in which an elongated dorsal fin is a characteristic feature, is the sole survivor of these Jurassic forms.

A number of other Jurassic groups, of which *Pholidophorus* (Fig. 68) and *Oligopleurus* are examples, had advanced still further toward the teleost type in the condition of the scales and caudal fin and were progressive in other respects, the centra of the vertebrae, for example, being often well ossified. Among these forms were presumably the ancestors of the teleosts, and it is difficult to establish a line of cleavage between the two groups.

Aspidorhynchus (Fig. 69) and a few related marine fishes of the Jurassic and Cretaceous constitute an extinct side branch of the holosteans which retained good ganoid scales but developed a forked tail which had, so to speak, prematurely attained a homocercal condition. The body was elongate and the dentition powerful, so that, despite the development of a rostrum in front of the mouth, these forms

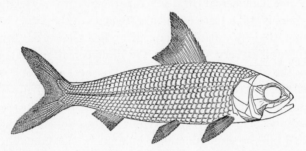

FIG. 68.—*Pholidophorus,* an advanced Jurassic holostean. About 9 inches long. (From Smith Woodward.)

FIG. 69.—*Aspidorhynchus,* an aberrant predaceous Jurassic holostean. About 2 feet long. (From Assmann.)

appear to have been fast-swimming active carnivores, preying on other holostean types.

Holostean history is essentially a Mesozoic story. Unquestionably derived from the older palaeoniscids, members of the order became abundant in the late Triassic, where *Semionotus* and its allies were the most common of fish types. From the base of the holostean stock were given off various side branches, such as the pycnodonts, *Aspidorhynchus* and the surviving gar pike. The Jurassic was the period of dominance of more progressive holosteans, of which *Caturus* was typical and of which *Amia* is a survivor. During that period appeared still more advanced forms leading to the teleosts. In the Cretaceous the holosteans were much reduced in numbers and have since all but disappeared. Holosteans were mainly marine forms, although the two living types inhabit fresh waters.

Teleosts.—The teleosts are the successful fishes today, the culmination of the series of phylogenetic changes seen in the more typical chondrosteans and holosteans. Although there are rare traces of primitive members of the group in the Upper Triassic, they are practically unknown until late Jurassic times. In the Cretaceous teleosts far outnumbered the holosteans and have since been the dominant fishes of both salt and fresh waters.

The diagnostic features of the order are merely the further expression of evolutionary tendencies already seen at work in the lower ray-finned fishes. The scales are so reduced that ganoine is no longer present, and fulcral scales have disappeared. The internal skeleton is composed almost entirely of bone, including complete ossification of the vertebrae (in contrast to the usual holostean condition). The tail has become homocercal (Fig. 3d); superficially it is perfectly symmetrical, but internally there is still a trace of the uptilted end of the axial skeleton, and the fin rays are supported by enlarged haemal arches known as "hypural bones." Functionally this tail is very similar to the diphycercal type attained in other fishes; but here the entire fin is developed from the lower lobe of the original heterocercal tail fin, whereas the diphycercal type is formed equally from upper and lower lobes. The primitive ray-finned forms, as we have noted, almost entirely lacked an upper lobe. The diphycercal type was thus difficult of attainment, but in the homocercal tail the same functional end has been attained by other means.

Within this group there has been a tremendous amount of variation. The primitive teleosts were undoubtedly marine types, but great numbers dwell in fresh waters, and many (the salmon and eel are familiar examples) divide their time between the two habitats. Others have become abysmal, deep-sea types. Primitive teleosts possessed a normal fusiform body shape; but later members of the group have evolved in almost every conceivable direction—into the elongate eel type of body, into deep-bodied types paralleling platysomids and pycnodonts, and into such weirdly shaped types as the sea horse. The scales may be lost entirely, as in catfish; or the body may be armored in bony plates superficially giving a resemblance to some of the old ostracoderms. The fin rays may be stiffened into spines, as is the case in all the higher members of the group. The median fins may coalesce; the pelvic fins in many groups tend to move forward and reach a position beneath the shoulder region or even, as an extreme, beneath the jaws. In the upper jaw the premaxilla tends to expand at the expense of the maxilla, which in advanced forms becomes toothless and reduced, migrating upward out of the margin of the jaw. The air bladder has lost all trace of breathing function and is purely a hydrostatic organ; and its connection with the gut may be lost altogether, the sac manufacturing gas within its own membranes.

The teleosts comprise not only some twenty-thousand or more living species but a vast array of fossil forms as well. How to arrange and classify this huge assemblage is a perplexing problem. Many students of living fishes have tended to divide the group into as many as twenty or more distinct orders. We shall here adopt a more conservative policy, treating the teleosts as a single but extremely complex order. We shall not attempt to give any comprehensive account of all the multifarious teleost types but will content ourselves with a brief review of the character and history of the principal suborders which are here adopted as units.

The more primitive forms, those which have departed least from the structure of their holostean ancestors, may be grouped as the Isospondyli. Their diagnostic characters are mostly of a negative and primitive nature. The fins are spineless;

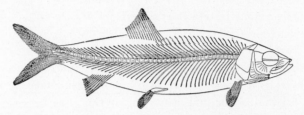

FIG. 70.—*Leptolepis dubius*, a primitive Jurassic teleost. Original about 9 inches long. (From Smith Woodward.)

the pelvic fins are in the original abdominal position; the air bladder still has an open duct; the maxilla is of a primitive structure. The earliest known teleosts were isospondyls; and *Leptolepis* (Figs. 70, 71), a small Jurassic form, may have been close to the ancestry of the whole order. The majority of Cretaceous sea forms were related types; some, such as *Portheus* (Fig. 72) of the Kansas Niobrara chalk, ran up to a length of 15 feet or more. This primitive group is still abundant and contains many common forms, mainly marine, such as the herrings, salmon, trout, and the tarpon.

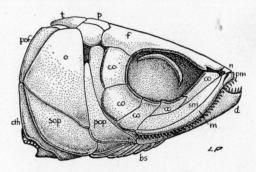

FIG. 71.—Skull of *Leptolepis knorri*, a late Jurassic primitive teleost; enlarged. For abbreviations see Figure 53. (After Jaekel.)

An early side branch of the primitive teleost stock is that which includes the carp and catfish and their relatives, the suborder Ostariophysi. These are fresh-water fishes which have retained many primitive structural features. A peculiarity is the development of a chain of small bones formed from parts of the anterior vertebrae which run from the air bladder to the ear and appear to register the air pressure in that organ; this odd structure is in itself sufficient to separate them from their more primitive relatives. In addition, the catfish have entirely lost their scales, which are replaced in some South American forms by a new bony armor. The oldest known fossils are from the Eocene; but the catfishes of that epoch were already highly specialized, and the group must have originated in the Mesozoic. The

Ostariophysi include about one-quarter of all teleosts, the carp family including a majority of all fresh-water fishes in the northern continents.

Another side branch from the main line of teleost development is that of the suborder Apodes, the eels. These are almost all marine forms, although the adult of the common eels enters fresh waters. The body is elongate, the pelvic and caudal fins are lost entirely in living eels, but were still present in the earliest known Cretaceous types.

Somewhat farther along in teleost evolution are the Percesoces, mainly marine fishes including the barracudas and flying fish. In these types the air bladder no longer connects with the gut, the maxilla is often pushed up out of the margin of the jaw, and spines are sometimes developed in connection with the dorsal fin. All these characters lead on toward the final group of spiny-finned forms. The pelvic fins are in the original abdominal position, but this may be a secondary rather

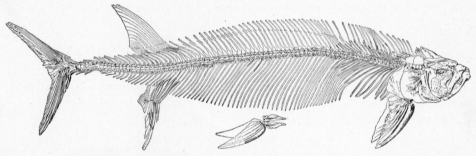

FIG. 72.—*Portheus molasse,* a giant Cretaceous teleost. Original about 12 feet long. (From Osborn.)

than a truly primitive feature. The other characters of the group suggest a relationship to the spiny-finned teleosts discussed below. Representatives of the Percesoces were already present in the Cretaceous.

Another side branch may be considered here, the suborder Hemibranchii, including such aberrant marine forms as the sea horses and pipefish, as well as the more normal appearing sticklebacks of fresh waters. These types have reduced the mouth to a small nibbling opening at the end of a tubular snout; the body is usually inclosed in bony armor plates. As in the last group, the air bladder does not connect with the gut and the pelvic fins are abdominal in position. We know little of the history of these small and mainly marine forms, but primitive types are found in the Eocene.

The Anacanthini (codfishes and their relatives), practically all marine types, are advanced teleosts in which, not only has the air bladder lost its duct, but the pelvic fins have migrated forward to the shoulder region; there are no spines present on the fins, however. These types are rare as fossils, but remains have been found at least as far back as the Eocene. They may have arisen from the Percesoces, as may have been the case with the last group.

A final, large, and most important suborder of the teleosts is that of the Acanthopterygii, the spiny-finned fishes. These are mainly marine forms and include many thousands of species, the largest teleost group in the number of contained types. Here, in addition to the various advances made in previous teleost groups (such as loss of teeth on the maxilla, closing of the air bladder, and forward movement of the pelvic fins), there have developed large stiff spines supporting the anterior part of the fins. A large number of familiar fish, such as the perch, bream, mackerel, tunny, sailfish, flounder, and trunkfish, are members of this group. A number of spiny-finned fishes, such as *Hoplopteryx* (Fig. 73), were present in the Upper Cretaceous. There are numerous Tertiary forms, and acanthopterygians are apparently at the height of their development at the present time.

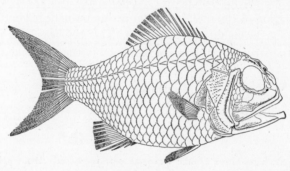

FIG. 73.—*Hoplopteryx*, a Cretaceous spiny-finned teleost. About 11 inches long. (From Smith Woodward.)

The history of many other groups of fishes is of interest in connection with the evolution of vertebrates as a whole; that of the later ray-finned fishes has no such interest, for these forms are quite unrelated to the development of further vertebrate types. But for the history of fish alone, no other group can approach them in importance. Since the Paleozoic almost all other fish groups have tended toward extinction, while the actinopterygians have remained dominant types, and group after group of them have flourished in succession. During the Paleozoic the primitive chondrosteans were the ruling order but have now disappeared except for a few aberrant forms. In the late Triassic and Jurassic the holosteans, their descendants, had taken their place and are found in great abundance and variety. By the Cretaceous the older types had been almost exterminated by the teleosts. Today among the teleosts the spiny types have attained dominance in the seas, the Ostariophysi in fresh waters.

Crossopterygians.—The Crossopterygii, or tassel-finned fishes, are a group of great interest. Entirely extinct today, they were the most common osteichthyan types in the Devonian. They seem to be close to the ancestry of the lungfishes; and, more important still, they are without question exceedingly close to the ancestry of the amphibians and hence all land-dwellers. The oldest and most typical forms, upon which our description will be based, are grouped as the order Rhipidistia. The early crossopterygians were fusiform actively swimming fresh-water fishes, carnivorous in habits and averaging a foot or two in length. A superficial feature which at once distinguishes them from actinopterygians is the presence of two dorsal fins. The most primitive forms possessed a heterocercal caudal fin, but in many crossopterygians there was a rapid shift to a diphycercal type with a characteristic three-pronged structure.

The paired fins always contained a well-developed fleshy lobe, scale-covered and fringed with dermal fin rays. The internal skeleton is not known in all cases but, when found, is seen to have had a considerable development of an axis (Fig. 56b). Only a single stout element attached to the shoulder girdle; a second segment contained a continuation of the main axis and a side branch; beyond this there was usually an irregular branching arrangement. This type of fin is presumably not as primitive as the structure of parallel bars seen in the ray-finned forms but is of

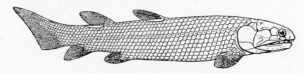

FIG. 74.—*Osteolepis*, a primitive Middle Devonian crossopterygian. About 9 inches long. (From Traquair.)

interest as the type to be expected in the ancestors of land vertebrates. In some of the early forms there was a long leaf-shaped fleshy lobe which presumably contained a long skeletal axis and side branches, a fin structure also found in the derived lungfish.

The dermal bones and scales (primitively rhomboidal, but often rounded in outline) were of the cosmoid type already described. The skull elements (Figs. 53, 55b) in general corresponded in their arrangement to the pattern laid down above. There were, however, variations in the circumorbital region, and the snout was often covered by a large rostral plate or plates. There are clear indications of internal openings for the nostril in the roof of the mouth, presumably in relation to lung breathing. A notch above the cheek region indicates the position of the spiracle; a pineal opening was present between the frontals. There was a well-developed series of teeth on the margins of the jaws. In addition to small teeth on the palate there was usually a set of teeth of exceptional size along the outer series of dermal palatal bones. These palatal teeth were few in number; each was accompanied by a pit from which the tooth's successor arose. These large teeth, and often the marginal teeth as well, had a labyrinthine structure (Fig. 75); there are longitudinal furrows along the tooth, into which the enamel is folded, sometimes in a very complicated pattern. Such teeth are not common in other bony fish but are found in the more primitive land vertebrates.

A peculiar feature of crossopterygians lies in the fact that there was seemingly considerable freedom of motion between the back part of the skull and the upper jaws. On the roof of the skull there appears to have been a somewhat movable joint between frontal and parietal; below, on the bottom of the braincase, there is an unossified gap, suggesting that there was a joint clear through the skull in this level. No such peculiarity is present either in other fish groups or in land forms.

Seemingly the most primitive of rhipidistians was *Osteolepis* (Fig. 74) of the Middle Devonian. The scales were thick and rhombic in shape. The caudal fin was heterocercal, and the other median fins well separated from it. The paired fins had a comparatively short lobe. The enamel of the teeth was but little folded.

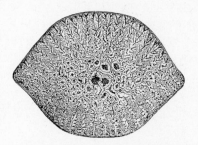

FIG. 75.—Section of tooth of *Holop-tychius*, a Devonian crossopterygian, to show the labyrinthine infolding of the enamel. (After Pander.)

More specialized were the dendrodonts, of which *Holoptychius* (Fig. 76) is typical. The sharp-pointed teeth were much more compli-cated in their folding than in *Osteolepis*. The median fins had moved far back toward the caudal fin, which was still of a heterocercal nature; the pectoral fin was a long leaf-shaped structure. The scales

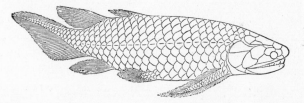

FIG. 76.—*Holoptychius*, a late Devonian crossopterygian with heterocercal tail and leaf-shaped ap-pendages. About 2½ feet long. (From Traquair.)

were rounded rather than quadrilateral in shape, and the pineal opening was absent. In many respects this form is much like the early lungfish.

Still a third type is that of the rhizodonts represented by *Eusthenopteron* (Fig. 77) and a number of other Devonian and later types. The scales were thin and rounded, the caudal fin was diphycercal, and the paired fins were short lobed. In tail and scale structure intermediate types are known indicating the origin of these forms from the *Osteolepis* type.

The crossopterygians were the most common of Devonian bony fishes; a number of different genera were already present when the group appeared in the middle of that period, and closely related types are common in Upper Devonian deposits as well. Presumably the peculiar climatic conditions of the times were especially favorable for these lung-breathing forms. But with the coming of the Carboniferous there is an abrupt decline. Rhipidistians were comparatively rare in the pools of the coal swamps; and only one rather large form, *Megalichthys*, survived until the Lower Permian as the last representative of its line.

Coelacanths.—The remaining crossopterygians constitute the order Coelacanthini. These types appeared in the Upper Devonian and persisted until the Cretaceous with comparatively little change in structure. Their derivation from the rhipidistians is shown by numerous points in their anatomy. There were two dorsals; the tail, like that of many rhipidistians, was diphycercal and trifid, with a central elongation. The paired fins (in which the bony elements apparently were unossified) had only a short fleshy lobe but long dermal rays. In some instances the wall of the lungs appears to have calcified, and their outline is seen in the fossils. The skull was essentially like that of the ancestral rhipidistians, even in

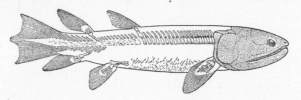

Fig. 77.—*Eusthenopteron*, an Upper Devonian crossopterygian with a diphycercal tail. (After Gregory, modified from Bryant.)

the presence of the peculiar joint between front and back portions. The most obvious peculiarity was the height and shortness of the skull, with a sharp downward bend at the joint giving these fishes a somewhat semitic appearance. There was a long series of small bones running back and upward from the nostrils, apparently in relation to the long beak; otherwise the skull elements were rather similar to those of the rhipidistians.

Diplocercides of the late Devonian appears to have been a type transitional between rhipidistians and coelacanths. *Coelacanthus* was a common Carboniferous genus which persisted into the Permian. At first fresh-water forms, the coelacanths seem in the Triassic to have taken to a marine existence; and Jurassic and Cretaceous types, such as *Undina* and *Macropoma* (Fig. 78), were salt-water fishes. The earlier forms did not average more than a foot in length; later types grew to perhaps twice that size.

The history of the crossopterygians is, like that of so many of the fish groups previously considered, one of early importance, followed by rapid decline and extinction. But they are an exceedingly important group for the student of vertebrate history, for they were certainly close to the line of development not only of the lungfish but of the ancestors of all land vertebrates.

Lungfish.—The lungfish, constituting the subclass Dipnoi, have never been an abundant group, but nevertheless they have persisted throughout the known history of the Osteichthyes from the Middle Devonian to the present day. Remarkably conservative in such features as their specialized teeth, in others, such as scale reduction and median fin structure, they exhibit an interesting series of evolutionary changes. Many structural features suggest that they have descended from unknown early Devonian crossopterygians.

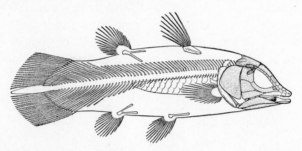

FIG. 78.—*Macropoma*, a Cretaceous coelacanth. Original about 22 inches long. (From Smith Woodward.)

In the earliest known Devonian form, *Dipterus* (Fig. 79), two dorsals, a heterocercal caudal, and an anal comprised the median fins. In this *Dipterus* resembled the contemporaneous crossopterygians. But in later types the first dorsal tended to disappear, the second to enlarge and to move back and join the caudal. Meantime the tail fin had tended to become diphycercal and to fuse with the anal, the

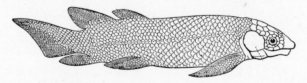

FIG. 79.—*Dipterus*, a Devonian dipnoan. About 14 inches long. (From Goodrich, after Traquair.)

final result in the living forms being a continuous and symmetrical median fin around the posterior part of the body.

The paired fins (Fig. 56a) have a long slim fleshy lobe containing a jointed central axis and side branches (in two of the modern genera the fins are much reduced). This type of fin is quite probably a specialized, rather than a primitive, structure. We have seen in the crossopterygians stages in the probable development of this sort of fin from a broad-based type, and *Holoptychius* had fins quite similar in shape to those of lungfish.

The scales primitively were of the cosmoid types, as in the Crossopterygii; but they were always rounded in outline, never rhomboidal. In later forms they became thinner, larger, and lost the enameled surface.

In the most primitive dipnoans the covering of the head with dermal bones was nearly complete, but no premaxilla or maxilla has been discovered, and the dentary was quick to disappear; in consequence there is almost never any trace along the margins of the jaws of the set of teeth which play the major part in the dentition of other bony fish. Instead there is a concentration of the teeth on the roof of the mouth and on the inner surface of the jaw into fan-shaped tooth plates which function in feeding on small invertebrates (Fig. 80b). There is a pair of these fan-shaped plates on the pterygoids above and the coronoids below, with another and smaller pair above on the prevomers. Each plate consists of a number of radiating ridges which in the embryo and in the adult of some of the older forms exhibit a series of cusps each of which was originally a separate tooth.

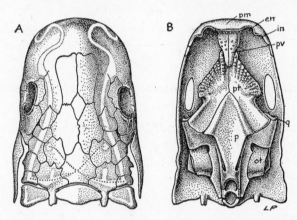

FIG. 80.—*A* dorsal and *B*, ventral views of the skull of *Dipterus*, a primitive Devonian lungfish. The homology of the dermal roofing elements is in doubt, and hence these have been left unlabeled. Anterior part of braincase, including nasal capsules, unossified. For abbreviations see Figure 53. (After Pander, Watson, and Goodrich.)

The pattern of the skull top (Fig. 80a) in some early types resembled that of crossopterygians; in others there was a considerable number of small elements. In later times the dermal bones are much reduced in number and form but a very incomplete covering for the roof of the head; they are reinforced by large scales which grow forward from over the body.

While in the early forms there was a considerable amount of ossification in the internal skeleton, there is in later types a tendency for degeneration into a cartilagenous condition. One of the distinctive features of the group as a whole is the fact that, in contrast with all other bony fish, the cartilagenous primary upper jaw is fused to the braincase. Perhaps here (as in the chimaeras) this may be related to the presence of large tooth plates.

Well-developed lungs are present in the living forms (Fig. 57), and here only among living fishes do we find internal openings for the nostrils. The gills are somewhat reduced, and the spiracle absent. Many features in the embryonic development of these forms are quite comparable to those in the primitive land vertebrates.

Modern lungfish live under conditions of seasonal aridity presumably comparable to those under which all the primitive bony fish lived. The Australian lungfish *Neoceratodus* cannot survive the complete drying-up of the streams but in foul and stagnant pools may come to the surface and breathe air. The African lungfish *Protopterus* and *Lepidosiren* of South America are able to retreat into a burrow and withstand a complete drying-up of the water; the more highly specialized shape and structure of these two forms suggest that this habit was not one characteristic of the Paleozoic forms.

Dipterus (Fig. 79), common in the Middle Devonian, was the oldest, and in many ways the most primitive, dipnoan. The heterocercal tail, the separate dorsals and anal, the shiny cosmoid scales, and the completely roofed skull render it difficult to tell this form from a primitive crossopterygian in the absence of knowledge of the teeth and the details of the skull roof.

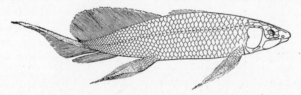

Fig. 81.—*Scaumenacia*, an Upper Devonian dipnoan from Canada, Length about 9 inches. (After Hussakof.)

In the Upper Devonian specialization was under way. In such forms as *Scaumenacia* (Fig. 81) and *Phaneropleuron* the tail was becoming diphycercal, the posterior dorsal was moving toward the caudal and joined it, and the scales had lost the shiny cosmoid layer. In *Ctenodus* and *Sagenodus* (Fig. 55c) of the Carboniferous the tail was definitely diphycercal, the anal had also united with the caudal, and a continuous median fin had been formed.

Ceratodus was known from tooth plates from the Triassic of Germany nearly a century ago; only much later was there discovered the very similar living form from Australia now distinguished as *Neoceratodus* (Fig. 82). There has been little change in this type since the beginning of the Mesozoic. The cranial bones are further reduced and fused in *Neoceratodus*, and the tooth plates have lost in the adult the originally separate tubercles on the ridges.

More divergent are the existing *Lepidosiren* and *Protopterus*. The body is more eel-like; the fins, reduced. The bony skeleton is still more degenerate; the teeth have ridges reduced to two or three in number. Little is known of the pedigree of these types, but they may have diverged from the line leading to *Ceratodus* as early as the Carboniferous.

Apart from the fact that they give us the most complete phylogenetic series of any fish group, the lungfish have been of great interest because of the light which they shed on the origin of land forms. They have been by some regarded as the ancestors of the amphibians. It is true that they, unlike most other fish, resemble the primitive tetrapods in the presence of functional lungs and that they, in con-

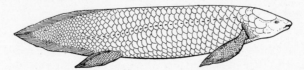

Fig. 82.—*Ceratodus* (*Neoceratodus*), a Mesozoic to Recent dipnoan. (From Goodrich, *Vertebrata craniata*.)

trast to other living fishes, have internal nostrils. Further, in many features of the soft anatomy and developmental history they alone among modern fishes show many resemblances to amphibian conditions. But their specializations in teeth and other structures debar them from any ancestral position. The truth of the matter seems to be that the features in which they resemble the tetrapods are very probably inheritances in the lungfish from their ancestors, the primitive crossopterygians. Were members of this latter group alive today they would presumably be even more highly comparable to land vertebrates. The lungfish are, so to speak, not the parents but the uncles of the tetrapods.

CHAPTER V

AMPHIBIANS

We now turn from a consideration of the fishes, primitive vertebrates for whom water is the natural habitat, to the history of land vertebrates, the tetrapods. These forms have made one of the most radical advances in vertebrate history in the development from the fish fin system of limbs capable of being used for progression on land. The change from water to land life, first initiated in the Devonian by the ancestral amphibian stock, was completed by the reptiles in late Paleozoic days; later, from reptilian types, were developed the birds and mammals. Once the water was left behind, wide and repeated radiations of tetrapod types occurred. The four-footed vertebrates have adapted themselves to almost every conceivable type of land habitat and have, moreover, taken to the air and, backed by the advances made in land life, have reinvaded the seas. Snakes, birds, men, and whales are but a few examples of the widely varied types which evolved from the primitive and ancient forms which in late Paleozoic times first left the stream and pools to walk upon the land.

Amphibian life.—Most primitive and earliest known of tetrapods are the amphibians, which as a class are, without question, the basal stock from which the remaining groups of land vertebrates have been derived. Living amphibians include but three comparatively unimportant vertebrate groups: the frogs and toads, the salamanders and newts, and some rare worm-like types. All are highly specialized and have in many respects departed far from the primitive type described below.

The life-history of a typical frog, however, shows the essential characters of the class. The eggs are usually small and without the protective membranes or shell found in the eggs of reptiles and higher types. Typically they are laid in the water, whereas the reptilian egg is laid on land. The young embryo, without any great supply of yolk for nourishment, hatches out at a very immature stage as a tadpole and must find its own food as it grows in the water. Later, when the frog approaches maturity, the structure of the body changes radically; the gills disappear, lungs and limbs develop rapidly, and the animal becomes a land, instead of a water, type.

But the amphibian is not even then freed entirely from an aquatic environment, for the eggs normally must be fertilized and laid in that element. Consequently the amphibian must return to the water at the breeding season, and complete adaptation to land life alone is impossible. Various devices have been developed by amphibians which tend to avoid, to some extent, this necessity for a double mode of life and a double set of adaptations, but never with complete success. It is not to be wondered at that among the salamanders, and apparently among many extinct groups as well, there have been numerous types which have, so to speak, given up the struggle and have reverted to a permanent water life and a retention of gill breathing.

The type of reproduction and development is the best definitive feature of the class. For living groups, certain other characters (particularly those of the skeleton) have been used to distinguish the group from the reptiles; but among the fossils practically all anatomical differences break down.

Among existing types the salamanders and newts approach most closely the body form which is probably the primitive one (the frogs, tailless and with elongate hind legs, are among the most highly specialized of vertebrates). The body and tail are elongate; median fins have disappeared; but the tail is often high and flattened and may be used as a swimming organ in rather fish-like fashion. The paired fins of the ancestral fish have been transformed into tetrapod limbs which in salamanders are usually quite small and feeble as compared with those of reptiles and other higher tetrapods but are quite large as compared with fish appendages. While these limbs are capable of a great amount of independent motion, it is of interest that a salamander progresses more or less in fish fashion on dry ground, the body being thrown into S-shaped curves which may advance the limbs with very little movement on their own part.

Structure of a primitive amphibian.—But while a salamander may resemble the probable tetrapod ancestors superficially, the internal anatomy of all modern amphibians is very much modified from primitive conditions. The structure of some primitive fossil types will be described below in some detail, since the fundamental pattern of the skeleton of those forms is basic not only for an understanding of the history of later amphibians but for that of reptiles and higher tetrapods as well. Almost every skeletal element of a bird or of a man may be traced back to these primitive types. Later forms have modified the shape and relationships of parts greatly and there have been frequent losses of bones, but the fundamental pattern laid down in the early tetrapods still persists.

Our description will be based in great measure upon such types as *Palaeogyrinus* (Fig. 86), *Eogyrinus* (Fig. 83), *Orthosaurus* (Fig. 87), and *Diplovertebron* (Fig. 84), members of the Embolomeri, a group of very primitive Paleozoic amphibians. These types were common inhabitants of the coal swamps. *Diplovertebron* appears to have reached a maximum length of about 2 feet; but most of the group were much larger, some being as large as modern crocodiles. The general proportions were not unlike those of a modern salamander, but the body was somewhat higher and more rounded in section. Most of the life of such an archaic tetrapod was still spent in the water, and the small palaeoniscid fish then abundant may have served as a major source of food supply. There was still much resemblance to the fish type both in structural features and in a continuation of the ancestral aquatic mode of life. But the development of tetrapod limbs rendering land locomotion possible is an obvious and striking difference.

Bony scales, present in the fish ancestors, have tended to be reduced in land forms, although horny scales may functionally replace them in reptiles and other

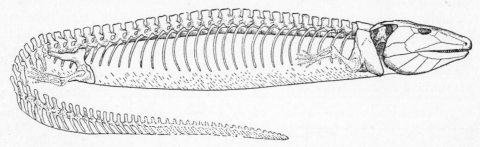

FIG. 83.—*Eogyrinus*, a Carboniferous embolomerous amphibian. Estimated length about 15 feet. (After Gregory, modified from Watson.)

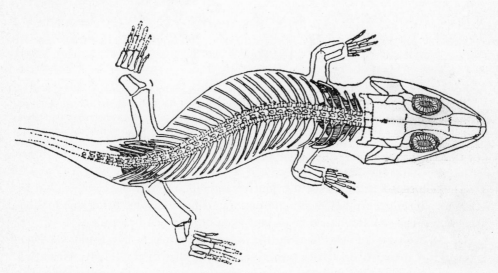

FIG. 84.—Dorsal view of the skeleton of *Diplovertebron*, a small embolomerous amphibian from the late Pennsylvanian of Bohemia. (From Watson.)

types (modern amphibians have a soft moist skin). The old fish scales were still present in primitive amphibians and even many early reptiles, but confined to the belly, where they were arranged in V-shaped rows. This ventral armor undoubtedly was of use in protecting the low-slung body while traveling over rough ground.

Axial skeleton.—In the vertebral column of most tetrapods the centra are well ossified in contrast to the usual fish condition; the backbone must carry the weight of the body, and cartilage could not stand the strain. But in the Embolomeri

(Fig. 85*a*, *b*), instead of the usual single centrum, there are two checker-shaped elements for each segment of the body. The posterior member of each pair appears to correspond to the single element found in higher classes and thus may be called the "true" centrum (or pleurocentrum); the anterior one is the intercentrum (or hypocentrum). Neural arches are well developed, and in the tail Y-shaped haemal arches (chevron bones) develop from the intercentra. The segments of the column connect with each other not only by juxtaposition of the centra but also by special articular processes, zygapophyses, on the arches. At the back of each arch there is a pair of round flat surfaces, facing down and somewhat outward. These posterior zygapophyses articulate with corresponding anterior zygapophyses, flat surfaces on the anterior side of the arches, facing upward and inward.

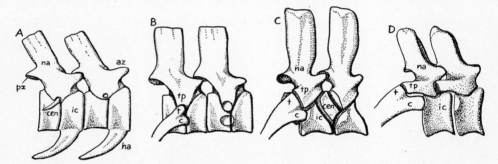

FIG. 85.—Vertebrae of labyrinthodonts. *A*, caudal vertebrae of the embolomere *Cricotus*. *B*, dorsal vertebrae of the same. *C*, dorsal vertebrae of the rhachitome *Eryops*. *D*, dorsal vertebrae of the stereospondyl *Mastodonsaurus*. *az*, anterior zygapophysis; *cen*, centrum; *cap*, capitulum of rib; *ha*, haemal arch; *ic*, intercentrum; *na*, neural arch; *pz*, posterior zygapophysis; *t*, tubercle of rib; *tp*, transverse process. (*A–C* mainly after Williston, *D* after von Meyer.)

The notochord still persists in primitive amphibians, and the circular disks of the embolomere central elements are perforated by a small central hole for this structure. This condition also holds true even in many early reptiles.

Of the two types of fish ribs, only the dorsal set is present in a tetrapod. Two-headed ribs appear to have been primitive, the true head or capitulum articulating with the intercentrum, and the tubercle meeting a transverse process from the neural arch. The ribs are found along nearly the whole length of the body from the first vertebra in the neck to the proximal part of the tail. The longest ribs are in the thoracic (chest) region, but there is little differentiation of a cervical (neck) or lumbar (waist) region. Opposite the pelvic girdle a specialized rib, the sacral, gives attachment for the girdle in most amphibians; in higher classes there are usually two or more such sacral ribs.

Skull.—The skull of *Palaeogyrinus* (Fig. 86) and its allies is completely roofed by dermal bones; in life these apparently lay close below the surface, barely covered by the skin. The skull pattern is essentially that described for primitive

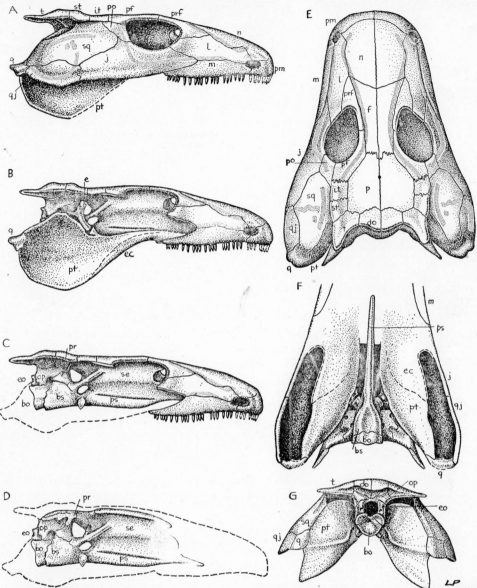

FIG. 86.—The skull of the embolomerous amphibian *Palaeogyrinus*, to show the structure of the primitive tetrapod skull. Length of original about 7½ inches. *A*, lateral view. *B*, the same, semi-diagrammatic, dermal bones of the cheek region removed to show the primary upper jaw (quadrate epipterygoid, and associated dermal bones—pterygoid and ectopterygoid). *C*, the same, primary upper jaw removed. *D*, the braincase (and parasphenoid), skull outlines in dashed line. *E*, dorsal view of skull. *F*, posterior part of palate. *G*, occiput. (*A*, *D–G* after Watson, *B* and *C* reconstructed from his data.) Lateral line canals stippled. Abbreviations for this and other amphibian and reptilian skulls: *a*, angular, *ar*, articular; *bo*, basioccipital; *bs*, basisphenoid; *c*, coronoid; *d*, dentary; *do*, dermal supraoccipital; *e*, epipterygoid; *ec*, ectopterygoid; *en*, external nares; *ex*, exoccipital; *f*, frontal; *fm*, foramen magnum; *in*, internal nares; *ina*, internasal; *it*, intertemporal; *j*, jugal; *l*, lacrimal; *m*, maxilla; *n*, nasal; *o*, opisthotic; *on*, otic notch; *or*, orbit; *p*, parietal; *pa*, prearticular; *pd*, predentary; *pf*, postfrontal; *pl*, palatine; *pm*, premaxilla; *po*, postorbital; *pop*, preopercular; *pos*, postsplenial; *pp*, preparietal; *pr*, proötic; *prf*, prefrontal; *ps*, parasphenoid; *pt*, pterygoid; *pv*, prevomer; *q*, quadrate; *qj*, quadratojugal; *r*, rostral; *s*, stapes; *sa*, surangular; *se* sphenethmoid; *sm*, septomaxillary; *so*, supraorbital; *soc*, supraoccipital; *sp*, splenial; *sq*, squamosal; *st*, supratemporal; *t*, tabular.

bony fishes. Nasals, frontals, and parietals are large; the pineal opening lies between the parietals (rather than between the frontals as in crossopterygians).
There are well-developed premaxillae and long maxillae. Five bones are present
in the circumorbital series. The lacrimal primitively extends all the way from the
eye to the nostril and carries the tear duct (a fish eye is naturally bathed in water,
but that of a land form must be kept moist and have a duct to carry off superfluous liquid). A large squamosal and a quadratojugal are present on the cheek,
the latter overlying the quadrate. At the side of the parietal lie intertemporal and

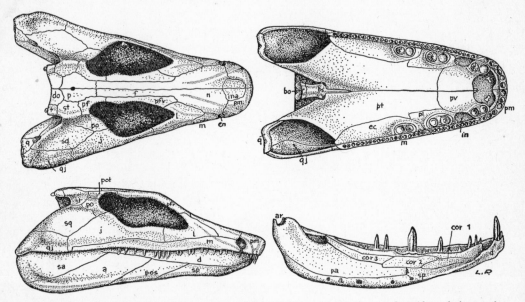

FIG. 87.—The skull of the embolomerous amphibian *Orthosaurus*, dorsal, ventral, and lateral views and
inner view of jaw. Length of original about 12 inches. Lateral line canals stippled. For abbreviations
see Figure 86. (After Watson.)

supratemporal elements, while at the back of the skull roof are dermal supra-
occipitals and tabulars.

With the loss of the gills the operculum which covered them has disappeared,
breaking the sheet of bones which originally extended unbroken from the skull
to the shoulder region. The disappearance of the operculum has converted the
slit in which the spiracle lay into an open otic (ear) notch bounded by the tabular
above and the squamosal below.

The external nares are on the dorsal surface, bounded by the premaxilla, the
maxilla, the nasals, and the lacrimal.

The palate (Figs. 86*f*, 87) resembles that of the primitive bony fish. The premaxilla and maxilla bear a marginal row of sharp teeth. Inside them lie the prevomers, palatines, and ectopterygoids, which in primitive types usually carry

large labyrinthine teeth and associated pits just as in the crossopterygians. The pterygoids are large and stretch back to the quadrates; toward the mid-line, processes from them form a movable articulation with the braincase. Of the old primary (shark) upper jaws there remain only the quadrate and a small epiptery-goid farther forward above the pterygoid (Fig. 86b). The front end of the brain-case is bounded below by a slim parasphenoid between which and the pterygoids are small openings, the interpterygoid vacuities. The internal opening of the nostrils is between premaxilla, maxilla, prevomer, and palatine.

The braincase itself (Fig. 86c, d) is well ossified in primitive amphibians. At the back are the four occipital elements—the median basi- and supra-occipitals and the paired exoccipitals. A single rounded surface mainly on the basioccipital, the occipital condyle, joins the skull with the first vertebra. At the sides the opisthotic (paroccipital) extends upward to the tabulars; in front of this is the proötic, the two inclosing the inner ear region. Ventrally in front of the basioccipital lies a well-developed basisphenoid which articulates with the pterygoids laterally and in front is covered by the parasphenoid. The front end of the braincase (through which the nerves pass to the nostrils) usually has a tubular ethmoid ossification.

The lower jaw of the Embolomeri (Fig. 87) resembles that of the crossop-terygians. On the outer surface lies the long dentary, and below this a row of dermal elements including two splenials, angular and surangular. On the inner side within the dentary are coronoids (variable in number) usually bearing an inner series of teeth. There is a long prearticular; and, as in most fish, the pri-mary jaw is represented only by the small articular.

With the loss of gill breathing in the adult the gill arches naturally are reduced, although these elements are still well developed in many amphibians. In higher types there is much further reduction, although even in mammals the cartilages of the tongue and throat are remnants of this skeletal system. They are, however, seldom found in fossils, and need little further consideration. The fate of the hyo-mandibular is discussed below.

Limb girdles.—The skeleton of the limbs and girdles is naturally highly de-veloped. The shoulder girdle (Fig. 88a, b) lies close behind the head; but in most tetrapods the original connection with the skull has been lost, for in a land animal independent movements of head and shoulder are a necessity. The cleithrum, the large upper bone of the dermal girdle, is retained in primitive land forms, as is the clavicle; in addition there is developed a median ventral dermal element, the inter-clavicle, lying on the under side of the chest between the collar bones. These der-mal elements tend to be much smaller than they are in the fishes, while the primary shoulder girdle beneath tends to increase in size, since there had been a great in-crease in the musculature passing from it to the limb. The upper portion of the primary girdle is a flat scapular blade below which is an articular surface for the humerus, the glenoid cavity. Ventrally there is a large flat coracoid plate turning

in toward the mid-line of the under side of the body. Primitively the primary girdle appears to have included but a single ossification, the scapula. In later types
(seldom in amphibians) one or two additional coracoid ossifications are often developed.

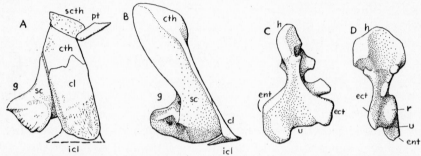

FIG. 88.—Shoulder girdle of *A*, the embolomerous amphibian *Eogyrinus*, *B*, the rhachitomous amphibian *Eryops*. *cl*, clavicle; *cth*, cleithrum; *icl*, interclavicle; *pt*, postemporal (connecting with skull);
sc, scapulo-coracoid (primary girdle); *scth*, supracleithrum. *C*, dorsal and *D*, anterior views of the humerus of *Eryops*. *ect*, ectepicondyle; muscular process on the outer or front side of the humerus; *ent*, entepi-
condyle on the inner or back side; *h*, head; *r*, articular surface for radius; *u*, articular surface for ulna.
(*A* after Watson.)

The pelvic girdle (Fig. 89) is a far larger structure than the small plate present
in fishes. It has been enlarged to accommodate more muscles; and while the fish

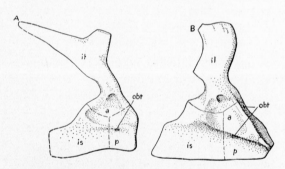

FIG. 89.—Pelvic girdles of *A*, an embolomere (? *Baphetes*) and the rhachitome *Eryops*. *a*, acetabulum; *il*, ilium;
is, ischium; *obt*, obturator foramen in pubis; *p*, pubis. (*A*
after Watson.)

plate is confined to the ventral
side of the body, the primitive
tetrapod girdle extends far dorsally and is usually joined to the
backbone by one or more specialized sacral ribs. This extension
is a functional necessity for land-
dwellers, for the hind legs in a
primitive tetrapod must not only
support much of the weight but
must also give most of the push
that propels the body forward.
The dorsal extension of the girdle
is usually a separate ossification,
the ilium. The head of the limb rests in a cavity known as the acetabulum. Below
this is a broad ventral plate which joins its fellow of the opposite side in a medium
symphysis; this plate consists of two ossifications, the pubis (containing a nerve
foramen) in front and the ischium behind; the former is often unossified in amphibians.

Limbs.—The limb skeleton is, of course, large in comparison with that of the paired fins of fishes. In the pectoral limb (Fig. 90b) the first segment is a broad and powerful element, the humerus (Fig. 88c, d). Its head fits into the glenoid cavity of the shoulder girdle; distally it articulates with two elements which form the second segment of the limb, the radius and ulna. The former lies on the inner side of the forearm and rests directly under the humerus, supporting much of the weight. The ulna lies outside and usually has a head, the olecranon ("funny bone"), extending above the edge of the humerus; muscles pulling on this open out the arm.

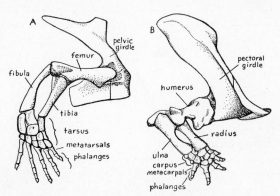

The radius and ulna articulate below with a complex of small elements which constitute the carpus, or wrist (Fig. 91a). Typi-

FIG. 90.—A, lateral view of the pelvic girdle and limb of a primitive labyrinthodont (composite). B, lateral view of the pectoral girdle and limb of Eryops. (After Miner.)

cally there is a proximal row of three elements, the radiale lying under the radius, the ulnare beneath the ulna, and an intermedium lying between the two. Below the last is a large central element, followed by a row of three smaller centrals (sometimes termed medials) lying toward the radial side and finally by a series of five distal carpals, each of which lies opposite the head of a toe.

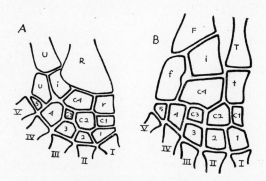

FIG. 91.—Nomenclature of the carpal and tarsal elements. A, diagram of the right carpus of a primitive amphibian, B, diagram of the right tarsus. I–V, metacarpals or metatarsals; 1–5, distal carpals or tarsals; c1–c4, centralia; F, fibula; f, fibulare; i, intermedium; R, radius; r, radiale; T, tibia; t, tibiale; U, ulna; u, ulnare.

The toes, or digits, of land forms consist of a first segment, a metacarpal, lying within the palm region of the front foot and beyond this a variable number of elements, phalanges, making up the joints of the free portion of the toe. Five toes are present in the front foot in Diplovertebron (Fig. 92a) and probably in all primitive forms. Most living amphibians and many fossils have but four; there are, however, in some cases traces suggesting that there may have been as many as seven toes originally. The inner digit, corresponding to the human thumb, receives the special name of the pollex. The number of phalanges varies, although the inner toes tend to be shorter than the outer ones. Reptiles typically have a phalangeal formula (counting the number of joints from the pollex out) of 2–3–4–5–3 (or 4); amphibians generally have less.

The pelvic limb (Fig. 90a) may be compared part for part with the pectoral, although a different set of names is used for the bony elements. The femur, usually longer and slimmer than the humerus, constitutes the proximal segment. The next consists of the tibia within and the fibula on the outside. The ankle is the tarsus (Fig. 91b); and the names of the tarsal elements are similar to the carpal ones, except that of course the names tibiale and fibulare replace radiale and ulnare.

The pose of the primitive land limbs (Fig. 90) is quite unlike that found in most living forms, although the straddling walk of a turtle is comparable and indeed

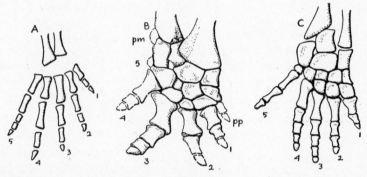

FIG. 92.—The feet of amphibians. *A*, manus of *Diplovertebron*, a small embolomere. *B*, manus of the rachitomous amphibian *Eryops*. *C*, pes of the rachitomous amphibian *Trematops*. *pp*, prepollex; *pm*, postminimus. (*A* after Watson, *B* after Gregory, Miner and Noble, *C* after Williston.)

may have been retained from those early days with comparatively little modification. The proximal segments of the limbs are extended nearly straight out from the body, with the forearm and lower leg extended down at right angles. It is obvious that in such a position only short strides could be taken, and that a great deal of the animal's strength was used merely in keeping the body off the ground. Walking must have been a slow and difficult process, especially for an animal of any size.

Other organs.—The probable condition of organs of other systems in such a primitive vertebrate may be deduced from conditions still found in living forms. In the adult, gill breathing would have gone and the lungs alone been functional; internal nostrils were, of course, present. Usually in tetrapods all the gill openings except the spiracle disappear. In connection with this change the circulatory system has been considerably modified, for, instead of passing to the gills, the blood must now pass to the lungs to be purified. This results in the destruction of most of the aortic arches which passed up between the gills. The last one is enlarged and forms part of the passage for blood to the lungs; more anteriorly another persists to carry the blood which has returned from the lungs to the heart up to the dorsal aorta and so to the body. With this double flow of blood through the heart there is the beginning of a division of this organ into two separate sets of compartments; this division, however, is incomplete in amphibians.

The brain of amphibians is still small, especially the cerebral hemispheres, which are still entirely concerned with smell. The sense organs have undergone considerable modifications. The nostrils are adapted for smell under the changed circumstances of air instead of water for a medium. The eyes are usually large; the sclerotic plates already mentioned as present in many fish groups were retained in primitive tetrapods. A pineal eye was present in all early forms but tended to be lost in post-Paleozoic tetrapods of most groups.

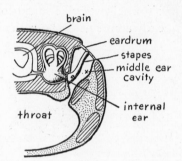

The ear region has undergone great change. The balancing function is, of course, retained. Hearing, however, is more difficult in a land type, for air vibrations are so delicate that they cannot effectively set up pulsations which reach the ear through the thickness of the skull. We find in relation to this situation that tetrapods have developed a new mechanism (Fig. 93) which amplifies the vibrations and transmits them to the internal ear. The spiracular opening is retained but near its outer end it is closed by a thin tight membrane, the ear drum, which picks up the sound vibrations. This drum primitively lies in the otic notch, which corresponds to the spiracular slit of the fish. Attached to the drum is a small bone, the stapes, or stirrup (sometimes termed the columnella), which at its inner end abuts on the otic region of the skull. Beneath this inner end is in most tetrapods a foramen leading into the liquid-filled spaces of the internal ear, so that air waves caught and amplified by the drum and transmitted by the stapes set up vibrations in the internal ear, and hearing thus results. The stapes is the fish hyomandibular which was similarly propped up against the otic region of the fish skull. With the tightening of connections between jaws and skull its old function of a jaw support became superfluous; and, lying in the region just behind the spiracle, it was free to be adapted to this new function (cf. Fig. 98, bottom).

Fig. 93.—Diagrammatic section through an amphibian skull to show the relations of the ear region.

The lateral line system of fishes is still retained in the amphibia, and grooves for head canals can often be seen on fossil skulls. Higher in the scale, however, these canals are lost entirely; and even among the amphibians adult forms which are land-dwellers lose them. Their presence or absence in a fossil is a good clue to its habits, for this sensory system is of use only in the water.

Tetrapod ancestors.—From the description above, it is obvious that among the bony fishes the extinct crossopterygians were the closest to the ancestors of the tetrapods. The lungfish of today are very similar to the amphibians in their embryology and certain soft parts, but this merely indicates the retention of characters present in their crossopterygian ancestors; in such respects as teeth and skull structure the lungfish are definitely on an evolutionary side line and cannot themselves be tetrapod ancestors. As regards the actinopterygians, such features as the absence of internal nostrils and the lack of a large fleshy fin from which a land limb might develop rule this group out of consideration.

In almost every respect the crossopterygians fulfil the requirements for tetrapod ancestors. The skull elements of these fishes were almost exactly the same as those of early amphibians and with similar relations. Even the details of the dentition,

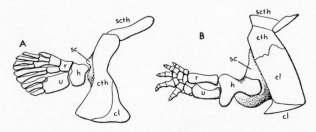

Fig. 94.—*A*, the pectoral girdle and fin of the Devonian crossopterygian *Sauripterus* (after Gregory). *B*, diagrammatic representation of a tetrapod limb "untwisted" and placed in the comparable original position. The palmar or ventral surface of the manus (and fin) is turned outward in the fish position; in land limbs the limb has been twisted outward and rotated at the elbow so as to bring the forearm forward and the palm down to reach the position shown in Figure 90*B*. For abbreviations cf. Figures 88 and 90.

with the labyrinthine structure and the peculiar pit and tooth arrangement on the palate, were identical in the two groups. The paired fins of these fishes were smaller than those of tetrapods, but in some cases at least the structure of the skeleton of the fins was essentially similar (Fig. 94). In some crossopterygians there was a single proximal bone (corresponding to the humerus or femur of tetrapods), two bones in the next segment (as in the forearm or lower leg of land forms), and beyond this an irregular subdivision which is roughly comparable to the foot skeleton of primitive land types. Although the known members of this fish group appear to have been too specialized or too late in time to have been the actual ancestors, the crossopterygians seem unquestionably to represent the stock from which land vertebrates have sprung.

Origin of tetrapods.—The "why" of tetrapod origin has been often debated. The earliest amphibians appear to have been fairly large forms of carnivorous habits, still spending a large portion of their time in fresh-water pools. Alongside them lived their close relatives, the crossopterygians, similar in food habits and in many structural features and differing markedly only in the lesser development of the paired limbs. Why did the amphibians leave the water? Not to breathe air, for that could be done by merely coming to the surface of the pool. Not because they were driven out in search of food—they were carnivores for whom there was little food on land. Not to escape enemies, for they were among the largest of vertebrates found in the fresh waters from which they came.

Their appearance on land seems to have resulted as an adaptation for remaining in the water.

The earliest known amphibians lived much the same sort of life as the related contemporary crossopterygians. Both lived normally in the same streams and pools, and both fed on the same fish food. As long as there was plenty of water the crossopterygian probably was the better off of the two, for he was obviously the better swimmer—legs were in the way. The Devonian, during which land adaptations originated, was seemingly a time of seasonal droughts when life in fresh waters must have been difficult. Even then, if the water merely became stagnant and foul, the crossopterygian could come to the surface and breathe air as well as the amphibian. But if the water dried up altogether, the amphibian had the better of it. The fish, incapable of land locomotion, must stay in the mud and, if the water did not soon return, must die. But the amphibian, with his short and clumsy but effective limbs, could crawl out of the pool and walk overland (probably very slowly and painfully at first) and reach the next pool where water still remained.

Once this process had begun, it is easy to see how a land fauna might eventually have been built up. Instead of seeking water immediately, the amphibian might linger on the banks and devour stranded fish. Some types might gradually take to eating insects (primitive ones resembling cockroaches and dragon flies were already abundant) and, finally, plant food. The larger carnivores might take to eating their smaller amphibian relatives. Thus a true terrestrial fauna might be established.

Amphibian classification.—As treated below, the amphibians may be grouped in some six orders (Fig. 96). Three of them (Labyrinthodontia, Phyllospondyli, and Lepospondyli) are typically late Paleozoic groups; the other three are the living orders, of which there are no fossils back of the later part of the Mesozoic. Not only were the older and younger groups present at different times, but in other features also they were in contrast, for the modern forms are degenerate and specialized in many ways. For example, in most existing amphibians many of the dermal elements of the skull have disappeared, and the orbital and temporal regions are unprotected by bone. In contrast almost all members of the three older orders had a completely roofed skull. The term "stegocephalian," referring to this fact, is often used as a designation for the older amphibians. This, however, is inappropriate as a taxonomic term, for it simply means the retention of a primitive character which later types have lost. The three older orders were already quite divergent in vertebral structure at the time of their first appearance and hence deserve separate consideration.

Until lately the oldest known skeletal remains of amphibians dated from about the middle of the Carboniferous. At that time, however, the main groups of Paleozoic amphibians were already quite distinct from one another, and it was obvious that their point of divergence must have lain much farther back, in De-

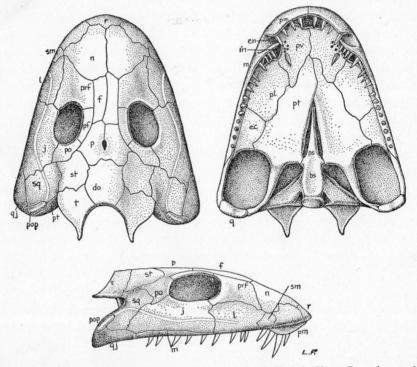

Fig. 95.—*A*, dorsal, *B*, ventral and *C*, lateral views of the skull of the Upper Devonian amphibian *Ichthyostega*. Braincase restored. Length of originals about 8 inches. For abbreviations see Figure 86. (After Säve-Soderbergh, composite.)

vonian times. Of these earlier forms we knew nothing but their footprints—fairly numerous in the Mississippian, but in the late Devonian only a single example.

Recently, however, exploration in Greenland has resulted in the discovery of a number of Upper Devonian amphibians which appear to be related to the phyllospondyls described later in this chapter (Fig. 95). This discovery pushes back our knowledge of land forms a full period.

Labyrinthodonts.—While the order Labyrinthodontia, whose known members range in time from late Mississippian to Triassic, is thus not the oldest of amphibian groups, it nevertheless merits first consideration. The members of this group included practically all of the larger amphibians of the Carboniferous, Permian, and Triassic. The more primitive types resembled greatly the primitive reptiles and are unquestionably ancestral to that group and thus to all higher tetrapods. More than that, the earlier representatives of the order are, in every respect except the vertebrae, exceedingly primitive forms structurally close to the ideal tetrapod ancestor.

The structure of a rather primitive labyrinthodont has been described above in some detail. But the labyrinthodonts were not, so to speak, any more disposed to remain idealized ancestral types than any other group of organisms which are of importance as phylogenetic connecting links. The labyrinthodonts themselves underwent a very considerable series of evolutionary developments between their first appearance in the Carboniferous and their extinction in Triassic times. It is of interest that many of the progressive changes seen in successive labyrinthodont types were closely paralleled in other amphibian groups.

In the history of this order may be seen an interesting sequence of stages. The earliest types were primitively aquatic forms of which *Diplovertebron and Eogyrinus* are fairly typical. Even in the Carboniferous, however, there appears to have been a trend toward stouter-limbed land types; from such forms may have sprung the reptiles.

But in the Permian regression took the place of progress in limbs and other structures, and the Triassic end-forms of the order were degenerate types, incapable of leaving the water.

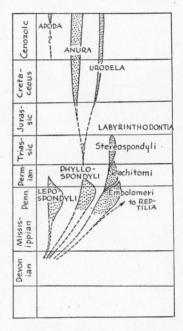

Fig. 96.—The phylogeny of the amphibian orders.

Many structural trends accompanied this sequence of stages. The body shape was primitively well rounded and rather fish-like; in later types a depressed body and a stumpy tail became common. The skull, at first comparatively high and narrow, tended in later forms to flatten out and become very broad and depressed. A single occipital condyle was present at first; in time this divided into two separate articulations. On the palate the primitively small openings between the pterygoids and the parasphenoid opened out into huge interpterygoid vacuities, and the movable joint between the pterygoids and braincase became a broad firm union of these bones. Ossifications in the braincase were much reduced. The limbs tended early to increase in size, but in later types dwindled into insignificance. In the shoulder region the clavicles and interclavicle expanded into broad plates on the flat lower surface of the chest. At first, progress, and the throwing-off of lines leading to other tetrapod groups; then degeneration into flat, sluggish water types; finally extinction. Such seems to have been the history of the laby-rinthodonts.

The vertebrae (Fig. 85) are the most important feature for diagnostic purposes. The primitive labyrinthodonts had the double type of centrum described above. Later both rings became incomplete; the top part of the intercentrum tended to disappear, leaving a notch at the upper side for the notochord, and the true centra became paired lateral elements above, as well as behind, the intercentra. Finally the pleurocentra disappeared entirely in the common Triassic forms.

This is the basis for a division into three subgroups which follow one another in time and in which can be seen the working-out of the other structural tendencies noted above.

Embolomeri.—The earliest and most primitive division of the labyrinthodonts is the suborder Embolomeri. Its members were types mainly of large size which were abundant in the coal-measures swamps. A diagnostic feature of the Embolomeri is the presence of two complete disk-shaped centra in each segment of the back-bone (whence the name, "thrown-in segments"). *Diplovertebron, Eogyrinus,* and *Palaeogyrinus* described above as primitive tetrapod types are all typical members of this suborder. The skull was rather high and narrow. The occipital condyle was single. There was a well-ossified supra-occipital and a large basioccipital; the basisphenoid was a large bone with a small splint-like parasphenoid at its front end. The interpterygoid vacuities were small, and the pterygoids movably articu-lated to the braincase. The limbs were small or moderately developed. Whereas in later amphibian types there are never more than four well-developed fingers in the front foot, the only embolomere in which the hand is known had five fingers. There was a considerable amount of variation in the group. A number seem to have been rather generalized in nature. Others, such as *Cricotus* of the American Lower Permian, were long-snouted fish-eating types. A curious cranial develop-ment is that illustrated in *Loxomma* and *Orthosaurus* (Fig. 87) and a number of other Carboniferous forms—the orbit was very much elongated, with the eye pre-sumably in the posterior part; the front end may perhaps have been occupied by some type of gland or sense organ.

Very interesting are the primitive structural features found in a few early forms such as the Carboniferous *Eogyrinus*. In contrast with fish the shoulder girdle of most tetrapods is separate from the head, while the pelvic girdle, free in fish, has become attached to specialized sacral ribs in land types. In some of the Embolo-meri (Fig. 83), however, the shoulder was still in contact with the skull by means of dermal supra-cleithral and post-temporal elements (Fig. 88a); and while in these very primitive forms there was a dorsal iliac process on the pelvic girdle, there were no specialized sacral ribs, there being probably only an attachment by ligaments to the ribs. Again, in the transformation of the hyomandibular into the stapes, we have noted that in rendering it effective as a transmitter of sound vibrations a fenestra had opened beneath its base into the skull beneath its base. In a few of the Embolomeri, however, there is no opening at all, merely a hollow at the base of the bone; hearing obviously must have been imperfect.

Embolomerous types were important and numerous in the Carboniferous. At the end of that period, however, they declined in importance, and disappeared early in Permian times.

The Rhachitomi.—The main line of labyrinthodont evolution was continued by the members of the suborder Rhachitomi. These were the typical large amphibians of the Permian, although they made their appearance in the Pennsylvanian and a straggler or two persisted into the early Triassic. *Eryops* (Figs. 97, 98) of the Lower Permian of Texas was a typical form. In the vertebral column (Fig. 85c), as the name ("cut-up segments") suggests, both intercentra and pleurocentra

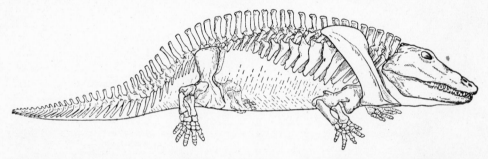

FIG. 97.—*Eryops*, a large lower Permian rachitomous amphibian about 5 feet in length. (From Gregory.)

were reduced, the former being large ventral wedges, the latter consisting of paired lateral pieces. The limbs in *Eryops* were powerful, although short; and such a type presumably spent much of its life on land, although it probably kept near the water. There were only four well-developed fingers in the front foot (Fig. 92b), as is the case in all remaining amphibians, although there were still indications of a former higher number. Here and in other types discussed hereafter the shoulder girdle was separate from the head, and the pelvic girdle was firmly united to a single sacral rib, as is common in amphibians. The skull was slightly degenerate, for it was somewhat depressed; and the condyle was tending toward a double condition, since the basioccipital which formed its central part was small. The interpterygoid vacuities were considerably enlarged, and the pterygoids were now firmly attached to the broad parasphenoid which stretched back over the reduced basisphenoid.

There were numerous side branches of the rachitomous stock in the Permian. An interesting type is that shown in *Cacops* (Fig. 99) and its allies. These forms were the most terrestrial in habits of the Rhachitomi, with well-developed legs and a much reduced tail. Presumably as a defense against carnivorous reptiles (already abundant in the Lower Permian) dermal armor plates were present on the

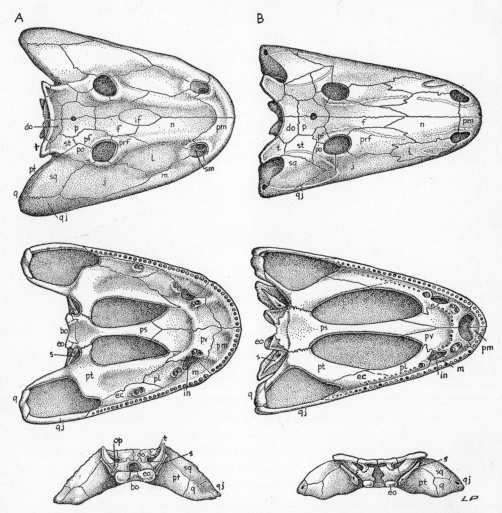

FIG. 98.—The skulls of *A*, the rhachitomous labryinthodont *Eryops* and *B*, the stereospondyl *Capitosaurus*—dorsal, ventral, and occipital views. For abbreviations see Figure 86. (*Eryops* mainly after Broom, Watson, and Williston; length about 18 inches. *Capitosaurus* after Schroeder and Watson; length about 12 inches.)

back above the neural spines. This is the first instance of the development of armor in land animals; we shall find similar structures again and again in reptilian groups and in certain mammals as well. The otic notch of some of these forms was inclosed behind, giving a complete ring of bone around the ear drum.

Even among the Permian Rhachitomi many forms were already degenerating, slumping back into the water, with very depressed skulls and much reduced limbs. *Trimerorachis* was a typical form of this sort, which structurally led to the final stage in labyrinthodont evolution.

Stereospondyls.—The last, largest, and most degenerate of the labyrinthodonts are grouped in the suborder Stereospondyli. The diagnostic feature lies in the fact that the true centra (which were to be the most important elements in reptiles) had completely disappeared (Fig. 85*d*); the intercentra had expanded again into large elements nicked at the top for the passage of the notochord.

Found only in the Triassic, the stereospondyls tended to grow to large size. The head was large, the body and tail short, and the limbs were tiny and obviously inadequate to support the body on land. The trunk was very broad and flat, and the interclavicle and clavicles formed a broad chest plate upon which the animals pre-

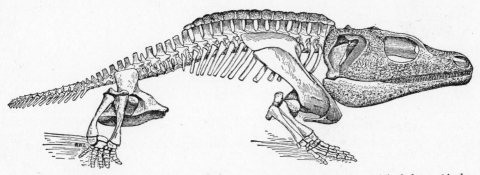

FIG. 99.—*Cacops*, a small rachitomous amphibian from the Lower Permian. Original about 16 inches long. (From Williston.)

sumably rested. The skull (Fig. 98) too was much flattened, and the eyes (as in all bottom-living forms) looked directly upward. The ossifications in the braincase had almost entirely disappeared, save the exoccipitals which formed the two distinct condyles. Beneath, the huge parasphenoid covered the entire braincase area, and there was a broad immovable connection between this bone and the pterygoids. The interpterygoid vacuities were very large.

These last and most degenerate of labyrinthodonts are common in Triassic deposits throughout the world. A maximum in size was reached by the appropriately named *Mastodonsaurus*, with a skull over a yard in length. In many forms, such as *Capitosaurus*, the skull was of "orthodox" outline. However, in *Brachyops* and its relatives there was excessive shortening, the breadth greatly exceeding the length. The opposite tendency is found in *Trematosaurus* and other still more extreme genera, in which there was a very long beak. Evidence from Spitzbergen indicates that some of these last were actually marine in habitat, a situation unparalleled among other amphibians, for salt water is fatal to larval forms.

Despite their abundance, the stereospondyls did not survive the Triassic. Their extinction is perhaps to be correlated with the fact that at that time there were developing numerous reptilian types of similar aquatic habits with which the more lowly organized amphibians could not successfully compete.

Lepospondyls.—As members of the order Lepospondyli may be grouped a series of forms, mainly of small size, which flourished greatly in Pennsylvanian times, and a few of which survived into the early Permian. In contrast with the comparatively conservative labyrinthodonts the lepospondyls were by Carboniferous times already highly specialized in various directions. The oldest remains of the group date from the end of the Mississippian, but the lepospondyls must have diverged far earlier from the primitive tetrapod stock. The most diagnostic character is found in the vertebral structure, which even at the first appearance of the group was quite dissimilar to that of the contemporary labyrinthodonts.

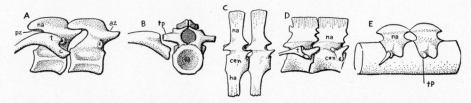

FIG. 100.—Vertebrae of Permian lepospondyls and phyllospondyls. *A, B,* lateral and anterior views of vertebrae of *Lysorophus. C, D,* caudal and dorsal vertebrae of *Crossotelos,* an elongate nectridian. *E, Branchiosaurus,* the notochord restored. For abbreviations see Figure 108. (*A, B* after Sollar, *C, D* after Williston, *E* after Whittard.)

In the lepospondyls the vertebral centrum (Fig. 100*a–d*) was a single hollow spool-shaped ossification with which even the neural arch was united in most cases. It is difficult to compare this structure with the two disk-shaped central elements and separate arch of labyrinthodonts, and the ossifications may have arisen quite differently in the two groups.

We feel certain that the primitive lepospondyls would have possessed the generalized body shape found in such widely divergent types as embolomeres and salamanders; and there are a few types of this sort, such as *Microbrachis,* all of them of small size, in deposits from the Pennsylvanian coal swamps. In these forms limbs were moderately developed, and the skull was of normal proportions. Such forms, which we may provisionally group as the suborder Micramphibia, are poorly known and often confused with the contemporary branchiosaurs.

The divergence of the various lepospondyl groups from the orthodox type of skull and body structure must have taken place at an extremely early date, for they were at the peak of their development in the Pennsylvanian coal swamps. Degeneration, too, must have set in early, for it is doubtful if any of these lepospondyls ever left the water.

Grouped in the suborder Aistopoda are a number of forms, such as *Ophiderpeton* and *Dolichosoma*, in which the limbs had been lost and an elongate snake-like body developed, sometimes with over one hundred vertebrae. Details of structure are poorly known, but in the former type one peculiar development was the replacement of the normal bones of the cheek region by a mosaic of small plates.

A more varied series of amphibians is that included in the suborder Nectridia. Its members are characterized by the fact that the caudal vertebrae (Fig. 100c, d) had elongated fan-shaped neural and haemal spines which opposed one another symmetrically, so that it is often difficult at first glance to tell which is the top and which the bottom of the body. The nectridians had diverged into two very distinct types in the Pennsylvanian. In such forms as little *Sauropleura* (Fig. 101)

FIG. 101.—*Sauropleura*, a snake-like Carboniferous lepospondylous amphibian. About 7½ inches long. (After Stein.)

the body was very long and, as in the aistopods, the limbs had been almost or entirely lost, while the skull was long and pointed. These eel-like types were locally very abundant in the coal-measures swamps.

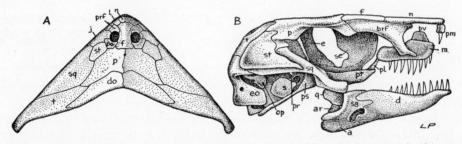

FIG. 102.—Left, dorsal view of the skull of *Diplocaulus*, a "horned" Permian lepospondyl. About one-fifth natural size. Right, the skull of *Lysorophus*, a worm-like Lower Permian amphibian; about three times natural size. For abbreviations see Figure 86. (*A* after Williston, *B* after Sollas.)

A second group of nectridians were forms with small limbs and with grotesque "horned" skulls. *Diplocaulus* (Fig. 102a) of the Lower Permian was the last and most highly specialized of these forms. The body in some cases was 2 feet or more in length. As in stereospondyls there was a large parasphenoid and huge interpterygoid vacuities, two very distinct condyles were developed, the braincase was almost unossified, and the skull as a whole was very much flattened. The greatest specialization, however, lay in the fact that the tabulars were, so to speak, pulled out backward and laterally to form the major part of huge horn-like extensions of the skull roof. The jaws, however, had not elongated, and lay far forward on the under side of the skull; while the eyes also had retained their anterior position but looked directly up out of the flat skull roof. The limbs were quite small, and the clavicles and interclavicle expanded into huge flat plates. Obviously this grotesque creature was a bottom dweller; the whole body may have been so broad and flat that a skate-like up-and-down undulation of the body was possible.

Several related forms, morphologically ancestral to *Diplocaulus*, are found in the Pennsylvanian. In these the "horns" were not so long, the skull a bit higher, the interpterygoid vacuities not so large, the limbs not so disproportionately small, and the body less flattened. In every way they suggest that here, as in other groups, descent can be traced back to a form with a structure like that of the Embolomeri. Many of the structural changes seen in *Diplocaulus* are strangely similar to those seen in later labyrinthodonts; we shall see further examples of parallel trends in later types.

Somewhat doubtfully to be included here in a subordinal position are the Lysorophia, a group including only a few small types; *Lysorophus* (Figs. 102*b*, 100*a*, *b*) of the Lower Permian was a last survivor found in enormous numbers in some Texas pool deposits. Here again the limbs were much reduced and the size and proportions much like those of a large worm. A characteristic feature of the group lies in the fact that, although there is a spool-shaped centrum, the neural arch was separated from it and tended to be divided into two lateral halves. In contrast to almost all other Paleozoic amphibians, there was no pineal opening; and the skull was no longer completely roofed, for most of the circumorbital bones were gone and the orbit was open below. The parasphenoid was large, as in most degenerate amphibian types, but the occipital condyle had remained single. In the throat the branchial arches were large and ossified, suggesting that this form retained gill breathing throughout life, a feature probably true of many other lepospondyls.

Related forms were already present in the Mississippian, making this type one of the most ancient of known tetrapods. The earliest forms, however, had a completely roofed skull. This fact suggests that here, too, the skull pattern originally was similar to that of the Embolomeri.

It has been suggested that *Lysorophus* was an ancestor of the reptiles. This is almost out of the question. Many features of the skull structure are comparable to those of modern amphibians. It is possible that this type might have been an ancestor of, for example, the modern worm-like apodous amphibians or the urodeles, but there is no positive evidence for this.

Lepospondyls of all the types discussed above flourished greatly in the Carboniferous coal swamps, where they outnumbered all other amphibians combined. Their history, however, was then nearly at an end. There were but three survivors in the earliest Permian; not a one in later deposits.

Phyllospondyls.—While the labyrinthodonts are of great interest as the best known of archaic tetrapods and as ancestors of the reptiles, and the lepospondyls are spectacular in illustrating the diversity of types possible in an early stage of amphibian history, the members of the order Phyllospondyli are of still greater importance in the history of amphibians per se. On the one hand, they include not only the branchiosaurs and many other common forms from the Carboniferous and Permian but also, seemingly, the oldest known Devonian amphibian types; on the other hand, the group very probably was the stock from which some, if not all, of the modern amphibian orders have been derived.

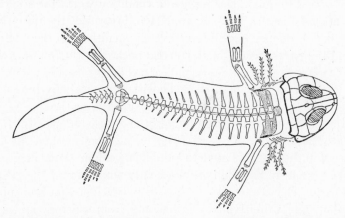

FIG. 103.—*Branchiosaurus*, a small phyllospondylous amphibian from the Lower Permian. About $2\frac{1}{2}$ inches long. (After Bullman and Whittard.)

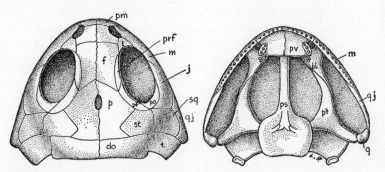

FIG. 104.—Skull of *Branchiosaurus*, dorsal and ventral views. Enlarged. For abbreviations see Figure 86. (After Bullman and Whittard.)

We shall begin our account of the order with a description of the branchiosaurs of the Lower Permian. *Branchiosaurus* (Figs. 103, 104) and related genera were amphibians of small size, only a few inches in length. Their appearance in life was probably similar to that of a modern newt. The limbs and girdles were well developed and, as far as can be determined, seem to have resembled those of the labyrinthodonts. But perhaps in relation to their small size and aquatic habits there was a much greater development of cartilage and a consequent loss of preservable parts in the skeleton.

In the head there were numerous parallelisms with the labyrinthodonts. The skull in typical Permian forms was rather broad and depressed, the orbits large; a pineal opening was present, as was an otic notch. The dorsal surface of the skull was completely roofed with bones, and practically all the primitive elements are found in much the same arrangement as that in the labyrinthodonts.

The braincase, however, was entirely unossified in most cases; the branchiosaurs, in the Lower Permian, had reached a condition which the labyrinthodonts had hardly attained in the Triassic. Here, too, instead of the primitive type of palate, there had developed huge interpterygoid vacuities like those in the stereospondyls, and the parasphenoid had extended back over the braincase in a broad plate, with the large triradiate pterygoids attaching to its sides. The ectopterygoids were lost. There were pointed teeth with traces of labyrinthine structure along the edges of the jaws and often numerous palatal teeth.

Back of the head there have been found in many cases lines of little denticles which indicate the presence of external gills in the younger stages at least. Such gills are present in the young of modern amphibians and in larval lungfish and presumably were present in the embryos of all early amphibians.

Such features as we have seen would lead us to conclude that branchiosaurs had descended from small primitive labyrinthodonts, from which group they differ in a more accelerated drift toward degeneracy. But the structure of the vertebral column (Fig. 100e) shows that, although they may have come from a common stock, the branchiosaurs were a very distinct group. Good neural arches were present, although the spines were low and rounded. Below, however, we find no central elements of any sort but merely thin extensions of the arch which sheathed the upper part of the notochord and terminated in a transverse process bearing short straight single-headed ribs.

It is quite probable that these small Paleozoic types were the ancestors of the frogs and salamanders. There are no skeletal features which debar them from consideration in this connection. Further skeletal degeneration would bring a branchiosaur close to the salamander condition, and adaptations for hopping are the only major changes required to convert such a form into a frog. Positive evidence, however, is lacking; a long gap exists between the time of the last known branchiosaur and the first known fossils of the modern types.

The branchiosaurs were, however, merely one terminal branch of the phyllospondyls; back of these small and degenerate forms lay a long history.

In the Carboniferous phyllospondyls were abundant and varied. Some small forms of that period were ancestral branchiosaurs, similar in many features to the Permian forms but with a more primitive palatal structure. There were many other types, one exceedingly long headed, another with a very short, broad skull.

Of greater interest were such types as *Erpetosaurus* and *Colosteus*, which were much more primitive types, with high narrow skulls superficially similar to those of the early labyrinthodonts but with typical phyllospondyl specializations. *Colos-*

teus had, as an adult, a skull a foot or so in length and was thus as large as most contemporary labyrinthodonts.

Here the pedigree of the phyllospondyls ceased, until recently the Upper Devonian of Greenland yielded remains of what are now the oldest known amphibians. Of these forms (*Ichthyostega* [Fig. 95] and *Ichthyostegopsis*) only portions of the skulls have so far been described; the remainder of the skeleton should reveal many points of interest. The skull material seems to show that we are dealing with ancestors of the phyllospondyls, although with forms of a very primitive nature and close to the fish ancestors of the tetrapods.

These were animals of fairly good size—the rather high and narrow skulls half a foot or so in length. Except for the intertemporal, every element of the cranial roof found in tetrapods was present, as well as certain additional elements such as a rostral bone at the front of the snout and, interestingly, a remnant of the gill covering, a tiny preopercular. The palate, with very tiny interpterygoid vacuities, was very primitive and essentially comparable to that of the embolomeres. The dermal pattern was comparable to that of Pennsylvanian branchiosaurs and different from the embolomeres in many ways, as, for example, the fact that the cheek region was tightly fused to the top of the skull in front of the shallow otic notch. Of particular interest is the nasal region. Presumably the ancestral fishes had as nostrils paired ventral pockets on the under side of the snout, each pocket opening to the outer surface by two openings, much as in living sharks. In the lungfish we see, seemingly, how internal nostrils have developed. The openings are still on the under side of the head, but the jaws have extended forward so that one opening to each pocket lies just inside their margins. In normal land forms the outer opening has migrated to the top of the snout; but in these Devonian amphibians, as in dipnoans, they were still on the under side, barely separated by a thin bar of bone from the internal nares.

These Devonian types are of great interest as the oldest known tetrapods. They show us, however, that even at that early date the line leading to the phyllospondyls had already separated from that leading to other land groups. It is to be hoped that future discoveries may reveal the Devonian ancestors of the lepospondyls and labyrinthodonts.

Modern amphibians.—Most of the older amphibian groups disappeared in the Lower Permian, and even the last labyrinthodonts disappeared in the Triassic. Later amphibians belong to three existing groups—the frogs and toads (order Anura), the salamanders (order Urodela), and the worm-like Apoda. It is difficult to connect living groups with the ancient forms, for the Apoda are unknown paleontologically and the other orders are rare as fossils; the salamanders do not appear until the Cretaceous, and the earliest frogs are of late Jurassic date. We have suggested that the modern types may have been derived from branchiosaurs, and many structural features in the frogs and toads are in agreement with this belief (the highly specialized Apoda are difficult to correlate). In both groups we see results of the degenerative skeletal trends visible not only in the branchiosaurs but in almost all of the older types.

The skull of the Anura and Urodela is much flattened, and there has been much reduction in ossification of the braincase. Exoccipitals bearing the paired condyles and a sphenethmoid are almost universally present, and there is usually an opisthotic but other braincase elements, such as basioccipital, supraoccipital, and basisphenoid, are practically unknown. The pineal opening is lost, and many roofing bones have disappeared; the skull is no longer solidly roofed. Almost without exception every bone of the circumorbital series has vanished, together with the temporal elements, tabulars, and dermal supraoccipitals, leaving of the dermal bones only a reduced central row and a lateral rim along the jaw. As in the late members of the older groups, there are in the palates of frogs and salamanders large interpterygoid vacuities separated by an expanded parasphenoid. Both ectopterygoids and epipterygoids disappear, and the other elements may be much modified; the pterygoids are immovably attached to the braincase. The jaw elements are much reduced; at the most we find a dentary, angular, prearticular, articular, and a single coronoid, as compared with the ten bones present in early labyrinthodonts; and there may be still further reduction.

The vertebral construction found in frogs and salamanders is derivable from the branchiosaur condition, as is that of the ribs which are short or absent. There is much loss of ossification in the limb skeleton; the pubis is never ossified, and the carpus and tarsus may remain largely formed of cartilage. There are never more than four typical digits in the front foot. There is no trace of scales in either frogs or salamanders.

Frogs and toads.—But while the two larger modern orders show many common characters, they have diverged remarkably from one another in many adaptive features and merit separate, if brief, consideration.

The tailless amphibians, constituting the order Anura, or Salientia, include the various modern types of frogs and toads. The absence of a tail and the extremely long, hopping hind legs, in which an extra joint has been formed from elongated tarsal elements, are the most obvious specializations. The internal structures are also highly modified. There are often only six or eight vertebrae in the entire backbone, although at the posterior end of the column, beyond the sacrum, there is a peculiar long spike of bone which appears to represent a dozen or so tail vertebrae fused into a solid mass. The short ribs presumably present in the ancestors of the frogs have almost universally disappeared and are replaced by long transverse processes.

The ilium is extended into a long rod which reaches forward a considerable distance to connect with the last of the vertebrae. The hind legs are very long and powerfully developed for jumping, and tibia and fibula are fused into a single element, as are the radius and ulna in the front leg.

The shoulder girdle retains all the primitive parts, although it is rather peculiar in form and seemingly strengthened to take up the jars caused by the hopping gait. There is even a separate coracoid ossification, a rather unusual feature in amphibians. Alone among living tetrapods, the frogs apparently have a vestige of the cleithrum in a partially ossified area above the scapula proper.

The frogs are the most successful of modern amphibians. Their history can be followed back to the Jurassic; but the oldest frogs were essentially modern in build, with all the specializations of the living forms. There are no intermediate types to help us to trace them back to the small normal-legged Paleozoic amphibians from which they must have come, although there is little in the anatomy of the branchiosaurs to debar them from an ancestral position.

Urodeles.—The newts and salamanders included in the order Urodela (or Caudata) are in appearance much more primitive types than the anurans. In most cases limbs of normal build are present, although they are usually rather small. Externally the salamanders, with a long body and well-developed tail, resemble primitive amphibian types. Internally, however, the skeleton shows many modifications and regressions. The limb girdles are largely cartilagenous (there is only one ossification in the shoulder), and the dermal shoulder girdle has disappeared completely. There is usually a well-developed branchial arch skeleton, for there is a general tendency in the group to persist in a water-living mode of life; and a number of types never leave the water, continuing to breathe with gills throughout life.

Typical salamanders have been found as far back as the lowest Cretaceous; it is of interest that one large Tertiary form (*Andrias*) was, some hundreds of years ago, regarded as the skeleton of a poor human sinner drowned in the flood, "Homo diluvii testis."

The Apoda.—A final order of amphibians is that of the Apoda (or Gymnophiona), comprising a few genera of small tropical burrowing forms of very peculiar build. There are no limbs, and the general appearance is that of a large earthworm. Alone among living forms the Apoda have retained scales, although these are small and buried in folds of skin. The skull is technically roofed, for there is a complete covering to the top and sides. But there has been a considerable loss of elements and much change in the shape and position of those remaining. The orbits are very small, for these forms are practically blind; and there are instead pits lodging tentacles which functionally take their place. This solidly built little head is quite possibly derived from one in which much of the dermal covering had been lost; it seems likely that there has been a secondary fusion of the remaining elements resulting in the formation of a more effective burrowing organ.

There are no fossils of this group known, and we have no clues whatever as to the pedigree of these modern types, although they may have come from some such small Paleozoic forms as *Lysorophus*.

CHAPTER VI

PRIMITIVE REPTILES

There is no more interesting story in the fossil record than that of the rise and fall of the reptiles. Springing from the primitive amphibians during the Carboniferous, they became the dominating group of vertebrates during the whole of the Mesozoic and gave rise to many curious and spectacular types. Now they are in decay; but it must not be forgotten that the birds and mammals which have triumphed over them are their descendants.

Class characteristics.—Reptiles have numerous features which serve to distinguish them from other tetrapods. Like the amphibians, but unlike the birds and mammals, they are cold-blooded, that is, there is no effective mechanism for the regulation of body heat and in consequence the activity of the animal varies with the temperature. In relation to this reptiles are characteristically tropical forms and become increasingly rare as we proceed toward the polar regions.

The most distinctive feature of the reptiles, as contrasted with amphibians, is the type of developmental history, for the egg can be laid on land. It is protected against drying and against mechanical injury by a series of membranes and fluids surrounding the developing embryo. Further protection is afforded by a firm shell. This shell, however, is porous; and one of the membranes within acts as an embryonic lung, extracting oxygen from the air. Since the young reptiles must emerge fully equipped for life on land, considerable growth is necessary; this is rendered possible because of the fact that the egg is large and contains a good supply of nourishing yolk.

The initiation of this new mode of development was an epochal event in vertebrate history. Only with the appearance of the amniote egg did a true terrestrial existence become possible. The amphibian is, from one point of view, nothing but a rather aberrant fish type. It may exist for a time on land but is chained to the water; it cannot stray far from that element, and must pass its early life as an aquatic form. The reptile, however, can develop directly into a terrestrial animal, and a much better opportunity is given for the perfection of a higher type of organization. This organization is apparent in every part of the body—in skeleton, in muscle, in the circulatory system. Even in the brain the reptile is on a higher plane, for, while this structure is still small compared with that of birds or mammals, it is nevertheless a much better organ than the amphibian brain; in its small cerebral hemispheres appear for the first time the rudiments of the higher mental centers which have become predominant in the brains of mammals.

Reptiles living today can easily be distinguished from amphibians by means of soft parts, and among living types it is also feasible to distinguish between these classes by means of skeletal features. Reptiles, for example, have but one condyle on the skull, modern amphibians two; reptiles typically have five toes in the manus, living amphibians four or less. The sacrum in reptiles includes at least two ribs, one in amphibians.

But the fossil evidence obliterates these and other supposed differences. Primitive Paleozoic reptiles and some of the earliest amphibians were so similar in their skeletons that it is almost impossible to tell when we have crossed the boundary between the two classes.

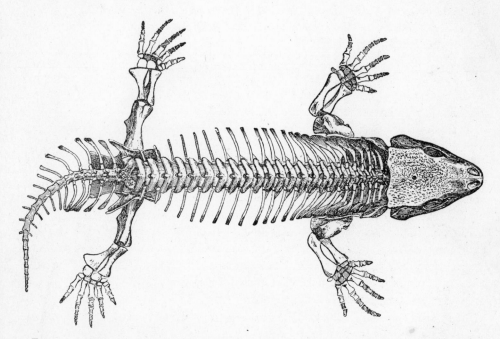

FIG. 105.—*Seymouria*, a primitive Permian cotylosaur. Dorsal view. Original about 20 inches long. (From Williston.)

Structure of a primitive reptile.—As an introduction to the study of the reptiles we may first consider the structure of one of the most primitive of known reptiles, *Seymouria*, of the Texas Lower Permian (Figs. 105, 106), and then discuss briefly some of the many variations to be found in the reptilian orders.

Seymouria is a small form, about 2 feet in length, with a rather chunky body, somewhat higher and narrower in shape than the usual amphibian and with a fairly long and strong tail. It was probably a carnivore, as seems to have been the case with most early reptiles, although from its size it is probable that large insects, rather than other vertebrates, may have formed its food.

In the skull, which is of moderate height, the arrangement of the roofing elements is exactly that found in the most primitive embolomerous amphibians; even such variable elements as the intertemporal and supratemporal bones are still present. The pineal is well developed; the lacrimal extends the full distance from the orbit to the nares. Most striking is the fact that a typical amphibian otic notch is still present and of good size.

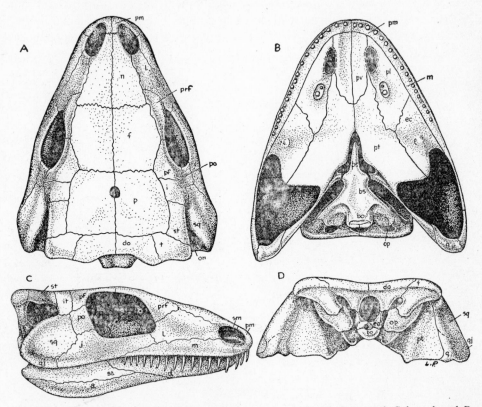

FIG. 106.—The skull of the primitive reptile *Seymouria*, *A*, dorsal, *B*, ventral, *C*, lateral, and *D*, posterior views. Length of original about 4½ inches. For abbreviations see Figure 86. (After Williston and Watson.)

The palate is also remarkably like that of the primitive amphibians, and contrasts with later members of that class, for there are very small interpterygoid vacuities, and the pterygoids articulate movably with processes of the basisphenoid. The braincase elements are well ossified; there is, as in primitive amphibians, a single rounded condyle at the back of the skull.

In the jaws the primitive elements are all present, except that there is but a single splenial element and a single coronoid. The teeth of the jaw margins are long and pointed and still with some labyrinthine structure; while on the palate, in addition to a number of tiny teeth, there are several pairs of teeth with adjacent pits of the type which can be traced all the way from the crossopterygian ancestors of the tetrapods.

In *Seymouria* and other very primitive reptiles (Fig. 108) the neural arches are very broad with the zygapophyses wide apart, rather in contrast with primitive

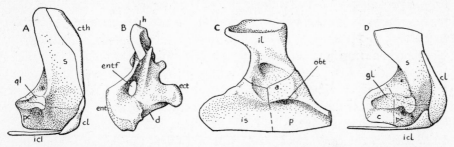

FIG. 107.—*A*, shoulder girdle of the cotylosaur *Diadectes*. *B*, right humerus of *Diadectes*. *C*, pelvis of *Diadectes*. *D*, shoulder girdle of the advanced cotylosaur *Labidosaurus*. Abbreviations for *A*, *D*: *c*, true coracoid; *cl*, clavicle; *cth*, cleithrum; *gl*, glenoid cavity (for head of humerus); *icl*, interclavicle; *pc*, precoracoid (anterior coracoid); *s*, scapula. *B*: *d*, articular surface for ulna; *ect*, *ent*, processes (ectepicondylar, entepicondylar) above the distal articular surfaces for muscles running to the leg; *entf*, entepicondylar foramen (common in primitive reptiles); *h*, head of humerus. *C*: *a*, acetabulum for head of femur; *il*, ilium; *is*, ischium; *obt*, obturator foramen piercing pubis; *p*, pubis.

amphibians. The true centra are complete disks, while the intercentra, although still quite large, are incomplete ventral wedges. This retention of the centra and reduction of intercentra is in sharp contrast with amphibian tendencies. In other respects the column is still rather amphibian in nature; there is little regional differentiation, for ribs may be found from the beginning of the neck to the base of the tail. The ribs are still double headed as in primitive amphibians, the head attaching to the intercentrum, the tubercle to the transverse process; in the chest region the ribs from which the shoulder girdle is slung are longer and heavier than the others.

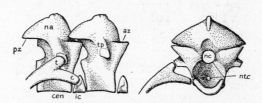

FIG. 108.—Vertebrae of the primitive reptile *Seymouria*, natural size, right side and anterior views. *az*, anterior zygapophysis; *c*, capitulum of rib; *cen*, centrum; *ha*, haemal arch; *ic*, intercentrum; *na*, neural arch; *nc*, opening in arch for nerve cord; *ntc*, notochordal pit; *pz*, posterior zygapophysis; *t*, tubercle of rib; *tp*, transverse process. (After Williston.)

The limbs are of the short, stubby, massive type found in many primitive amphibians, with the proximal elements projecting at right angles to the body. The massive shoulder girdle is close behind the head, there being almost no neck. It is very similar in many respects to that of such an amphibian as *Eryops*. However, in reptiles the ventral part of the primary girdle (Fig. 107*a*) is (in contrast with almost every amphibian group) a separate coracoid element, and the interclavicle has a long posterior stem for the attachment of powerful breast muscles. In most primitive reptiles the cleithrum is present, although reduced (it is absent, however, in *Seymouria*). The pelvic girdle in primitive reptiles (Fig. 107c) consists of the usual three elements; but the ilium is larger, more expanded than in amphibians, a feature presumably related to greater walking powers and increased musculature. *Seymouria* has but a single sacral rib, but almost all other reptiles possess at least two.

The limb bones are in many respects similar to those of a well-developed ancient amphibian such as *Eryops*. One distinctive feature is the presence of an entepicondylar foramen, an opening for nerve and blood vessels on the back (or inner) side of the humerus near the distal end. Such a structure is found in all primitive reptiles (Fig. 107b) but present in only one known amphibian type.

In *Seymouria* the carpus and tarsus still contain all the elements found in the most primitive amphibians. Five fingers are present in both hand and foot, in contrast with all except the most primitive of amphibian types. The phalangeal formula is 2–3–4–5–3 in the manus and 2–3–4–5–4– in the hind foot—the typical reptilian number (cf. Figs. 213a, 214a); amphibians, as far as known, always have a smaller number of joints.

As will be noted, there are but few points in which *Seymouria* can be distinguished from a primitive amphibian. Our only sure criterion would be a knowledge of the beast's development; but of this we, of course, know nothing. So close is the structure of this little reptile to that of amphibians that it has sometimes been claimed that it belongs to that group. The evidence, however, although not positive, suggests that it is in reality a primitive reptile which is but little removed from the ancestral amphibian stock.

From such a structural type as that of *Seymouria* there have been enormous variations in the fifteen or so orders of reptiles. The development of bipeds from quadrupeds and the evolution of flying forms and of many marine types have caused many startling changes in the general body organization. We shall here outline some of the main trends.

The reptile skull.—The skull in reptiles has tended in general to become progressively higher and narrower in shape in contrast with the flattening found among amphibians. Many of the dermal roofing elements may disappear. The supratemporal and intertemporal, and later the tabulars and dermal supra-occipitals, tend to become reduced and lost. The pineal may be absent, and there may be considerable variation in the bones about the orbits. The otic notch disappears or is considerably modified in structure. With the elimination of this notch, the opisthotic tends to extend farther sideways and form a more effective brace across the back of the skull (cf. Fig. 114d).

Especially to be noted is an interesting series of variations in the cheek region of the skull. The temporal muscles closing the jaws have their attachment under the bones covering this region. It appears that when a muscle arises from a broad plate of bone, its action is facilitated if an opening (fenestra) develops through which the muscle may bulge when contracted. In correlation with this we find that in most later reptiles the cheek is fenestrated, that is, openings appear between various bones. These fenestrae vary considerably, apparently being related to different developments of the temporal muscles (Fig. 109). Frequently there is but one opening. In some cases this is high up on the skull and bounded below by the squamosal and postorbital; in others (mammal-like forms) it is low on the side, and these two bones are in contact above it. These two types of opening are termed the upper (superior) and lateral temporal vacuities. In a large number of types (the crocodiles and dinosaurs, for example) both openings may be present, with the postorbital and squamosal meeting between the two.

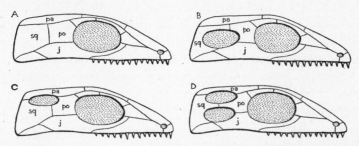

Fig. 109.—Diagrammatic side views of reptilian skulls to show various types of temporal opening. *A*, no opening—"anapsid" condition. *B*, a lower opening with postorbital and squamosal meeting above— "synapsid" condition. *C*, an upper opening with postorbital and squamosal meeting below—"parapsid" condition. *D*, both openings present—"diapsid" condition. *j*, jugal; *pa*, parietal; *po*, postorbital; *sq*, squamosal.

There are many variations in the palate. In some types the palatal bones may fuse into a nearly solid plate. In several groups the internal nostrils may be shifted back from their original anterior position by the construction of a shelf in the roof of the mouth. In contrast with amphibians the braincase is always well ossified and the occipital condyle almost always remains single. In the lower jaw one or two elements may be lost in various cases. The dentition varies enormously with adaptations for feeding on plant and invertebrate life. Never, except in a few primitive types such as *Seymouria* itself, does the old tooth-and-pit arrangement occur on the palate, although some forms (as ichthyosaurs) may have teeth of labyrinthine construction.

Axial skeleton.—In the backbone there is a universal tendency for the reduction of the intercentra. Even in most Permian forms they are merely small ventral crescents, and they usually disappear completely in Mesozoic types. The true centra tend to lengthen. They are primitively hollow at both ends (amphicoelous), but the opening for the notochord usually disappears; the ends may be flush across (platycoelous), while in many cases articulations are developed between successive centra, one end being hollowed, the other swelling out to fit into this socket. Various terms have been devised to describe this and other conditions. If, for example, a vertebra is concave in front, convex behind, it may be termed procoelous; the opposite condition is opisthocoelous.

The ribs vary greatly in structure (cf. Figs. 123, 149, 198). The attachments of the two heads may shift, or a single-headed condition may result. With the development of a true neck region in most reptiles, the ribs in this region may shorten or even disappear, and a well-marked cervical region be formed. Two or more sacral vertebrae are almost universal in contrast to the amphibian condition.

In addition to the ventral continuation of the ordinary ribs, reptiles often have independent structures called "abdominal ribs," dermal bony splint-like elements, ranged along the belly in V-shaped rows. These structures are seemingly the last remnants of the old fish scales which were developed in amphibians in a similar position on the under side of the body. While reptiles are scaled (in contrast with living amphibians), the scales are really horny scutes (although plates of bone often develop beneath them) and are not homologous with fish scales.

Limbs.—There is, of course, much variation in the limb structure. In the shoulder girdle the cleithrum tends to disappear very early in reptile history (it is found in but a few Triassic forms and in none today), and the other dermal elements may be lost as well. In most reptiles a scapula and a single coracoid constitute the elements of the primary girdle; but in one major group (mammal-like reptiles) a second, posterior coracoid element is added (Fig. 196). The peculiar screw-shaped glenoid of primitive types disappears by the close of Permian times. There is never any change in the number of pelvic bones, but in many cases a fenestration of the ventral plate occurs in relation to the origin of a large limb muscle, a development comparable to the fenestration seen in the skull (cf. Figs. 116c, 132b, 211b, c).

The limb bones in general tend to become much slimmer than in primitive forms, and many variations in structure occur in relation to varied locomotor needs. In the humerus the ectepicondylar foramen characteristic of primitive reptiles usually disappears, but there often develops an ectepicondylar foramen on the outer side of the distal end of the bone (Fig. 210b, c). Reduction takes place in carpus and tarsus (cf. Figs. 213a, 214a, etc.). Of the central and medial elements there is seldom more than one, while the last distal carpal and tarsal usually disappear. In the hind foot the tibiale almost always vanishes, leaving but two proximal elements, often called by their mammalian names of "astragalus" and "calcaneum." The number of joints in the toes is in general remarkably uniform. The outer toe, especially in the hind foot, tends to be set off at an angle and may disappear.

Reptile radiation (Fig. 110).—The earliest certain remains of reptiles are found in the Pennsylvanian. From that period known specimens are few, but practically all our knowledge of carboniferous fossils is gained from coal-swamp deposits, and we know nothing of the life of higher and dryer regions where reptiles might well have been already numerous. Dating from the end of the Pennsylvanian and the beginning of Permian times are deposits (Red Beds) of a more terrestrial type in which are found abundant reptiles, including not only such primitive forms as *Seymouria* but more advanced types. Amphibians were then still numerous, but long before the close of the Permian they had been pushed into the background, and the radiation of the reptiles was under way. Almost every known reptilian group made its appearance before the end of the Triassic. In the Jurassic and Cretaceous these groups increased in size, in abundance, and in diversity. Toward

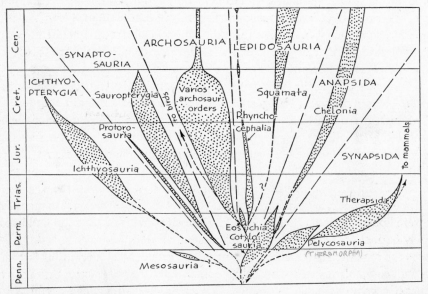

Fig. 110.—The phylogeny of reptiles. (The archosaurs are shown separately in Figure 162.)

the close of the Cretaceous, however, the great reptilian orders waned; and the beginning of the Cenozoic is marked by the end of the reptilian dynasties and the radiation of the mammals. Only a few reptilian groups have survived—the lizards and snakes, the turtles, the crocodiles, and the rhynchocephalian *Sphenodon*.

These varied reptilian types have been arranged in from fifteen to twenty or more orders by different authors. It is probable that they did not all spring directly and independently from the base of the reptile stem, and various workers have attempted to assemble larger groups of presumably common parentage as subclasses or superorders. It is difficult to select a proper basis for such classification; the most obvious differences between groups lie in the varied construction of the limbs and other superficial features which are closely related to environmental adaptations and are hence untrustworthy (seagoing reptiles, for example, are all likely to develop paddle-like legs, but this means merely convergent adaptation and not real relationship). It was early suggested that the nature of the temporal openings was a better criterion, and attempts to work out reptilian phylogenies have been based mainly on this feature. It was once thought that all reptiles originally had two temporal openings, and hence forms with two openings (or two bars across the temple, which amounts to the same thing) were termed "diapsid" (two-arched); and forms with one opening (in which it was presumed that the two openings had fused into one), "synapsid" (fused-arched) reptiles. But it soon became obvious that this division was inadequate. Truly primitive forms must have possessed a completely roofed skull like that of their amphibian ancestors, and for this condition the term "anapsid" was coined. Further, the single opening found in a number of groups is obviously not homologous throughout, being sometimes a superior, sometimes a lateral, one; and temporal fenestrae may shift in position or become secondarily closed. These structures may be used for purposes of classification—but used, like any other single character, with caution.

Cotylosaurs.—*Seymouria* was an exceedingly primitive reptile; the stock to which it belongs may well be the stem from which the other reptilian orders have arisen. This group constitutes the order Cotylosauria, and its members have been appropriately called "stem reptiles." The few fragmentary reptilian remains from typical Pennsylvanian deposits presumably pertain to cotylosaurs. At the very end of that period and the lower part of the Permian they had become common and diversified. But other reptilian groups had already evolved from them, and from that time on the cotylosaurs began steadily to lose in importance. Comparatively few were left in the later Permian, and by the late Triassic the group had become entirely extinct and had given place to more advanced types.

As is the case with primitive ancestors of any group, a "stem reptile" is difficult to define; cotylosaurs are distinguishable mainly by the presence of primitive and comparatively unspecialized features, the lack of the peculiarities found in derived groups. The one certain criterion is the fact that the roof of the skull is not pierced by fenestrae in the temporal region. This is the anapsid condition, and the stem reptiles may be placed in a subclass Anapsida, in which the turtles are perhaps to be included as well.

The cotylosaur limbs are usually short and stubby, the feet generally little modified. The dermal shoulder girdle is usually complete, and the cleithrum often of considerable size. There are usually two sacral ribs. In the skull the otic notch may be much modified or lost completely; there is but little loss of skull elements. In the backbone a characteristic feature of almost every cotylosaur, and one by which they may be distinguished from almost all other reptilian groups, is the fact that the neural arches are very broad and swollen with the zygapophyses far apart and with horizontal articular faces.

Despite certain common characteristics, mostly of a primitive character, there is such a wide range of variation in these primitive reptiles that by some the cotylosaurs are considered as constituting a superorder in themselves. We shall not go to this extreme here but shall use a classification dividing these forms into a few suborders based on representative types.

Seymouria, described above, was an exceedingly primitive reptile and may serve as the type of a group, the Seymouriamorpha, which presumably represented the basal reptilian stock and was characterized by a number of archaic features such as the large intercentra, the single sacral vertebrae, and especially the retention of the typical amphibian otic notch. Presumably this group flourished during the Carboniferous, but we have only a few fragmentary reptilian remains from typical deposits of the period. A member of this group has been found in the late Coal Measures of Bohemia; *Seymouria* itself is from the Lower Permian; and late survivors appear to have been present in Russia in Upper Permian times. These archaic forms seem early to have been displaced by their more progressive and diversified descendants.

Diadectomorphs.—Primitive cotylosaurs presumably were carnivores; the flesh-eating rôle, however, appears soon to have been taken over by the mammal-like reptiles, to be discussed later; and the majority of Permian cotylosaurs were herbivorous or mollusk-eating types.

Fairly representative of an important side line of cotylosaurs, the Diadectomorpha, were *Diadectes* and its relatives of the Lower Permian of North America and Europe. *Diadectes* (Figs. 111a, 107a–c) was a rather large form, about 5 feet in length. In trunk and limb structure there were many resemblances to *Seymouria*. But the skull was much modified, particularly the region of the otic notch. For an effective bracing of the quadrate and its jaw articulation on the skull the presence of the otic notch was a hindrance, weakening the structure greatly. Greater strength was obtained in this form by shifting the whole jaw articulation forward, thus placing the quadrate vertically under the cheek region. This obviously resulted in greatly exaggerating the size of the otic notch, now widely open below.

In addition these types are characterized by the development of crushing cheek teeth, widened transversely into several cusps, probably for the eating of invertebrate food such as small mollusks.

A more advanced type which appears to be closely related to the diadectids, although not directly descended from them, is that of the pareiasaurs of the Middle and Upper Permian of Europe and Africa (Fig. 112). These were the largest of cotylosaurs, ranging up to 10 feet or so in length. With increase in size the problem of weight support becomes a serious one. It would have been physically impossible for such a large animal to have walked with its limbs spread out at the sides, and in relation to this we find that in pareiasaurs the limbs had rotated in toward the body and bore the weight more vertically. This change in pose was accompanied by changes in the limb bones similar to those which we shall see in the reptilian ancestors of mammals. While the feet of most cotylosaurs were of a very primitive character, those of the pareiasaurs tended to be considerably modified; the fifth toe, for example, tended to be reduced or lost in many cases.

The skull was very large and grotesque, often with warty or horn-like protuberances. The teeth along the margins of the mouth were serrated and leaf shaped, and there were rows of small teeth on the palate. The otic notch at first sight ap-

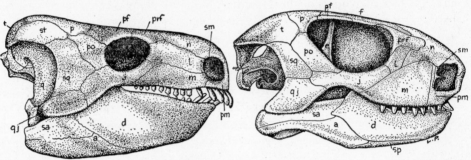

FIG. 111.—The skull of diadectomorph cotylosaurs. Left, *Diadectes* of the American Lower Permian, skull length about 8 inches. Right, *Procolophon* of the Lower Triassic of South Africa, skull length about 2 inches. For abbreviations see Figure 86. (*A*, after Williston, *B*, after Watson.)

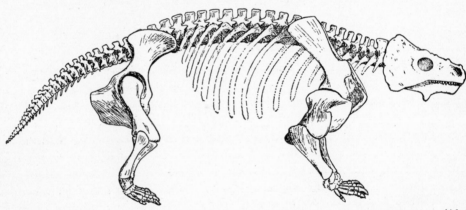

FIG. 112.—The skeleton of the Middle Permian pareiasaur *Bradysaurus*. Length about 8 feet. (After Broom.)

pears to have been absent. In reality it was present and large but covered superficially by a great development of the cheek bones, so that it opened out backward. These forms were slow and harmless herbivores, and for defense there were usually plates of bone studded along the back.

Numerous remains of pareiasaurs, such as *Bradysaurus*, have been found in the Middle Permian beds of South Africa, the skeletons often complete and right side up in the position in which they presumably became mired in their native swamps. In later Permian times they appeared in Europe as well, but were then rarer, generally smaller, and more heavily armored. Competition with more efficient herbivores and the development of various carnivorous reptile types may have been responsible for their extinction by the end of the period.

A final group of diadectomorphs, and the last survivors of all the cotylosaurs, was that including *Procolophon* (Fig. 111*b*) and its allies of the Early Triassic. These were small reptiles, usually a foot or two in length, and rather slim-limbed. Like the other members of the suborder, *Procolophon* apparently was an invertebrate or plant-feeder, and had transversely elongated cheek teeth. The otic notch was exceedingly well developed. Smaller and swifter than the pareiasaurs, they lacked armor for protection against carnivores. In some early Triassic strata they are comparatively abundant, but before the close of the period these last stragglers of the cotylosaurs had vanished.

Captorhinomorphs.—Early in Permian times, however, a much more advanced group of cotylosaurs had appeared, the Captorhinomorpha, of which *Captorhinus* (Fig. 114) and *Labidosaurus* (Fig. 113) are typical. These were small forms not

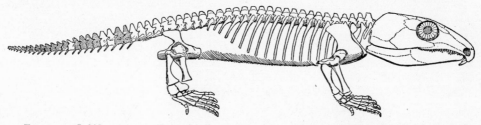

Fig. 113.—*Labidosaurus*, a progressive Lower Permian cotylosaur. Original about 26 inches long. (From Williston.)

exceeding a foot or two in length. Their postcranial skeleton was essentially similar to that of other cotylosaurs, except that the limbs were comparatively slim, and almost all the primitive skull elements were present. The dentition was specialized, the cheek teeth placed in several close-set rows, while those at the tip of the snout were long and overhanging, all suggesting an arrangement for catching and crushing small mollusks; these forms probably lived along the margins of the Permian seas.

There was one strikingly advanced condition in the skull, for the otic notch had been done away with altogether; the back margin of the skull formed an unbroken line from top to quadrate, and a good brace for the jaw had been secured. As seen in rear view, the whole skull structure was then much more solid than before. The opisthotics which connect the braincase laterally with the dermal roof formerly had, of necessity, extended upward as well as outward to terminate at the tabulars; the otic notch prevented them from passing more laterally. Now, however, these elements ran out laterally toward the jaw joint to form effective side braces fusing the whole skull into a solid compact mass. The ear drum in such a form apparently lay just behind the corner of the jaws, for the long stapes ran out and articulated with the quadrate, just as in many fish types.

These changes in the ear region of the skull are similar to those found in a number of other more highly evolved reptilian groups, particularly the ancestors of the mammals. It has been suggested that *Captorhinus* and its relatives were the ancestors of mammal-like types. This may be true in a broad sense, but the known captorhinids apparently had already become specialized mollusk-eaters, and the primitive mammal-like reptiles were their contemporaries.

Most of the varied cotylosaurs discussed above did not lead to later reptilian types. They appear to represent merely part of an archaic radiation of the reptiles

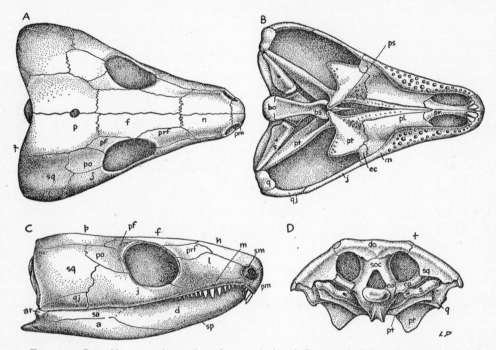

FIG. 114.—*Captorhinus*, an advanced cotylosaur. *A*, dorsal, *B*, ventral, *C*, lateral, and *D*, occipital views of skull. Length of original about 2¾ inches. For abbreviations see Figure 86. (Data from Case, Sushkin, Gregory.)

into various modes of life at a very early date, soon after they had shaken off the encumbrances of the old amphibian mode of development. They are very important members of the Permian fauna, for, together with mammal-like forms, they constituted an overwhelming majority of Permian reptile types. But their importance waned rapidly, and they soon gave place to members of a second wave of reptilian radiation which included the orders which were to dominate the Mesozoic.

Chelonians.—The turtles, the order Chelonia, may be considered here despite their obvious specializations, since it is probable that they have retained the primitive solid skull roof and hence may be placed in the subclass Anapsida with the cotylosaurs.

The chelonians are the most bizarre, and yet in many respects the most conservative, of reptilian groups. Because they are still living, turtles are commonplace objects to us; were they entirely extinct their shells, the most remarkable defensive armor ever assumed by a tetrapod, would be a cause for wonder. From the Triassic the turtles have come down to present times practically unchanged;

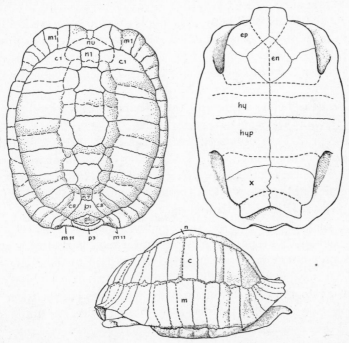

FIG. 115.—*Testudo ammon*, a giant tortoise from the early Tertiary of Egypt. Carapace (upper left), plastron (upper right), and lateral view, to show shell structure of chelonians. Sutures in solid line; outline of overlying horny scutes in dashed lines. Carapace, bony elements: *c*, costal plates; *m*, marginal plates; *n*, neural plates; *nu*, nuchal; *p*, pygal. Plastron: *en*, entoplastron; *ep*, epiplastra; *hy*, hyoplastra; *hyp*, hypoplastra; *x*, xiphiplastra. Original about 39 inches long. (After Andrews.).

they have survived all the vicissitudes which have swamped most of the reptilian groups and are in as flourishing a condition today as at any time in the past.

The turtle shell (Fig. 115).—The armor plate of the ordinary modern turtle is composed of two materials—horny scutes representing the ordinary reptilian scales on the surface, and bony plates underneath. The arrangement of the outlines of scutes and bones does not coincide; in general there is an alternating arrangement, which gives greater strength to the combined structure. The scutes are not, of course, preserved in fossils, although the outlines are often indicated by grooves in the bones which lay beneath them.

The bony shell is divisible into a dorsal carapace and a ventral plastron, connected by a bridge at the sides. At the center of the carapace is a row of eight bony neural plates fused to the neural arches of the vertebrae beneath. Lateral to them on either side is a row of longer plates, also eight in number; these are fused to the eight underlying ribs and are hence known as costals. Circling the edge of the carapace is a ring of small elements, the marginals. In addition, there may be in the central row an extra nuchal element in front of the neurals and two pygals behind them.

A much smaller number of bony elements is present in the ventral shield, the plastron. Near the front is a median plate, the entoplastron. The other elements, which are paired, consist (from front to back) of epiplastra, hyoplastra, in some primitive types one or two pairs of mesoplastra, then hypoplastra and xiphiplastra.

The shell is widely open in front for the withdrawal of the head and front legs; behind, for the hind legs and the stubby tail.

It would seem that the carapace, at least, has arisen through the development of new plates of dermal bone. Such plates are developed in many crocodiles and some lizards, as well as in other groups now extinct. The turtles differ from them in the consolidation of the plates into a complete compact covering. As regards the plastron, however, it may be that no new elements were needed. The old fish scales had been retained in many primitive reptiles as the so-called "abdominal ribs." It is possible that the turtle plastron for the most part arose by an enlargement and consolidation of these elements. With regard to the front of the plastron, it is interesting to note that the paired epiplastra articulate internally with the scapula, as do the clavicles of ordinary reptiles, while between them the single entoplastron lies in the position of an interclavicle. The anterior elements of the shield thus appear to represent the old dermal shoulder girdle.

Body skeleton.—The backbone is, of course, much modified in connection with the development of the shell. The tail is short and easily tucked away. There are two sacral vertebrae and only ten trunk vertebrae in front of it, all except the first immovably attached to the median plates of the shell. This represents a great shortening of the body from primitive conditions; probably nearly a dozen vertebrae have dropped out. There are eight ribs which, as has been stated, are fused to the under side of the costal plates; this fusion, and that of the neural arches with the median elements, effectively braces the shell. There are eight cervicals in the neck; in modern forms, in which the head is withdrawn into the shell, these have very complicated articular arrangements.

Limbs.—The limbs and girdles are of rather peculiar construction, as might be expected from the requirements of a shell-inclosed life. The limbs spread out at the sides, giving a broad trackway and a short stride, much as was the case in the cotylosaurs; and it is not improbable that this old-fashioned method of walking was present in the group when the shell first appeared and has become permanently fixed. In detail, however, the limbs are far from primitive.

In the shoulder girdle the dermal bones have been taken over into the plastron. The primary girdle (Fig. 116b) is a triradiate structure with the glenoid cavity at the union of the branches; the scapula includes a slim ascending blade and a long projection which goes down to touch the clavicles (the epiplastra); while the third prong is a single coracoid. In the pelvic girdle (Fig. 116c) much of the ventral region, instead of being a solid plate of bone, is occupied by a large opening or fenestra which has separated the pubis and ischium almost completely from one another. The feet are in general quite specialized; there is especially a tendency (rather unusual among reptiles) for a general reduction of the number of phalanges in the toes, so that there is never a higher phalangeal formula than 2–3–3–3–3.

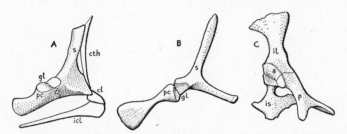

Fig. 116.—Limb girdles in chelonians. *A*, shoulder girdle of the primitive *Triassochelys*. The girdle still close to the primitive reptilian type; a cleithrum is present; the dermal elements forming part of the plastron are shown *B*, shoulder girdle of *Toxochelys* (Cretaceous). *C*, pelvic girdle of the Oligocene *Testudo laticunea*. For abbreviations see Figure 107. (*A* after Jaekel, *B*, *C* after Hay.)

Skull (Fig. 117).—The skull is also highly specialized in a number of ways. Modern turtles entirely lack teeth, their function being taken over by a horny beak which sheaths the edges of the jaws. The palatal bones have fused and united so as to give a solid structure quite different from that of primitive reptiles. The pineal eye no longer pierces the roof of the skull, and the two external nostrils have a common bony opening. A number of elements are lost, not only the dermal supra-occipitals and tabulars and the two temporal elements which have disappeared in almost all types considered later, but also the postfrontals, lacrimals, and usually even the nasals as well. The cheek is rather puzzling in many respects. In many forms most of this region is bare of dermal bones. The hole so formed is not a true temporal opening, for it has no back rim of superficial dermal bone. Seemingly there has been merely an eating-away of the skull roof from the back. From this point of view the turtles are technically anapsid and to be associated with the cotylosaurs. It has been argued that this hole was once a true temporal opening, and that its posterior margin has later disappeared; but some living turtles have a solidly roofed skull, and so did the oldest known fossils.

Primitive turtles.—The previous description has been based on the more normal turtles. The oldest forms are found in Triassic deposits, and here in such a form as *Triassochelys* we meet with types which were in some respects more primitive.

All the shell elements of later turtles were already present, and their arrangement was essentially that of later forms. In addition several pairs of mesoplastra, intermediate plastral elements not found in the modern turtles of northern continents, were present. It is probable that the limbs could not be withdrawn, but some protection was afforded them by a series of scutes projecting beyond the normal marginal region. Head and tail, as well, were not capable of being retracted and were covered with spines. The limb girdles were rather primitive, particularly

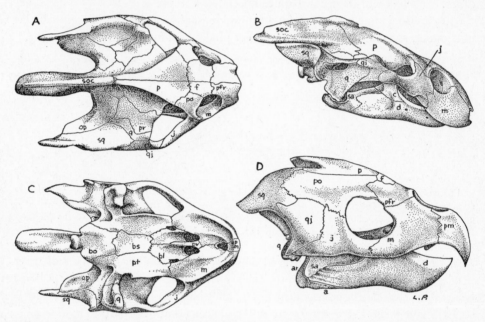

Fig. 117.—The skull in chelonians. *A*, dorsal, *B*, lateral and *C*, ventral views of the skull of *Amyda tritor*, an Eocene trionychid turtle, jaw restored from a related species. Skull length about 6 inches. *D*, lateral view of *Archelon*, a Cretaceous marine turtle, skull length about 2½ feet. For abbreviations see Figure 86. (*A–C* after Hay, *D* after Wieland.)

the shoulder girdle (Fig. 116*a*). The clavicles and interclavicle were already incorporated in the plastron but show their original character clearly, and there was possibly even a small cleithrum. In most of these primitive forms the pelvis was fused to both carapace and plastron. In the skull (Fig. 118) nasals were still present; the temporal region was completely roofed, while the most striking feature of all is that, although a horny beak was apparently already developed, there were still tiny teeth on the palate.

These Triassic forms were primitive representatives of the oldest group of turtles, the suborder Amphichelydia, which included the dominant forms in the Mesozoic. There were a number of families, which differed in many respects. Teeth were unknown except in *Triassochelys*, and the Jurassic forms were more modernized in many features, but mesoplastra continued to be present in turtles of this group until they finally disappeared in the Eocene.

Pleurodires.—Most direct descendants of these archaic chelonians are the members of the suborder Pleurodira, the "side-neck" turtles. The distinguishing feature of the Mesozoic types included in the previous suborder was the impossibility (as shown by the structure of the neck vertebrae) of drawing the head into the shelter of the shell. This has been accomplished in the pleurodires, but in contrast with most living turtles the head is withdrawn by a sideways bending of the neck.

Although present in the north in Cretaceous and Eocene times, pleurodires are now confined to the three southern continents. In many ways they seem to be little-changed survivors of the Mesozoic forms; mesoplastra, for example, are often present and the pelvic girdle fused to the shell. We have here an instance, re-

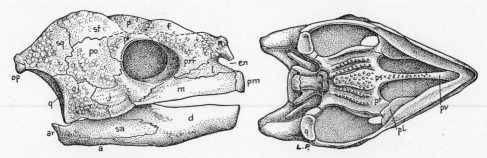

FIG. 118.—The skull of *Triassochelys*, a primitive Triassic turtle still retaining teeth; lateral and ventral views. Length of original about 5¼ inches. For abbreviations see Figure 86. (After Jaekel from *Palaeontologische Zeitschrift*, Vol. II, Gebrüder Borntraeger, Berlin.)

peated in many other groups, of the late survival in the tropics of archaic types. A Pleistocene Australian form, *Miolania*, reached a very large size; the shell is incompletely known, but some idea may be gained from the fact that the skull was 2 feet broad.

Cryptodires.—More progressive and successful has been the suborder Cryptodira, in whose members the head is withdrawn straight back into the shell by means of an S-shaped curvature of the neck vertebrae. Mesoplastra are never present, nor is the pelvis ever attached to the shell. Types intermediate between the amphichelydians and the cryptodires appeared in the Jurassic, and by the end of the Cretaceous typical cryptodires appeared and have since become the dominant types in northern areas and have invaded the seas as well.

Best known today of all the chelonians are the tortoises and terrapins, such as *Testudo* (Fig. 115) and *Emys*. Many of these forms are completely terrestrial, while others are marsh tortoises. In the land types especially, the back may be highly arched; and in all of them both carapace and plastron are very well ossified. Remains of these forms are very common in most Tertiary beds. Included in this group are a number of species of very large tortoises which have been found on various isolated islands where the absence of land enemies has afforded turtles even more protection than that which is given them by the shell.

The marsh turtles of the *Dermatemys* type, now confined to America, but known as fossils in the Old World Tertiary as well, are fairly similar to the tortoises in structure and differ mainly in their more aquatic habits, more depressed shape, and their somewhat paddle-like limbs. Their type of habitat is probably that of the primitive turtles generally and suggests the initiation of the aquatic adaptations which have been taken up in a number of turtle families.

An early stage in aquatic life is that illustrated by *Chelydra* and related snapping turtles, somewhat aberrant river-dwellers now confined to North America and the East Indies but apparently widespread in the northern continents in the Miocene.

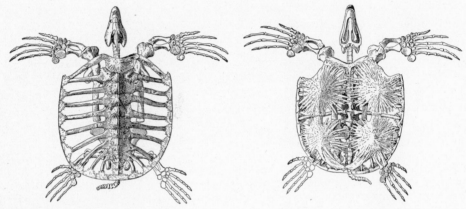

FIG. 119.—*Archelon*, a Cretaceous marine turtle, dorsal and ventral views. Original about 12 feet long. (From Wieland.)

Full aquatic adaptations have been attained by a series of marine turtles. A number of such types appeared in the Cretaceous, and a few are present in the oceans today. Of the extinct forms the best known are *Protostega* and the related *Archelon* (Fig. 117d, 119) of the Cretaceous. These old sea turtles were large types, up to a dozen feet in length. Land turtles seldom grow to any great size; but in the water, of course, many of the problems of support do not arise. The heavy armor of a turtle however, means a much increased specific gravity and a consequent expenditure of energy in maintaining the body in the water; it would be highly advantageous if the armor were lightened and the weight consequently reduced. This was rendered possible by the fact that in taking to the sea many land enemies were left behind, and for a large form there were few or no marine enemies; it was consequently possible for a marine turtle secondarily to reduce its armor to a considerable extent, leaving a small amount of bony framework.

The compact shape of a turtle's body and the small size of the tail renders swim-

ming by a fish-like movement out of the question. Consequently it was necessary
for the feet to develop into powerful swimming paddles by which the turtle might
row itself through the water. The proximal part of the limbs of these oceanic
forms is short but powerful, while the fingers are elongated and broadened to form
large webbed flippers.

Of a number of such turtle types which evolved in the Cretaceous most are extinct; but *Chelone* and a few related forms have survived to modern times. This
living genus is in general still similar in build to the oldest forms.

A second marine type present in the oceans today but almost unknown as a
fossil is *Dermochelys*, the leathery turtle. In this form there is almost no connected
dermal skeleton at all, merely a series of small bony plates studded in the skin of
the back. It has been argued that this really represents the primitive chelonian
condition and that the leathery turtle is the most primitive known member of the
entire order. But there is no fossil evidence to substantiate this, for the complete
development of the armor had taken place by the Triassic. On the contrary, we
have just seen that other marine turtles tend to reduce their armaments; and it is
probable that *Dermochelys* is merely a marine type in which reduction has gone
much farther than is usually the case.

These oceanic turtles are the first example that we have encountered of a reptile
returning to a marine existence. Later, however, we see many examples of this
type of adaptation in other reptilian groups.

Trionyx, the living soft-shelled turtle, is a river-dwelling type with a very flat
body in which the armor is somewhat reduced and on which horny scutes are entirely lacking, the plates being covered only with a leathery skin. Sometimes
placed in a separate suborder, these turtles are perhaps also to be regarded merely
as aberrant cryptodires. Related types had developed by the Cretaceous, very
probably from relatives of the snapping turtles. *Amyda* (Fig. 117) is a common
fossil form.

Turtle origins.—But little light is shed on the ultimate origin of the turtles
from a study of fossil members of the order. Some early Triassic forms, such as
Triassochelys, show a structure slightly more primitive than that of most later
turtles. But already at that time the armor was nearly perfectly developed; we
are dealing definitely with a true turtle and not with a transitional type. The ancestors of the group must be sought farther back, in Permian times.

A possible connecting form has been found in the shape of *Eunotosaurus* (Fig.
120), a small reptile from the Middle Permian of South Africa. Unfortunately the
roof of the skull is unknown; we cannot settle the problem of the presence or absence of a temporal opening. Teeth were still present. The limbs too are poorly
known, but the girdles appear to have been of a primitive character. The greatest
point of interest lies in the skeleton of the trunk. There was only a small number
of vertebrae, a fact suggesting the reduction which has taken place in turtles.

Especially significant seems to be the fact that following the small first rib were eight exceedingly broad ribs which extended far laterally and almost touched one another at their edges. This may be compared with the condition in turtles in which there are eight ribs supporting the costal plates which make up the most of

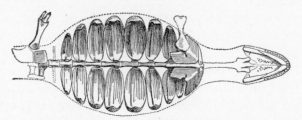

FIG. 120.—Ventral view of *Eunotosaurus*, a small Permian reptile possibly ancestral to the chelonians. About ⅔ natural size. (From Watson.)

the carapace. There is one marked difference, for in *Eunotosaurus* the plates were an expansion of the rib itself, while in turtles there is a separate dermal ossification. But it is not improbable that this form was closely related to the turtle ancestry, and the development of separate plates may have been preceded by the stage seen here. This creature was not, of course, a true turtle; on the other hand, it was far from the typical cotylosaurs. Perhaps we may include it in the Chelonia in a broad sense but place it in a separate suborder, the Eunotosauria.

CHAPTER VII

VARIED REPTILIAN TYPES

When we turn from the anapsids to a consideration of the evolution of higher reptilian groups we at once meet with difficulties. In the Mesozoic flourished many reptilian types: on land the archosaurian reptiles (including dinosaurs, flying reptiles, and crocodiles), together with lizards and rhynchocephalians as minor faunal elements; in the seas the ichthyosaurs and the plesiosaurs and allied forms. Typical members of all these groups are well known, often to the smallest details of structure. But when we attempt to discuss their mutual relations and evolution from the primitive reptilian stock we meet with serious difficulties. Most of these forms appeared in the Triassic, and their early development must have taken place in the Permian. But known fossils of the latter period (apart from cotylosaurs already too aberrant to be ancestral types) consist almost entirely of forms leading to the mammals. Of possible ancestors of other reptilian groups we have remaining but a few small obscure types, most of which are represented by fragmentary remains and are very inadequately known.

The archosaurs and the mammal-like reptiles will be considered at a later time. In the present chapter we shall discuss the various other reptilian types mentioned above, together with some less prominent but presumably related forms. We shall make some attempts at classification and suggestions as to mutual relationships (cf. Fig. 110). But it must be remembered that in doing so we are treading in many cases upon uncertain ground.

Mesosaurs.—While reptiles originated as land forms, many groups took again to water. Earliest of all aquatic types were *Mesosaurus* (Fig. 121) and its allies constituting the order Mesosauria (or Proganosauria). These were slimly built little reptiles about a yard in length which apparently were active fish-eating forms, inhabiting bodies of fresh water. Their remains are known only from deposits in South Africa and South America which appear to be of late Carboniferous age. This distribution has been used as an argument for the former union of those continents. But it may merely mean that they lived in larger bodies of water than the coal-swamp pools from which specimens of contemporary vertebrates have been recovered in Europe and America, and may possibly have been widely distributed.

The mesosaur skull was long and slim, the neck and body elongate, and there was a long powerful laterally compressed tail. The last seems to have been the principal swimming organ. But while the front legs were not particularly long and presumably functioned merely as steering organs, the hind legs were long and strong suggesting that they also were of considerable use in locomotion.

The vertebrae were of a primitive type with broad arches like those of cotylosaurs. The dorsal ribs were curiously thickened, rather banana-like; a similar structure is found in some marine sirenians among mammals, and this "pachyostosis," it is suggested, is due to some physiological change connected with aquatic life.

The shoulder girdle had the usual reptilian elements—a single coracoid and a scapula, clavicle and interclavicle. As was general in aquatic forms, the scapula was short and broad, the coracoid large. The pelvis was rather primitive, but was partly unossified. The limbs were not much modified for aquatic life; the long bones were little shortened. Presumably the spreading digits of the feet were webbed. In the toes of such marine forms as the ichthyosaurs and plesiosaurs there was a tendency for increase in the number of joints. Here, however, the phalangeal formula was normal except for an extra joint or two in the fifth toe in the pes.

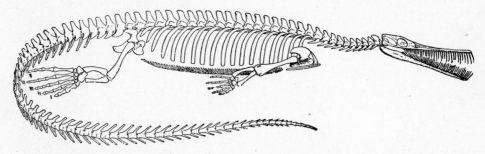

FIG. 121.—The skeleton of *Mesosaurus*, a late Carboniferous aquatic reptile from the Southern Hemisphere. Length of original about 16 inches. (After McGregor.)

There was a long slender fish-eating type of snout; the nostrils were pushed far back, an aquatic adaptation for easier breathing; the teeth were very long and sharp and set close together; the tooth-bearing palate is derivable from the generalized type seen in most primitive reptiles. The temporal region is, unfortunately, poorly known. It is believed that there was a single upper opening, but this is still uncertain.

The very early appearance of this group suggests that they were an extremely early offshoot of the stem reptiles, the cotylosaurs. They do not reappear in typical Permian deposits, and hence had a very short span of life. It is thought by some that they may have been ancestral to the ichthyosaurs. This is not improbable, although many of the resemblances may be parallel developments related to aquatic life, and in ichthyosaurs the hind legs were markedly reduced rather than enlarged as in mesosaurs.

Ichthyosaurs.—Of all reptiles, the group most highly adapted to an aquatic existence were the ichthyosaurs, which well deserve their name of "fish reptiles." They seem to have occupied the place in nature now taken by the dolphins and porpoises. They were particularly numerous in the Jurassic, but their life-span seems to have covered the greater part of the Mesozoic.

The typical Jurassic forms (Fig. 122) seem to have been very fish-like in their superficial appearance. There was a large fish-like caudal fin. The body was short

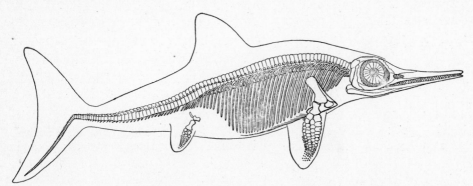

FIG. 122.—A Jurassic icthyosaur. Much reduced. (Simplified from E. v. Stromer, *Lehrbuch der Palaeozoologie*, Vol. II, G. Tuebner, Leipzig.)

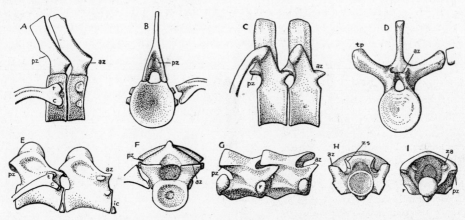

FIG. 123.—Dorsal vertebrae of various reptiles. *A, B*, lateral and posterior views of vertebrae of the ichthyosaur *Ophthalmosaurus. C, D*, lateral and anterior views of vertebrae of the plesiosaur *Cryptocleidus. E, F*, lateral and anterior views of vertebrae of the protorosaur *Araeoscelis. G, H, I*, lateral, anterior, and posterior views of vertebrae of the Cretaceous snake *Coniophis. az*, anterior zygapophysis; *c*, capitulum of rib; *ic*, innercentrum; *pz*, posterior zygapophysis; *r*, rib articulation on centrum in squamata; *t*, tubercle of rib; *tp*, transverse process of neural arch; *za, zs*, zygantrum and zygosphene, additional articular processes of neural arch. (*A–D* after Andrews, *E, F* after Williston, *G–I* after Marsh.)

and deeply fusiform and apparently somewhat compressed laterally. Perfectly preserved specimens show the body outline and reveal the presence of a large dorsal fin, unsupported by bone. The limbs were reduced (especially the pelvic ones) to short steering paddles, the main swimming motion being a fish-like undulation of the body and the tail fin. The vertebral centra (Fig. 123*a, b*) were short amphicoelous disks to which alone the two-headed ribs attached. The caudal series of vertebrae appear to be broken in fossil specimens, with the tip of the tail bent downward. This was once thought to be a post mortem effect, and the tail was restored as a straight structure. But we now know that this seeming break was natural and that ichthyosaurs had developed a reversed, but otherwise shark-like, heterocercal tail fin (Fig. 126).

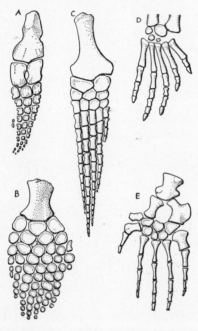

All the bones of the girdle were present but none too well ossified; and the elements were small, especially the dorsal ones. The pelvis had lost its connection with the sacral vertebrae. The long bones of the limbs were much shortened and, except for the humerus and femur, tended to become hexagonal or circular disks, as did all the more distal limb elements (Fig. 124*b*). The paddle seems to have moved as a unit, flexible in structure but without any great motility between individual bones. There was always considerable hyperphalangy, or addition of extra finger joints, as in many marine forms. In addition the number of toes varied; in some cases there was a decrease to three, in others hyperdactyly, with as many as seven or eight digits; sometimes a single toe is observed to divide into two, part way down the paddle.

FIG. 124.—Limbs of various aquatic reptiles. *A*, pectoral limb of the Triassic ichthyosaur *Merriamia*. *B*, same of the Jurassic *Ophthalmosaurus*. *C*, same of the Cretaceous plesiosaur *Elasmosaurus*. *D*, pes of the nothosaur *Lariosaurus*. *E*, pectoral limb of the mosasaur *Clidastes*. (*A*, after Merriam *B–E* after Williston).

The skull (Fig. 125) was, of course, highly modified for aquatic life. The beak was long, the external nostrils had moved far back; the eyes were very large, with well-developed sclerotic plates; a pineal opening was present. With the enormous enlargement of the eyes, the temporal region had become much shortened. There was a large temporal opening which lay high on the skull at either side of the parietals and was thus an upper temporal fenestra. But in contrast with other reptiles, its lateral border was formed by the postfrontal and tabular (or supratemporal) bones; the postorbital and squamosal lay farther down the cheek region and did not enter into its borders. The stapes, usually slim in reptiles, had a massive structure, suggesting that these types had undergone considerable change in their mode of hearing, as have the whales and other secondarily aquatic forms.

These creatures were extreme in their marine adaptations, and their limbs obviously unfitted for use on land. It was long ago suggested that reproduction must have taken place in the water (in many snakes, for example, and in lizards, the eggs are retained in the mother's body until they are hatched). In agreement

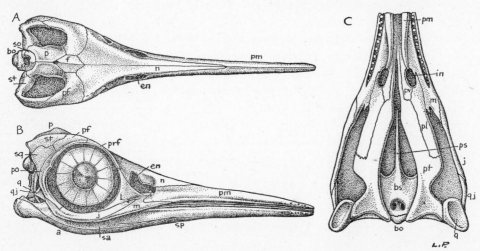

FIG. 125.—The ichthyosaur skull. *A, B*, dorsal and lateral views of the skull of *Ophthalmosaurus*, skull length about 40 inches. *C*, posterior portion of palate of *Stenopterygius*. For abbreviations see Figure 86. (*A, B* after Gilmore, *C* from Abel after Owen and Smith Woodward.)

with the idea that the young were born alive are specimens which actually show skeletons of young ichthyosaurs inside the body of a large individual. It has been argued that these may have been youngsters which had been eaten by mistake.

But recently several specimens have shown the young partially emergent from what would have been the cloacal region in life. The mother here apparently died during childbirth or (there are human parallels) labor may have taken place after the death of the mother.

The description above is that of a typical Jurassic form. The

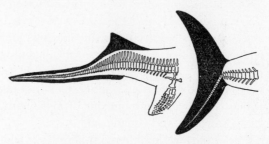

FIG. 126.—Tails of *Mixosaurus* (Triassic) and a Jurassic ichthyosaur, to show development of shark-like tail. (From Williston, after Wiman.)

typical Triassic forms, such as *Mixosaurus*, were more primitive. The tail (Fig. 126) was much straighter with little development of the fish type of caudal fin; the limbs were somewhat less specialized (Fig. 124a); the face shorter.

These forms are found in the later Triassic beds of California and Spitzbergen. From these same deposits come fragmentary remains of *Omphalosaurus*, which represented a short-lived, shell-eating side branch of the group. The skull was in sharp contrast with that of ordinary ichthyosaurs, short and strongly built with flattened, button-like teeth for crushing mollusks. These forms seem to have paralleled the contemporary placodonts discussed later; like them they did not persist beyond the Triassic.

Most of the later ichthyosaurs have usually been included in a single genus, *Ichthyosaurus*. There were, however, a number of distinct types, deep-bodied and slender forms, broad-finned (*Eurypterygius*) and narrow-finned (*Stenopterygius*) series; and there was one ichthyosaur, *Eurhinodelphis*, with a short lower and long upper jaw like those of a swordfish.

In the Cretaceous the ichthyosaurs became rarer; they are quite unknown in the very well-known Upper Cretaceous fauna of the Kansas chalk, where plesiosaurs and mesosaurs abound, and they seem to have become extinct well before the close of the period.

Although the Triassic forms of ichthyosaurs were slightly more primitive than their Jurassic descendants, they were already very highly specialized marine types. No earlier forms are known. We have mentioned the possibility of a descent from the mesosaurs of earlier times. There is no strong objection to this theory, particularly since the peculiarities of ichthyosaur structure would seemingly have required a long time for their development and hence a very early origin for the group.

Apart from the aquatic features of the skeleton, the odd type of temporal opening shows that the ichthyosaurs were far removed from any other reptile orders, even other forms with an upper temporal fenestra. Provisionally, at least, we may regard them (and perhaps the mesosaurs) as the types of a distinct subclass which might be termed the Ichthyopterygia.

Protorosaurs.—Except for the anapsids and the mammal-like forms, an upper temporal vacuity has developed in all reptiles, sometimes alone, sometimes accompanied by an additional lower opening. In the ichthyosaurs an upper fenestra was present but of an unusual type. We shall now treat of another series of forms with an upper opening but one of more normal construction, bounded below by the postorbital and squamosal.

One of the few small Permian reptiles of which we have any adequate knowledge is *Araeoscelis* (Figs. 127, 128) of the Lower Permian beds of Texas. This was a small and lightly built creature little more than a foot in length, with very slender limbs; it may have appeared in life somewhat like one of the more agile lizards. The vertebrae (Figs. 123e, f) were still amphicoelous as in primitive forms; the ribs, however, had but a single head in the cervical region, although there were two heads in the trunk. Despite the slim build, there were still many primitive features in the limbs; the pubis and ischium, for example, formed a solid plate and lacked the large opening which developed there in many reptile types.

The skull had retained many primitive features, particularly in the palate. But a small opening had developed high up in the side of the temporal region, bounded above by the parietal, behind by a small bone which may be a tabular,

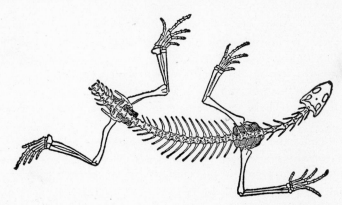

Fig. 127.—*Araeoscelis*, a small Lower Permian protorosaur. About ¼ natural size. (From Williston.)

below by the postorbital and squamosal. This last element was very large and occupied almost the entire surface of the broad cheek region, and the quadratojugal seems to have disappeared.

This little form is quite different from its better-known large contemporaries and merits being made the type of an order which has been termed the Protorosauria. With this form have been associated, with various degrees of probability, other rare and early reptilian types. *Protorosaurus*, for example, was an Upper Permian form from Europe seemingly somewhat aquatic in habits, twice the size of *Araeoscelis* but also rather slimly built. There was definitely an upper temporal opening, and hence an association with *Araeoscelis* has seemed reasonable. Some Jurassic types have been placed in this same group. This association, however, is open to doubt.

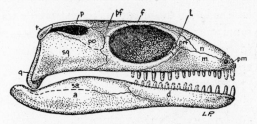

Fig. 128.—Lateral view of the skull of *Araeoscelis*. Length of original about 1¾ inches. For abbreviations see Figure 86. (After Williston.)

It has been suggested that *Araeoscelis* is an ancestor of the lizards, since these forms also have an upper temporal opening. But as will be seen, it is possible that the lizards have really been derived from two-arched types with a different pedigree. Another and seemingly more probable suggestion is that in *Araeoscelis* we are dealing with an early land-dwelling ancestor of the plesiosaurs next to be considered. In both cases there is a single upper temporal opening bounded below by a broad cheek plate formed by the squamosal bone, a type of construction not repeated in other groups; and there are other suggestions of relationship in the skeleton. There are no indications in *Araeoscelis* of a tendency toward an aquatic life, but *Protorosaurus* was a water-dweller, and the Triassic relatives of the plesiosaurs were still imperfectly adapted to a marine existence.

Sauropterygians.—The plesiosaurs, one of the most important of marine reptilian types, may be included with related Triassic forms, such as the nothosaurs and placodonts, in an order Sauropterygia.

In almost all of these reptiles aquatic adaptations were developed, and in addition there were a number of common structural features which tend to show their mutual relationship. There was a single upper temporal opening which, as in *Araeoscelis*, lay above a broad cheek plate formed mainly by the squamosal, while the quadratojugal was absent. The pineal eye had been retained, while the nostrils had, as in many marine forms, moved well back along the top of the skull. There was no secondary palate, but the interpterygoid vacuities were nearly or entirely closed by a fusion of the pterygoids in the mid-line below the old roof of the mouth. The vertebrae (Fig. 123*c, d*) were rather primitive in build, amphicoelous or, at the most, flat-ended. The ribs of the trunk region had but a single head which, in contrast to most of the other types considered in this chapter, articulated with the transverse process of the neural arch rather than the centrum. The old ventral rib system had (as in *Araeoscelis*) been retained and powerfully developed to form a basket-like structure along the belly.

The limbs and girdles were usually considerably modified for aquatic life. The dorsal elements of the girdles (scapula, ilium) were reduced in size; the ventral ones tended to be expanded. The sacral articulation was reduced in relation to the lessened need of support as terrestrial life was abandoned. The limbs of the nothosaurs and placodonts were still more or less primitive in structure and not ill suited to walking as well as swimming; in the plesiosaurs they were long paddle-like structures.

Plesiosaurs.—The plesiosaurs are the best-known members of the Sauropterygians, as well as the last to survive and the most specialized for aquatic life; they are common in many Jurassic and Cretaceous deposits. Many of them were of considerable size, with a maximum length of about 50 feet. Although they were obviously well fitted for marine life, their adaptations were very different from those of the rival ichthyosaurs. The latter swam by a fish-like undulation of the body, the fins were merely for steering, and the head did not move independently of the body as a whole. In the plesiosaurs, however, the body (Figs. 129, 130) was comparatively broad and flat, and the tail seems to have been of comparatively small importance; swimming seems to have been accomplished through rowing the body along by means of the well-developed paddles. The head, usually small, was set on the end of a flexible neck and could dart sidewise to seize the prey. A plesiosaur has been compared to "a snake strung through the body of a turtle" by an old writer.

The skull (Fig. 131) was variable in shape, most forms having a short face, while in others shortness of the neck was compensated by an elongated beak. The

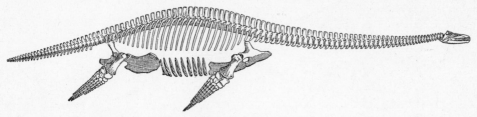

FIG. 129.—*Muraenosaurus*, a long-necked Jurassic plesiosaur. About 21 feet in length. (From Andrews.)

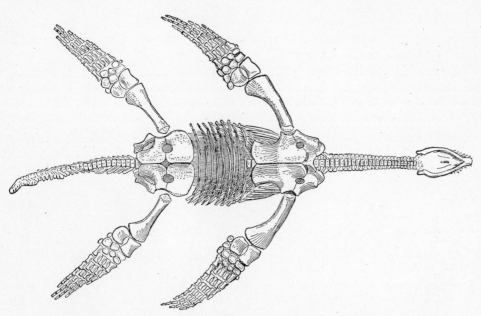

FIG. 130.—*Thaumatosaurus*, a Jurassic plesiosaur, ventral view, to show the abdominal ribs and expanded girdles. About 11 feet long. (After Williston, adapted from Fraas.)

external nares had been pushed back to a position comparable to that found in ichthyosaurs. The palate was highly modified; the two pterygoids met each other beneath the basisphenoid, separated to disclose a small interpterygoid vacuity, and then met again further forward. The pointed teeth, set in sockets, were confined to the margin of the jaws. As in most aquatic forms well-developed sclerotic plates were present.

The scapula (Fig. 132a) had only a small dorsal blade, but ventrally it and the coracoid had expanded into a huge ventral plate for the attachment of strong muscles which gave a powerful down-and-back stroke to the paddle. In the pelvic girdle (Fig. 132b) the ilium was very short and but loosely attached to the tip

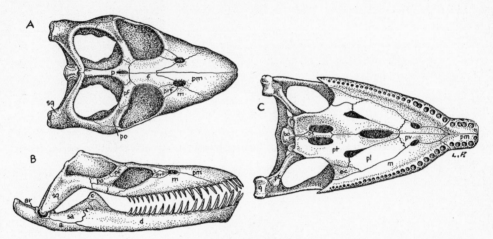

FIG. 131.—The skull in plesiosaurs. A, dorsal view of skull of *Muraenosaurus*. B, lateral view of same; skull length about 14 inches. C, palatal view of *Thaumatosaurus*. Skull length about 14 inches. For abbreviations see Figure 86. (A, B after Andrews, C after Fraas.)

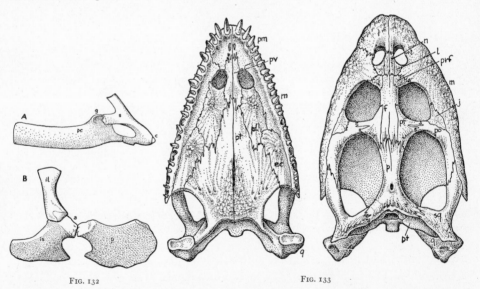

FIG. 132   FIG. 133

FIG. 132.—Above, shoulder girdle of the plesiosaur *Microcleidus*. The scapula has grown downward and backward to gain a ventral contact with the coracoid. Below, pelvis of *Muraenosaurus*. a, acetabulum; c, clavicle; g, glenoid; il, ilium; is, ischium; p, pubis; pc, precoracoid; s, scapula. (A after Watson, B after Andrews.)

FIG. 133.—The skull of the nothosaur *Simosaurus*, dorsal and ventral views. Length of original about 12 inches. For abbreviations see Figure 86. (After Jaekel.)

of the sacral ribs. The pubis and ischium, however, had developed to form a very large plate containing a small vacuity.

The humerus and femur were long, while the bones of the distal segment of the limb were much shortened. The paddles (Fig. 124c) were very long but less specialized than the fins of the ichthyosaurs, for, although there was considerable hyperphalangy, there was never any hyperdactyly, and the phalanges retained the shape of normal finger joints.

Plesiosaurs first appear in the Rhaetic deposits, laid down at a time transitional from the Triassic to the Jurassic. In the marine Liassic deposits of the Lower Jurassic of Europe there are numerous types such as *Plesiosaurus* and *Muraenosaurus*, the long-necked *Thaumatosaurus*, and *Pliosaurus* with a short cervical region and a long beak. The group still flourished in late Cretaceous times and is well represented in the Kansas chalk deposits. Variations in neck development were

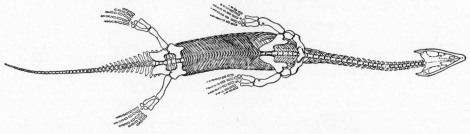

FIG. 134.—*Ceresiosaurus*, a Triassic nothosaur, ventral view. Original about 3½ feet long. (From Peyer.)

very marked at that time, and there is a great contrast between such forms as *Elasmosaurus* with a whip-like neck of seventy-six vertebrae and *Brachauchenius* with a modest thirteen. The forms found in the chalk beds were, however, among the last members of their race, and no plesiosaur is known to have survived the close of the Mesozoic.

Nothosaurs.—Much more primitive sauropterygians are present in the Triassic strata, particularly the marine beds of the Middle Triassic of Europe. *Nothosaurus*, *Simosaurus* (Fig. 133), *Ceresiosaurus* (Fig. 134), and a number of other genera of that age were types of considerably smaller size which were not yet completely adapted to aquatic life. The general proportions of the body and the structure of the girdles were quite similar to those of the plesiosaurs. The limbs, however, were little specialized for aquatic life, except that the distal segments were somewhat shortened. The digits (Fig. 124d) were of rather normal build but were probably webbed. In the skull the nostrils were "in transit" between the normal position and that found in plesiosaurs. The palate shows much the same general type of construction but was a quite solid structure, for the two pterygoids met in the mid-line for their entire length to form a continuous plate. In this respect they

were already more specialized than the plesiosaurs, and hence no known form of nothosaur can have given rise to these later types. A nothosaur, however, in which this pterygoid union had not been quite completed would make an ideal plesiosaur ancestor.

Placodonts.—*Placodus* is the best-known member of a small group of aberrant Triassic sauropterygians which had taken up mollusk-eating as a livelihood. Connected with this is the most remarkable specialization of *Placodus* (Fig. 135), the

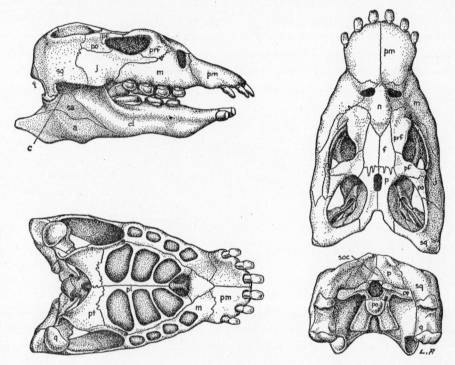

FIG. 135.—The skull of the placodont reptile *Placodus*. Original about 10 inches long. For abbreviations see Figure 86. (After Broili.)

development on the palate and lower jaws of enormous flat teeth capable of crushing mollusk shells. These teeth were not unlike those of some of the pavement-toothed sharks, and indeed were long thought to pertain to fish. Presumably there were very powerful jaw muscles for this heavy work, for the coronoid bone of the jaw forms a long upwardly directed process for muscular insertion. This remarkable development simulates that found in mammals and is almost without parallel in ordinary reptilian types. The front teeth were heavy projecting pegs across a broad muzzle in *Placodus* and may have served to root up mussels; in another form, *Placochelys* (Fig. 136), there were no anterior teeth and the sharp beak may have functioned like a pair of forceps.

Apart from adaptations for this specialized diet, *Placodus* was not dissimilar to the nothosaurs; the stout trunk and but slightly modified limbs were much alike in the two groups, and the skulls were essentially similar in such features as the position of the nostrils and the solid palate; in *Placodus*, however, the tooth-bearing palatines have pushed back at the expense of the pterygoids.

There was, however, one further peculiarity of the placodonts in that numerous nodules of bone have been found associated with some skeletons which seem to show the development of armor on both upper and lower surfaces of the body in a rather turtle-like fashion. It has been suggested that the placodonts were related to the turtles, although not, of course, directly ancestral to them. This, however, assumes very marked changes in the construction of the skull roof, for which we have little evidence.

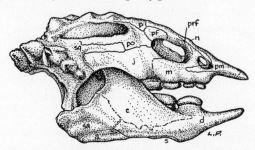

FIG. 136.—Lateral view of the skull of the placodont *Placochelys*. Length of original about 6 inches. For abbreviations see Figure 86. (After Jaekel and von Huene.)

Primitive sauropterygians.—*Trachelosaurus* of the early Triassic of Europe appears to represent a terrestrial ancestor of the sauropterygians. This little reptile is incompletely known but shows a number of diagnostic sauropterygian features; the neck was considerably elongated, containing about twenty vertebrae. The limbs, as far as known, indicate that this was a purely land-dwelling type.

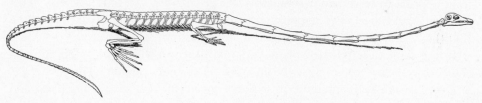

FIG. 137.—*Tanystrophaeus*, a long-necked Triassic sauropterygian. About 2½ feet long. (From Peyer.)

Tanystrophaeus (Fig. 137) of the European Middle Triassic was a small form similar to the last in structure but with extremely elongated neck vertebrae. The contrast between the cervical region and the stubby body and rather normal limbs is so extreme that, when recently a complete skeleton was found for the first time, it proved that the front part of the animal had been described by earlier writers as pertaining to a flying reptile, while the trunk had been thought to be that of a primitive dinosaur!

In the known sauropterygians we see, from the beginning of the Triassic on, a series of stages leading from terrestrial to purely marine reptiles, together with various side lines. Seemingly here aquatic life was a much later specialization than in the ichthyosaurs, and the ancestors of the sauropterygians are presumably to be sought among the land animals of the Permian. As we have seen, *Araeoscelis* of that period is a land form which might well have been the ancestral type. While such a conclusion is, of course, to be regarded as a provisional one, we may be justified in associating the Protorosauria with the Sauropterygia in a common subclass Synaptosauria.

Eosuchians.—The forms described in the earlier sections of this chapter have been one-arched reptiles, forms with a single temporal opening. But except for marine types, the great bulk of Mesozoic reptiles were two-arched forms, with a temporal opening both above and below a bar formed by the postorbital and squamosal bones. This is the diapsid condition (cf. Fig. 109), and all forms with this double opening have often been grouped as members of a single subclass (the Diapsida). But many of the diapsids were advanced types showing evidences of close relationship to one another but not especially to more primitive two-arched types. We prefer to regard the advanced forms—the crocodiles, dinosaurs, and pterosaurs—as members of a subclass Archosauria which will be considered in later sections. In this chapter we will treat only of some primitive two-arched forms and types perhaps derived from them which we may regard provisionally as constituting the subclass Lepidosauria.

No two-arched reptiles are known from the early Permian. First of such types to appear were a number of small reptiles from the Upper Permian and Lower Triassic of South Africa of which *Youngina* (Fig. 138) is the best known. This form appears to have had a comparatively primitive postcranial skeleton, with moderately slender limbs, normal reptilian foot structure, and (as far as can be told) body proportions not unlike those of typical lizards.

In the skull were retained many primitive features which bring this form in contrast to the archosaurians to be described in the next chapter. The palate was of a very generalized reptilian type with pterygoids movable on the braincase and with teeth on the palatal bones in addition to a row of teeth set in sockets on the jaw margins. Small dermal supra-occipital and tabular bones were still present at the back of the skull, a pineal eye had been retained, and (unlike many archosaurs) there was no opening between the bones in the side of the slim snout.

Youngina, nevertheless, had two temporal openings—a lateral one far down the side of the cheek region, and a large upper opening on the top of the broad skull table. We are dealing with a diapsid reptile but a very primitive one, and it seems fitting that *Youngina* and its few small and inadequately known relatives should constitute a separate order, the Eosuchia.

Rhynchocephalians.—Still primitive in many features, but with a few characteristic specializations which mark them as an aberrant group, are the Rhynchocephalia, which first appeared in the Triassic and still survive in the shape of a small reptile *Sphenodon* inhabiting a few islands off the coast of New Zealand. *Sphenodon* (Fig. 139) looks very much like a lizard, and indeed resembles the lizards greatly in many features; while on the other hand, it appears, in the retention of many primitive characters, to have departed little from the structure of the Eosuchia. By the presence of two temporal openings it is sharply marked off from the lizards, in which the cheek is bare beneath the upper opening and bar; from the eosuchians it is easily distinguished by two specialized features: the teeth are fused to the edge of the jaws rather than set in sockets, and there is a small overhanging beak on the upper jaw, a characteristic to which the group name refers.

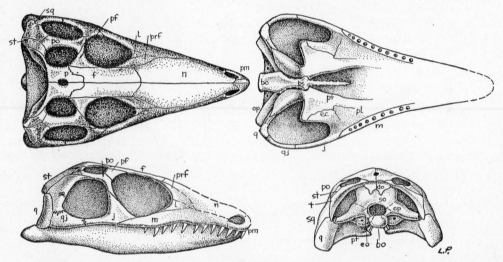

FIG. 138.—*Youngina*, a primitive two-arched reptile from the Upper Permian of South Africa; dorsal, palatal, lateral, and occipital views. Length of original about 2½ inches. For abbreviations see Figure 86. (After Broom and Watson.)

Most of the diagnostic characters of the rhynchocephalians are primitive ones to which little reference need be made. The palate is as primitive as that of *Youngina*, the pineal eye is still present, the vertebrae are amphicoelous rather than having the solid structure of most land reptiles of post-Triassic times. There have been some changes from primitive conditions, however: the lacrimal, supratemporal, and tabular bones have disappeared; the ribs attach to both arch and centrum by a single broad head rather than a double one; and (as in many other types) a large opening has developed in the primitively plate-like ventral part of the pelvis.

Sphenodon appears to be a persistent survivor of an ancient group, for *Homaeosaurus* (Fig. 140) of the Jurassic appears to have been almost identical in structure, and the ancestry of this type may without doubt go back through some imperfectly known Triassic genera to such a form as *Youngina*. Very few changes are needed to make a rhynchocephalian out of an eosuchian.

Early offshoots of the stock were the rhynchosaurs of the Triassic (Fig. 141*a*). These tended to be of comparatively large size, but the postcranial skeleton and

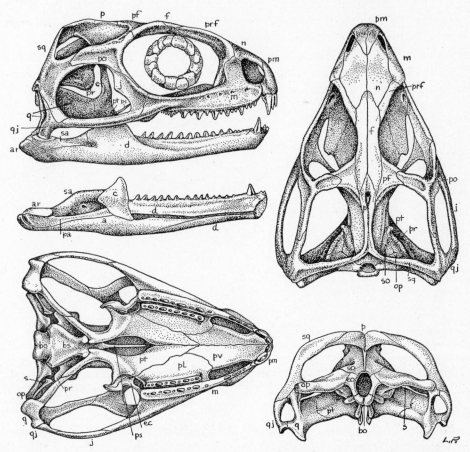

FIG. 139.—The skull of the living rhynchocephalian *Sphenodon*. For abbreviations see Figure 86.

most of the skull were essentially similar to that of *Sphenodon*. The pineal opening had disappeared, however, and the beak was much elongated and toothless, with the nares fused into a single opening above it. *Rhynchosaurus*, *Hyperodapedon*, and related forms appear to have been shell-eating shore-living types; they have been found in nearly all continents except North America.

An isolated but rather interesting group is that represented by *Champsosaurus* (Fig. 141*b*) of late Cretaceous to early Eocene times. The nostrils were at the tip of the long slim skull; the internal nares were carried far back, although there was no development of a real secondary palate. The pineal was absent. The limbs were little modified; there was a long flat tail. Structural features and the nature of the deposits in which the remains are found indicate that these forms were sub-aquatic fresh-water fish-eaters which do not appear to be closely related to other rhynchocephalian types.

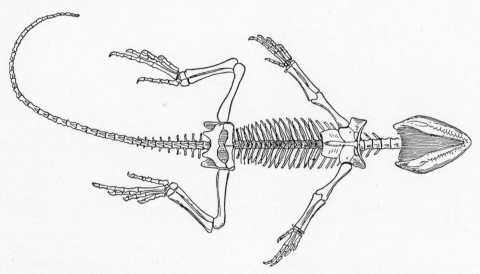

FIG. 140.—*Homaeosaurus*, a Jurassic rhynchocephalian about $7\frac{1}{2}$ inches long. (From Williston's *The Osteology of the Reptiles*, by permission of the Harvard University Press.)

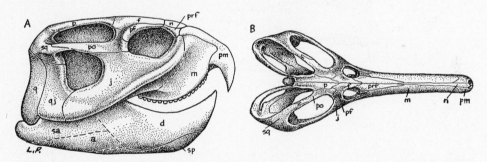

FIG. 141.—The skull of extinct rhynchocephalians. *A*, *Hyperodapedon*, a Triassic beaked type, skull about $7\frac{1}{2}$ inches long. *B*, dorsal view of skull of *Champsosaurus*, a late Cretaceous and early Tertiary amphibious form, length about $13\frac{1}{2}$ inches. (*A* after Huxley and von Huene, *B* after Brown.)

A group placed here with very great doubt is that of the Thallatosaurs, rather small and poorly known aquatic reptiles from the marine Upper Triassic of California. The limbs of *Thallatosaurus* were paddle-like, but otherwise the postcranial skeleton is inadequately known. The skull was rather elongate, and sclerotic plates were present in the eyes. In the temporal region there was certainly a lower opening, but the presence or absence of an upper opening is uncertain due to the

fragmentary nature of the specimens. Their position is quite dubious; it may be
that there was only a lateral opening and that they are really an aquatic offshoot
of the pelycosaur stock.

The Squamata.—The order Squamata includes the lizards and snakes, the most
successful of modern reptiles. The lizards may be traced back to the Jurassic and

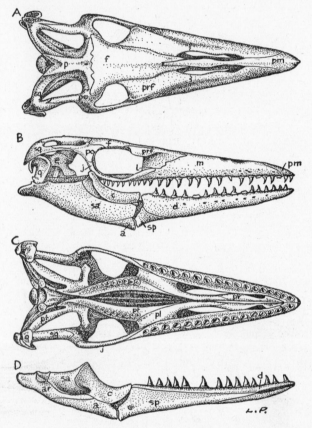

Fig. 142.—The skull of mosasaurs. *A*, *Tylosaurus*, dorsal view, original about 38 inches long. *B*,
Clidastes, lateral view, original about 20 inches long. *C*, *Platecarpus*, ventral view, original about 22
inches long. *D*, inner view of jaw of *Clidastes*. (After Williston.)

had an interesting marine development in the Cretaceous. The snakes, last evolved
of any reptilian group, appeared only in the Cretaceous and have obviously been
derived from a lacertilian stock. A diagnostic feature of the group lies in the fact
that there is but a single temporal opening present, the upper one, lying above a
bar formed by the postorbital and squamosal (Fig. 142). Instead of a lower opening being present, we find that the cheek region lies open at the side behind the
eye; the quadratojugal has disappeared, and the squamosal is much reduced. As a
result of this loss of cheek covering, the quadrate bone is freely movable, giving

greater flexibility to the jaws. The pineal eye persists in most lizards. The lacrimal bone is small or absent, the dermal supra-occipital has gone, and so has either the tabular or the supratemporal (there is a single bone to represent the two). On the other hand, some lizards have developed a whole series of new dermal bones which may cover the whole skull roof.

The palate is of the primitive type seen in many Permian reptiles and in *Sphenodon*. The teeth are not set in sockets but are fused to the edge or inner sides of the jaws and are thus specialized in character.

The primitive amphicoelous type of vertebra has persisted in a few living lizards, but in most of the Squamata a good articulation between the centra has been brought about through the development of the procoelous condition in which the swollen posterior end of one vertebra fits into a socket in the one behind (Fig. 123g). The ribs have, as in *Sphenodon*, a single head, but in contrast this is here narrow and articulates only with the centrum. In other than these features the general structure is not unlike that just described for the Rhynchocephalia and may not be far from that of the eosuchians.

Origins.—With regard to the origin of lizards there are two sharply contrasted views. There is but a single temporal opening, and this has been held by many authorities to be a primitive character. Under this hypothesis the lizards are but remotely related to a majority of the other reptile groups and must have had a long independent history. We have noted that *Araeoscelis* of the Permian had a single temporal opening, and it has been suggested as a possible lizard ancestor. But the temple of that little reptile shows none of the excavation at the side characterizing the lizards, and there are few positive resemblances.

On the other hand, we have noted many resemblances between the lizards and *Sphenodon*. The one difference of importance is that *Sphenodon* has a lateral temporal opening and the lizard has not. This seems a fatal bar to relationship. But it may not be as serious as it first appears. If we were to suppose that in *Sphenodon* the thin bar below the lower opening were to disappear, there would result an appearance of the cheek region almost identical to that of lizards. It is not improbable that this has occurred and that these one-arched types have in reality descended from two-arched forms in which the lower bar has vanished. We may consider the lizards as having been quite possibly derived, together with the rhynchocephalians, from the primitive eosuchians. We may therefore provisionally group the Squamata with those orders in a subclass Lepidosauria.

Lizards.—The Squamata are divided into two suborders: the Lacertilia, the lizards; and Ophidia, the snakes. The first are, of course, the more primitive of the two and the first to be represented in the fossil record. Even the lacertilians, however, were comparatively late in appearance, for there are no certain fossil lizards in rocks older than the Jurassic, and it was only at the end of the Mesozoic and in Tertiary times that the group became a flourishing one.

There is a large number of families of lizards, few of which need be considered in detail. We shall merely make brief mention of a number of superfamily groups into which these may be assembled, using a simple and rather conservative system of classification.

The largest of these groups is that of the superfamily Kionocrania, many of whose members are rather generalized and primitive lizards, such as the geckoes, agamids, and true lizards of the Old World and the iguana type of the New. More aberrant forms include the Gila monster, the glass "snake," and skinks. This group appears to have been represented in the Jurassic.

The superfamily Amphisbaenia comprises a number of worm-like burrowing forms, often limbless, with a blunt tail and small eyes. The temporal arches have disappeared, but the rest of the skull is fused tightly together to form a burrowing organ. Little is known of them as fossils.

The Chamaeleons of the superfamily Rhiptoglossa are a highly specialized arboreal group inhabiting the Old World tropics of which fossils are found as far back as the Eocene in northern continents. The most obvious superficial specializations are the long tongue for insect-catching, the prehensile tail, and the grasping foot in which two toes are opposed to the other three. The skull is of rather peculiar structure; many bones are fused or vestigial.

A fourth major group of lizards is the superfamily Platynota, of which the living members are all included in the family Varanidae. These forms, the monitors of the Old World tropics, are interesting in that they are close to the ancestry of both the marine lizards (mosasaurs) and the snakes. They include the largest of living and fossil terrestrial lizards, one from the East Indies today measuring a dozen feet in length, while *Megalania*, a fossil form, was perhaps double that size. Suggestions of relationship to the snakes are found in the fact that a joint tends to develop in the middle of the jaws and that, unlike most reptiles, the front part of the braincase is nearly completely inclosed by bone.

Marine lizards.—Placed in the same superfamily and seemingly derived from varanids (which unfortunately are little known as fossils, although presumably of early origin) are a number of interesting types of Cretaceous marine lizards.

Two groups of aquatic lizards appear in the Lower Cretaceous. The dolichosaurs, including *Adriosaurus* (Fig. 143) and the somewhat later *Dolichosaurus*, were small forms with a very long neck and with limbs of a fairly normal structure which show that these lizards were not completely adapted for marine life. These elongated types cannot have been the ancestors of the other water-living lizards. The aigialosaurs were a second early Cretaceous group, also fairly small and also only semi-aquatic in their probable habits. Here the neck was short; there was a powerful swimming tail.

From the last, apparently came the mosasaurs (Figs. 142, 144), Upper Cretaceous marine lizards, world-wide in distribution but especially common in the chalk rocks of Kansas; *Platecarpus* and *Tylosaurus* are among the best-known types. They were of large size, averaging about 15–20 feet in length. There was a long head, a short neck, and a long slim body and tail. The tail was the main swimming organ, the limbs functioning as steering organs. In the paddles (Fig. 124e), as usual in aquatic forms, the proximal bones were much shortened; but the toes were well developed, spreading, and presumably webbed. The normal number of

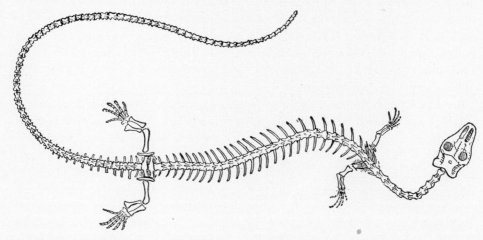

Fig. 143.—*Adriosaurus*, a Lower Cretaceous semi-aquatic lizard. Original about 16 inches long. (From Williston's *The Osteology of the Reptiles*, by permission of the Harvard University Press.)

Fig. 144.—*Tylosaurus dispar*, a mosasaur from the Niobrara Chalk of Kansas. Original about 26 feet long. (From Osborn.)

digits were present, but there was a slight increase in the number of joints. The skull was much like that of the varanid lizards; and as in them there was a well-developed joint midway of the jaws, between angular and splenial. The teeth were rather unlike those of most lizards in that they were set in pits rather than fused to the jaws.

The mosasaurs were mainly fish-eaters, probably existing on the large variety of primitive teleosts found in the chalk deposits. There were various types, presumably diving, deep-sea, and surface forms. A more divergent form was *Globidens*, which is poorly known except for the jaws. The teeth had peculiar spheroidal crowns, and it would seem that this form was a mollusk-eater.

Despite the profusion of mosasaur types in the late Cretaceous rocks, they perished as soon as did their contemporary fellow-fishermen, the plesiosaurs.

Snakes.—The Ophidia, the snakes, are the newest of reptilian groups. Obviously derived from varanid types, they first appeared in the Cretaceous but are not well known as fossils.

In snakes almost all traces of limbs are lost, as in some of the true lizards. The limbless condition seems to be associated with the fact that in all slimly built reptiles locomotion, even with limbs, utilized to some extent the sinuous motion of the body held over from the fish stage; the legs merely held the ground gained by twisting the body. With the addition of horny scales which could hold onto the surface and prevent a backslip the loss of legs became a possibility, and a new type of locomotion made its appearance.

In snakes the vertebrae may increase in number up to several hundred with, of course, little regional differentiation, and extra articulations are present between the vertebrae (Fig. 123*g–i*). The skull (Fig. 145) has been highly modified in the direction of greater motility of its components for swallowing of large prey. Even the upper arch of the cheek is lost, leaving the quadrate very loosely attached to the skull. The quadrate also has but a loose connection with the palate, while the palate and the

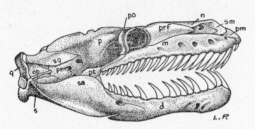

FIG. 145.—Skull of a primitive living snake, the python. (After Williston.)

anterior portion of the skull may both move freely on the braincase region. The dentary is freed considerably from the more posterior elements of the jaws, and the two branches of the jaw are connected only by ligaments. These all make for the possibility of a wide jaw gape. The teeth are usually directed backward so that alternate jaw movements tend to push the prey down the throat. The pineal opening is lost. The parietal and frontal have grown down so that, together with a new ossification, they completely inclose the front of the braincase, a rather necessary feature for brain protection during the swallowing of large objects.

The oldest known snakes of the late Cretaceous and Eocene, such as *Palaeophis*, appear to have been rather primitive forms with fairly short bodies and stout build; the boas and pythons are apparently comparatively unmodified descendants. The harmless smaller snakes, such as the grass snakes and many other types, appear only in the Tertiary. Comparatively late seem to have appeared poisonous types with hollow fangs. In more primitively built poisonous types, such as the cobras, the fangs are fixed. A final development in snake evolution seems to have resulted in the vipers, of which the rattlesnakes are American representatives, in which the palatal bones are so arranged that the fangs are automatically turned down and in when the mouth closes, and are erected when it opens.

CHAPTER VIII

RULING REPTILES

The mutual relations of many of the reptilian types are, as has been seen, none too clear; and the establishment of superordinal or subclass groups a dubious matter. In contrast are the groups now to be considered, a series of orders including the crocodiles, dinosaurs, flying reptiles, and related primitive forms which may be unified in the subclass Archosauria, the ruling reptiles (Fig. 162).

Diagnostic characters possessed by all these forms are few. All possess two temporal openings, the diapsid condition; but two openings are also present in rhynchocephalians and other reptiles which seemingly have little to do with the groups under consideration. Of greater importance are the comparable evolutionary trends seen in the development of the various orders and indicative of the potentialities inherent in the ancestral stock. Many similarities in structural features among end-forms of different archosaurian lines have not been inherited as such from a common ancestor but have been independently acquired. This, however, does not debar such characters from consideration as indications of relationship. Study of fossil forms increasingly indicates that there has been an enormous amount of parallelism in development; but this study also appears to demonstrate that close parallelism occurs only in closely related forms.

Bipedalism.—The most characteristic archosaurian evolutionary tendencies are to be seen in the limb-and-girdle structure and are connected with significant changes in the locomotion of most members of the group.

The clumsy style of walking of the primitive cotylosaurs was improved upon by later reptiles in various ways. Most reptilian orders tended merely to improve a four-footed style of progression; the archosaurs are unique in that they tended toward a bipedal gait, the animal running semi-erect on its hind legs. Some of the most primitive archosaurs had hardly begun the changes leading to bipedalism, and some groups never attained this condition. Others, having once acquired a bipedal gait, have slumped back to a four-footed pose; but even in such forms the group history has left structural marks.

In the archosaurian bipedal pose the anterior part of the body tilts forward at a considerable angle from the pelvis. This posture could not be maintained without a tail as a balancing organ, and this structure is almost always long and powerful. In addition to its balancing function, it also sheaths powerful muscles which move the hind limbs.

This changed position has entailed many structural changes in the limb bones. The entire weight of the body in bipeds is supported from the hips; and the sacrum is strongly built, a number of ribs in addition to the primitive two usually being incorporated in it. The ilium is elongated, and the acetabulum lies high up near the backbone. The body could not, of course, be supported in a biped with the legs spread out at the side of the body. Instead the hind legs have been turned forward, giving them a fore-and-aft motion, and are considerably straightened, so that they essentially form two long and powerful pillars extending from the pelvis to the ground.

The head of the femur now lies under the upper margin of the socket of the acetabulum and no longer pushes in against it, and the bottom of the cavity usually becomes open. The femur (Fig. 147), originally straight, develops a head at the side of its upper end to fit into the acetabulum, while part way down an extra process, a fourth trochanter, is often developed for the attachment of tail muscles.

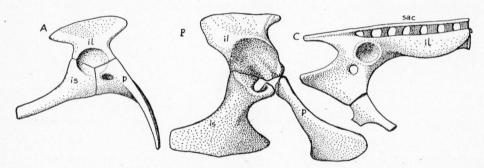

FIG. 146.—The pelvic girdle of archosaurians. *A*, the thecodont *Aetosaurus*. *B*, the Jurassic crocodile *Steneosaurus*. *C*, the Cretaceous pterosaur *Pteranodon*. *il*, ilium; *is*, ischium; *p*, pubis; *sac*, sacrum. In *C* the homologies of the ventral element are uncertain. (*A* after Broom, *B* after Andrews, *C* after Eaton.)

The tibia tends to become long; the fibula, reduced in importance. An extra joint, making for additional speed, may be added to the leg by an elongation of the metatarsal elements. The tarsal bones, which might become an element of weakness in this new type of limb, tend to be reduced, the proximal ones sometimes fusing with the tibia and fibula, the distal ones becoming associated with the heads of the metatarsals; this leaves but a single movable joint in the middle of the tarsus. The foot is now not at all twisted on the leg, and the central toes tend to be the more highly developed. The third toe often becomes the longest of the set; the second and fourth, at either side, slightly shorter. The remaining toes usually become comparatively unimportant, the fifth often disappears entirely, while the first is sometimes turned backward, apparently acting as a prop. Although the comparative length of the toes may be greatly changed, the number of joints has tended to remain constant; and in forms as far apart as carnivorous dinosaurs and birds the feet are almost identical in structure and also in phalangeal formula.

A characteristic series of modifications takes place in the pubis and ischium

(Fig. 146a). Instead of retaining the primitive plate-like structure, both bones tend to be elongated and directed downward, giving, with the ilium, a triradiate type of pelvis. This structural feature is probably related to the fact that, with the femur playing back and forth close to the body, the muscles running to it from these bones must shift fore or aft to gain a longer play. Even the most primitive of archosaurians show at least the beginning of this tendency, while some forms have a still more complicated pelvic structure.

The front legs have naturally become less important with the development of the bipedal gait. They are usually considerably shorter and much weaker than the hind legs. There is some tendency toward a loss of fingers in the more advanced

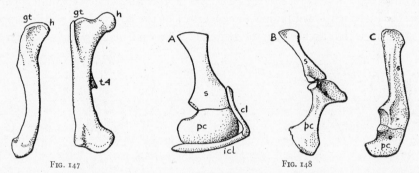

FIG. 147.

FIG. 148.

FIG. 147.—Anterior views of right femur of A, a crocodilian, B, a trachodont dinosaur. gt, greater trochanter for attachment of iliac muscles; h, head, fitting into acetabulum; t4, fourth trochanter for attachment of caudal muscles.

FIG. 148.—Shoulder girdles of archosaurians. A, the thecodont *Euparkeria*. B, the Jurassic crocodile *Steneosaurus*. C, the sauropod dinosaur *Morosaurus*. cl, clavicle; icl, interclavicle; pc, precoracoid; s, scapula. (A after Broom, B after Andrews, C after Marsh.)

forms, and but two or three of the inner ones may persist. Certain forms which have become quadrupedal again seem to have effected some secondary redevelopment of the front legs, but even in most of these the anterior limbs are much shorter than the hind ones. In the shoulder (Fig. 148) there is only a single coracoid bone, and the scapula tends to be rather long and slim. The cleithrum is lost, as in most advanced reptiles; and clavicles or interclavicle or both may drop out.

Skull.—The primitive archosaurs were carnivores with simple pointed teeth set in separate sockets on the margins of the jaws; in contrast with most other reptiles teeth were never present on the palatal bones. In some cases there is a tendency for some or all of the teeth to be lost and to be replaced by a horny bill, and the cheek teeth were sometimes modified for plant feeding. A pineal opening is invariably absent. With the effect of lightening the skull an anteorbital fenestra is usually present between the orbit and nostril. The quadrates are large and extend far up the back corners of the skull. The two pterygoids have tended to meet to form a median plate in the roof of the mouth, with palatal vacuities present at either side. In the lower jaw appears a fenestra between dentary, angular, and surangular.

The ribs almost always retain the primitive double-headed condition. But a common archosaurian feature is the tendency in the dorsal region for the two heads to crowd close together with a common attachment to the transverse process (Fig. 149).

Thecodonts.—The characters and tendencies just discussed are seen in the various advanced archosaur types—the dinosaurs, pterosaurs, and crocodiles—and in the primitive birds (which seem clearly derivable from the archosaurs). These forms make their appearance in the late Triassic and Jurassic. We would expect to find in the first-mentioned period the ancestors of the later ruling reptiles, a common stock in which archosaurian characters were first making their appearance.

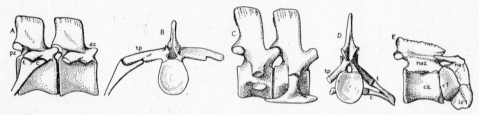

Fig. 149.—Vertebrae of the Jurassic crocodile *Steneosaurus*. *A*, dorsal vertebrae. *B*, same, anterior aspect. *C*, cervicals. *D*, same, posterior aspect. *E*, atlas and axis. *az*, anterior zygapophysis; *c*, capitulum of rib; *c1, c2*, centra of first and second vertebrae (atlas and axis); *icl*, intercentrum of atlas; *na1, na2*, neural arches of atlas and axis; *t*, tubercle of rib; *tp*, transverse process of neural arch. (After Andrews.)

Such a group is that which we shall here consider as comprising the order Thecodontia (or Pseudosuchia). In it are included a number of types of Triassic reptiles which vary considerably among themselves but which, as a whole, show the initiation of archosaurian tendencies.

The two-arched condition of the skull had already been acquired by some reptiles in late Permian times. The early diapsids which we have treated as constituting the Eosuchia are quite possibly ancestral to the primitive ruling reptiles; and *Youngina* is, for example, sometimes accorded a place among the thecodonts. But such Permian types show almost no indication of true archosaurian characters.

Primitive thecodonts.—Quite in contrast were a number of Triassic forms, such as *Euparkeria* (Fig. 150a, b), *Ornithosuchus* (Fig. 150c), and *Saltoposuchus* (Fig. 151). Such types are well known from both Europe and South Africa and were probably world-wide in distribution. They were, in the main, small reptiles with about the range of size seen in modern lizards, and the general appearance as well may have been rather lizard-like. Here, however, the comparison ends, for not only the bipedal gait which seems to have been developing but many internal features emphasize their position as ancestors of the later ruling reptile orders.

These forms were active little carnivores with sharp teeth set in sockets in the thecodont fashion characteristic of the subclass. The skull was long and slim with the nostrils near the front end. In contrast with the two-arched reptiles considered in the last chapter, an anteorbital vacuity was developed, the upper temporal opening was comparatively small, the pineal eye had disappeared, and the tabulars and dermal supra-occipitals were gone; on the under side of the skull palatal teeth had vanished, palatal vacuities were present, and the two pterygoids were in close contact. In all these skull characters the members of this group were typical archosaurs.

In their postcranial skeletons they exhibited the beginnings of typical archosaurian bipedal tendencies. The hind legs were very much longer than the front ones. The pelvis (Fig. 146a), while always somewhat plate-like, showed some elongation and down-turning of both pubis and ischium; the metatarsals were somewhat elongated, the third toe tended to be longer than the others, and the fifth toe seems to have been considerably reduced. These little reptiles ap-

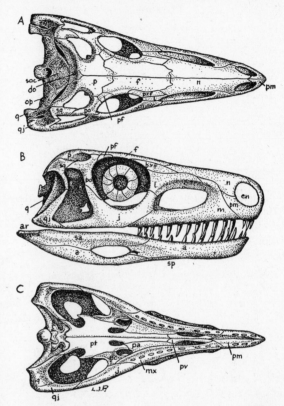

FIG. 150.—The skull in primitive thecodonts. *A*, dorsal, and *B*, lateral views of *Euparkeria*. Skull length about 6 inches. *C*, palate of *Ornithosuchus*. For abbreviations see Figure 86. (*A*, *B* after Broom, *C* after Newton and von Huene.)

parently were subject to attack by larger foes, for in almost all of them there were rows of small bony plates down the back.

Types such as these were apparently numerous in early Triassic times and persisted to the end of the period. It is obvious that they occupy a central position in archosaurian evolution. Almost no structural features need to be changed to turn some forms into a primitive carnivorous dinosaur, and other related genera seem to show the beginning of the secondary palate which characterizes the crocodiles. Known forms are somewhat farther in structure from the other archosaurian types, but there is nothing in their structure to debar them from a position of ancestry to pterosaurs or birds or the "bird-like" dinosaurs.

Other thecodont types.—In addition many sterile side branches developed among the Triassic thecodonts. *Aetosaurus*, for example, represents a group of small rep-

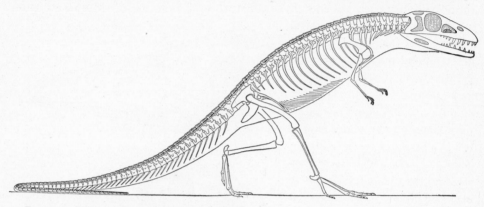

FIG. 151.—*Saltoposuchus*, a lightly built Triassic thecodont, about $3\frac{3}{4}$ feet in length. (From von Huene.)

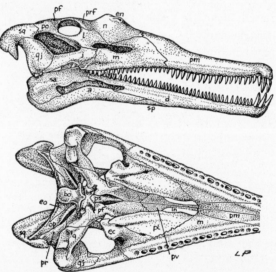

FIG. 152.—Lateral view of skull and posterior part of palate of the phytosaur *Machaeroprosopus;* skull length about $3\frac{1}{2}$ feet. For abbreviations see Figure 86. (After Camp.)

tiles quite similar to the last in most structural features but covered solidly on the top and sides of the body by expanded bony plates. There also developed a number of large aberrant members of the order.

Phytosaurs are among the most abundant of fossil reptiles from the later Triassic. They appear to have been quite similar in habits and general appearance to the modern crocodiles and were ecologically the predecessors of these forms, although not in themselves directly ancestral. The skull (Fig. 152) was much elongated in correlation with probable fish-eating habits, and the jaws were armed with a powerful battery of sharp teeth. The position of the nostrils was one that we have seen in certain other water-living types, the external openings being far back, almost between the eyes. The two openings were close together near the top of the skull and were in some cases situated in a sort of crater rising above the level of the skull top; this seems to have been a device for breathing with most of the body under water.

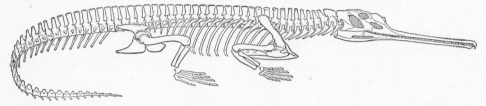

FIG. 153.—*Mystriosuchus*, a Triassic phytosaur. Original about $11\frac{1}{2}$ feet long. (From McGregor.)

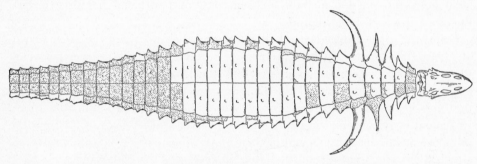

FIG. 154.—*Desmatosuchus*, an armored thecodont from the Triassic of North America, dorsal view. Part of body illustrated about 12 feet in length. (From Case.)

The body (Fig. 153) was crocodilian in general shape. The limbs were short, and the pelvis quite primitive in structure. But the hind legs were considerably longer than the front ones, although, with the taking up of an aquatic life, these animals had completely given up any aspirations toward bipedalism.

A considerable variety of these forms—*Phytosaurus, Mystriosuchus, Machaeroprosopus*, and many other genera—were present in Europe and North America, although apparently absent from the Southern Hemisphere. Comparatively successful for the time, they apparently failed to succeed in competition with the crocodiles and disappeared at the close of the Triassic.

Desmatosuchus (Fig. 154) was a large thecodont of the American Triassic. In some features it seems allied to the phytosaurs and like them may have been largely aquatic. But there were interesting specializations. Armor, present to some extent in phytosaurs, was highly developed in *Desmatosuchus*. Broad plates had completely covered the back, and the limbs were protected by horn-like bony processes which curved down over them and must have hindered an attack by carnivores. The skull was short, and while difficult of interpretation, not at all like that of phytosaurs.

Seemingly an overgrown offshoot from the early thecodont stock was *Erythrosuchus*, a large South African Lower Triassic form in which bulkiness was the structural keynote. The body was stout, the tail short, the limbs comparatively heavy, and the hind legs but little longer than the front. The skull was comparatively short, although rather high. It has been suggested that the creature was a marsh-dweller. Its sharply pointed teeth lead us to assume that it was a carnivore, but with its clumsy build it is difficult to imagine its source of food supply.

Confined exclusively to the Triassic, the history of the thecodonts was a brief one. But the development of these forms was an event of the greatest importance in the evolution of Mesozoic life, a necessary prelude to the later expansion of ruling reptile types.

Of the forms descended from this group, the dinosaurs and birds will be treated in later chapters; we shall include here an account of the other archosaurian orders. the crocodiles and flying reptiles.

Crocodiles.—The crocodiles and alligators and their relatives, the order Crocodilia, have been among the least progressive of ruling reptiles but nevertheless are the only members of the archosaurian stock which survived the end of the Age of Reptiles. Derived from one of the Triassic thecodont families, they appeared in the Jurassic and have undergone comparatively little modification in later times. In general body form and in many structural features they are not far from the primitive archosaurian type, and in their amphibious mode of life they resemble greatly their somewhat distantly related predecessors, the phytosaurs.

The skull (Fig. 155) is in many respects of a primitive archosaur pattern; it is always rather elongate and extremely so in fish-eating types such as the living Indian gavial. The palate, however, is much modified. We have seen that in the phytosaurs breathing difficulties were overcome to a considerable extent by shifting the external opening of the nostril far back, the internal opening beneath consequently lying in the back part of the mouth. In the crocodiles the external nares are at the tip of the snout, so that breathing can be accomplished even if only this part of the body is exposed, while internally the danger of shipping water into the air supply is prevented by the development of a secondary palate. Below the original inner opening of the nostrils the premaxillae, maxillae, and palatines have formed a secondary shelf below the original level of the roof of the mouth, leaving above them a tube through which the air passes back to the posteriorly situated internal nares. In modern forms even the pterygoids have met in the mid-line and formed a further prolongation. As a result the inhaled air does not enter the

mouth proper at all, but passes back separately into the throat, which can be
closed off by a flap of skin. A similar secondary palate has been formed in mammals but almost never developed to the extent seen in the crocodiles.

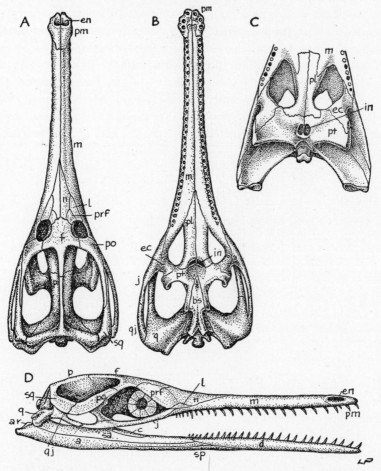

FIG. 155.—The skull in crocodilians. *A*, dorsal and *B*, ventral views of the Jurassic *Steneosaurus*, skull
length about 30 inches. *C*, part of palate of the Eocene *Crocodilus affinis*, to show posterior movement of
internal nares. *D*, lateral view of the Jurassic marine crocodilian *Geosaurus*, skull length about 15 inches.
For abbreviations see Figure 86. (*A*, *B* after Andrews, *C* after Mook, *D* after Fraas.)

The general body shape is rather lizard-like, with a long flattened tail which is
the main swimming organ. In modern forms the vertebrae are no longer hollowed
or flat-ended structures but are procoelous. There is always a well-developed set
of dermal armor plates down the back beneath the horny scales, and sometimes
down the ventral side as well—a feature which is an inheritance from the primitive thecodonts.

The modern crocodiles are quadrupeds and, as ordinarily observed, have a slow sprawling gait. Fast locomotion, however, is accomplished with the body high off the ground and the limbs straight under the body, as in all advanced archosaurians; and while crocodiles are not bipeds, it is suggestive that the front legs are always much shorter than the hind. The contrast in length was very strongly marked in the earliest Jurassic types, and it is highly probable that some degree of bipedal locomotion had developed in the archosaurian ancestors of the group before a trend toward an aquatic life appeared. In the shoulder (Fig. 148b) an interclavicle is retained but the clavicles lost. The two outer fingers of the front foot are reduced in a common archosaurian fashion, while as in dinosaurs the carpals are much reduced, leaving only two proximal and one distal element; the proximals are usually much elongated (Fig. 156a). There are but two sacral ribs,

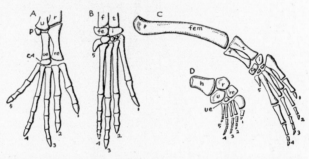

FIG. 156.—Limbs of crocodilians. A, manus, and B, pes, of the Jurassic *Alligatorellus*. C, D, hind and front legs of the Jurassic marine crocodile *Geosaurus*. The digits are numbered. c4, fourth distal carpal; f, fibula; fe, fibulare; fem, femur; h, humerus; i, intermedium; p, pisiform; r, radius; re radiale; t, tibia; u, ulna; ue, ulnare. (A, B after Lortet, C, D after Fraas.)

a primitive feature. The pelvis (Fig. 146b) has a triradiate structure, with pubis and ischium extending down separately from the acetabular region much as in the saurischian dinosaurs. The crocodile pelvis is peculiar, however, in that the pubis has been excluded from the acetabulum by the ischium. The hind legs are quite long; as in most archosaurians there is some elongation of the metatarsals, and the fifth digit is reduced to a stump of the metatarsal. But the foot (Fig. 156b) is somewhat divergent from that of many other archosaurs in that the first toe is still in line with the others, the fourth toe is slightly reduced, and the tarsus has a joint at its proximal end rather than in the middle.

Early crocodiles.—Crocodiles were already a flourishing group when they first appeared in Jurassic times. The forms of that period obviously pertained to the order but were somewhat more primitive than Tertiary and recent types. The upper temporal openings were not as small as in living forms; the internal nostrils still lay between the palatine bones, for the pterygoids had not yet been pressed into service to continue the secondary palate, the vertebrae still retained flattened or even slightly hollowed ends, and the anteorbital opening found in many other archosaurs had not disappeared in some cases (it is absent in all later crocodiles).

There were already several distinct types. Conspicuous were a number of rather slimly built long-snouted forms with heavy armor such as *Steneosaurus* (Fig. 155*a*, *b*) and *Teleosaurus*, which appear to have been active fish-eating forms, while there were also small short-nosed types such as *Atoposaurus* and *Alligatorellus*, the latter less than a foot in length.

Noteworthy were the marine crocodiles of the Jurassic. These were the only archosaurians of any sort that ever became purely aquatic types, for, while the ruling reptiles were supreme on land and in the air during the Mesozoic, most of the marine reptiles belonged to other groups. *Geosaurus* (Figs. 155*d*, 156*c*, *d*) and *Metriorhynchus* were unarmored crocodiles in which the limbs were considerably modified to serve as paddles. The main swimming organ was the tail, which had redeveloped into a fish-like tail fin rather similar to that of early ichthyosaurs, with the backbone turned down into the lower lobe of the fin, the upper lobe presumably being supported by toughened skin. These aquatic crocodiles were not uncommon in the late Jurassic seas, but for some reason they do not seem to have been as successful as were other reptilian marine types and soon disappeared.

Later crocodiles.—Besides the various types mentioned, crocodiles more directly ancestral to later forms were present in Jurassic times; such types, represented by *Goniopholis* and others, were common in the Cretaceous. During that period there was a strong trend toward modernization in such respects as the completion of the secondary palate (Fig. 155*c*) and the development of procoelous vertebrae. At the beginning of the Tertiary crocodiles and alligators had practically reached their modern status.

The crocodiles have been the most unprogressive of archosaurians but have survived while their progressive relatives have become extinct. What is progress?

Flying reptiles.—While the archosaurians did not succeed in an invasion of the sea, in the air they had better success, for they not only gave rise to the birds but produced within their ranks a second aërial type, the flying reptiles of the order Pterosauria. These curious forms flourished greatly in the Jurassic, and some large types survived to late Cretaceous times. Although there may have been pterosaurs on land, practically all known remains have been found in salt-water deposits, suggesting a fish-catching mode of life somewhat like that of terns today.

The structure of the pterosaurs may perhaps be best appreciated by taking as a type the fairly representative, but rather primitive, Jurassic form *Rhamphorhynchus* (Figs. 157, 158). This little reptile was about a foot and a half in length, with a long skull, a short body, a long tail, and, as the most striking feature, the development of the arms into elongate wings. The body appears to have been practically naked; some specimens preserved in sediments which show many delicate structures show no trace of scales (or of feathers), although there are indications of small rather hair-like structures. The wings were composed of a membrane of skin, as in the bats, but supported only by an attachment to a single elongated finger.

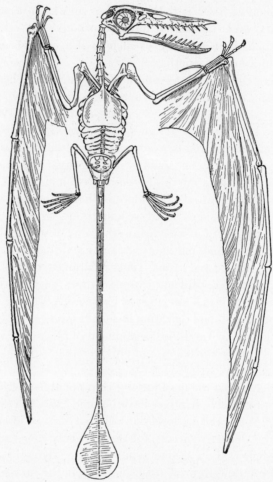

FIG. 157.—*Rhamphorhynchus*, a long-tailed Jurassic pterosaur. About ¼ natural size. (From Williston's *The Osteology of the Reptiles*, by permission of the Harvard University Press.)

Skeleton.—The head (Fig. 158) was typically archosaurian in structure, although (as in birds) the bones tended to be fused together and the sutures obscured. There were two temporal openings, below which the quadrates slanted forward so that the jaw articulation lay below the eyes. The orbits were large, and the eyes were protected (as in many flying or diving forms) by a ring of sclerotic plates. The nostrils were situated well back on the long beak. The teeth were sharp and pointed, for these forms appear to have been fish-eaters; *Rhamphorhynchus* was peculiar in that the teeth sloped forward rather than backward as in most carnivorous reptiles. The neck was elongated and the cervical ribs small, giving the head great freedom of motion; the trunk, on the other hand, was very short, with only ten or so dorsal segments; there was a long sacral region of more than half a dozen vertebrae and an elongate tail. This last structure was stiffened by strong ligaments and, as we know from impressions, bore a small steering rudder of skin.

The limbs were, of course, quite highly modified, the "arms" particularly so; many of the bones were hollow and air-filled, as in birds, thus decreasing the weight. There was a very large sternum on the ventral surface of the chest from which arose (as in birds) the main muscles having to do with wing movements. The der-

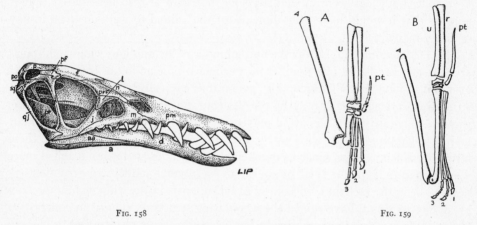

FIG. 158   FIG. 159

FIG. 158.—The skull of the pterosaur *Rhamphorhynchus*. Length of original about 5 inches. For abbreviations see Figure 86. (After Jaekel.)

FIG. 159.—Forearm and manus of pterosaurs. *A*, *Rhamphorhynchus*. *B*, *Pterodactylus*. The distal digits of the wing finger are omitted. *pt*, elements supporting the membrane between arm and neck; *r*, radius; *u*, ulna; 1-4, first to fourth digits. (After Williston.)

mal shoulder elements were absent, but scapula and coracoid were well developed. The shoulder girdle was, of course, subject to considerable stress during flight, and in this group tended to be better attached to the body than is usually the case; not only was the bottom of the coracoid propped against the edge of the sternum, but in some pterosaurs (cf. Fig. 161) the upper edge of the scapula fitted into a notch on the side of a fused series of dorsal vertebrae.

The humerus was short and powerful, usually with a large process for the attachment of breast muscles, the radius and ulna long and placed close together. The carpus (Fig. 159) was much shortened and reduced and apparently without much motion in it; at its front edge attached a small splint-like pteroid bone which seems to have supported a span of skin running up on to the neck. There is no trace of a fifth finger. The other four metacarpals ran out close together to the bases of the fingers. Three of the fingers were quite short but with the normal number of joints, and bore small claws at their ends. The fourth finger, however, was enormously elongated with four long phalanges; this fourth finger formed the entire support for the wing membrane, which ran back to attach along the side of the body and the thigh.

The pelvic limb was also quite peculiar in structure. There was the usual long ilium of archosaurs, tightly attached to the numerous sacral ribs (cf. Fig. 146c). Below lay a large plate which is sometimes thought to represent not only the ischium but the pubis as well. However, anterior to this there was attached a T-shaped element which met its fellow in the mid-line. This is thought by some to have been an extra element, a prepubis; by others it is considered to be the pubis itself. The hind legs were moderately long but slim and so articulated that it appears that it would have been difficult for the animal to walk on them in any ordinary manner.

Flight.—Obviously flight was the normal mode of locomotion; wing membranes are perfectly preserved in a number of specimens. The action of the wings, however, must have been considerably poorer mechanically than in birds. These structures were supported only by one elongate finger; and since the membrane was probably fairly soft, no partial movements could have been accomplished but merely a flapping of the whole structure. It seems highly probable that these forms did not move the wings as much as does the average bird, but relied more upon a soaring flight for their progression. An obvious fault in construction appears to lie in the fact that, without internal supports in the wing membrane, any break or tear would have ruined the whole wing structure. This is in contrast to birds, in which a few feathers may be lost without serious results, and to bats, in which several fingers are inserted in the membrane.

It is difficult to see how pterosaurs might have got about when not in flight. Older restorations show them walking about on all fours with the wings turned back and the three small front toes on the ground, but the structure of the hind legs makes such a pose almost impossible. A bipedal mode of progression is out of the question. It seems obvious that the small front fingers were used for clutching, and the animals may have rested hanging from a limb or a rock ledge. Perhaps, as in bats, the body may have been suspended upside down from a branch, in which case the hind legs would have made good clutching organs. But it seems difficult to assume that "emergency landings" would never have been necessary; and how the animal could get itself into the air again from level ground is difficult to understand.

The brain of the pterosaurs has been revealed by casts. It was exceedingly large for a reptile; very prominent are the regions which have to do with sight, while the olfactory areas are negligible, suggesting that, as in the birds, sight was all important and smell almost lost. The many other analogies with birds, and the real relationship of the two groups within the archosaurian stock suggests that perhaps other bird characters may have been present. These forms quite probably were somewhat warm blooded, for it seems very necessary that there should have been a continual supply of energy for flying; and it is not impossible that the "improvements" in the circulatory system found in birds may have been present here (they are foreshadowed in the crocodiles, the only living archosaurians).

Rhamphorhynchoids.—The pterosaurs are divided into two suborders—the Rhamphorhynchoidea and Pterodactyloidea. The former, of which *Rhamphorhynchus* is typical, is the more primitive group and is exclusively Jurassic in age. Its members agree in a number of primitive features. The originally long reptilian tail was still present, teeth were usually well developed, the metacarpals in the wing were comparatively short (Fig. 159a), the last toe in the foot was unreduced, and the fibula was present although small.

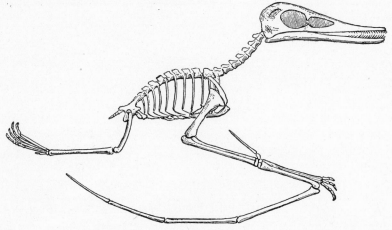

FIG. 160.—*Pterodactylus*, a small short-tailed Jurassic pterosaur. (From Williston's *The Osteology of the Reptiles*, by permission of the Harvard University Press.)

Pterodactyloids.—But already in the Jurassic there appeared a second, derived group, the pterodactyloids. *Pterodactylus* (Fig. 160) was a small form, some specimens being no bigger than a sparrow. The most prominent difference from the primitive types lay in the fact that there was but a stub remaining of the originally long tail. The fifth toe in the hind leg was reduced; the wing metacarpals were much elongated (Fig. 159b). The teeth tended to be lost from the back part of the mouth at least and presumably were succeeded by a horny beak. These little pterodactyls appear to have been common along the Jurassic shores. In the Cretaceous but a few forms survived, but among them were remarkable types. The size tended to increase, the skull tended to elongate and to develop a crest extending back from the occipital region. Teeth were entirely lost. The culmination of these tendencies is seen in *Pteranodon* (Fig. 161) of the Upper Cretaceous of Kansas, a form with a wing spread of as much as 25 feet, a long toothless beak, and a crest nearly as long as the main part of the skull, extending back from the head.

This was the end of the pterosaurs; the group became extinct before the close of the Cretaceous.

Pterosaur history.—The structure of these forms clearly indicates that they were derived, as were other archosaurians, from some member of the Thecodontia in which a bipedal gait had been evolved. The arms were freed from the necessity of functioning in terrestrial locomotion and were available to take up other employment. Possibly the pterosaurs were small climbing types; and a membrane may have developed, as in a number of other tree-dwelling vertebrates, as an aid

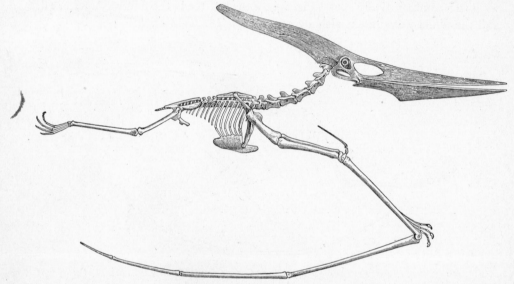

Fig. 161.—*Pteranodon*, a giant Cretaceous flying reptile. Maximum wing spread about 27 feet. (From Eaton.)

in planing from tree to tree and breaking the fall on landing. The fifth finger was often reduced in archosaurians; and the fourth, the longest of the series, was well adapted, after the loss of the claw joint, to support a wing membrane. Why, however, the loss of ordinary walking powers should have taken place is not clear. Some light may be shed on this and other problems if ever the missing connecting types which must have been present in the Triassic are found as fossils.

It seems obvious that these forms were not as well adapted for a flying existence as the birds. The feathered structure of the bird's wing seems much better than the pterosaur membrane. The pterosaurs appeared first in the field, for, when the first primitive birds appeared in the Jurassic, the flying reptiles were at their peak. But by Upper Cretaceous times highly developed flying birds had been evolved; competition with them may have been a factor in the elimination of the last of the pterosaurs.

CHAPTER IX

DINOSAURS

Most interesting of ruling reptiles, and perhaps the most spectacular fossil animals of any age, were the dinosaurs. Springing from the primitive thecodont stock in the early Triassic, dinosaurs were already abundant by the end of that period and were the dominant land types during the remainder of the Mesozoic. Among their numbers is included almost every large terrestrial vertebrate of the Jurassic and Cretaceous.

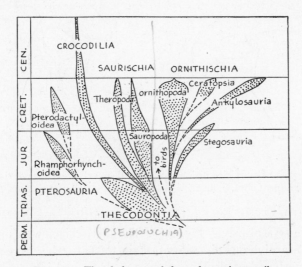

Fig. 162.—The phylogeny of the archosaurian reptiles

The popular conception of the dinosaurs is that of a single group of large reptiles. This is, however, inaccurate. Most dinosaurs were large—some reaching a weight of 40 or 50 tons—but some true dinosaurs bulked no larger than a rooster. Further, the dinosaurs were not a single group but were already divided at their first appearance into two distinct stocks related only in that both were archosaurs descended from the primitive ruling reptiles, the Thecodontia. The term "dinosaur" is thus one which can be used only in a popular sense, and scientifically the dinosaurs are arrayed in two separate orders defined below.

Certain of the dinosaurs were carnivores, as had been their thecodont ancestors; a majority, however, abandoned this mode of life and became herbivores. All the earlier and more primitive members of both orders were bipeds, as were the more advanced thecodonts from which they had sprung. Although a majority remained bipedal until the end of dinosaurian history, many herbivorous forms in both orders reverted to a four-footed gait. But even if we know nothing of the pedigree of such quadrupedal forms, many features of their limb construction would tell us of their descent from bipedal ancestors.

The dinosaurs are divided into two orders, the Saurischia and Ornithischia, both included in the subclass Archosauria but no more closely related to one another than to the other members or descendants of the ruling reptile group—the crocodiles, pterosaurs, and birds. The distinctions between the two dinosaurian orders were clean-cut from the first. A key character (to which the names refer) is that, while the Saurischia have the triradiate pelvic structure (Fig. 163) devel-

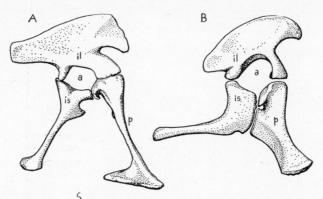

FIG. 163.—The pelvis of saurichian dinosaurs: *A*, the theropod *Allosaurus*. *B*, the sauropod *Morosaurus*. *a*, acetabulum (perforate); *il*, ilium; *is*, ischium; *p*, pubis. (*A* after Gilmore, *B* after Marsh.)

oped in many thecodonts, the Ornithischia have a two-pronged pubis, resulting in a tetraradiate type of pelvis (Fig. 164). The saurischians were primitively carnivores, and all carnivorous dinosaurs pertain to that order. Some saurischians, however, became four-footed plant-eaters and developed into great amphibious forms, among which are the largest of all reptiles. The ornithischians, on the other hand, were herbivorous from the first. Many of them remained bipeds; the well-known duck-billed dinosaurs of the Cretaceous are end-forms of this line. But in this order also there was reversion to a quadrupedal gait in various armored types and the horned dinosaurs of the Cretaceous.

Saurischians.—The order Saurischia perhaps merits first consideration, since many of its members were still exceedingly close in structure to the small bipedal thecodonts from which all the dinosaurs presumably sprang. The typical triradiate pelvis is present in all members of this order. A majority of the group, including all the more primitive forms, were bipedal and carnivorous. Almost all (in contrast with ornithischians) had teeth present throughout the length of the jaws. The teeth were in general of a simple nature, primitively sharp conical structures but compressed and knife-like in some of the carnivores and blunted in herbivorous

types. In correlation with the usually carnivorous mode of life the end-phalanges
were generally compressed and curved, indicating the presence of powerful claws.

Various systematic arrangements of the order have been proposed. We shall
here use a conservative classification which divides the saurischians into two suborders: the Theropoda, including all the bipedal forms, mainly carnivorous in
habits; and the Sauropoda, constituting a side branch of large quadrupedal amphibious types.

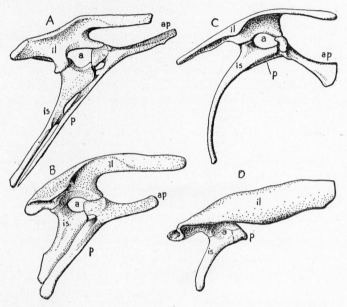

FIG. 164.—The pelvis of ornithischian dinosaurs. *A, Thescelosaurus,* a primitive ornithopod. *B,*
Stegosaurus. C, Monoclonius, a horned dinosaur. *D, Ankylosaurus,* a Cretaceous armored form. *a,*
acetabulum; *ap,* anterior process of pubis; *il,* ilium; *is,* ischium, *p,* main body of pubis. (*B, C* after Gilmore, *D* after Brown.)

Primitive theropods.—The theropods (using this term in a broad sense) include
all the characteristic terrestrial reptilian carnivores of the late Triassic, Jurassic,
and Cretaceous. These reptiles were flesh-eating successors to the carnivorous
synapsids of the Permian and early Triassic (to be described in a later chapter)
and ecologic predecessors of the carnivorous mammals of the Cenozoic. All were
bipeds, with long hind legs which tended to assume a rather bird-like structure
and with short front limbs in which the outer digits were usually much reduced.

Most primitive of saurischians were a number of small forms of the late Triassic
and Jurassic. Typical genera were *Procompsognathus* of the European Upper Triassic; the contemporary American *Podokesaurus;* and *Compsognathus* and *Ornitho-*
lestes (Figs. 165, 166), which occur in the late Jurassic in Europe and America, respectively. All were of small size; *Podokesaurus,* even including the long tail, was

little over a yard in length; *Compsognathus* was even smaller. These little forms were obviously active, fast-running bipeds. The lightness of their build was emphasized by the fact that many of the vertebrae and limb bones were hollow and

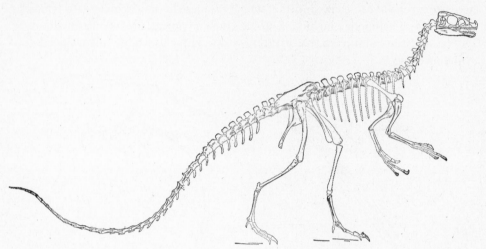

FIG. 165.—*Ornitholestes*, a small late Jurassic carnivorous dinosaur (coelurosaur). About 6 feet long. (From Osborn.)

presumably (as in birds) filled with air spaces. In reference to this fact the term "coelurosaur" is often applied to these types.

The skull of early theropods (Figs. 166, 167) was in general fairly small in comparison to the size of the body, and lightly built. In most respects the cranial

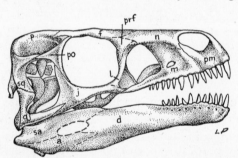

FIG. 166.—The skull of a small theropod, *Ornitholestes*. The braincase imperfect. Original about 5 inches long. For abbreviations see Figure 86. (After Osborn, modified.)

structure was very similar to that of such thecodonts as *Ornithosuchus* and *Euparkeria*. Such characteristic archosaurian structures as a large anteorbital opening and a fenestra on the outer side of the jaw were present both here and in later and more specialized saurischians. The thecodont teeth were long, sharp, often somewhat compressed and recurved, and usually well adapted to a carnivorous diet.

The vertebrae were primitively amphicoelous or with flat ends on the centra (platycoelous); in Jurassic and Cretaceous saurischians opisthocoelous vertebrae were common, particularly in the front end of the vertebral column. The backbone included about ten rather elongate cervicals, thirteen or so trunk vertebrae, usually four sacrals united with the expanded ilium, and a long slim tail. Seemingly the neck was held well erect, with the head bent forward at a right angle. The tail served as a balancer and (as indicated by many specimens of footprints of carnivorous dinosaurs) was held clear of the ground. In many theropods the tail was stiffened by long processes which extended forward from each prezygapophysis to interlock with the preceding vertebra. Slim ventral ribs have been found along the belly in many specimens.

The theropod pelvic girdle (Fig. 163a) was of a simple triradiate pattern. The pubis was presumably rather broad in the most primitive theropod ancestors but generally had the form of a long slim rod somewhat dilated distally, and the

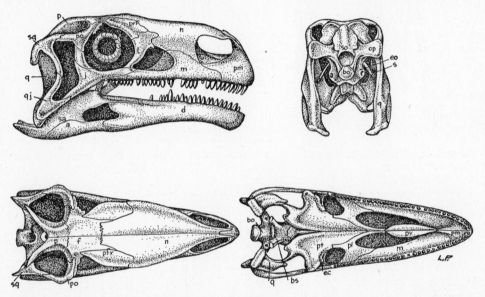

FIG. 167.—The skull of the Triassic saurischian dinosaur *Plateosaurus*. Length of original about 13 inches. For abbreviations see Figure 86. (After von Huene.)

ischium was similarly elongated. The hind legs were long and slim and presumably were restricted to a straight fore-and-aft type of movement with a high development of the adaptations for bipedal locomotion discussed in the preceding chapter. The femur in primitive theropods was generally somewhat shorter than the tibia; in life this would have resulted in the development of considerable speed, a short swift stroke of the thigh muscles being accompanied by a long swing of the tibia (in slow and ponderous tetrapods the femur is long, the tibia short). In the foot (Fig. 168) the fifth toe (as in most archosaurs) had been reduced to a short metatarsal with, at the most, a vestigial nubbin or two representing the digits. In many theropods the first toe as well was considerably shortened and tended to be set off at an angle from the other three. In the second to fourth toes the metatarsals tended to be much elongated and closely appressed and the central digit was somewhat longer than its neighbors, resulting in a very bird-like foot structure. So similar are the feet of theropods to those of the avian relatives that when numerous dinosaur footprints were discovered a century ago in the Triassic rocks of the Connecticut valley they were thought to pertain to ancestral birds.

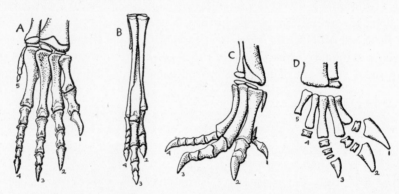

FIG. 168.—The pes of saurischian dinosaurs. *A, Anchisaurus. B, Struthiomimus. C, Allosaurus. D, Camerasaurus.* (*A* after Marsh, *B* after Osborn, *C, D* after Gilmore.)

The shoulder girdle in these and other dinosaur types (Fig. 148*c*) consisted merely of an elongated scapula and a single rounded coracoid. No dinosaur has preserved any trace of the original dermal elements of the girdle; this is one of the

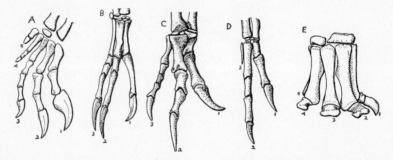

FIG. 169.—The manus in saurischian dinosaurs. *A, Anchisaurus. B, Struthiomimus. C, Allosaurus. D, Gorgosaurus. E, Diplodocus.* (*A* after Marsh, *B, E* after Osborn, *C,* after Gilmore, *D* after Lambe.)

few diagnostic characters by which the early carnivorous dinosaurs can be distinguished from their more primitive thecodont relatives. The fore limb was much shorter than the hind. In every known form the fifth digit had been much reduced (Fig. 169). The remaining four fingers were all still well developed in *Procompsognathus;* but in *Podokesaurus* and the Jurassic genera the fourth digit was also reduced, leaving only the three inner ones functional. Presumably the front limb was used little, if at all, in supporting the body (except in a resting pose) but may have aided in feeding.

There were a number of small theropods of this general type in the latter part of the Triassic. They appear to have been not far from the ancestral thecodonts in most structural features and in some cases can scarcely be distinguished from members of that group. In the Jurassic small "coelurosaurs" were comparatively rare and were tending to specialize in various directions. *Compsognathus*, known from a skeleton from the lithographic stone of southern Germany, is the only known European Jurassic type. This was a very small and lightly built dinosaur with about the bulk of a fowl. In the manus there were three well-developed digits subequal in length and rudiments of the two outer ones. *Ornitholestes* of the late Jurassic Morrison beds was a considerably larger form, with a total length of about 6 feet and a rather stouter build. Here only the three inner digits of the manus were preserved; the inner one was shorter than the others, and somewhat divergent; seemingly this form had developed a grasping type of hand. The obvious agility of this little dinosaur and the clutching power of the hand led to a belief that this form might have preyed upon the contemporary primitive birds (a suggestion preserved in the generic name). This is improbable; presumably small reptiles such as lizards and perhaps the small early mammals may have been the staple articles of diet of this and other tiny dinosaurs.

Ostrich-like dinosaurs.—Almost no remains of such small theropods are known from Cretaceous deposits, but descendants of the coelurosaurs are to be recognized in *Ornithomimus* and *Struthiomimus* (Fig. 170) of the North American Cretaceous and related Old World contemporaries. *Struthiomimus* was about the size of an ostrich and (as the name implies) not unlike that bird in general proportions, with very long slim hind legs, a long neck, and a small head. The foot (Fig. 168b) was three toed and very bird-like. The three metatarsals were very long and closely appressed; the central one was much reduced proximally, its neighbors taking over most of its weight-supporting function. Despite the fact that these forms were obviously purely bipedal in habits, the front limbs were quite long. The three inner fingers were all well developed, and the first was seemingly opposable to the other two, forming an effective grasping organ (Fig. 169b). The skull is imperfectly known but was quite small and very lightly built, with a superficial bird-like appearance. This resemblance is greatly heightened through the fact that, almost alone among dinosaurs, *Struthiomimus* and its relatives had entirely lost their teeth and presumably had replaced them functionally with a horny bill. The jaws were short and weak.

The odd combination of specializations found in these ostrich-like forms—great swiftness, a grasping ability in the well-developed "hands," and the weak and toothless jaws—has caused considerable discussion as to their mode of life. The happiest idea put forward was that these forms made a living by robbing eggs from the nests of other dinosaurs. Teeth are unnecessary for egg-eating, and the shell can be effectively broken with a horny beak; the "hands" would be of great use in handling the eggs, and the speed was necessary to escape the enraged parents! As if in confirmation of this suggestion was the subsequent discovery in Mongolia of a crushed skull of an ostrich-like dinosaur in a nest of fossil eggs belonging to a dinosaur of a different group. It would almost seem as if this reptile had actually been caught in the act of egg-stealing.

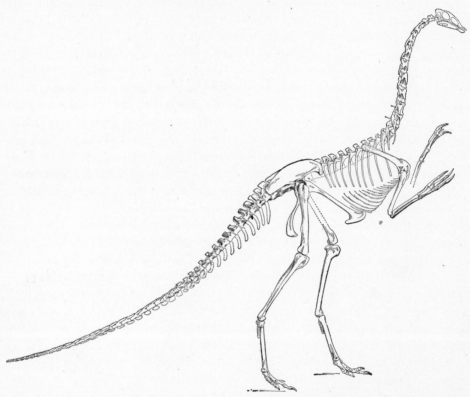

FIG. 170.—*Struthiomimus*, an ostrich-like Cretaceous saurischian dinosaur. About 5 feet in height. (From Osborn.)

Larger carnivorous types.—While the ancestral theropods were presumably small forms such as those described above, more powerful carnivores began to make their appearance at an early date. A number of carnivores with a much larger size and a heavier build have been described from the Upper Triassic of South Africa, and there are numerous footprints (but unfortunately few adequate skeletal remains) of other large dinosaurs in beds of that age in Europe and North America. Many of these types are probable ancestors of the sauropods. However, *Zanclodon*, a large form from the Triassic of Europe which is incompletely known, was distinguished from most of its contemporaries by the possession of a skull very large in proportion to its body and by large compressed and recurved teeth. It is from some such form that there arose the large flesh-eating dinosaurs of the Jurassic, the megalosaurs.

There are numerous scattered finds in European deposits representing nearly every stage of the Jurassic to which the generic term *Megalosaurus* is usually applied. Most of these remains are, however, fragmentary and tell us little beyond the fact that large flesh-eaters were abroad in the land. Well-preserved specimens of the megalosaurs are found only in late Jurassic Morrison beds of North America; from these beds have been obtained nearly complete skeletons of two large carnivores, *Allosaurus* and *Ceratosaurus*.

Allosaurus was an animal with a total length of about 34 feet; it was seemingly powerful enough to have attacked any of its herbivorous contemporaries, even the giant sauropods. The skull (Fig. 171*a*), in contrast with that of most smaller or earlier theropods, was quite large in proportion to the body, the teeth large and sharp, the jaws long and deep. A curious feature is found in the fact that the quadrate was loosely united to the other skull elements, and there appears to have been also some possibility of movement between the frontal and parietal bones. Seemingly this was an adaptation for bolting large masses of flesh, a type of structural modification which we have seen carried to an extreme in the snakes and which is also present to some extent in birds.

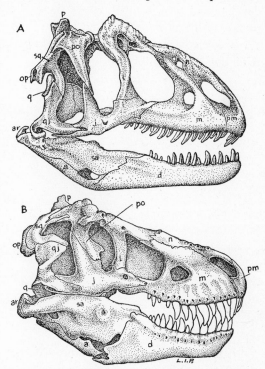

FIG. 171.—*A*, skull of *Allosaurus*, a large late Jurassic carnivorous dinosaur. Length of original about 27 inches. *B*, *Tyrannosaurus*, a late Cretaceous type. Skull length about 50 inches. For abbreviations see Figure 86. (*A* after Gilmore, *B* after Osborn.)

The body was rather massively built. The neck vertebrae were opisthocoelous, and extra articulations in addition to the normal zygapophyses tended to add to the strength of the backbone. The hind legs, in correlation with the size of the creature, were stout and only moderately long, and the femur was somewhat longer than the tibia. The metatarsals were rather short, but otherwise the foot (Fig. 168*c*) was quite bird-like with three well-developed toes and a small first toe turned backward as a prop, much as in many avian types. The fore limb was short but fairly stoutly built, with three spreading claw-tipped digits (Fig. 169*c*); it was obviously not a supporting structure but may have been of considerable use in feeding.

Ceratosaurus was a somewhat smaller related type in which the most striking feature was the development of a small median horn on the nasal bones. There was a somewhat more progressive condition in the feet of this form, for all three metatarsals had partly fused to form a single solid bone. This is parallel to the development seen in birds, where these elements have fused completely; but the process of fusion was carried no farther in any known dinosaur. The front foot of *Ceratosaurus* was, on the contrary, comparatively primitive, for there was little reduction of the outer two digits.

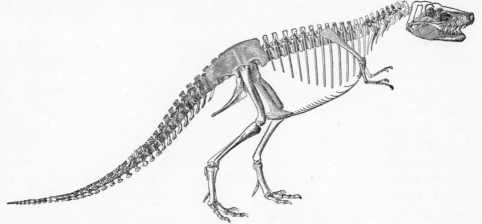

FIG. 172.—*Deinodon* (*Gorgosaurus*), a gigantic Cretaceous Theropod dinosaur. Length about 29 feet. (From Lambe.)

Little is known of the carnivores of the early Cretaceous, and it is doubtful whether the Jurassic megalosaurs gave rise to the typical large carnivores of the later part of that period. From them, however, may have been derived *Spinosaurus* of the Cretaceous of Egypt. This large flesh-eater is poorly known but was remarkable in that the neural spines were greatly elongated rather after the fashion of some of the Permian pelycosaurs described in a later chapter; some spines had a length of about 6 feet.

Cretaceous carnivores.—Successors in the late Cretaceous to the megalosaurs were the still larger and more powerful carnivores of the deinodont group of which *Tyrannosaurus* (Fig. 171b) and *Deinodon* (*Gorgosaurus*) (Fig. 172) of Western North America are the best-known forms. *Tyrannosaurus* reached a length of some 47 feet and stood about 19 feet high in walking pose, while *Deinodon* was nearly as large. These reptiles were the largest terrestrial flesh-eaters known from any period in the history of the world. The body was heavy in its construction; the hind legs, massively built. The metatarsals were moderately elongated, and (as in the contemporary ornithomimids) the middle one was much reduced in size. The front legs were absurdly small and weak and seem to have been practically useless; they were too short to reach the mouth and seemingly too weak to have been of any assistance in seizing or rending the prey. Only two small digits were present in *Deinodon* (Fig. 168*d*), and probably the same was true in *Tyrannosaurus*.

The skull was very large and massively built, with the fenestrae of small size. The jaws were armed with powerful scimitar-like teeth, some half a foot in length, recurved and with serrate edges. The cervical vertebrae, which bore the weight of the heavy head, were short and broad.

These forms, although agreeing with the megalosaurs in many adaptive features, are thought by some not to be their descendents. Certain structural features, such as the metatarsal construction mentioned above, suggest that they represent a parallel development from the primitive stock of small bipeds. Some comparatively small deinodonts (one with a skull only 8 inches long) from the Upper Cretaceous seem to be rather primitive in character and may represent transitional types.

The reign of the deinodonts was a brief one, for they disappeared at the end of the Cretaceous. Their extinction was obviously consequent upon the extermination of the herbivorous dinosaur types which presumably formed their food supply.

Sauropod ancestors.—We have still to consider the history of the sauropods, Jurassic and Cretaceous saurischians which became herbivores, reverted to a quadrupedal pose, and reached gigantic proportions. The ancestors of these forms are unquestionably to be sought among the larger Triassic theropods.

A first step in sauropod development is perhaps illustrated by *Anchisaurus* of the Upper Triassic of North America. This was a small dinosaur (the largest specimen was but 7 or 8 feet long), and many of the bones were still hollow in coelurosaur fashion. There are many suggestions, however, of sauropod relationships. The teeth were comparatively blunt and straight; and the jaw was short, the quadrate slanting forward as well as down to reach the jaw articulation; these are sauropod features. Highly suggestive is the persistently primitive construction of the limbs. Despite the small size of this animal the hind legs were comparatively short and clumsy and the metapodials were not greatly elongated (Fig. 168*d*). While the fifth toe had been reduced the other four were all well developed; and the hallux was not, as in the majority of carnivores, turned back and separated from the three middle digits. The front legs were comparatively little shortened; they were still about two-thirds the length of the hind limbs and were stoutly built. The fifth digit in the hand (Fig. 169*d*) was considerably reduced, and the fourth reduced to some extent as well. Probably these forms were not purely bipedal in habits and may have walked on all fours much of the time.

Farther along the line toward the sauropods was *Plateosaurus* (Figs. 167, 173) of the Upper Triassic of Germany, a much larger form of which complete skeletons with a length of as much as 20 feet are known. The build of the body was quite clumsy and ponderous, with much the same set of structural features as those found in *Anchisaurus*. The head was very small in proportion to the bulk of the body, as in the sauropods themselves.

Sauropods.—From such forms seem to have descended the sauropods of the Jurassic and Cretaceous, a series of forms which include not only the largest of all reptiles but the largest four-footed animals of any time. Among the better-known

FIG. 173.—*Plateosaurus* a Triassic ancestor of the sauropod dinosaurs. Length about 21 feet. (From von Huene.)

sauropods are *Brontosaurus*, *Diplodocus* (Figs. 174, 176), and *Camarasaurus* (Figs. 175, 177), forms whose remains are among the most spectacular attractions of many museums.

The most obvious contrasts between the sauropods and their carnivorous relatives lie in the quadrupedal pose of the body and in the bodily proportions. The sauropods were massively built, with powerful limbs (the front ones almost always considerably the shorter), a long tail, and a long neck terminating in a small head.

The skull (Figs. 176, 177) in sauropods seems absurdly out of proportion to the size of the animal. It was generally quite lightly built, with large temporal fenestrae and a large anteorbital opening (there was a second smaller one in *Diplodocus*). The orbits were of good size and were situated high up on the side of the head. In *Camarasaurus* the external nares were very large and reached high up on the short skull; in *Diplodocus* the two openings were fused and situated at the top of the skull between the eyes. The position of these organs, analogous to that

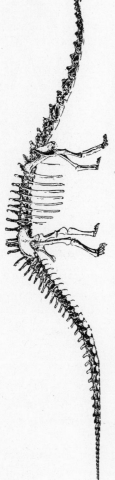

FIG. 174.—*Diplodocus*, lengthiest of late Jurassic sauropod dinosaurs (87½ feet). (From Holland.)

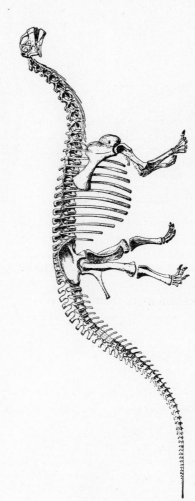

FIG. 175.—*Camarasaurus*, a comparatively small late Jurassic sauropod dinosaur. Original of figure about 18½ feet long. (From Gilmore.)

in many water-living tetrapods, suggests an amphibious mode of life for the sauropods; the animal could breathe and look about with only the top of the skull exposed above the water.

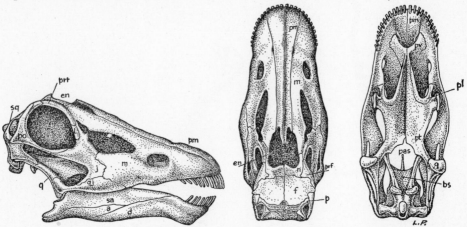

FIG. 176.—The skull of the sauropod dinosaur *Diplodocus*, lateral, dorsal, and palatal views. Length about 2 feet. For abbreviations see Figure 86. (After Holland.)

The jaws were short and weak, the quadrate slanting downward and forward to the jaw articulation. The teeth were small and slim, peg-like or spoon-shaped; there were seldom more than a dozen or so in each jaw half. It seems almost im-

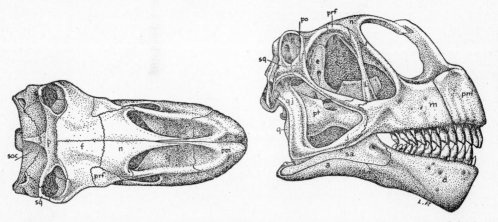

FIG. 177.—Dorsal and lateral views of the skull of the sauropod dinosaur *Camarasaurus*. Length about 1 foot. For abbreviations see Figure 86. (After Gilmore.)

possible that this dental and jaw apparatus could have been capable of cropping enough fodder to supply such a huge body, although the food material may have been some soft type of water vegetation which could be eaten with little effort.

The brain was small in size in all dinosaurs but excessively small, proportionately, in the sauropods, in which the endocranial cavity was but a small recess in the posterior part of the small skull. Presumably the brain had few functions other than working the jaws, receiving sensory impressions, and passing the news back down the spinal cord to the pelvic region, from which originated the nerves working the hind legs. Here there was situated an enlargement of the spinal cord several times as big as the entire brain.

A monumental construction of the backbone was required to carry the weight of the enormous body and transfer it to the legs. The anterior vertebrae, which had only the tiny head to support, were small; but in the trunk the centra of the vertebrae become progressively massive as we pass up over the arch of the back to the hip region. The neural spines, low in front, increase rapidly in height and reach a maximum at the top of the arch just in front of the pelvis. Presumably an interlacing series of ligaments and tendons passed between these spines and helped to strengthen the back. In many sauropods the neural spines of the anterior vertebrae were cleft at their upper ends, and probably a stout longitudinal ligament lay between the two prongs.

FIG. 178.— A dorsal vertebra of the sauropod dinosaur *Diplodocus*. (After Hatcher.)

But the dead weight of the backbone itself was a great burden; in correlation with this we find that adaptations had developed which greatly increased the weight of the vertebrae (Fig. 178). These structures were generally cavernous; great areas were hollowed out at the sides of the centra and arches; these were presumably filled with air sacs connecting, as in birds, with the lungs. Weight was thus much reduced, but all the essential frame work of the vertebrae was left in tact.

The pelvic elements (Fig. 163*b*) were short but stoutly constructed; the ventral elements had more of the primitive plate-like aspect than was the case in most theropods. The hind-limb bones were massive, with the femur considerably longer than the tibia; presumably the limbs extended straight down from the body in elephantine fashion. The front legs were generally much shorter than the hind, a feature suggestive of the probable bipedal ancestry of the sauropods. They bore less of the weight than the hind limbs and may have been less straight, the elbows projecting somewhat. In both front and hind feet (Figs. 168*d*, 169*d*) the metapodials and phalanges were short, stout, and spreading; probably the limbs terminated, as in elephants, in a broad pad in which the toes were incased. The details of foot construction are poorly known in most cases, but from one to three of the digits in each foot bore a large claw which presumably was of use in preventing slipping.

The pose of sauropod limbs has been a much debated subject. It has been argued that, since in most reptiles the femur projects sideways from the body, the sauropods, too, should be mounted in this fashion. As a matter of fact, this cannot be done without doing violence to the articular surfaces of the bones. But more than this, it would have been impossible for the animal to have supported an enormous weight with any type of limb other than a straight column. With the limbs sprawled sideways, no mere muscles could have withstood the direct pull of the score or more of tons that the hind legs of a big sauropod had to support; the animal would have sagged to the ground.

But even granting the columnar position of the legs, it is difficult to see how these dinosaurs ever walked on land; the elements of physics show that there are natural limits set to the possible size of a four-footed vertebrate.

An elephant does not and cannot have the slim limbs of a gazelle; *Deinodon* and *Tyrannosaurus* could not have the slender hind legs of the little coelurosaurs. The weight of an animal varies in proportion to the cube of a linear dimension. But the strength of a leg, like that of any structural supporting element, is proportionate to its cross-section, which increases only by squares. If a reptile doubles his length, his weight is approximately eight times as great, but his legs are but four times as strong. Hence in large animals the bulk of the legs must increase out of all proportion to the rest of the body.

The legs of sauropods were large, but even so it seems doubtful whether they could have borne so many tons of weight. For this reason, as well as because of cranial features noted earlier, it appears probable that the sauropods were amphibious types which spent most of their lives in lowland swamps and lagoons where, buoyed up by the water, problems of support and locomotion were greatly simplified.

Sauropods are unknown in the Triassic, although we have noted some seemingly ancestral types and some late Triassic South African forms which appear to have been even closer to the sauropod condition. In the earlier part of the Jurassic there are fragmentary remains, particularly in Europe, to most of which the name *Cetiosaurus* has been applied. In the Morrison beds of North America and beds of similar age in East Africa have been found a considerable number of well-preserved specimens of a variety of sauropod types. *Camarasaurus* of North America was a comparatively small and unspecialized form. *Brontosaurus* was a bulkier relative which reached a length in one specimen of some 67 feet and an estimated weight of perhaps 30 tons. *Diplodocus* was a slimly built form which may not have been nearly as heavy as the last but which, with a whiplash at the end of his tail, reached the record for length—87½ feet. *Brachiosaurus*, known both from North America and East Africa, was the real giant of the group. The tail was comparatively short, but even so the body may have been close to 80 feet in length. The body was extremely stout, and (in contrast with almost all other sauropods) the front legs were long. Above the shoulders there extended a long neck which could place the head above the level of the roof of a three-story building; this build presumably was an adaptation for life in deep waters. A rough guess at the weight of this great animal would be somewhere close to 50 tons.

In Cretaceous deposits sauropods are comparatively rare. Only a very few fragmentary finds have been reported from all of North America in that period. In the southern hemisphere, however, sauropods remained more abundant and may have been common throughout the Cretaceous. Most of them, included in the genus *Titanosaurus*, were forms of comparatively small size, although one giant is reported from South America.

The decline and final disappearance of these great reptiles may perhaps be correlated with geologic events. Their environment seems to have been a restricted one and if, as seems likely, continental elevation toward the end of the Mesozoic greatly restricted the area of the lowland swampy regions in which the sauropods dwelt, their extinction was almost inevitable; changes taking place in the vegetation at this time may also have been of great importance.

Ornithischians.—Members of the second order of dinosaurs, the Ornithischia, never reached the size attained by some of their saurischian cousins but are perhaps of even greater interest because of the variety of bizarre types into which they developed. The most characteristic feature of the order, one by which the skeletons of these forms may be told at a glance, was the tetraradiate type of pelvis (Fig. 164). The ilium and ischium were roughly comparable in shape and position to those elements in the saurischians, but the pubis was peculiarly constructed. Its main portion had not only rotated downward but also backward, so that it lay parallel to and close beside the ischium while, presumably in relation to the need for support of the abdomen, a broad new process had developed which projected forward and outward along the margin of the belly.

The limbs in ornithischians were never as efficiently developed for bipedal locomotion as those of the theropods, and the front legs never as much reduced or shortened as in those forms. It is probable that few ornithischians were entirely bipedal in habits; the front legs were very likely used in locomotion at times in even the most lightly built types. A great number of ornithischians, apparently representing several independent phyletic lines, reverted completely to a quadrupedal gait.

The ornithischians were, even at their earliest appearance, herbivorous forms. The teeth were invariably leaf-shaped, thin and with crenulated edges. In only a few known genera were there teeth in the front part of the mouth; in the vast majority this region was toothless and presumably covered with a horny beak. In the lower jaw the beak capped a median predentary bone, an element not found in any other reptilian group.

The Ornithischia may be divided into (1) the suborder Ornithopoda, bipedal forms; (2) the Stegosauria, quadrupedal forms with a double row of protective plates and spines down the back and tail; (3) the Ankylosauria, heavily armored, rather turtle-like quadrupeds; and (4) the Ceratopsia, horned dinosaurs.

Primitive ornithopods.—*Camptosaurus* (Figs. 179, 180), common in the late Jurassic and early Cretaceous of Europe and North America, may be used as a

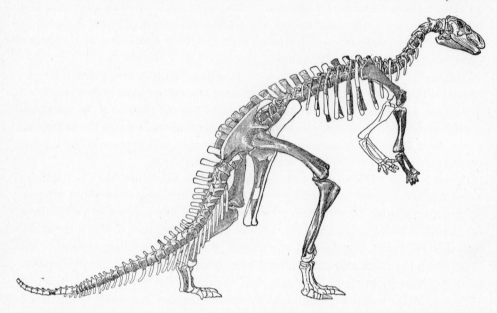

FIG. 179.—*Camptosaurus*, a Jurassic bipedal ornithischian dinosaur. (From Gilmore.)

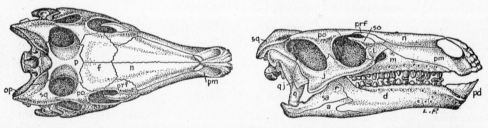

FIG. 180.—Dorsal and lateral views of the skull of the ornithopod dinosaur *Camptosaurus*. Skull length about 16 inches. For abbreviations see Figure 86. (After Gilmore.)

basis for the consideration of the ornithopods, the most primitive of ornithischian suborders; some of its contemporaries and predecessors were smaller and somewhat more primitive in structure but are less adequately known. Various specimens of this genus show a range in length of from 7 to 17 feet.

The skull was long and low and, as compared with saurischians of similar dimensions, rather heavy in its construction. An anteorbital opening was present but was of small size. The external nares were oval openings much larger than those of most reptiles and were nearly completely surrounded by the enlarged pre-maxillae; the nasals, which bounded them above, were also elongated and stretched back along the top of the skull to the level of the orbits. An extra element, a supra-orbital bone, lay in the upper anterior margin of the orbit.

As in sauropods (but in contrast with carnivorous dinosaurs) the jaws were rather short and did not reach the full length of the skull. The lower jaw was heavily built, and a powerful musculature is suggested by the fact that a coronoid process (seen elsewhere among reptiles only in placodonts and mammal-like forms) extended up beneath the edge of the cheek region of the skull for the attachment of the temporal muscles, while a process projecting back from the articular region was developed for the muscles opening the jaws. There was a well-developed pre-dentary bone in the lower jaw. The front part of the mouth was toothless and pre-sumably covered by a horny beak; the teeth were confined to a single row in the cheek region. Teeth, however, were still present in the premaxillary region in a smaller contemporary.

The normal position of the body was presumably the bipedal one, with the neck well erect, for the occipital condyle of the skull projected downward rather than backward, indicating that the head was held at right angles to the backbone. The neck vertebrae were opisthocoelous in *Camptosaurus*, as were the anterior trunk vertebrae as well in many more advanced forms. The arch of the back was stiff-ened in ornithopods by a latticework of tendons which (particularly in the duck-billed dinosaurs) were often ossified and thus preserved in fossil specimens.

The primitive ornithopods had the typical tetraradiate type of pelvis described above (Fig. 164a). The ilium was considerably lengthened; both pubis and ischium were greatly elongated and of subequal length, and the former bone had a long anterior process. The limbs in *Camptosaurus*, as in ornithopods in general, were somewhat more massive and shorter than those of saurischians of equal size; pre-sumably in these herbivores the demand for speed was not as great as in carnivo-rous types. The tibia never exceeded the femur in length; and, although the or-nithopods were digitigrade types, walking on their toes rather than the flat of the foot, the metapodials were but little elongated. In primitive ornithischians, as in saurischians, the fifth toe was functionless and the first was reduced in length (Fig. 181d). Claws appear to have been present, but were usually rather blunt.

The front legs were not as short as in most bipedal saurischians; in *Campto-saurus* they were about two-thirds the length of the hind limbs. All five digits were present but in even the most primitive of known ornithischians the outer two were reduced, much as in the early theropods (Fig. 181a). The terminal phal-anges of the manus in *Camptosaurus* and more advanced forms were broadened and presumably were covered by small hoof-like structures rather than claws. Very probably the front legs were used for support while feeding or walking slowly.

In contrast with the saurischians, the ornithischians were rare in the early days of dinosaurian history. There are no intermediate types known which serve to connect them with any of the better-known thecodont families. From the Triassic there are only two fragmentary specimens which appear to pertain to the present order, and we know almost nothing of ornithischians during most of the Jurassic. A number of forms, however, appear in late Jurassic and early Cretaceous deposits in both Europe and North America.

Hypsilophodon of the Lower Cretaceous Wealden beds of Europe is among the most primitive of known ornithopods. This animal was scarcely more than a yard in length, and some structural features suggest arboreal habits comparable to those of the tree kangaroo of Australia. Teeth were still present in the premaxilla in *Hypsilophodon*, and an interesting feature is the fact that there appear to have been two rows of small bony plates running down the mid-line of the back, much as in many thecodonts. There are several other incompletely known small forms of this general type in the Morrison beds of North America and even from the Upper Cretaceous. *Camptosaurus*, as described above, was a somewhat larger and more advanced form.

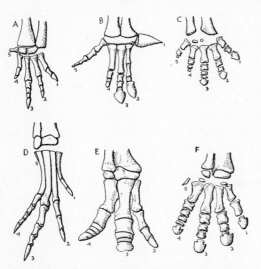

Fig. 181.—*A–C*, manus, and *D–F*, pes, of ornithischian dinosaurs. *A, D, Hypsilophodon. B, Iguanodon. C, F, Monoclonius. E, Trachodon. (A, D* after Hulke and Abel; *B* after Dollo; *C, E, F* after Brown.)

Best known of European ornithopods is *Iguanodon* of the Wealden, a form twice the size of *Camptosaurus*. Numerous remains have been found both in England and on the continent. The most striking of European dinosaur finds was the discovery of more than a score of individuals pertaining to this genus in the process of excavation of a Belgian coal mine. Seemingly a herd of these large reptiles had fallen into a crevasse in the older Carboniferous rocks and were buried there. An interesting specialization in *Iguanodon* is that the terminal phalanx of the short "thumb" is a stout but pointed spike of bone which may have been an excellent defensive weapon (Fig. 181*b*).

Duck-billed dinosaurs.—Most prominent of ornithopods in the Upper Cretaceous were the trachodonts, or duck-billed forms, which appear to have been almost universal in distribution and are represented in modern museums by numerous skeletons from Western North America. The skull structure in these forms varied enormously, but the skeleton was similar in all types. The length of the body averaged about 30 feet; and, while in many structural features they were similar to *Camptosaurus* of the preceding period, the build was somewhat heavier. In the pelvic girdle the main body of the pubis was much shortened. The hind foot (Fig. 181*e*) had but three toes, which terminated in hoofs rather than in claws. In the manus the fifth finger had disappeared and the first was reduced; the remaining three digits ended in small hoofs.

In several instances trachodont mummies have been discovered in Western deposits. These appear to represent specimens which had dried and mummified before burial, so that a natural cast of the skin has been preserved. This shows that the trachodonts were unarmored, although the skin was covered with a mosaic of small scales. A web of skin was present between the digits of the manus, and the same condition probably held true for the feet. This indicates that the trachodonts were amphibious in habits, probably feeding in swampy pools or about their margins. The hind limbs and the stout tail with long neural and haemal arches were probably effective swimming organs.

The skull in such types as *Trachodon* and *Edmontosaurus* (Fig. 182*a*) is readily comparable with that of a camptosaur despite some specializations. The toothless beak was flat but greatly broadened and was presumably covered by a duck-like bill. The nostrils had pushed far back along the facial region; they were completely surrounded by the premaxillae and nasal bones.

The teeth had remained simple leaf-like structures but had multiplied enormously in numbers to form a seemingly efficient grinding apparatus for tough vegetable food. In each jaw half there was not one, but several, parallel longitudinal rows of teeth closely pressed against one another, and beneath each tooth in these series its successors were already formed and ready to function. It has been estimated that in some cases there were as many as five hundred compactly arranged teeth in a single jaw ramus, giving a total of about two thousand teeth present in the mouth of a single animal.

The appearance of numerous crested types was a peculiar feature of trachodont history. In some forms, such as *Gryposaurus*, a peculiar swelling, a sort of "roman nose," developed above the external nares, here situated well up the forehead. In *Corythosaurus* we find a peculiar thin hollow dome-like structure capping the skull. This was shaped like a rooster's comb but formed of bone, the premaxillae and nasals being the elements concerned. In *Lambeosaurus* (Fig. 182*b*) this crest was present but smaller, and there was in addition a backwardly directed horn-like prolongation of the same bones; while in *Parasaurolophus* the crest was absent but the backward projection was a very long tubular structure, formed entirely by the premaxillae and nasals, which thus stretched the entire length of the skull.

The details of these peculiar crests and prongs are imperfectly known, but seemingly they formed part of some peculiar type of breathing apparatus; it will be noted that they were composed solely of the bones originally surrounding the nostrils. Quite possibly the crests were air-storage chambers which permitted the head of these amphibious forms to remain under water for some time while the animal was feeding. The backwardly directed "horn" of some of these forms is known to have contained a pair of tubes, and it is not impossible that these opened at the end to give the animal a means of breathing while the skull itself was totally immersed!

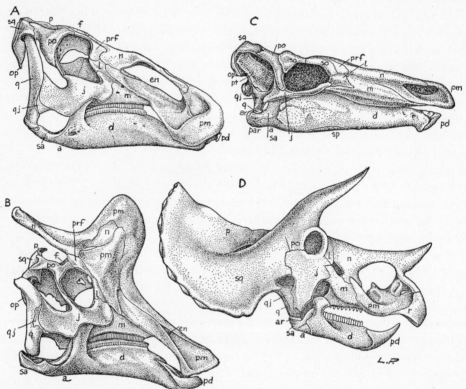

FIG. 182.—The skull in various ornithischian dinosaurs. *A, Edmontosaurus*, an Upper Cretaceous duckbilled ornithopod, length of skull about 3½ feet. *B, Lambeosaurus*, a contemporary crested duckbill, skull length about 32 inches. *C, Stegosaurus*, skull length about 16 inches. *D, Triceratops*, an Upper Cretaceous horned dinosaur, skull length (including frill) about 5⅔ feet. For abbreviations see Figure 86. (*A, B* after Lambe; *C* after Gilmore; *D* after Marsh, Hatcher.)

Trachodonts were exceedingly numerous in the late Cretaceous but died out completely at the end of the period. Perhaps their disappearance, like that of the sauropods, may be partly accounted for by continental elevation and the consequent drying of their marshy haunts. But not improbably a main cause for extinction may have been the contemporary gradual replacement of the Mesozoic plant types by modern types of vegetation to which they were not well adapted.

Stegosaurs.—Since the front legs were probably used to some extent in locomotion in most ornithopods, it would seem that reversion to a four-footed pose might readily occur. Such was the case in many ornithischian forms. But these slow-moving quadrupeds, left thus at the mercy of the carnivores, universally acquired some type of protective device in the way of armor or horns.

Earliest in appearance of quadrupedal ornithischians were members of the sub-order Stegosauria, of which *Stegosaurus* (Figs. 182c, 183) of the late Jurassic Morrison beds is the most familiar. This was a fairly large dinosaur, with a length of 20 feet or more. The skull was small, the front legs short, the back arched high over the long hind limbs. The most conspicuous peculiarity of this quadruped lay in the series of plates and spines arranged in a double alternating row down the

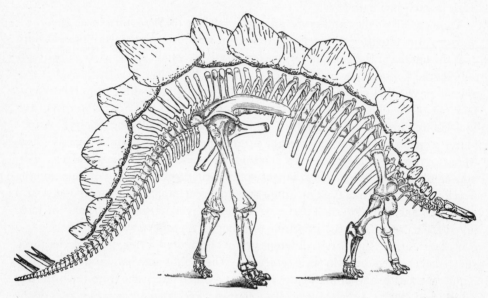

FIG. 183.—*Stegosaurus*, a Jurassic armored dinosaur about 18 feet in length. (Modified after Marsh and Gilmore.)

entire length of the neck, trunk, and tail. The tip of the tail bore two pairs of long spikes which may well have been effective weapons. The remainder of the body was protected by a series of flattened plates which projected nearly vertically above the back. These plates were roughly triangular in outline, with thickened bases which were presumably tied into the skeleton by tough ligaments. The largest plates lay above the hips, the size decreasing from this point fore and aft. These structures would seem to have afforded protection against an attack aimed from above on the backbone and spinal cord. But there is little indication of any armor over the remainder of the body, and it would seem that *Stegosaurus* might have been easily crippled by a flank attack.

The vertebrae were still somewhat amphicoelous or, at the most, had flat-ended centra. In the pelvis (Fig. 164b) the recurved ilium extended far forward; the pubis and ischium were both quite flat and broad. The hind legs were exceedingly long, giving the creature a very high hip region; the limb bones were straight with a columnar build. The front legs, on the contrary, were very short, seemingly an indication of the probable bipedal ancestry of the stegosaurs. All five digits were present in the manus, but the outer two were reduced; the foot was three-toed. The toes terminated in flattened hoof-like structures.

The skull was very small and long but low; here, as in the sauropods, the brain was exceedingly tiny and was vastly exceeded in size by a swelling of the spinal cord in the sacral region. There was but a single row of about two dozen small teeth in each jaw half.

A somewhat smaller and more primitive relative of *Stegosaurus* was *Kentrurosaurus* of the late Jurassic of East Africa. In this form plates were present only over the middle of the back and were comparatively small; spines were present not only on the tail but also over the anterior part of the body. It is thought that this animal may still have been somewhat bipedal in habits. A still earlier relative (in fact, one of the oldest known ornithischians of any sort) was *Scelidosaurus*, of the Lias (Lower Jurassic) of England, a reptile with a length of about 13 feet. Armor plates were present, but their exact arrangement is uncertain. Probably there were two rows of oval plates with longitudinal keels which in the shoulder region appear to have developed into longer spiny structures. The potentiality for the development of such a type of armor was inherent, apparently, in the ancestral ornithischians; dorsal dermal plates were present even in thecodonts, and we have noted their presence in the primitive ornithopod *Hypsilophodon*.

Ankylosaurs.—An entirely different group of armored forms, the Ankylosauria, succeeded the stegosaurs in the Cretaceous. These dinosaurs had an armor of quite a different nature and probably originated at a much later time from the primitive ornithopod stock. *Ankylosaurus*, *Palaeoscincus*, and *Nodosaurus* (Fig. 184) of the Upper Cretaceous are among the better-known members of the group. They have been termed, not inappropriately, "reptilian tanks," for with the exception of the turtles they were the best armored of any reptiles and show many analogies to the shelled glyptodonts of the Age of Mammals.

The body was broad and flattened, the proportions not unlike those of a "horned toad." The entire back was covered by a tough mosaic of larger and smaller bony plates which formed a seemingly efficient carapace. The front legs, which projected somewhat at the sides, were afforded protection by long spines extending outward from the shoulder region; and the tail was incased in rings of bone and sometimes armed with long bony spikes.

The skull was large and broad but rather short. The temporal openings had been closed over, and the flat skull roof so formed was further reinforced by an extra layer of polygonal bony plates. The dentition was weak, and the teeth were seemingly entirely absent in some cases. The limbs were short but stout. In the pelvic region (Fig. 164d) the ilium flared out widely over the hip region and, rein-forced by bony plates on its upper surface, effectively sheltered the thighs. The pubis had become reduced to form merely a part of the acetabulum.

In both the Lower and Upper Cretaceous of Europe have been found somewhat smaller armored types, such as *Acanthopolis*, *Struthiosaurus*, and *Polacanthus*, which seem to be rather more primitive members of the same group. There have been found in connection with them numerous plates and spines indicating the presence of a carapace somewhat similar to that of the large forms described above. The temporal openings were still present in the skull but were quite small.

Troödon of the Upper Cretaceous of North America was a small form with a broad, but peculiarly swollen, skull which shows resemblances to that of the ankylosaurs. With a skull of this sort was found a rather lightly built skeleton of

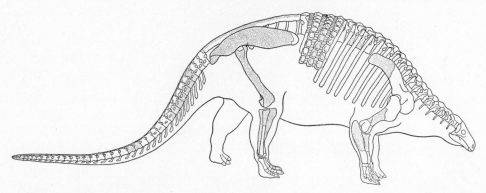

FIG. 184.—*Nodosaurus*, a Cretaceous armored dinosaur, 17½ feet in length. A few segments of the armor are indicated. (From Lull.)

bipedal types. This association has been disputed; if correct, it may be that *Troödon* was a late survivor of the bipedal stock from which the ankylosaurs have been derived.

Horned dinosaurs.—Last of the ornithischian groups in time of appearance were the horned dinosaurs, the suborder Ceratopsia. The entire history of this group is confined, so far as known, to the Upper Cretaceous; and almost all known forms are from North American deposits. *Triceratops* (Fig. 182d) and *Monoclonius* (Fig. 185) are representative forms. These were quadrupedal dinosaurs of moder-ate size, *Triceratops*, for example, ranging from about 16 to 20 feet in length.

The main point of interest in these forms is the cranial structure. The head ap-pears to be exceedingly large, making up a third or so of the total length of the body. But half of this structure is really not part of the true head region but a great frill of bone formed by extensions of the parietals and squamosals which has extended back over the neck nearly to the shoulders. This frill obviously must have afforded considerable protection to the neck region, a favorite point of attack by carnivores. Sometimes, as in *Triceratops*, this frill is a solid plate of bone; in other cases is found a probably more primitive condition in the presence of large openings on either side.

A second curious feature of the skull lay in the development of horns. The bony horn cores are not dissimilar in appearance to those of a modern bison, and indeed the first discovered specimen of ceratopsian horns was ascribed to that ruminant! In *Triceratops* there was a pair of large horns on the frontal bones over the orbits and a median horn over the nasal region. The degree of development of these horns varied considerably. In *Monoclonius*, for example, the nasal horn is very large and the frontal horns undeveloped; in another ceratopsian the reverse is true.

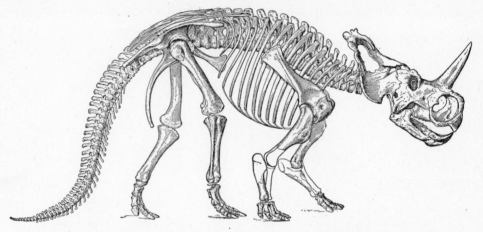

FIG. 185.—*Monoclonius*, a ceratopsian dinosaur. About 17 feet in length. (From Brown.)

In relation to the development of these defensive structures the remainder of the skull was much modified. The temporal openings had been reduced almost to the vanishing point. The nasal region of the skull was greatly enlarged, and the powerful beak was formed by a newly developed rostral bone comparable with the predentary in the lower jaw. Only a single row of teeth was present in the cheek region.

The vertebrae were platycoelous. The neck was short. In the pelvis (Fig. 164c) the main body of the pubis had been reduced to a short spike, although the anterior process of that bone was well developed. The hind legs were, as in all ornithischian groups, much shorter than the front and terminated in four stubby, hoof-capped toes (Fig. 181f) (the inner toe appears to have been reduced in some cases). All the digits were present in the manus, but the outer two were reduced (Fig. 181c).

Until recently nothing was known of the pedigree of these forms. But recent work in Mongolia has brought to light a small primitive ceratopsian, *Protoceratops*

(Fig. 186), of which there have been found numerous specimens ranging from un-hatched embryos to adults, as well as a number of "nests" of eggs. *Protoceratops* belies its name, for there are not the slightest indications of horns. In contrast, however, the frill was well developed although fenestrated. The structure of the frill in this form suggests that it originated primarily as a pulling-out of the back margin of the temporal region for the better accommodation of the jaw muscles

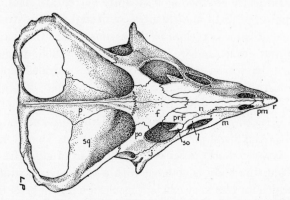

FIG. 186.—Dorsal view of skull of *Protoceratops*, a primitive ceratopsian dinosaur from Mongolia. Length of original, a young individual (including frill), about 14 inches. For abbreviations see Figure 86. (After Gregory and Mook.)

and that its function as a neck protection was a secondary one. *Protoceratops* ex-hibits a very primitive feature in the presence of teeth in the premaxilla.

No earlier stages in ceratopsian history are definitely known. But *Psittaco-saurus*, of an earlier Mongolian Cretaceous deposit, while a small biped which shows no indication of either horns or frill, has (as the name implies) a large beak and other features suggestive of ceratopsian affinities.

Numerous as were the horned dinosaurs in the late Cretaceous, they disappeared as completely at the close of the period as did the other dinosaur groups. Except for the stegosaurs, all of the major types of dinosaurs were still in existence in the closing phases of the Mesozoic; but by the beginning of the Cenozoic all had van-ished. The reign of the dinosaurs was over; the Age of Reptiles was at an end.

CHAPTER X

BIRDS

Although the birds are grouped as a separate vertebrate class, Aves, they are, apart from the power of flight and features connected with it, structurally similar to reptiles. Indeed, they are so close to the archosaurians that we are tempted to include them in that group, and we may perhaps preferably discuss them here.

Feathers.—Birds have been called by an old writer "glorified reptiles." Feathers are in reality almost the only distinctive feature of the class, for almost every other character can be matched in some archosaurian group. Large quills form the expanse of the wing, taking rise from the back of the forearm and from the fused fingers which form the distal part of the wing support. On the tail (which, as a bony structure, is very short) is set a spreading fan of stout feathers used as a rudder. The rest of the body is covered with a thick overlapping set of smaller softer feathers which forms a very efficient insulation for the retention of the bird's bodily heat.

But, although the feathery covering of birds seems to be in contrast with the horny scales which normally cover a reptile body, the difference is in reality not great, for feathers are only modified scales in which the edges have been frayed out into a large number of fine interlocking subdivisions.

Flight adaptations.—Unlike ordinary reptiles, birds are warm blooded; maintenance of a high body temperature is a necessity, for flight requires a great energy output over a long period. Also connected with this necessity, which demands a large oxygen supply and an efficient circulatory system, is the fact that the heart is divided completely into four chambers, with those receiving fresh blood from the lungs and leading it to the body completely separated from those taking used blood from the body to the lungs. This is a condition also found in mammals, but in birds the great arch of the aorta which carries the blood from the heart to the body passes over and down the right side of the chest, rather than the left, as in ourselves.

The nesting habit, contrasting with the usual lack of care of reptilian eggs, seems also to have been developed in connection with flight. The eggs must be kept warm for the maintenance of body temperature in the embryo. Further, while a young reptile makes its own way in the world from birth, the necessity of training for the complicated business of flight seems to have rendered essential the care and feeding of the fledglings in the nest. Brain and sense organs are much modified in relation to flight. Birds depend for their main contact with the world upon sight rather than smell (in contrast to reptiles and most mammals). The eyes are large, and sclerotic plates are commonly developed in the eyeball. The bird brain is vastly enlarged compared with that of a reptile; but this enlargement appears to result not so much in an increase in intelligence as in the development of centers having to do with sight, balance, and the delicate muscular co-ordinations necessary for flight.

Skeleton.—In the skeleton (Fig. 187) there are many modifications connected with flight. With the result of lessening the specific gravity, not only are there air sacs within the body connected with the lungs, but many of the skeletal elements, including portions of the skull and neck vertebrae, the humerus and femur, are hollow, air-filled bones.

Wings.—The anterior limbs as the actual supports of the flying organs have been much modified. There is a long, slim, backward-slanting scapula and a single coracoid attached to the edge of the sternum. There are slim clavicles which fuse in the mid-line to form the wishbone. The sternum is a large plate, usually with a great keel in the middle; and to it are attached the powerful chest muscles which exert the main propulsive pull on the humerus during flight (these muscles form the white meat of the chicken).

The humerus is short and stout in a typical modern flying bird, with a heavy process near the head for the at-

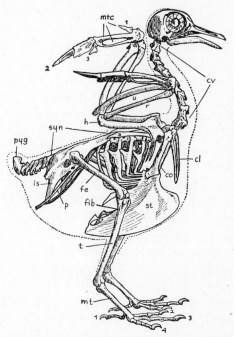

FIG. 187.—The skeleton of a modern bird. *cl,* clavicle; *co,* coracoid; *cv,* cervical vertebrae; *fe,* femur; *fib,* fibula; *h,* humerus; *il,* ilium; *is,* ischium; *mt,* metatarsus (including distal tarsals); *mtc,* metacarpals; *p,* pubis; *pyg,* pygostyle; *r,* radius; *s,* scapula; *st,* sternum; *syn,* synsacrum; *t,* tibia. Digits of manus and pes numbered. (Modified from *The Origin of Birds* by Gerhard Heilmann [copyright, D. Appleton & Co., New York], used by permission.)

tachment of the chest muscles. Both bones of the lower arm are well developed and rather long; but the ulna, which carries important wing feathers at its back, is the stronger. There are four carpals, the two distal ones fused with the metacarpals. We find a reduction in the hand rather similar to that in dinosaurs, for only the three inner fingers are represented; the fourth and fifth have vanished completely. Even the three remaining are not complete. The pollex is short and usually has but one phalanx. The second and third metacarpals are longer and fused together; the second finger usually has two free phalanges; the third, but one. Almost never do these fingers bear claws; they are buried in the flesh and function only as supports for the feathers.

Backbone.—As was presumably the case with its archosaurian ancestors the modern bird walks in a semi-erect position. The free vertebrae usually have a complicated but easily movable saddle-shaped set of central articulations in addition to the zygapophyses. The neck usually comprises about fifteen elongate vertebrae; the dorsal region, however, is very short, with only about six to ten vertebrae; and of these, several in front are usually fused as in some pterosaurs, with the effect of giving a stronger support to the muscles running to the wings. A number of posterior dorsals and the proximal caudals as well are joined to the original sacral vertebrae to make up an elongate synsacrum. The tail is short, for following a half-dozen small free vertebrae, the few remaining ones are fused into the pygostyle, which forms a support for the spreading tail feathers.

Legs.—The hind legs are reminiscent of the dinosaurs in their structure. The ilium is very much elongated and firmly bound to the synsacrum. As in dinosaurs, the acetabulum is perforated. The pubis passes down and backward, as in the ornithischian dinosaurs; there is, however, no forward branch, although this may be represented by a small process. The slim ischium passes down and back parallel to the pubis. There is usually no ventral union of the bones of the two sides, but the ischium is usually braced by an upward extension which meets the posterior end of the ilium, and pubis and ischium may join one another distally. The femur is short and stout, but the tibia is elongated, while the fibula is always reduced and attached to the tibia and may disappear completely. As in the dinosaurs, the main joint with the foot lies in the middle of the tarsus; the proximal elements are fused with the tibia, the distal ones with the metatarsal elements. The foot, too, is essentially like that of many dinosaurs. The three middle toes are well developed; the fifth has gone without leaving a trace; and the first, often reduced or absent, has only an incomplete metatarsal and usually is turned to the rear where it may aid in clutching a perch. The three principal metatarsals are firmly fused into a single element with separate distal ends for the toes which, as in dinosaurs, have the original count of 3, 4, and 5 phalanges, although the central one is the longest.

Skull.—The distinctly unreptilian appearance of the bird skull (Fig. 188) is due principally to the large orbits and large braincase; its structure is one easily derivable from the archosaurian type. Most of the sutures between bones become obliterated early in life, making the identification of elements difficult. The condyle, as in reptiles, is single; and there is no pineal opening. The orbits are very large and incompletely surrounded by bone. In front of the orbits (again as in dinosaurs) is an anteorbital opening; lacrimal, postfrontal, and postorbital are lacking. Behind the orbit is a seemingly single temporal opening which, however, is presumably the two diapsid openings fused into one by loss of the bar separating them. Because of the incomplete nature of the circumorbital ring, the temporal opening usually communicates freely with the orbit. The jugal and quadratojugal pass forward as a slim bar from the quadrate; this last element is freely movable on the skull, having loose joints with squamosal, pterygoid, and quadratojugal.

The palatal structure (Figs. 188, 189) is easily derivable from the archosaurian type. There is never any secondary palate, but the internal nares (and the external ones as well) are usually well back in the skull. Prevomers, palatines, and parasphenoid are present; but there are no ectopterygoids. In the higher birds the prevomers are small, the pterygoids short; the palatines extend back to a suture with the base of the braincase and have movable articulations with the pterygoids. This type of palate, termed "neognathous," is markedly different from that of rep-

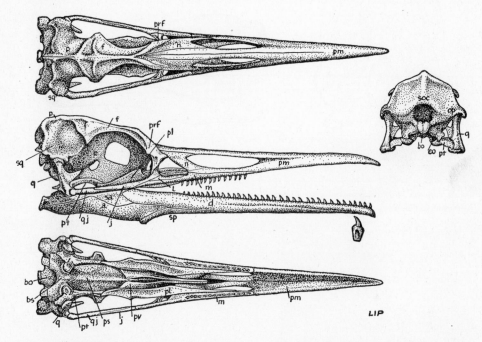

Fig. 188.—Restoration of the skull of the Cretaceous toothed bird *Hesperornis;* dorsal, lateral, ventral, and occipital views. Length of original about 4 inches. For abbreviations see Figure 86. (After Heilmann, *The Origin of Birds* [copyright, D. Appleton & Co., New York], used by permission.)

tiles. An intermediate type, however, the palaeognathous, is found in certain presumably primitive types such as the ostrich-like forms and in *Hesperornis*. This type is considerably closer to the reptile palate in that the prevomers are much larger, the palatines do not come in contact with the braincase, and the pterygoids are longer and have an immovable union with the palatines. In the lower jaw all six typical reptilian bony elements are present; and, as in most archosaurians, there is an external opening between angular and surangular. Modern birds are, of course, toothless, and the beak is covered with a horny bill.

Jurassic birds.—Modern birds show many reptilian features; but even closer to the archosaurians were the earliest birds, known only from two skeletons of animals about the size of a crow from the Jurassic lithographic stone of Germany. The remains, which pertain to two related genera, *Archaeopteryx* and *Archaeornis*

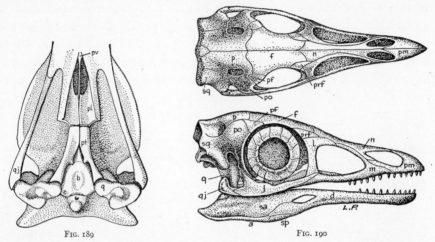

FIG. 189   FIG. 190

FIG. 189.—The palate of a neognathous bird, based upon *Phororhacos*, *b*, basicranial region; *qj*, quadratojugal; *pl*, palatine; *pt*, pterygoid; *pv*, prevomers; *q*, quadrate. (Data from Andrews.)

FIG. 190.—Attempted reconstruction of the skull of the Jurassic bird *Archaeornis*. Length of original about 2 inches. For abbreviations see Figure 86. (After Heilmann, *The Origin of Birds* [copyright, D. Appleton & Co., New York], used by permission.)

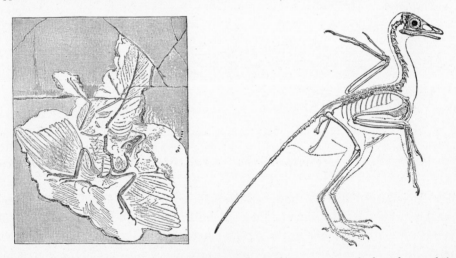

FIG. 191.—*Archaeornis*, an archaic Jurassic bird. Left, specimen as preserved, about ⅛ natural size. Right, restoration. (Left after Evans. Right after Heilmann, *The Origin of Birds* [copyright, D. Appleton & Co., New York], used by permission.)

(Figs. 190, 191), so closely resemble those of some of the smaller bipedal dinosaurs that they might well have been taken for reptiles were it not for the impressions of feathers which surround them on the stone slabs on which they are preserved.   The

skull, as far as it can be seen, was already rather bird-like, with an expanded braincase; and as in modern birds the sutures were mostly closed. However, well-developed teeth, implanted in sockets, were present in the jaws. None of the bones
were pneumatic. The backbone was quite simple in structure, for the centra had
the primitive amphicoelous character, and all were free to the sacrum, which included only five or six vertebrae. The tail still had the long structure of the typical
dinosaur; and the feathers, instead of being bunched at its tip, were arranged in
two rows along its sides. As would be expected, the hind legs were quite like those
of archosaurs, for they are but little changed even in modern birds. The wings
had not yet completed their transformation. The sternum was small and without
a keel, indicating weak pectoral muscles (incidentally, ventral ribs were still present). The front limb was still a hand rather than a wing, for the three fingers which
it possessed were very similar to those of the carnivorous dinosaurs; the metacarpals were quite separate, the number of joints was complete, and each finger was
clawed. It would hardly be suspected that this appendage was used for flight had
not the impression of wing feathers been found back of the ulna and manus. The
flying powers, however, must have been slight, for the spread of the wing was much
less than that of rather poor fliers, such as the pheasant, among modern birds.
These early forms probably were forest types and did little more than plane from
tree to tree or to the ground.

Archaeopteryx and Archaeornis were already definitely birds but were still very
close to the archosaurian reptiles in most of their structures, and it is obvious that
they were descended from that group. Their exact ancestors among the small
thecodonts which include the ancestors of all the later archosaurians are unknown.
The structure of the pelvis suggests that they arose from a stock close to that
which gave rise to the Ornithischia. There were, however, in the limbs many features suggestive of a parallelism, if not an actual relationship to the saurischian
dinosaurs.

There has been much discussion as to the origin of flight. The most generally
held theory is that the ancestral bird was a tree-dweller and that flight started as a
slight parachute effect as the "proavis" jumped from branch to branch, the developing wings breaking the fall on landing. A second theory is that the ancestors
were ground types and that the feathered arms and tail helped increase running
speed by acting as planes.

The early birds of the Jurassic were obviously sharply marked off from later
types by several features which are not met with in birds of later geological times.
These include the absence of pneumaticity, the primitive reptilian structure of the
wing bones, and especially the long reptilian tail. They are the only known forms
included in the subclass Palaeornithes.

Cretaceous toothed birds.—All other birds may be included in the subclass Neornithes, characterized by such features as a reduced tail with a fan of feathers

usually arising from a pygostyle, a well-developed sternum usually with a good keel, and the reduction and fusion of the fingers to the typical bird condition.

Our next glimpse of bird life is gained from the chalk beds of the Cretaceous, the only complete fossils being from the marine Niobrara formation of Kansas. This is in a sense unfortunate, for we know in consequence only sea birds, and the more generalized land types are almost unknown. Two forms are known from adequate skeletons. One, *Ichthyornis* (Fig. 192), was a small form about the size

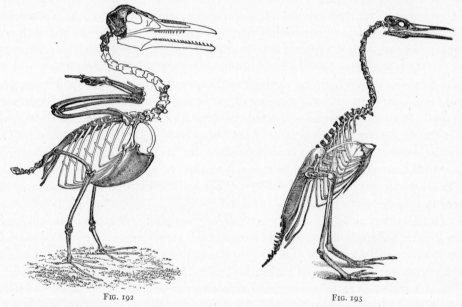

FIG. 192   FIG. 193

FIG. 192.—*Ichthyornis*, a small Cretaceous toothed bird with well-developed wings. About 8 inches in height. (From Marsh.)

FIG. 193.—*Hesperornis*, a Cretaceous flightless diving bird. About $\frac{1}{12}$ natural size. (The feet should be directed laterally.) (From Marsh.)

of a tern, seemingly rather similar to a tern in habits and not unlike it in many structural features. In *Ichthyornis* the vertebrae were still amphicoelous. The wings were highly developed and quite like those of later birds, and the sternum was large and keeled. Here, as in *Archaeopteryx*, however, teeth arranged in separate sockets were still present; and consequently we are dealing with a type intermediate between the Jurassic forms and modernized birds. A second and considerably larger bird from these deposits is *Hesperornis* (Figs. 188, 193). This remarkable form was probably much like the modern loon in habits, for it seems to have been a diving bird with powerful hind legs which spread out sidewise at the ankles to give a powerful swimming stroke. But this form had already degenerated in connection with its water life, for the wings had been almost completely lost, and of the arm bones there remains only a slender humerus, while the sternum was unkeeled. This form is the first of the many types of birds which have taken up a water life. As in *Ichthyornis* teeth were present, although here placed in a groove rather than in sockets; and also as in that form there were no teeth in the premaxilla; probably the horny beak was already in process of formation.

These two forms may be gathered together in a superorder Odontognathae, in contrast with all other post-Jurassic birds; and the two known types are certainly far enough apart, judging by avian standards, to be placed in two separate orders. The incomplete glimpse which they give us of Cretaceous bird life at least shows us that the radiation of the group must have been far under way at this time to have already produced such dissimilar forms.

Tertiary birds.—All later birds may be distinguished from those already discussed by several characters: loss of teeth; the fact that the two halves of the jaw, separate until then, are fused; and a union of the posterior end of the ischium with the ilium. Such birds we know had come into existence by the end of the Cretaceous; but our remains of them are very poor, and it is not until the beginning of the Tertiary that we have much information about them.

And even here, it must be confessed, our knowledge is none too good. Birds are mostly small forms, and their bones and skulls are very fragile; consequently we have but few remains, mostly of water birds. With mammals and reptiles we know more fossil forms than living ones; but among birds, as against about ten thousand living species, we have but four or five hundred fossil forms. Even these are for the most part known only from a fragmentary bone or so. This leads to great difficulties in attempting to work out the paleontological history of the group, for the birds of today, despite their varied plumage, are very similar to one another in their structure. They are divided into many orders; but the differences, for example, between a humming bird and an ostrich or an albatross are much less than those between a seal and a cat, or between a stegosaur and a duck-billed dinosaur, forms which are commonly placed in a single order. The different orders have in general no more differences between them than exist between families in other classes of vertebrates, and anatomically generic differences are so slight that fossils are very hard to place.

Palaeognathous birds.—Of all the post-Mesozoic birds, the most interesting from the paleontological point of view are the flightless forms, represented today only by the ostrich, rhea, cassowary, emu and kiwi, but including a large number of interesting fossil types. These forms, here grouped together with the tinamous as a superorder Palaeognathae, have a number of common features. Most of them, however, are associated with the fact that they have lost the power of flight; the wing skeleton in flightless forms is naturally reduced; the sternum, with weak pectoral musculature, lacks a keel; and the hind legs are powerful running organs. The tail not being used for flight, there is usually no pygostyle. The feathers, presumably in connection with the loss of flight, are usually soft and curly. But in addition some presumably primitive features are found in the lack of the distal fusion of pubis and ischium found in most modern birds and in the palaeognathous palatal structure described above.

Perhaps representing the central stock from which the ostrich-like birds have arisen are the tinamous (Crypturiformes) living in South America today and unknown as fossils. These forms have the appearance of quail or grouse but are quite different from those game birds in their structure. They are essentially ground-dwellers and take to the air only in an emergency. They are exceedingly poor fliers, having little control over their flight and seldom going more than a hundred yards or two. Tail feathers are reduced or absent, but unlike other ostrich-like birds, there is a keeled sternum.

Ratites.—From such a stock may have come the remaining, flightless members of the superorder, often grouped as ratites. Most familiar are the ostriches (order Struthioniformes), the largest of living birds. Now found only in Africa and Arabia, they are known to have existed in Eurasia in the Pliocene, while eggs of a gigantic ostrich-like bird have been found in the Pleistocene in that region; there are remains of a possible ancestor in the early Tertiary of Egypt. A distinguishing feature of the ostrich, in contrast to other flightless types, is the fact that there are only two toes—the third and fourth.

On the South American pampas the place of the ostrich is taken by the rhea (order Rheiformes) with a somewhat different structure (including a three-toed foot) and smaller size. Rheas are known from the Pleistocene, but farther back their history is quite unknown.

In Australia and New Guinea are the emus and cassowaries (order Casuariiformes). Among their distinguishing features is the fact that the wing is more reduced than in either of the last two orders, there being only one digit preserved and this projecting but little from the body. These forms were present in the Pleistocene of Australia, and there appears to have been a member of the group in India in the Pliocene.

Still more interesting were certain fossil types present in the Pleistocene of two island regions. In Madagascar lived a number of species of "elephant-birds" (*Aepyornis*, order Aepyornithiformes), some of them as large as an ostrich, with greatly reduced wings and heavy legs. There have been found numerous egg-shells, some with a capacity of two gallons. It is possible that these large birds lived until quite recent times, and their extermination may have been due to man.

New Zealand is remarkable today for flightless birds, for there are found not only the kiwi but numerous flightless rails and other ground-dwellers. In the past there were much larger birds, the moas (order Dinornithiformes) (Fig. 194), which ranged in size from species no larger than a turkey to creatures 10-11 feet in height. Of these birds numerous remains have been found, and even feathers have been preserved. There is proof from native camp sites that these forms were still alive when man reached the island and that they were used for food.

Quite different from the ostrich-like groups in size and general appearance are the kiwis of New Zealand (order Apterygiformes). These small birds are also practically wingless ground types with a very long bill and small eyes. They are known as fossils from the Pleistocene of New Zealand and apparently from Australia as well.

Origin of flightless types.—It has been suggested that these various groups of flightless birds are really primitive forms that have descended from some primitive types in which flight had never been developed. But upon reflection it is obvious that such a theory is highly improbable. Even in the Cretaceous the toothed *Ichthyornis* had already developed powerful wings, and such a form as *Hesperornis* was obviously specialized rather than primitive. Further, we know that in many other higher groups of birds certain types have also lost the power of flight; the dodo, the great auk, and the flightless rail of New Zealand are all types which cannot fly and have reduced wings but yet are surely descended from flying forms.

The clue to the matter seems to be that for many birds which seek their food on the ground flight is necessary mainly as a protection from enemies. With freedom from carnivores there is no reason why flight should be maintained. Almost all these flightless forms are so situated as to be practically free from enemies. There are no carnivorous mammals in New Zealand; until the arrival of man there

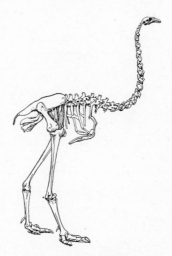

Fig. 194.—*Dinornis maximus*, a New Zealand moa. Height about 7 feet. (After Andrews.)

was no ground-living enemy of any kind for the moas and kiwi. In Australia the only carnivores before the arrival of man and his dog were comparatively harmless primitive mammalian types (marsupials). The island of Madagascar is almost devoid of carnivores. The ostrich and rhea are in a worse situation, but they live in open country where carnivores cannot approach without being seen, and the speed of these forms enables them to outrun their enemies. It would thus seem that birds are liable to return to a ground life wherever conditions permit. When flight is thus abandoned, most of the common adaptations seen in these forms, such as reduction of wings and tail and powerful legs, would naturally follow. The resemblances between the various ostrich-like types need not, then, really indicate relationship; and below are mentioned other large birds, now extinct, which in the past evolved along similar lines.

However, certain anatomical features, such as the palate, tend to show that these forms are really related. A probable suggestion is that there existed in the early Tertiary a group of birds in which teeth had been lost but the palate had remained primitive, and which had complete wings and a keeled sternum but were comparatively poor fliers. The living tinamou may be a comparatively unchanged relict of this primitive type. In parts of the world where favorable conditions existed these forms might have tended to stay on the ground, lose the power of flight, and develop into ostrich-like forms; in other regions they would have lost out in competition with better flying types and have disappeared.

There is little fossil evidence for such a history; but, as has been said, our knowledge of early fossil birds is very inadequate.

Neognathous birds.—All remaining birds may be grouped together as the superorder Neognathae. In these forms there is but seldom any tendency toward a flightless condition; almost always the wings and tail are well developed. As a common key character may be cited the fact that the palate is of the advanced neognathous condition described earlier.

As was noted above, the members of numerous living groups are essentially similar in internal structure, and the taxonomic position of many fragmentary fossil types is dubious. Nevertheless, it appears probable that most, if not all, of the avian orders were in existence in early Tertiary times; and some inadequately known Cretaceous types appear to be ancestors of the modern bird groups.

Below we shall merely list the more generally accepted orders of birds and here and there discuss a few of the more interesting fossil types.

1. *Order Colymbiformes.*—This includes the loons and grebes—diving birds which, in contrast to the penguins, use the hind legs rather than the wings (which are capable of normal flight) as swimming organs. The loons are confined to the Northern Hemisphere and are of moderate to large size. The webbed feet are unusual in that the first toe, usually placed at the back in birds, is turned forward with the other three. The grebes are smaller, with a cosmopolitan distribution; the toes are not connected by a web, but each toe has flaps of skin at the sides.

2. *Order Sphenisciformes.*—The penguins, although primitive in many respects, are in others among the most highly specialized of birds. The wings are totally incapable of functioning in flight but are powerful flippers used in swimming. The wing bones are flattened and fused into a compact powerful fin. The foot, too, is modified for swimming; it is webbed, and the metatarsal bones, usually fused in birds, have secondarily become more or less separated.

The penguins are confined to the Southern Hemisphere; and very numerous fossil remains, including some forms as large as a man, have been found on southern islands, many from beds supposed to be Eocene in age. An interesting suggestion has been put forward as to their origin. At the end of the Mesozoic most of the world's reptilian fauna died off; and while in most of the world mammals rapidly evolved and took their place, it is possible that members of this class did not reach the Antarctic land areas. We have seen that many birds tend to return to the ground in the absence of enemies, and the presumably empty Antarctic continent would have presented an excellent opportunity for such a venture. But while this region presumably had originally a temperate climate, at the beginning of the Tertiary must have begun, here as elsewhere, the gradual cooling of the polar regions. With the loss of flight, these birds could not escape by air from an increasingly inhospitable and isolated land. Escape into the sea, however, was possible. Such may have been the history of the penguins.

3. *Order Procellariiformes.*—Albatrosses and petrels. Strong-flying oceanic birds with long narrow wings and webbed toes.

4. *Order Pelicaniformes.*—Pelicans, cormorants, man-o'war birds, etc. Aquatic, often oceanic fish-eating forms. An early Tertiary type (*Odontopteryx*) is of interest in that the lost teeth were functionally replaced by a saw-toothed edge to the jaw.

5. *Order Ciconiiformes.*—Herons, storks, flamingos. Long-legged and usually long-billed wading birds, mainly fish-eaters.

6. *Order Anseriformes.*—Ducks, geese, swans. In general these are aquatic birds, good swimmers with webbed feet, but also good fliers; the bill is broad and flat.

7. *Order Falconiformes.*—The diurnal birds of prey: falcons, hawks, eagles, vultures. This order and that comprising the owls include the truly carnivorous bird types. The short stout curved beak and the strong sharply clawed feet are among the adaptations for seizing and tearing their prey. A Pleistocene vulture from the California tar pits, *Teratornis*, is the largest of all known flying birds.

8. *Order Galliformes.*—Contains not only the common fowl but also many familiar game birds such as pheasants, pea fowl, quail, grouse, and turkeys. The members of this group are, for the most part, predominantly terrestrial in their habits and are capable of only short flights. An interesting member of the order is the hoactzin (*Opisthocomus*) of South America, in which claws are present on the first two digits of the nestling's wing. This adaptation, which permits the young bird to clamber about the tree, appears possibly to be a reversion to the condition found otherwise only in the oldest fossil birds.

9. *Order Gruiformes.*—The order includes the rails, coots, cranes, bustards, and a number of other forms, mainly tropical. Many are wading birds, and at the best they are heavy fliers. The cariamas, existing South American running birds, are of some interest because of the possible relation to them of certain large fossil flightless types mentioned below. They are long-legged forms about 2 feet in height with short wings and are poor fliers.

Perhaps distantly related to the cariamas was *Diatryma* (Fig. 195a) of the Lower Eocene of North America. This was a gigantic running form about 7 feet in height with greatly reduced wings and powerful four-toed legs. Although in mode of locomotion it resembled the ostriches, its structure shows that it is probably related to the present order. The neck was short, the head large, and there was a massive overhanging beak.

The appearance of this great bird at a time when mammals were, for the most part, of very small size (the contemporary horse was the size of a fox terrier) suggests some interesting possibilities—which never materialized. The great reptiles had died off, and the surface of the earth was open for conquest. As possible suc-

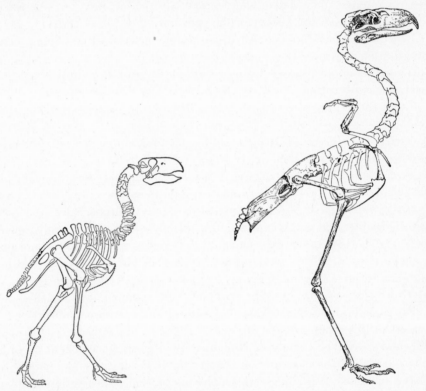

FIG. 195.—Left, *Diatryma*, an Eocene flightless bird about 7 feet in height (from Matthew and Granger). Right, *Phororhacos*, a giant flightless bird from the Miocene of South America. Original about 5 feet in height. (From Andrews.)

cessors there were the mammals and the birds. The former succeeded in the conquest, but the appearance of such a form as *Diatryma* shows that the birds were, at the beginning, rivals of the mammals.

Phororhacos (Figs. 195*b*, 189) and its relatives, large bird types apparently also related to the cariamas, were present in South America in somewhat later times (Oligocene and Miocene). *Phororhacos* was also flightless and with a large beaked skull as large as that of a horse. Its ability to survive on the ground was rendered possible by the fact that until later times in South America its possible carnivorous enemies were only comparatively ineffective marsupials related to the opossum.

10. *Order Charadriiformes.*—Plovers, snipe, sandpipers, gulls and terns, and auks. The more primitive types appear to have been shore-living forms, while a number of members of the group have become oceanic birds, good fliers and divers and often good swimmers. An interesting form, now killed off by man, was the great auk. This large bird had become flightless but could use its wings in swimming, thus paralleling in the Northern Hemisphere the penguins of the Antarctic.

11. *Order Columbiformes.*—The doves and pigeons, related to the last order. Most are good fliers; but several large forms inhabiting Mauritius and other islands in the Indian Ocean had, in the absence of enemies, become flightless types. These, best known of which was the dodo, became extinct following the settling of the islands.

12. *Order Cuculiformes.*—Cuckoos and road-runners, related to the parrots.

13. *Order Psittaciformes.*—The parrots, a well-defined group of forms which presumably have been tropical types throughout their history; in consequence little is known of them as fossils.

14. *Order Coraciiformes.*—A large and heterogeneous assemblage, often divided into half a dozen distinct groups. Included are the night birds of prey (owls, etc.), nighthawks, swifts, humming birds, kingfishers, woodpeckers, and many others.

15. *Order Passeriformes.*—The perching birds, the "highest" bird order, including a great wealth of types of small to medium size and comprising about half the bird population of the world. Almost all are good singers (in contrast with the usual simple cries of previous orders), while the powers of flight are usually quite highly developed. A characteristic feature is the perching type of foot, with the very large first toe directed straight back and opposed to the other three, giving an effective grasp on the limb.

Summary.—The history of birds may be summarized as follows: (1) the appearance in the Jurassic of primitive arboreal types with feathers and a feeble type of flight but with an essentially reptilian skeleton; (2) the development by the Cretaceous of birds which still possessed teeth but in which the skeleton was essentially like that of modern birds and flight well developed; (3) a primitive dispersal of birds in which teeth had been lost but in which the power of flight was comparatively poor; these are represented today only by a few ostrich-like flightless birds and the tinamous; (4) the appearance and radiation, by the beginning of the Tertiary, of more modernized orders which now make up the vast majority of the world's bird population.

CHAPTER XI

MAMMAL-LIKE REPTILES

The relatively late time at which the mammals took over the world's supremacy from the reptilian dynasties would lead one to think that the stock from which they sprang would have been one developed at a comparatively late date in reptilian history. This, however, is exactly the reverse of the true situation. The mammal-like reptiles, constituting the subclass Synapsida, were one of the earliest to appear of known reptilian groups and had passed the peak of their career before the first dinosaur appeared on the earth.

Primitive synapsids were already present in the late Pennsylvanian and took a leading rôle in the archaic reptilian radiation of Permian times. Although the central types were carnivores, herbivores and invertebrate feeding forms developed as well. A majority of all known Permian reptiles were members of this group; apart from the cotylosaurs, all other reptile stocks were at that time represented only by small and seemingly rare forms.

In the Triassic, however, conditions altered. The herbivorous types rapidly disappeared, and the carnivorous forms were supplanted by the developing dinosaur stock. The synapsids rapidly dwindled in numbers during the period and vanished at its close. Many millions of years were to pass before the mammalian descendants of the synapsid group were to rise to a position of dominance.

Since the various synapsid types cover the entire range of the vast structural gap existing between the ancestral reptiles and forms extremely mammal-like, it is hardly to be expected that there would be many diagnostic features common to all members of the subclass. The central stock of the group, as has been said, consisted of carnivorous types. There was in the dentition a tendency toward a differentiation of the tooth row, the development of varied types of teeth to subserve various functions—a tendency which reached its climax in the mammals. Synapsids tended, too, to improve the primitive clumsy limb structure found in the stem reptiles. Here, however, the trend was solely toward improvement in quadrupedal locomotion; there were (in contrast to the archosaurs) no bipedal tendencies.

The one diagnostic feature of the group was the presence of a single lateral opening in the temporal region, a condition found in no other reptilian stock. This fenestra was primitively situated low down on the skull and was of small size, with the postorbital and squamosal joining above it; it became enlarged, however, and extended upward to border the parietal in more advanced forms. The pineal opening persisted in almost every synapsid. There was never an otic notch of any sort; and the stapes ran out to articulate with the quadrate, as in the captorhinids. The eardrum appears to have moved far down the side of the head and was situated in many synapsids in a notch in the angular bone near the back of the jaw. There was comparatively little loss of cranial elements; but the dermal supra-occipitals (usually fused into a single bone) were, with the tabulars, pushed down onto the back of the skull, and in advanced forms the elements surrounding the orbits were reduced in number. The vertebrae were primitively amphicoelous, and double-headed ribs were present the length of the trunk. There were usually two coracoid elements in the shoulder (Fig. 196), a new posterior one in addition to the

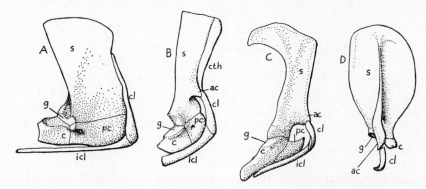

FIG. 196.—Shoulder girdles of synapsids and mammals. *A*, the pelycosaur *Ophiacodon*. *B*, the therapsid *Kannemeyeria*. *C*, the monotreme *Ornithorhynchus*. *D*, the marsupial *Didelphys*. *ac*, acromion; *c*, coracoid; *cl*, clavicle; *cth*, cleithrum; *g*, glenoid cavity; *pc*, procoracoid; *s*, scapula. (*A* after Williston, *B* after Pearson.)

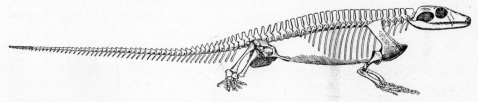

FIG. 197.—*Varanops*, a small Lower Permian pelycosaur about 2 feet long. (From Williston.)

anterior element which is alone present in most other reptiles. The dermal shoulder girdle was always retained and usually included a cleithrum in the older types.

The whole series should, perhaps, be divided into a considerable number of groups of equal rank. But it so happens that the primitive Lower Permian forms are found abundantly only in the Texas Red Beds of North America (more rarely in Europe), while the later Permian and Triassic types are almost exclusively from the South African Karroo series. This cleavage of the group may be used as a basis for a somewhat illogical but fairly convenient division into two orders—the Pelycosauria (or Theromorpha), primitive forms; and Therapsida, the advanced South African types.

Pelycosaurs.—The primitive synapsids are among the commonest animals found in the Red Beds of Texas, dating from late Carboniferous and early Permian times. One of the most primitive members of the group was *Varanops* (Fig. 197), a small form not a yard in length even including the well-developed tail. The proportions of this form were not unlike those of many lizards. In internal structure

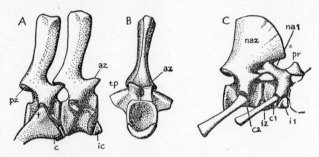

FIG. 198.—Vertebrae of a primitive pelycosaur, *Ophiacodon. A, B,* posterior cervical vertebrae, lateral and anterior views. *az,* anterior zygapophysis; *c,* capitulum of rib; *ic,* intercentrum; *pz,* posterior zygapophysis; *t,* tubercle of rib; *tp,* transverse process; *C,* atlas and axis, condyle of skull in dashed line. *c1, c2,* centra of atlas and axis; *i1, i2,* intercentra of the same; *na1, na2,* neural arches; *pr,* proatlas, a neural arch whose centrum is presumably fused into the basioccipital. (After Case and Williston.)

there were many similarities to the cotylosaurs from which these types had arisen. The limbs, while rather longer and slimmer than those of cotylosaurs, still resembled them in most features. The second coracoid element of the shoulder was variably developed in primitive pelycosaurs and was still unossified in *Varanops.* The neural arches of pelycosaurs (Fig. 198) were (as in most reptiles) narrower than those of the cotylosaurs, and the neural spines somewhat taller. Intercentra were still present throughout the column, and the old scales were still present on the ventral side as abdominal ribs in most pelycosaurs. The snout was rather

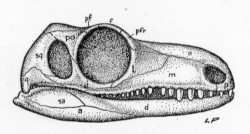

FIG. 199.—The skull of *Mycterosaurus,* a small pelycosaur, length about 3¼ inches. For abbreviations see Figure 86. (After Williston.)

long; the skull, rather taller and narrower than in the cotylosaur types. In *Varanops, Mycterosaurus* (Fig. 199), and other primitive pelycosaurs sharp-pointed teeth lay along the margins of the jaw in an almost uniform series. The pelycosaur palate (Fig. 200) was constructed on a primitive pattern not dissimilar to that of lizards and *Sphenodon,* with well-developed tooth-bearing flanges on the pterygoids.

A type somewhat larger and slightly more advanced than *Varanops* was *Ophiacodon* (Figs. 201, 196*a,* 198, 212*a,* 213*a,* 214*a*) of the Red Beds of New Mexico.

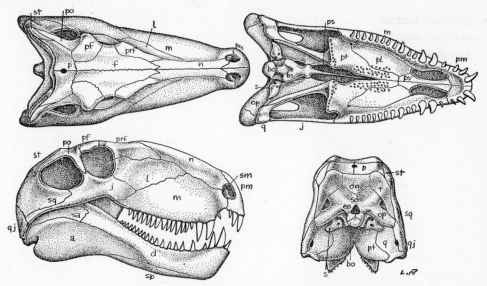

FIG. 200.—Skull of the Lower Permian pelycosaur *Dimetrodon* (composite). For abbreviations see Figure 86.

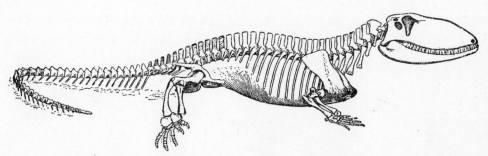

FIG. 201.—*Ophiacodon*, a pelycosaur from the Permo-Carboniferous of North America. About 6 feet long. (From Case and Williston.)

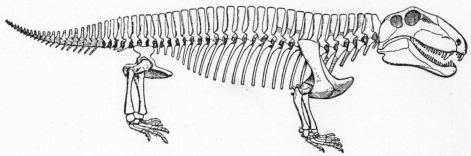

FIG. 202.—*Sphenacodon*, a large pelycosaur from the Lower Permian. Original about 6 feet long. (From Williston.)

The skull was very high and narrow, and the teeth at the front end of the maxilla slightly larger than their neighbors.

A stage further is represented by *Sphenacodon* (Fig. 202) from the same deposits. In this and the next form there had occurred considerable differentiation

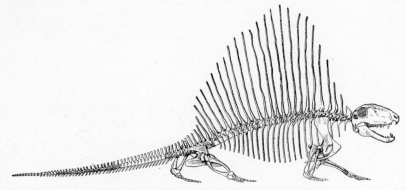

FIG. 203.—*Dimetrodon*, a long-spined Lower Permian pelycosaur. Original about 6 feet long.

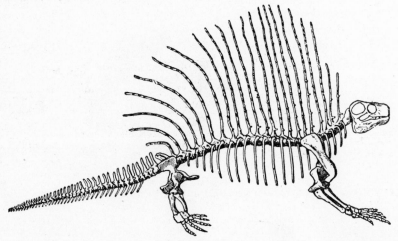

FIG. 204.—*Edaphosaurus*, a long-spined Lower Permian pelycosaur, about 6 feet long. (From Williston.)

in the tooth row. In the upper jaw there were nipping teeth of moderate size in front, then, following a gap in which fitted a large lower tooth, one or two enlarged stabbing canine teeth at the front end of the maxilla and a series of smaller cheek teeth. This foreshadows the tooth development seen in the related South African types and their mammalian descendants.

Dimetrodon (Figs. 200, 203, 209a, 210a, and 211a) was a creature in most respects quite similar to the last, although reaching somewhat greater size, the skull in some specimens being a foot and a half in length. It was one of the most common animals in the Texas Permian, where it was the largest and most powerful of carnivores. But we find a remarkable specialization which shows that *Dimetrodon* was off the main line of synapsid evolution, for the neural spines were enormously developed to extend a yard or so above the back. They were undoubtedly united by skin in life to form a sail-like structure; what function, if any, this served is doubtful.

There were other pelycosaur types besides these carnivores in the Red Beds. In *Edaphosaurus* (Figs. 204, 205), as in *Dimetrodon*, there were long spines; but here there were crossbars as well. This creature must have evolved the spines quite independently of *Dimetrodon*, for it differed markedly from that type in many ways, particularly in the dentition. The palate and inner side of the jaw were covered with a large number of small teeth; the food may have consisted of invertebrates of some sort. *Casea* (Fig. 206) was a small form which had little except the temporal opening to suggest association with the rest of the pelycosaurs. The body was stout and barrel-shaped; the skull, very short and broad with a large pineal eye. The palate was covered with a mosaic of small teeth which suggest a herbivorous diet.

These varied pelycosaurs were present only in the late Pennsylvanian and early Permian and, while abundant only in Texas, are known to have existed in Europe

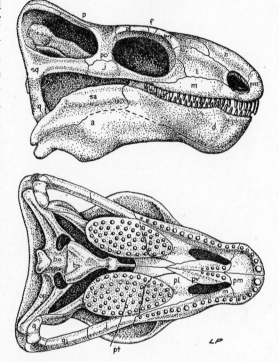

FIG. 205.—Skull of the aberrant pelycosaur *Edaphosaurus;* length of specimen about 6 inches. For abbreviations see Figure 86. (After Williston.)

and may have had a wide distribution (we know practically nothing of Lower Permian reptiles in other regions). *Dimetrodon* and most of the other Red Beds types were obviously specialized and soon disappeared. From some of the smaller and more primitive pelycosaurs, however, seem to have come the more progressive and more mammal-like synapsids which flourished for another full period.

Therapsids.—As members of the order Therapsida may be grouped the numerous mammal-like types which, best known from the richly fossiliferous Karroo beds of South Africa, flourished from Middle Permian to Lower Triassic times and survived in limited numbers until the end of the latter period. To this group be-

long all the carnivorous reptiles of the later Permian, as well as a host of herbivorous forms. So varied are these types that they are often considered to constitute a number of distinct (although closely related) orders.

Because of the wide radiation of the group, absolute diagnostic characters are
rare. The evolutionary trend of the main line of therapsid development may be
illustrated by a consideration of the structure of one of the later and more progressive forms.

Structure of Cynognathus.—*Cynognathus* (Figs. 207, 208) was a Lower Triassic
therapsid which we shall note later to be a member of the very mammal-like
cynodonts. This reptile was a rather lightly built and seemingly active four-
footed carnivore, with a maximum length of 4 or 5 feet.

FIG. 206.—*Casea*, a small aberrant Lower Permian pelycosaur, about $3\frac{1}{2}$ feet in length. (From Williston.)

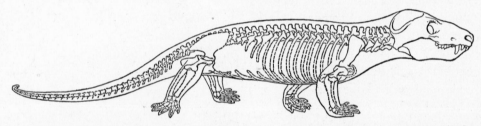

FIG. 207.—The skeleton of the Lower Triassic cynodont *Cynognathus*. About $\frac{1}{18}$ natural size. (From
Gregory and Camp.)

In the skull the pineal opening is small but still present. Many therapsids have
a small median bony element, the preparietal, associated with it; this is, however,
absent in *Cynognathus*. The temporal opening is much expanded and reaches up
to the parietal, the postorbital and squamosal no longer touching one another
above. The circumorbital series of bones has dwindled; the prefrontal and lacrimal
are small, and the postfrontal has disappeared. The quadratojugal is small and
closely attached to the equally reduced quadrate, and these two bones are rather
loosely connected with the rest of the skull. On the under side of the skull the most
obvious development is the presence of a secondary palate. The two prevomers
have fused into a single bar which sends up a process in the mid-line. Extensions
from the premaxillae, maxillae, and palatines have formed a flat plate extending
across below the old level of the roof of the mouth, so that a hard secondary palate
is formed with the internal opening of the nostrils passing backward through

the space above it. There are no longer any interpterygoid vacuities, for the two pterygoids have fused with each other to form a solid bar beneath the front end of the braincase; the parasphenoid is still present in its old position above and between them. The pterygoids have shortened and no longer extend back to the quadrates, although the epipterygoids above them may reach this far back.

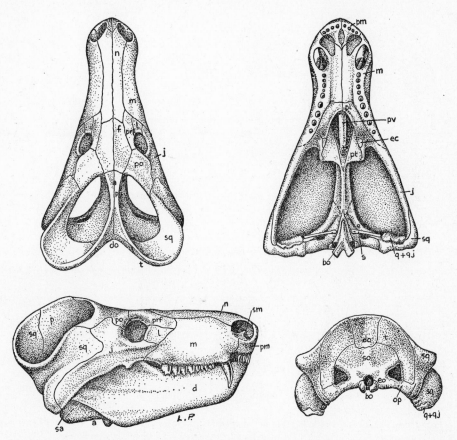

FIG. 208.—The skull of the cynodont *Cynognathus*, length of original about 18 inches. For abbreviations see Figure 86. (After Seeley, Broom, and Watson.)

The condyle has divided into a double structure in contrast with the primitive single condition. The occipital surface of the skull is a nearly solid plate made up of the combined occipital bones and the opisthotics together with the dermal supra-occipital and the tabulars above. In addition to the ordinary bones of the braincase the epipterygoid forms a flat plate applied to the side of the braincase in front of the proötic, and in the more anterior portion there appears to be a pair of ossifications corresponding to the mammalian orbitosphenoids. The stapes extends as a slim rod from the inner ear opening to the quadrate.

All the bones of the primitive lower jaw are present (Fig. 209c); but the dentary is greatly enlarged at the expense of the other elements, sending a large process backward and upward which nearly touches the squamosal.

The dentition is differentiated into a small number of nipping teeth, comparable with the human incisors in the premaxilla and front of the dentary; a large canine

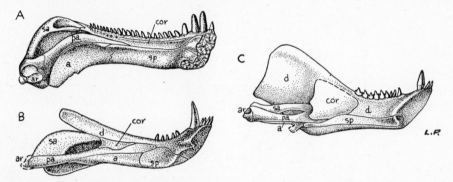

FIG. 209.—Jaws of synapsids, from the inner side. *A*, the pelycosaur *Dimetrodon*. *B*, the primitive cynodont *Cynariodes*. *C*, the cynodont *Cynognathus*. For abbreviations see Figure 86. (*A* after Williston, *B* after Broom, *C* after Broom and Watson.)

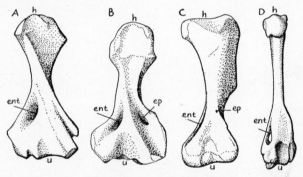

FIG. 210.—The humerus of synapsids and mammals: dorsal views. *A*, the pelycosaur *Dimetrodon*. *B*, the pelycosaur *Edaphosaurus*. *C*, a cynodont (? *Diademodon*). *D*, the Oligocene canid *Daphoenus*. *ent*, entepicondylar foramen; *ep*, ectepicondylar foramen; *h*, head; *a* articular surface for the ulna. (*C* after Watson, *D* after Hatcher.)

tusk; and a series of cheek teeth, most of them with several cusps. The teeth on the inside of the jaw and the palate have gone. While we do not know the conditions in *Cynognathus*, certain other therapsid specimens suggest that, instead of the teeth being replaced an indefinite number of times as in ordinary reptiles, these forms had but one set of replacement teeth. This corresponds to the mammalian condition where we find the milk teeth followed by a permanent set to which there are no further successors.

Intercentra have disappeared from the backbone, although the centra are still amphicoelous. There are still freely movable double-headed ribs all the way from the neck to the base of the tail.

The limbs in advanced therapsids are greatly changed from the primitive sprawling position. The elbow has been moved back and the knee forward, so that the legs tend to be more underneath the body, making support easier. Associated with this are many changes in the musculature and in the shape of many of the

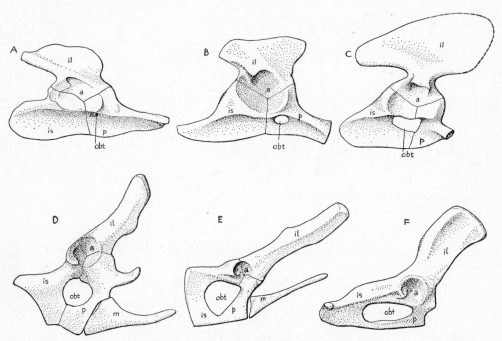

FIG. 211.—Pelvis of synapsids and mammals. A, the pelycosaur *Dimetrodon*. B, the gorgonopsian *Lycaenops*. C, the cynodont *Cynognathus*. D, the monotreme mammal *Ornithorhynchus*. E, the marsupial *Didelphys*. F, the Miocene canid *Daphoenodon*. *a*, acetabulum; *il*, ilium; *is*, ischium; *m*, marsupial bone; *obt*, obturator foramen—enlarging to form a fenestra in therapsids and mammals; *p*, pubis. (B after Broom, C after Gregory and Camp, F after Peterson.)

bones. The shoulder girdle (Fig. 196b) still consists of a dermal girdle including a stemmed interclavicle and clavicles (the cleithrum has disappeared) and a primary girdle of scapula and two coracoid elements. The front edge of the scapula is turned out (the beginning of the mammalian spine) with the clavicle attaching to the projecting spine at the lower end of the ridge. In the pelvis (Fig. 211c) the ilium extends forward rather than back, as primitively, in relation to a changed position of the muscles, and is attached to an increased number of sacral ribs. The pubis and ischium have shifted toward the back (also in relation to muscular changes), and a circular opening has appeared between and partially separating them. The femur (Fig. 212b) has developed a head at the side rather than the end of the bone in relation to its forwardly rotated position, and on the outer sides is a large trochanter for muscles which come from the ilium and aid in its backward push. The toes are all, except the first, of nearly equal length, in correlation with the more directly fore-and-aft motion of the limbs; and each has but three functional joints. But while this foreshadows the mammalian condition, the old rep-

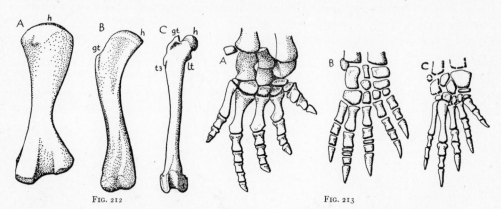

FIG. 212.—The femur in mammal-like reptiles and mammals. *A*, the pelycosaur *Ophiacodon*. *B*, a cynodont. *C*, the Oligocene canid *Daphoenus. gt*, greater trochanter; *h*, head of femur; *lt*, lesser trochanter; *t3*, third trochanter. (*A* after Case and Williston, *B* after Watson, *C* after Hatcher.)

FIG. 213.—The manus in mammal-like reptiles. *A*, the pelycosaur *Ophiacodon*. *B*, the gorgonopsian *Lycaenops*. *C*, the bauriamorphan *Ericiolacerta*. (*A* after Case and Williston, *B* after Broom, *C* after Watson.)

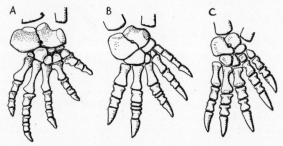

FIG. 214.—The pes in mammal-like reptiles. *A*, the pelycosaur *Ophiacodon*, *B*, the gorgonopsian *Lycaenops*, *C*, the therocephalian *Whaitsia*. (*A* after Case and Williston, *B, C* after Broom.)

tilian phalangeal formula of 2–3–4–5–3 still persists in *Cynognathus* and related types, for rudiments of the superfluous phalanges are still present in the third and fourth toes (Figs. 213*b*, 214*b*).

The skeleton of such a reptile approaches in many features that of the mammals. It would be of interest to know whether these forms resembled mammals as much in other features; but we know almost nothing of other organ systems, except that the brain was still small and apparently reptilian in organization. The warm-blooded condition of mammals is seemingly correlated with their active mode of life. Activity seems to have been a keynote in the development of these carnivorous therapsids, and it is not impossible that this physiological change had already begun in them. A cold-blooded reptile may cease breathing for a time without harm, but not a mammal. The secondary palate of mammals seems to be an adaptation preventing interference with breathing during mastication; the presence of this structure in advanced therapsids is suggestive. Whether hair was already beginning to replace scales is, of course, quite unknown. Nor have we any knowledge of reproductive processes, but since the most primitive living mammals are still egg-laying types, this was presumably also the case in *Cynognathus*. The nursing habit seems to have been earlier in appearance, but whether early enough to have been present in advanced therapsids cannot be guessed.

Primitive therapsids.—Having seen in *Cynognathus* one of the advanced types of the mammal-like reptiles, we may retrace our steps to review the early stages

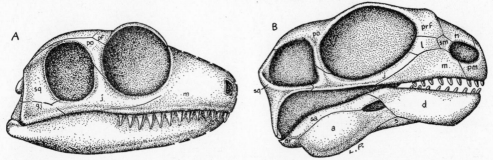

FIG. 215.—The skull of some primitive therapsids. *A, Anningia,* skull length about 3 inches. *B,* the dromasaur *Galepus,* length about 1½ inches. For abbreviations see Figure 86. (After Broom.)

in their history and the varied side branches that sprang from the therapsid stock.

Anningia (Fig. 215*a*) was a tiny form which is unfortunately known only from a single incomplete skull. Found in rocks of Middle Permian age in South Africa, it is one of the oldest and seemingly the most primitive of therapsids. In many respects it resembled the smaller pelycosaurs. The teeth were of nearly equal length throughout, the dentary was not very large, the quadratojugal and quadrate still well developed, the postfrontal present, postorbital and squamosal still met above the temporal opening, and the condyle was single. The presence of a separate pre-parietal bone in the region of the pineal shows that we are dealing with a true, although primitive, therapsid.

There are several small Permian types from South Africa grouped as the Dromasauria which appear to represent a very early sterile side branch of the therapsid group. The skull of such a dromasaur as *Galepus* (Fig. 215*b*) exhibits many of the primitive features of *Anningia,* such as, for example, the small temporal opening.

The teeth show no sign of differentiation and were even lost in one genus. The postcranial skeleton (unknown in *Anningia*) was in these little reptiles still quite primitive and similar to that of the pelycosaurs in some respects. But there was a single very progressive feature, in that the phalangeal formula had already been reduced to that of 2–3–3–3–3.

Dinocephalians.—The earliest group of therapsids to attain prominence were the "giant heads" of the suborder Dinocephalia. These were large forms known mainly from the Middle Permian of South Africa but also present in the Ural region of Russia. The name refers to a peculiar dome-like bony thickening of the roof of the head. The skull, except for this peculiarity, was rather primitive and pelycosaur-like in such features as the single condyle, lack of a secondary palate,

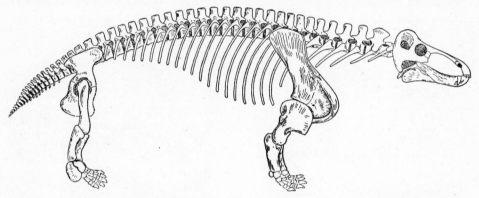

FIG. 216.—The skeleton of the dinocephalian *Jonkeria*. Length of original about 14 feet. (After Broom.)

the primitive paired prevomers, and a fairly small dentary. However, a number of therapsid changes had occurred, such as the fusion of the pterygoids and reduction of the quadratojugal. The limbs were turned well in toward the body, but the girdles were still quite primitive. The phalangeal formula is unknown but was probably the primitive one.

There are two main types of giant heads. One, typified by *Titanosuchus*, *Dinophoneus* (Fig. 217*b*), and *Jonkeria* (Figs. 216, 217*a*), were carnivores with a differentiated dentition including large canine tusks; the second type, to which belonged *Tapinocephalus*, *Moschops*, *Delphinognathus* (Fig. 217*c*), and other forms, were herbivores with small teeth. Both types are fairly common in the Middle Permian Karroo beds. Almost all were large forms; dinocephalians were the largest of mammal-like reptiles, and indeed the largest known Permian animals of any sort, being only rivaled in size by the contemporary pareiasaurs. These last probably furnished the main food supply of the carnivorous dinocephalians, while the herbivores probably competed with the pareiasaurs for plant food. Most of the dinocephalians were off the line leading to later therapsid types, but a few of the smaller carnivores appear to have departed little from the central stock.

Dicynodonts.—Most aberrant but most successful temporarily of therapsids were the "two-tuskers" of the suborder Dicynodontia. They appeared in the Middle Permian, and in late Permian and earliest Triassic times were by far the commonest of all reptiles. They were present not only in South Africa but in the Upper Permian in Russia and Scotland, and there are even fragments of such forms in Triassic deposits in both Asia and North America.

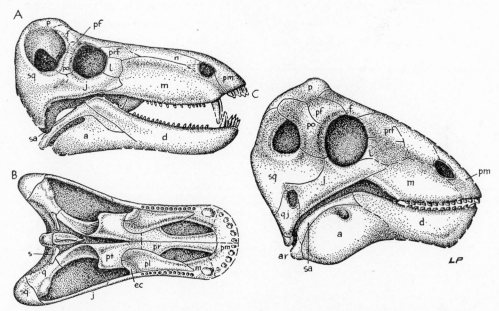

Fig. 217.—The skull of dinocephalians. *A*, lateral view of *Jonkeria*, skull length about 29 inches. *B*, palatal view of *Dinophoneus*, skull length about 28 inches. *C*, lateral view of skull of *Delphinognathus*, length about 15 inches. For abbreviations see Figure 86. (After Broom.)

The dentition was peculiar. In a few of the more primitive types there were small molars; but in most cases there remained only the tusk-like upper canine teeth, and even these were apparently restricted to the males in most genera. The jaws obviously were covered by a horny beak similar to that of turtles.

The skull was considerably specialized, rather broad and flat, with an odd arched construction of the cheek region. There was an incipient secondary palate, and other advanced features were present. The postorbital and squamosal, however, still met above the temporal opening. The postcranial skeleton was of an advanced character and resembled that of such a form as *Cynognathus* in many features, although the limbs were rather short and stubby. Here the phalangeal formula was reduced to the mammalian count of 2–3–3–3–3.

The dicynodonts appear to have been marsh-dwelling herbivores; one type, *Lystrosaurus*, appears to have been somewhat aquatic in habits, and has been called a "reptilian seal." They ranged in size from species with a skull not more than an inch or two in length to types with a skull 2 feet long.

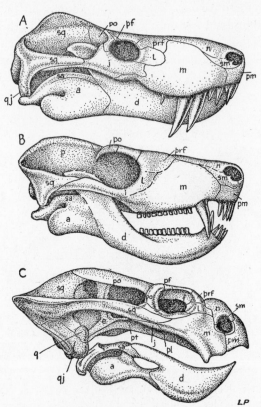

Many of the varied Permian types are included in the genus *Dicynodon* (Fig. 218c), with more than fifty described species. *Kannemeyeria* (Fig. 219) was a large Triassic survivor. These harmless plant-feeders seem to have held out well against their carnivorous relatives but disappeared with the advent of large flesh-eating archosaurians in later Triassic times.

Theriodonts.—The typical therapsids are the forms comprising the suborder Theriodontia; *Cynognathus* was one of the more progressive members of the group. Like that type, theriodonts were all active flesh-eaters of medium or small size with a differentiated dentition and a rather mammal-like limb structure. Except for a few types from the Upper Permian of Russia, the known remains of these forms are all from the African Karroo series, where they first appeared in the Middle Permian

FIG. 218.—Therapsid skulls. *A, Lycosuchus*, a therocephalian, skull length about 11 inches. *B, Bauria*, a bauriamorph, skull length about 6 inches. *C, Dicynodon kolbei*, a dicynodont. For abbreviations see Figure 86. (After Broom.)

and continued to be abundant until the Lower Triassic.

During their history there were many advances and differentiations among the theriodonts. Some four groups may be distinguished, forming two evolutionary series, the Gorgonopsia leading to the Cynodontia, the Therocephalia leading to the Bauriamorpha.

The gorgonopsians, such as *Scymnognathus* (Fig. 220), were perhaps the most primitive of the theriodonts and were common in Middle and Upper Permian times. There were many primitive features in the group. The postorbital and squamosal still met above the temporal opening; the postfrontal bone was still present; there was no secondary palate, although the prevomers had fused into a single bar; the condyle was still single; the dentary, although large and with an ascending branch, does not greatly exceed the other elements in size; the post-cranial skeleton was somewhat more primitive and more heavily built than in the cynodonts; the phalangeal formula was still 2–3–4–5–3, although the "extra" joints were small.

These forms led directly to the Cynodontia; *Cynognathus* described above was a typical cynodont and illustrates the advances made in this group over their more primitive relatives in the construction of the palate, jaws, and other features.

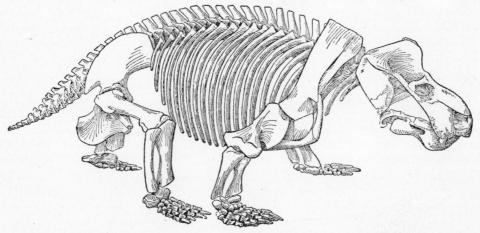

FIG. 219.—The skeleton of *Kannemeyeria*, a Lower Triassic dicynodont, length about 6 feet. (From Pearson.)

These forms were exclusively Triassic in age and were the dominant carnivores of the earlier part of that period. There was considerable variation in size, the smallest cynodont being not much bigger than a rat, the largest the size of a wolf. The posterior, or cheek, teeth of cynodonts varied widely. In contrast with most other therapsids, the teeth usually had several cusps, and in some cases a grinding surface or crown had developed much as in mammals.

The therocephalians (Fig. 218a) were contemporaries of the gorgonopsians and resembled them in many features. But they were already in advance of either gorgonopsians or cynodonts in one respect, for they had attained the mammalian phalangeal formula of 2–3–3–3–3 (Figs. 213c, 214c). A pecularity of these forms lay in the presence of openings perforating the palate.

Bauria (Fig. 218b) and other related forms in the early Triassic constituting the Bauriamorpha had become as advanced as the cynodonts and indeed even more so in some features, for in some members of this group the bar behind the orbit had broken down, as in primitive mammals, and the pineal eye had disappeared. However, these forms were less progressive than the cynodonts in other regards, such as the comparatively large size of many of the bones of the back of the jaw. The

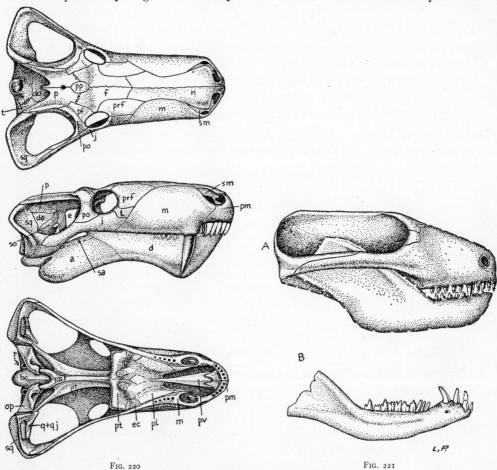

FIG. 220   FIG. 221

FIG. 220.—Dorsal, lateral, and ventral views of the skull of the gorgonopsian *Scymnognathus;* length of original about 1 foot. For abbreviations see Figure 86. (After Watson and Broom.)

FIG. 221.—Advanced therapsids. *A*, skull of a late Triassic ictidosaurian from South Africa. *B*, jaw of *Dromatherium* from the late Triassic of North Carolina; length of original about $1\frac{1}{2}$ inches. (*A* after Broom, *B* after Simpson.)

structure of the palate indicates that these forms had evolved from therocephalians and that the advanced features which they share with cynodonts had been evolved independently in the two groups.

Late therapsid tpyes.—The more progressive theriodonts flourished in the early Triassic but disappeared with the advent of carnivorous dinosaurs, and very few therapsid remains are known from late Triassic deposits. Among the last of the therapsids, however, were some small forms grouped as the Ictidosauria which appear to have been still closer to the mammalian type of organization. They are as yet known only from a few fragmentary specimens from the Upper Triassic of South Africa. Apparently in these little reptiles, as in some of the bauriamorphans, the pineal opening had been lost and the bar behind the orbit had broken down; and further, not only the postfrontal, but the prefrontal and postorbital bones as well, had disappeared from the circumorbital series of bones, leaving the skull roof in an essentially mammalian condition (Fig. 221a). A secondary palate had developed, as in other advanced therapsids, but was here much more like that of mammals. Practically the only diagnostic reptilian character remaining was the fact that some of the extra jaw elements (angular, surangular, articular, and prearticular) were present, although exceedingly small. While the postcranial skeleton is poorly known, it appears to have been very mammal-like. These forms may very well have been close to the actual ancestors of most of the mammalian groups; of mammals only the multituberculates are known from deposits of such an early age.

Also close to the mammals appear to have been *Dromatherium* (Fig. 221b) and *Microconodon*, known only from two jaws from the Triassic of North Carolina. These jaws are about an inch in length and, as preserved, consist of a dentary bone alone. There were three incisors, a canine, and about ten cheek teeth. The teeth of the molar series had elongated narrow crowns with a large central cusp and accessory cusps on the slopes of the main one. It was long held that these forms were true mammals with but a single bone in the jaw rather than the seven reptilian elements; and this belief was reinforced by the fact that there were thought to be two roots to the molar teeth. Recently, however, it has been shown that the roots were not yet truly divided and that, although the dentary was large, there were very likely other jaw elements present in life. These poorly known forms were perhaps therapsids of a very advanced type.

Synapsid history.—In these varied synapsid types we span nearly the entire evolutionary gap between a primitive reptile and a mammal. In the skull the more primitive pelycosaurs had few features (apart from the small lateral temporal opening) not present in cotylosaurs, but in one group or another of the more advanced therapsids almost every diagnostic feature of mammals had been attained. A considerable number of bony elements had been lost, the pineal eye had disappeared, the quadrate and quadratojugal were much reduced, the temporal opening had expanded, and the bar behind the orbit sometimes disappeared. The occipital condyle was double in higher types as in mammals, and the palate had evolved strongly in a mammalian direction. The jaw elements were never reduced to the dentary alone, as in a mammal; but the other elements had become quite small. The teeth were differentiated into incisors, canines, and molars, much as in mammals; and there are indications that there may have been a mammalian type of tooth succession.

The limb skeleton, too, approached the mammalian condition (cf. Figs. 196, 210–14). The pelycosaurs still had the primitive type of limb with the proximal elements held out horizontally from the body. In the higher therapsids the limbs had swung around practically into the fore-and-aft position of the mammals and gone through a series of structural changes which was a logical consequence of this changed posture, these changes including such features as the development of a spine and acromion on the scapula, a forward growth of the ilium, the development of an opening between pubis and ischium, and the reduction of the phalanges in some types to a formula of 2–3–3–3–3. The skeleton of the advanced therapsids was almost as mammal-like as that of such a primitive mammal as the duck-bill of Australia.

Just which therapsids were the ancestors of the mammals is a question which we cannot surely answer. We have noted that such mammalian characters as the reduction in phalanges and formation of a secondary palate have been independently acquired in several therapsid groups. The cynodonts are sometimes thought to be mammalian ancestors, but there are minor features which tend to debar them from such a position. Some of the poorly known later Triassic forms now seem to offer still closer approach. These, too, may eventually prove to be somewhat off the line of descent. But although the details of the phylogenetic history are still uncertain, the therapsid ancestry of mammals seems established.

CHAPTER XII
THE STRUCTURE OF MAMMALS

We now enter upon a consideration of the mammals, the most intelligent and the most successful of land vertebrates. Arising in the Triassic from the mammal-like reptile stock, the group remained comparatively unimportant until the extinction of the great reptiles at the end of the Mesozoic. From that time on, however, mammals increased rapidly in numbers and diversification, so that now they include the greater part of the animals with which one is ordinarily familiar. They not only inhabit the surface of the earth but have invaded the air (bats) and returned to the seas (whales, seals, sireneians). In size they range from tiny shrews and mice to certain of the whales which are the largest of all known animals, exceeding even the greatest dinosaurs in size. Mammals are of particular interest to man, not only because the group includes many of his animal friends and enemies and much of his food supply, but also because he himself is a member of this group.

Diagnostic characters.—Many of the diagnostic features of mammals lie in their soft anatomy and hence cannot be used in paleontology. As the name implies they alone among vertebrates suckle their young after birth. There is thus a period of infancy and "education" which, it would seem, enables mammals to make better use of their finer physical and mental equipment. The young are, except in the most primitive forms, born alive, the shell-less egg being retained within the mother's uterus. The yolk dwindles, and in most cases a connection, the placenta, is formed by which the young can be nourished by transfusion between the blood streams of the mother and the young. Mammals are warm blooded, that is, they maintain a high body temperature with a consequent potentiality of maintenance of continuous activity; the presence of hair (apparently originally developed between the scales) aids in the preservation of the body heat. Horny scales are only rarely present; superficial dermal ossifications are uncommon. There is a four-chambered heart, as in birds, with a perfect separation of the pure and impure blood, and only one arch of the aorta; but, whereas in birds the arch is the right, here it is the left.

The brain is much enlarged (Fig. 222), the growth of the higher centers in the cerebral hemispheres being the most characteristic change; the hemispheres grow upward and backward, cover the midbrain and often overlie the cerebellum, and usually further increase their area of superficial gray matter by a folding of the surface. In the brains of the higher mammals the entire dorsal surface of the cerebrum represents a new outgrowth and infolding of nervous tissue, collectively called the "neopallium" or "new brain"; this has overgrown the old brain, forming a "super control" system that dominates the old vertebrate brain beneath it. By its means memory is greatly enriched and the animal is enabled to make a more or less intelligent choice between conflicting sensory stimuli, so that it can be guided by memory of past reactions and of their results.

While here we must naturally pay chief attention to the skeleton, it must not be forgotten that the advances made in this system constitute but one of the many expressions of the high development of the mammals. Activity guided by intelligence is the keynote of mammalian success, contrasting with the sloth and stupidity of reptiles. The warm-blooded condition has rendered possible the activity without which the many skeletal adaptations of mammals would be useless; the mammalian mode of development has rendered possible the elaboration of the complicated brain structure.

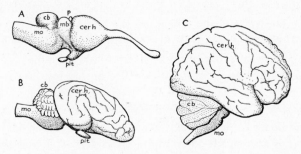

Fig. 222.—Side views of the brain of *A*, a reptile, *B*, a typical mammal (dog), and *C*, man, to show the increase in size of the cerebral hemispheres. *cb*, cerebellum; *cerh*, cerebral hemispheres; *mb*, midbrain; *mo*, medulla oblongata; *p*, pineal organ; *pit*, pituitary gland.

Among osteological characters which are usually considered as diagnostic are: the double condyle of the skull; the presence of epiphyses on certain, at least, of the bones; only one element (dentary) on each side of the lower jaw, this element articulating with the squamosal; the tympanic membrane supported by a tympanic bone; the presence of three auditory ossicles; the presence of only marginal teeth in the jaws; two definite tooth generations; two or more roots in the cheek teeth; and a single nasal opening. Some of these characters, however, were already present or foreshadowed in the therapsids.

Skeleton.—The study of the skeleton in mammals presents an entirely different problem from that encountered in the reptiles. In that class there is an extremely wide variation in skeletal patterns and in the elements present. The mammalian skeleton has developed from the type seen in the mammal-like reptiles and thus is, in a sense, highly specialized to begin with. Once established, however, it has varied but little. Almost never are new skeletal elements added, and seldom are elements lost, except in the distal portions of the limbs in relation to locomotor adaptations. But, although the bones of the skeleton are essentially stabilized, tooth structure is, as will be seen, exceedingly variable. Teeth are, from their composition, the hardest of skeletal materials and the parts most frequently preserved as fossils. In consequence, dentition and limb structure, as the two most variable and diagnostic features of the mammalian skeleton, will bulk large in our consideration of the various groups.

The mammalian skeleton is in contrast with that of reptiles in its thorough ossification; exceedingly little cartilage is present in the adult. One development in this regard deserves particular mention—the epiphyses (Fig. 223). In reptiles the articular ends of bones are frequently covered by cartilage; growth in length of the bones takes place by the gradual replacement of this cartilage by bone. Such a process, however, hinders the development of a firm articulation of one element with another. In mammals this difficulty has, so to speak, been solved; the articular surface is formed of bone and finished early in life. But between the ends and the main body of the bone there is a layer of cartilage in which additional bone is laid down. Lengthening of a bone may thus take place without interference with its articulations. When the element has reached its maximum size, this zone of cartilage disappears and the end-segments, known as epiphyses, fuse with the main body of the element. After their fusion growth is over. This is in contrast with reptilian conditions, where no definite adult size is attained and growth may continue, seemingly, throughout life.

Fig. 223.— The tibia of an immature seal, showing the terminal epiphyses (e) separated from the shaft (s) by cartilaginous bands in which growth of the bone continues.

Skull.—The interpretation of the mammalian skull (Fig. 224) is rendered easier if the reptilian ground plan upon which it is based be kept in mind. It is a highly complex structure, differing from that of therapsids mainly in features connected with the great expansion of the brain and with changes in the nasal apparatus and the auditory mechanism.

As seen in dorsal view, the greatest change from the reptilian condition is that caused by the growth of the brain and the consequent swelling out of the braincase; the temporal arches stand out from the sides of the skull as if they were appendages to it rather than part of the original roof. There is no pineal eye, and the bony external nares are fused into a common anterior opening. There is the normal tetrapod series of parietals, frontals, nasals, and premaxillae. The parietals spread down over the sides of the braincase. If the brain is small the jaw muscles meet above, causing a median sagittal crest to develop between them. This structure is more particularly liable to be present in large forms, for the brain does not increase in proportion to the rest of the body. There is no bar behind the orbit in primitive mammals, and the reptilian postorbital bone is gone. The bar may reform in advanced members of many groups, but this bone does not return. The prefrontal and postfrontal are likewise absent; the lacrimal is small and confined to the neighborhood of the orbit and the tear duct. The nasals project freely in

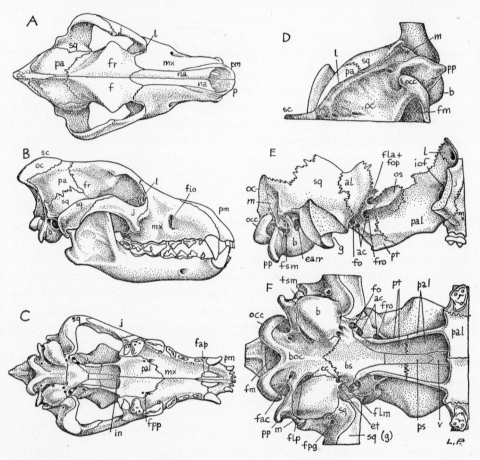

FIG. 224.—The skull of the Pleistocene wolf, *Canis dirus*, to show the structure of the mammalian skull. *A*, dorsal, *B*, lateral, and *C*, ventral views. *D*, occipital view of right half of skull (top at left of figure). *E*, lateral view of posterior part of skull with zygomatic arch and roofing bones removed. *F*, ventral view of same. *ac*, alisphenoid canal; *al*, alisphenoid; *b*, auditory bulla; *boc*, basioccipital; *bs*, basisphenoid; *cc*, carotid canal; *eam*, external auditory meatus; *et*, eustachian tube; *fac*, anterior condyloid foramen; *fap*, anterior palatine foramen; *fio*, infraorbital foramen; *fla*, anterior lacerate (sphenorbital) foramen; *flm*, median lacerate foramen; *flp*, posterior lacerate foramen; *fm*, foramen magnum; *fo*, foramen ovale; *fop*, optic foramen (here fused with *fla*); *fpa* anterior palatine foramen; *fpg*, postglenoid foramen (transmitting a nerve); *fpp*, posterior palatine foramen; *fr*, frontal; *fro*, foramen rotundum; *fsm*, stylomastoid foramen; *g*, glenoid fossa (jaw articulation); *in*, internal nares; *j*, jugal; *l*, lacrimal carrying tear duct, also lamboidal (transverse occipital) crest; *m*, mastoid portion of periotic; *mx*, maxilla; *na*, nasal; *oc*, occipital (including basi-, ex- and supra-occipitals); *occ*, occipital condyle; *os*, orbitosphenoid; *pa*, parietal; *pal*, palatine; *per*, periotic; *pm*, premaxilla; *pp*, paroccipital process of exoccipital; *ps*, presphenoid; *pt*, pterygoid; *sc*, sagittal crest; *sq*, squamosal; *v*, vomer.

front over the nares, but the premaxillae push up to meet them at the sides. The maxillae are large and deep, as they were in mammal-like reptiles. The jugal lies beneath the orbit and takes part in the formation of the temporal arch. The squamosal forms the hinder end of this bar and also forms the new jaw articulation, the glenoid cavity, as well as extending up over the lateral wall of the braincase. In contrast to reptiles, quadratojugal and quadrate are absent from their former place at the back corner of the skull.

As in reptiles, there is usually a considerable amount of fusion of the elements which make up the occipital plate. The basioccipital lying below the foramen magnum is fused with the exoccipitals. The latter form much of the paired condyles, extend out laterally into paroccipital processes, and may fuse in turn with the supra-occipital. Embryology often reveals a distinct interparietal (dermal supra-occipital) which usually fuses with the supra-occipital. There is usually a transverse (lambdoidal) crest across the upper margin of the occipit for the attachment of neck muscles.

On the under side of the braincase the basisphenoid lies in front of the basioccipital, bounded laterally by the auditory region. Anterior to it is a bone, the presphenoid, which is probably merely a separated part of the same original element (there is no reptilian homologue). At the side of the basisphenoid is the alisphenoid, which extends up as a wing around the side of the braincase and meets the roofing bones above. This element is apparently identical with the reptilian epipterygoid. Originally it was a plate rising at the side of the basisphenoid from the pterygoid but lying outside of the braincase (cf. Fig. 86). With the swelling out of the brain it has become merged with the braincase but still articulates with the pterygoids. In front of the alisphenoid, on the side of the braincase and inside the orbit, the wall is filled out by the orbitosphenoid, a comparatively new ossification which appears to have been present in some mammal-like forms.

In the front part of the mouth the bony structure is not unlike that of the higher therapsids. The secondary palate is formed by extensions from the premaxilla, maxilla, and palatine back to the internal nares. Behind the palatine is the pterygoid, closely articulated to the basicranial region. It no longer reaches back to the quadrate region, and ends behind in a wing-like structure. (The ectopterygoid has vanished.)

Below the front end of the braincase in front of the presphenoid and concealed from ventral view by the secondary palate is a long slim median bone of dermal origin, the vomer; this is presumably the reptilian parasphenoid. Above it, at the front end of the braincase, is the ethmoid. This element sends out into the nasal cavity scrolls of bone, turbinals, which are covered with mucous membranes in life, as are similar turbinals formed from the nasals and maxillae. The prevomers, important elements in the reptilian palate, occur only as occasional rudiments in mammals.

Auditory region.—The structure of the inner ear region is complicated. In reptiles and primitive amphibians (cf. Fig. 86) there are two otic bones, proötic and opisthotic, which lie in the side wall of the braincase. They inclose the cavity of the internal ear; and between them, on the outside, is an opening (fenestra ovale) from which projects the stapes. At the back the opisthotic joins the exoccipital and, above, the tabular. These two bones are still present in mammals. The proötic is now termed the petrosal and is much the larger of the two; it lies at the side of the braincase, above the basioccipital and basisphenoid, just as its reptilian predecessor did, and houses the internal ear. The opisthotic has become the mammalian mastoid, which is sometimes a separate bone exposed on the surface at the back corner of the skull. It is often fused with the petrosal; and this mass, called the periotic, may be usually combined further with the squamosal to form the so-called temporal bone.

We have noted that in mammal-like reptiles the eardrum appears to have been lodged in a notch in the angular bone on the under edge of the back part of the jaw (Fig. 225). In mammals this bone has become the tympanic, primitively a simple ring surrounding the eardrum, but may expand into a tube. Within this is the cavity of the middle ear, with three tiny ossicles (discussed below) instead of the single stapes of the reptile. This cavity and its delicate contents were primitively unprotected by bone. But in almost all mammals the surrounding bones tend to send out inclosing processes; and in most a complete inclosure, the tympanic bulla, protects the middle ear. Often part or all of this structure is formed by an inward growth of the tympanic bone, but in many groups a great part of it is formed by a separate and seemingly new ossification, the entotympanic bone.

Skull openings.—The various openings in the skull (foramina and fenestrae) are numerous, complicated, and important. They may be roughly divided into (1) openings out of the braincase for cranial nerves and (2) other openings for blood-vessels and various ducts.

Mammals possess twelve cranial nerves, passing directly from the brain to the sense organs and muscles of the head and throat. We shall briefly list these and their more usual relations to the skull openings (Fig. 224,*d e*). Nerve I, the olfactory, to the nose, does not reach the surface of the skull, but reaches the nostrils by perforating the ethmoid. Nerve II, the optic, passes out to the eye through the optic foramen in the orbitosphenoid. The three small nerves to the muscles of the eye (III, IV, VI) and part of the large nerve V (trigeminal) pass out through the foramen lacerum anterius (or foramen sphenorbitale) between orbitosphenoid and alisphenoid inside the cavity of the orbit. Two other branches of nerve V pass out through the foramen rotundum and foramen ovale, both in the alisphenoid bone. Nerve VII (facial) passes through the petrosal and emerges at the edge of the skull from the stylo-mastoid foramen. Nerve VIII, the auditory nerve, passes into the petrosal to the inner ear and does not, of course, reach the surface of the skull. Nerves IX, X, and XI (glosso-pharyngeal, vagus, and accessory) pass out through the posterior lacerate or jugular foramen between the basioccipital and the ear capsule, while XII (hypoglossal) sometimes accompanies them but primitively emerged through an anterior condyloid foramen in the exoccipital.

The lacrimal duct usually pierces the lacrimal bone and runs inward to reach the nose. An infraorbital canal carries blood vessels and nerves forward from the orbit through the maxilla into the face. On the palate the incisive foramen between premaxilla and maxilla and the palatine foramen in the latter bone transmit blood vessels. There is often an alisphenoid canal carrying an artery forward through the base of the alisphenoid bone. The internal carotid artery which supplies blood to the brain usually passes forward from the hind end of the skull through a carotid canal running forward under cover of the petrosal from near the posterior lacerate foramen, while at the front end of that bone the artery passes up into the braincase through the foramen lacerum medium, an opening between petrosal and alisphenoid. In this region there is an opening into the auditory bulla for the eustachian tube leading from throat to middle ear. In the jaw, there is a foramen (inferior dental) on the inner side near the posterior end through which enter nerves and blood-vessels and a mental foramen well forward on the outer side to give a blood and nerve supply to the chin and lower lip region.

Jaw and auditory ossicles.—In the lower jaw there is but a single element on each side, the dentary. This has an ascending ramus with a coronoid process (for the temporal muscle which closes the jaw) and an articular process. At the lower back corner of the jaw there is often an angular process for the attachment of muscles.

Of the other elements of the reptilian jaw (cf. Figs. 209, 225) the splenial, coronoid, and surangular seem to have disappeared in mammals. The angular, as we have noted, has become the tympanic bone. This leaves the articular (with which the prearticular is fused) and, in the upper jaw, the quadrate (to which in mammal-like reptiles the quadratojugal was fused). The fate of these two bones has been a curious one.

In mammal-like reptiles the sole auditory ossicle, the stapes, ran out to touch the quadrate; this element in turn was in contact with the articular bone of the jaw. In the mammalian auditory region this "stirrup bone" is the inner member of a chain of three ossicles, an outer one, the malleus or "hammer," receiving vibrations from the eardrum and transmitting them to the stapes through the incus or "anvil." The origin of these two "new" elements was long disputed. But a study of their embryology confirms the conclusion to which a consideration of the jaw changes undergone in the evolution of mammals leads us. The malleus is the old articular (with the prearticular as an anterior process); the incus, the reptilian quadrate. Once important bones, they had become useless for their original purpose and, lying close to the auditory region, were salvaged and put to a new use. This change was presumably facilitated through the fact that in the mammal-like reptiles the eardrum lay close to the jaw region. Very likely quadrate and articular had begun to function in sound transmission before they had lost their function as jaw elements.

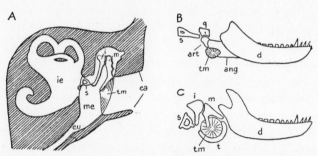

FIG. 225.—*A*, diagrammatic section through the ear region of man (after Weber, simplified). *B*, diagram of jaw region of a mammal-like reptile and *C*, a mammal, to show the origin of the bony elements of the auditory region of mammals. *ang*, angular (=tympanic); *art*, articular (=malleus); *d*, dentary; *ea*, external ear opening; *eu*, eustachian tube leading to throat; *i*, incus; *ie*, internal ear; *m*, middle ear; *q*, quadrate (=incus); *s*, stapes; *t*, tympanic; *tm*, tympanic membrane.

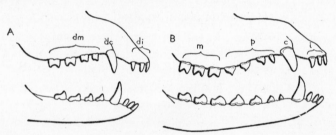

FIG. 226.—Diagrams to show the types and numbers of teeth in a primitive placental mammal. *A*, deciduous ("milk") teeth. *di*, deciduous incisors; *dc*, deciduous canine; *dm*, deciduous premolars ("milk molars"). *B*, permanent dentition. *i*, incisors; *c*, canine, *p*, premolars; *m*, molars.

The history of the auditory ossicles is one of the best examples of a change of function to be found in vertebrates. These elements, it will be recalled, were once part of the shark jaw apparatus; and this, in turn was derived originally from branchial bars. Accessory breathing organs were transformed into biting structures and these, finally, into part of the hearing apparatus.

Some portions of the reptilian branchial apparatus, especially the hyoid, remain in the tongue and throat of mammals but they are paleontologically unimportant.

Dentition.—Teeth in mammals are confined to the margins of the jaws. They consist (Fig. 226) of incisors, canines, premolars, and molars. All of these except the molars have, normally, a "milk" or deciduous set preceding the permanent ones. In the upper jaw the incisors are in the premaxilla, the others in the maxilla.

In a primitive placental mammal there were three incisors in each half of each jaw. No mammal has more than one pair of canines above and below. Four premolars and three molars in each half of the jaw is the number present in primitive placentals. This set of statements may be written simply as a dental formula, $\frac{3 \cdot 1 \cdot 4 \cdot 3}{3 \cdot 1 \cdot 4 \cdot 3} \times 2 = 44$; and a similar system may be used for any set of teeth. Primitive mammals may have a larger number of teeth; in placentals the formula given is usually the maximum and there is often a considerable reduction; our own formula, for example, is $\frac{2 \cdot 1 \cdot 2 \cdot 3}{2 \cdot 1 \cdot 2 \cdot 3} \times 2 = 32$.

The incisors are generally nipping teeth of moderate size. In some cases (as rodents) a pair may be developed as strong chisels, or they become tusks in the elephants. The canines are primitively long stabbing cone-shaped teeth. They are emphasized in carnivores; in herbivores they may be lost but are sometimes retained as defensive weapons. The cheek teeth, premolars and molars, usually have at least two roots in mammals. The four premolars are primitively simpler in structure than the molars. In many herbivore types they tend to become more complicated and may resemble the molars. In herbivorous mammals the molars tend to take on a complicated pattern, but in carnivores they tend to become reduced.

In primitive mammals there was a closed tooth row, without pronounced gaps; but herbivores tend to develop a gap, or diastema, between the front teeth which secure the food and the cheek teeth which masticate it.

Cheek teeth were primitively low crowned (brachyodont); but in many forms in which there is unusual wear, as in gnawing or grass-eating, they become high crowned (hypsodont). The roots primitively closed, limiting the amount of crown material formed, but in some forms part or all of the teeth may have a continuous growth.

Molar structure.—Reptilian teeth are generally simple cones. Mammalian molars generally have a broad crown bearing a number of cusps or ridges arranged in a complicated pattern which varies widely from group to group. It was only natural that there should have arisen various theories to account for the origin of molar patterns and to homologize the various cusps and crests found in different types. There have been some fantastic theories based on the idea that each cusp represents an originally separate tooth; however, the tritubercular theory set forth below is generally accepted today in at least certain of its aspects.

The theory starts with the type of molar teeth found in many primitive placentals, particularly Eocene forms (Fig. 227). In the upper jaws the molars are triangular in shape, with three cusps. A single cusp is found at the inner apex; this was originally believed to represent the original reptilian cone and hence is called the protocone. External to this is the paracone; back of the paracone is a third, the metacone. Between protocone and paracone there is often a smaller cusp, the protoconule, and inside the metacone a smaller one, the metaconule.

In the lower jaw there was a similar triangle, but with the base inside and the apex outside. Similar names are given to these cusps, but with the suffix -id: protoconid, paraconid, metaconid. Back of the triangle, or trigonid, is a low extension, the heel or talonid. This often bears two cusps, an external one termed the hypoconid and an internal one, the entoconid.

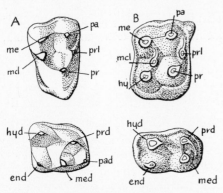

FIG. 227.—Molar teeth of primitive placentals. Upper row, right upper molars, lower row, left lower molars. A, *Omomys*, a Lower Eocene tarsioid, with a tritubercular pattern. B, *Hyracotherium*, a Lower Eocene horse, showing the evolved quadritubercular pattern. Abbreviations: upper molars—*hy*, hypocone; *me*, metacone; *mcl*, metaconule; *pa*, paracone; *pcl*, protoconule; *pr*, protocone; lower molars—*end*, entoconid; *hyd*, hypoconid; *med*, metaconid; *pad*, paraconid; *prd*, protoconid.

This primitive type of molar tooth, often with fairly sharp cusps, is usually termed "tuberculo-sectorial." The upper triangles are assymetrical, the front edge of the upper tooth and the hind edge of the lower trigonid being perpendicular to the edge of the jaw. Each upper tooth centers behind its proper lower mate (Fig. 228); and if it were not for the heel below which received the protocone in its basin, the two teeth would pass each other. A shearing action is obtained by this partial passage, while the partial opposition of the cusps gives a chopping effect.

In carnivorous mammals comparatively little change takes place. In herbivorous or mixed feeders with the development of a grinding surface, the pattern tends to become complicated (Fig. *227c, d*). In the upper molars the tooth tends to square itself up usually by the addition of a fourth cusp, the hypocone, at the inner back corner; the intermediate cusps may remain or drop out. The lower teeth tend also to square up but in a more complicated way, by building up the heel to a level of the rest of the tooth and dropping the paraconid from the front end so that the four definitive cusps are the protoconid, metaconid, entoconid, and hypoconid (a hypoconulid may also appear in the heel).

The cusps present may form various types of patterns. They may remain separate but low and rounded, a bunodont (hillock) type of dentition characteristic of such mixed feeders as men and pigs (Figs. 354, 355, 304a, b, etc.). Each cusp may tend to expand into a crescent (selenodont type) (Fig. 304c–h, etc.). Rows of cusps may tend to fuse into ridges (lophodont); for example, the two outer cusps of the upper molars may form a ridge, called the ectoloph, an anterior row of cusps may join to form a protoloph, or the back ones may form a metaloph (Fig. 229). Vertical ridges, or styles, may form on the edge of the teeth to add to the complication of the pattern.

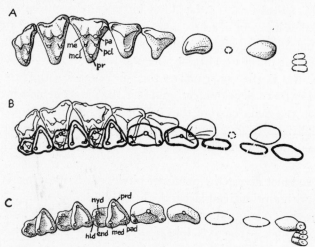

FIG. 228.—Cheek teeth and canines of *Didelphodus*, an Eocene insectivore, to show occlusional relations. *A*, right upper tooth row, *C*, left lower tooth row, *B*, the two superimposed to show occlusional relations. Each upper tooth lies behind and outside its homologue in the lower jaw. The two rows partially pass each other, with a shearing action along the diagonal line between each upper tooth and the lower tooth behind it. The passage of the upper tooth is stopped by the heel (talonid) on the corresponding lower molar; the protocone fits into the basin of the talonid. For abbreviations see Figure 227. (After Gregory.)

This tritubercular terminology affords an exceedingly useful method for the description of placental molar teeth. But the theory originally attempted also to explain the evolution of tritubercular placental teeth from the single cusped tooth common in reptiles. It assumed that there had developed three cusps in an anteroposterior row as in the triconodonts described in the next chapter (Figs. 238, 239). Then a rotation of the cusps into the triangular shape seen in the Jurassic symmetrodonts was thought to have taken place, and that from this condition through the Jurassic pantotheres, or trituberculates, arose the type of tooth found in primitive placentals.

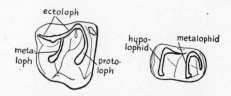

FIG. 229.—Right upper and left lower molars of a fossil rhinoceros, to illustrate a common type of lophodont tooth.

But this part of the tritubercular theory is far from acceptable. In the first place the triconodonts and symmetrodonts probably have nothing to do with the evolution of the remaining mammals, and there is no evidence of the supposed rotation of the cusps. Further, in the supposed rotation of cusps it was assumed that the original reptilian cone remained at the apex of the triangle, internal above and external below, and it was for this reason that the names "protocone" and "protoconid" were applied to the apical cusps. If this were true, it would be expected that this apical cusp, as the oldest historically, would appear first in the embryological development of teeth, and that when we trace forward in the tooth row of an animal this cusp would be homologous with the principal cusp of the premolars. This is true in the lower teeth; the protoconid appears to be the primitive reptilian cusp. But in the upper molars the paracone—not the protocone—is the first to appear in tooth development, and it is the paracone and metacone which are in line with the main cusp of the premolars (Fig. 228). Probably, then, the paracone is really the original reptile cusp; the protocone is a newer development at the internal border, while the metacone was formed by splitting off from the protocone.

But while we must divest the names of phylogenetic meaning, it remains true that, starting with a primitive placental, the tritubercular nomenclature is an excellent tool for the description and comparison of placental molars.

Postcranial skeleton.—The skeletal features of such a generalized mammal as an opossum or certain insectivores are the logical outcome of the adaptations for rapid quadrupedal progression seen in the therapsids; the opossum is a "living fossil," with a skeleton changed but little from the ancestral mammals of the Mesozoic. The reptilian ancestors of the mammals presumably were ground-dwellers. But the flexibility of the skeleton of the more generalized mammals, and the fact that "thumb" and "big toe" (pollex and hallux) tend primitively to be set off to a slight extent from the other digits as if some grasping power were early present, suggests a primitive arboreal stage.

In the axial skeleton (Fig. 230), there is greater regional differentiation than in reptiles. Ribless lumbar vertebrae are clearly set off from the rib-bearing dorsals. The cervical region also appears to be ribless, for the ribs are short and fuse in the embryo with the vertebrae. The tail is often long but is merely an appendage, not an integral part of the body, as in most reptiles. The sacral vertebrae tend somewhat to increase in number, and the originally separate sacral ribs tend to be lost and to be replaced by the transverse processes.

The number of vertebrae is much less variable than was the case in reptiles. On the average there are about twenty-five to thirty vertebrae in front of the sacrum. The number of cervicals is almost invariably seven; the long-necked giraffe and the neckless whale differ, not in number of neck vertebrae, but in their proportions. The number of rib-bearing dorsals commonly ranges from about twelve to fourteen, lumbars from five to seven, sacrals from two to five. The caudals are, of course, rather variable; there are seldom as many as two to three dozen.

The chief changes from the therapsid condition are seen to be: (1) fusion of the cervical ribs with the transverse processes, (2) loss of ribs in the lumbar region, (3) tendency for reduction of the tail. In addition, the breast bone, or sternum, which was unimportant in reptiles, becomes much more of a major feature of the skeleton in mammals. All the longer dorsal ribs attach firmly to it, and a tough membrane (the diaphragm) closes off posteriorly the barrel-like chest region. Continued breathing is a necessity for warm-blooded types; this is chiefly accomplished

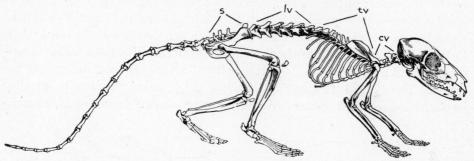

FIG. 230.—Skeleton of the living tree shrew *Tupaia*. *cv*, cervical vertebrae; *lv*, lumbar vertebrae; *s*, sacrum; *tv*, thoracic vertebrae. (After Gregory.)

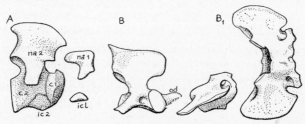

FIG. 231.—The atlas and axis in *A*, the therapsid *Moschops*, *B*, the Oligocene canid *Daphoenus*. Lateral views from right side. *B₁*, dorsal view of mammalian atlas, posterior end to the left. In both *A* and *B* the two elements are separated. The atlas consists of the neural arch and intercentrum of the first vertebra (separated in *A*) and form a ring-like structure in mammals (*B₁*). The centrum of the first vertebra is fused in mammals with the axis as the odontoid process, fitting into the cavity of the atlas. *c1*, *c2*, centra of the first and second vertebrae; *ic1*, *ic2*, intercentra of same; *na1*, *na2*, neural arches; *od*, odontoid process of axis (= *c1*).

by expansion and contraction of the diaphragm and ribs, held together by the breastbone.

The general contour of the backbone is similar to that of the therapsid ancestors. The cervical vertebrae slant downward from the head. Above the shoulder region, at about the beginning of the dorsal vertebrae, the curve of the back rises to descend through the lumbar region to the sacrum and tail.

The atlas and axis are of particular interest (Fig. 231). The atlas consists of a ring composed of its own neural arch plus its intercentrum. The axis has, in addition to its own proper elements, the centrum of the atlas attached to its front end as the odontoid process.

Limbs.—The limbs have continued the rotational process noted in our discussion of the therapsids, so that they lie parallel to the body and almost underneath the trunk. Humerus and femur work in a fore-and-aft plane (Fig. 232), functioning as a type of lever with the fulcrum (knee or elbow) at one end, the weight to be raised near the other end at the articulation with the girdle, and the major force (muscles) attached just beyond at the very tip (greater tuberosity of the humerus, greater trochanter of the femur). The chief muscles are consequently dorsal in position, and in consequence the limb girdles tend to be reduced ventrally and expanded above. This is particularly marked in the shoulder girdle (Fig. 196d). In typical mammals the interclavicle and the two ventral coracoids have disappeared except for a nubbin of the posterior (true) coracoid element underneath the scapula. The spine of the scapula with which the clavicle articulates is in reality its old front edge; the region anterior to the spine is a new development, an addi-

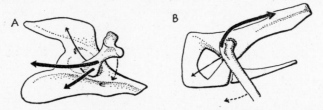

Fig. 232.—Diagram to show the differences in the musculature of the hip region between a pelycosaur (*A*) and a mammal (*B*). In *A* the principal muscles pulling the femur downward and backward (shown in heavy lines) attach to the tail and ventral part of the pelvic girdle. In *B* these muscles are reduced and replaced to a considerable extent by muscles attached to the greater trochanter and inserting on the ilium.

tion on the front for the accommodation of muscles moving up from the coracoid. In the pelvis, too (Fig. 211d–f,) there has been a rotation of bone related to rotation of muscles; and the ilium extends far forward, not at all back, while the pubis and ischium are as much behind as below the acetabulum.

The humerus and femur have, of course, changed considerably from the primitive condition because of their rotation. The humerus (Fig. 210d) has, near its proximal end, greater and lesser tuberosities for attachment of the muscles connecting it with the body; distally the primitive reptilian entepicondylar foramen is often present. The femur (Fig. 212c) has greater and lesser trochanters proximally for muscular attachment and often has a third trochanter more distally (a useful diagnostic character in many cases). In carpus and tarsus we lose, unfortunately, the simple and logical reptilian names for the elements and have to adopt a series of individual ones which vary considerably from author to author. In the carpus (Fig. 233b), instead of radiale, intermedium, and ulnare, we speak of scaphoid, lunar, and cuneiform, while an accessory bone on the outer side is called the pisiform. The centrale retains its name, while the four distal carpals are, in order, the trapezium, trapezoid, magnum, and unciform. In the tarsus (Fig. 233*d*) the intermedium and fibulare are termed the astragalus and calcaneum. The former develops a rolling joint over which the tibia moves freely; the latter projects back as a prominent heel bone to which the calf muscles attach. The

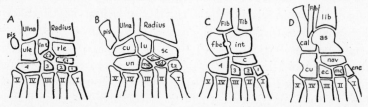

FIG. 233.—Diagrams to show the contrast in nomenclature of the carpal and tarsal elements in mammals and reptiles. *A*, carpus of reptile. *B*, carpus of mammal. *C*, tarsus of reptile. *D*, tarsus of mammal. Metacarpals and metatarsals in Roman numerals, distal carpals and tarsals of reptiles in Arabic. *as*, astragalus; *c*, centrale; *cal*, calcaneum; *cu*, cuboid; *ec*, ectocuneiform; *enc*, entocuneiform; *fib*, fibula; *fbe*, fibulare; *int*, intermedium; *lu*, lunar; *mc*, mesocuneiform; *mg*, magnum; *nav*, navicular; *pis*, pisiform; *rle*, radiale; *sc*, scaphoid; *td*, trapezoid; *tib*, tibia; *tz*, trapezium; *un*, unciform; *ule*, ulnare.

distal tarsals become the internal, middle, and external cuneiforms and the cuboid. The primitive phalangeal formula is that which we have seen develop in some mammal-like reptiles, namely, 2–3–3–3–3 (Fig. 234). The pollex and hallux are usually somewhat shorter and thicker than the other toes and diverge somewhat from them, suggesting a grasping power in the primitive mammals. The feet in primitive forms presumably were armed with sharp claws.

Locomotor adaptations.—From the type of skeleton described above there have been wide variations. Locomotor adaptations to different modes of life are varied and often striking. Among ground-dwellers fast running has evolved in many different groups. The beginning of such an adaptation is

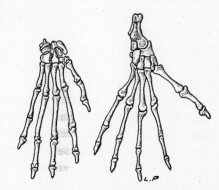

FIG. 234.—Manus and pes of *Notharctus*, an Eocene lemur. (After Gregory.)

seen in the dog; the horse or antelope shows an extreme development. The originally flexible skeleton becomes adapted almost entirely to a fore-and-aft motion of the legs, so that other motions become awkward or impossible. The foot, which originally lay nearly flat on the surface, in a semi-plantigrade (palm-walking) position, tends to be lifted from the ground; and the metacarpals and metatarsals elongate, forming an extra limb segment (as in the hind legs of some dinosaurs and birds); the divergent hallux and pollex tend to be reduced and disappear. The animal now walks on the toes (digitigrade). The clavicle tends to be lost, thus freeing the shoulder from any bony connection with the body and breaking the jar of landing on the front feet after a bound.

The dog has reached a stage such as that outlined above. But many forms have progressed beyond this, with the development of hoofs and further reduction of toes, to the ungulate (hoofed) condition to be considered in a later chapter; while heavy ungulates have, in relation to the carriage of weight, developed ponderous, straight legs analogous to those of the sauropod dinosaurs; these are the gravi-portal (weight-bearing) types.

Still other types which have progressed considerably toward fast locomotion on the ground are leaping forms, as the kangaroos and jumping rats, in which the body is held partially or fully erect and the propulsive force is a sudden spring with the hind legs.

In a number of groups, especially among primitive placental insect-eaters, underground burrowing types have developed in which the most prominent adaptation is the development of very strong front legs for digging purposes.

In tree-living forms the skeleton remains flexible in relation to the necessity for agility. Adaptations are present for holding onto the trees often by an opposable thumb and big toe but sometimes merely through sharp claws for digging into the bark. The tail is usually well developed as a balancing organ and is often prehensile. Some forms tend to swing more especially by the hands (brachiation), with interesting evolutionary results. These adaptations are discussed in detail in connection with the primates. A further tendency on the part of tree-living types has led in a number of groups to the development of gliding forms, in which a membrane has developed in connection with the limbs; and a final stage in this evolutionary process has resulted in the development of true flight in the bats.

Again (as in reptiles) mammals may tend to revert to an aquatic existence. A number of marine mammals, as seals, whales, sea cows, sea otters, have developed. The limbs are retransformed into fin-like organs; the fusiform body shape of the fish tends to be re-assumed; a tail fin, and even a dorsal fin, may be redeveloped.

Cenozoic subdivisions.—As noted on page 3, the Cenozoic, or age of mammals, includes but three periods, Tertiary, Pleistocene, and Recent. In studying the evolution of mammal groups, however, we shall have much occasion to refer to the main subdivisions, or epochs, of the Tertiary. These include: (1) the Paleocene epoch, a time of cool climates in the modern north temperate regions, with a duration estimated roughly at about 8 million years; (2) Eocene, with warmer climates, about 12 million years; (3) Oligocene, with moderate and moist climates, about 16 million years; (4) Miocene, somewhat cooler climates, about 12 million years; (5) Pliocene, colder climates heralding the approach of glacial conditions. This epoch marked the end of the Tertiary and was followed by the Pleistocene ice age, from which, in Recent times, we appear to be emerging.

CHAPTER XIII

PRIMITIVE MAMMALS

Classification.—Living mammals are easily divisible into: (1) monotremes (the duckbill and spiny anteaters of Australia), which are egg-laying types; (2) marsupials, including the opossums and a large number of Australian forms which bear the young alive but at an immature stage, (3) placentals, in which the young are retained longer within the mother's body and a highly developed placenta is present. The first have been called the subclass Prototheria, or primitive mammals; the second and third together, Eutheria, or true mammals. Under another system the marsupials have been called the Metatheria and the term Eutheria restricted to placentals. Still another terminology, based on the female reproductive system, calls the three types Ornithodelphia, Didelphia, and Monodelphia. These divisions are satisfactory for living forms. But the monotremes are almost unknown as fossils, and marsupials and rare placentals appear only at the end of the Cretaceous. Most Mesozoic fossil forms pertain to orders not particularly close to living groups; and since we have no knowledge of their mode of reproduction, they are difficult to classify.

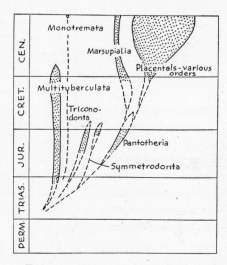

Fig. 235.—Chronologic distribution of the lower mammalian types.

The mammal-like reptiles which flourished in Permian and early Triassic times had disappeared by the end of the latter period. Mammals presumably came into existence during the Triassic, but we know extremely little about their history during almost the entire span of the Mesozoic. For the Triassic we have but a few fragmentary specimens of an extinct archaic group known as the multituberculates. In the Jurassic almost all known remains come from two English localities, and one small bone pocket at Como Bluff, Wyoming. Between the late Jurassic and the late Cretaceous, when marsupials and the first placentals appear, we know but two or three teeth. Further, almost all of the earlier Mesozoic remains consist of isolated teeth or, at the most, jaws; prior to the Upper Cretaceous we have not one single skeleton, not one complete skull. In consequence we are as yet in the dark as to much of the history of Mesozoic mammals. We can tell but little except the dental anatomy of the forms we know, and the sparseness of the record suggests that many groups may well have existed but have escaped discovery.

This absence of material is, presumably, not due to any great rarity of mammalian life during these times but to the small size of the Mesozoic mammals. On the average they were no bigger than a rat or mouse; and delicate bones of such forms would seldom be preserved and, even if exposed, would tend to be overlooked by collectors.

Monotremes.—Before considering these early fossil types, it will be advisable to discuss the living members of the order Monotremata, a group which is paleontologically almost entirely unknown but which must have had a long independent history. The duckbill (*Ornithorhynchus*) and spiny anteaters (*Echidna*) of Australia, the only living monotremes, are among the most bizarre and paradoxical of living vertebrates. They are unquestionably mammals, with such characteristic features as milk glands (of primitive structure), hair, and but one lower jaw element. However, they are exceedingly primitive in that, in contrast to all other mammals, they still lay eggs, while many other reptilian characters are present in their skeletons and soft anatomy. They are highly specialized in their modes of life and in consequent adaptations, such as the loss of teeth, development of a bill, and peculiar limb structure for digging or swimming. The brain is rather reptilian; the spiny anteater has a pouch like that of marsupials.

The duckbill has a broad bill; the anteater, a long slim beak suitable for ant-eating. Both are toothless as adults. The anteater has no trace of teeth; in the duckbill there are a few irregularly shaped molar rudiments in the young which have been compared to some extent with those of the fossil multituberculates. The braincase is moderately expanded; the frontal bones are unusually small, the nasals large. There is no lacrimal, and the jugal is reduced or absent. There is a large palatine covering the long secondary palate, a well-developed vomer which runs back to the basisphenoid and is readily comparable with the old reptilian parasphenoid, and there are even traces of the reptilian prevomers. The orbito-sphenoid is large. Both pterygoid and alisphenoid are present but peculiarly developed. There is no formation of an auditory bulla; the tympanic bone is a loose open ring, and the recess for the middle ear is only partially inclosed by extensions from the petrosal and alisphenoid. The jaws are reduced.

The presence of unfused cervical ribs is again a primitive feature. The shoulder girdle (Fig. 196c) is emphatically reptilian, for an interclavicle is still present, there are two large ventral coracoid elements, and in the scapula there is no spine or supraspinous area. In the pelvis (Fig. 211d) there are long marsupial bones extending forward from the front of the pubis, as in marsupials. The limbs are highly specialized for digging.

There is a large *Echidna* in the Pleistocene of Australia; beyond this we know nothing about the history of this group. It may be that they are related to some of the known Mesozoic types; but the absence of teeth, coupled with their other specializations, renders comparison almost impossible. Certainly they are very primitive, as well as highly specialized; and it has been suggested that they represent a line of descent from mammal-like reptiles entirely separate from that of other living forms. Their survival in the Australian region may be attributed partly to their specialized mode of life and partly to the long isolation of that region from other continents.

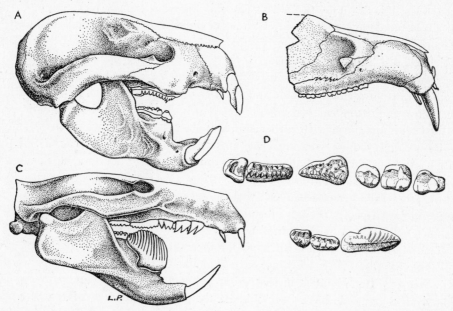

FIG. 236.—Multituberculates. *A*, skull of *Taeniolabis taoensis*, original about 6¾ inches long. *B*, *Tritylodon longaevus*, front end of skull, about ⅔ natural size. *C*, *Ptilodus* skull, original about 3 inches long. *D*, upper and lower teeth of same, about 2⅔ natural size. (*A, D* after Simpson, *B* after Broom, *C* after Gidley.)

Multituberculates.—Of the Mesozoic fossil types the most isolated are those which comprise the order Multituberculata (Fig. 236). They were in general the largest of Mesozoic forms, some the size of a woodchuck, and were rodent-like in many adaptive features and perhaps in habits as well. The multituberculates had the longest history of any known mammalian order, for they appeared in the Triassic as the oldest known forms of mammals and persisted through into the Lower Eocene. They were already very highly specialized at their first appearance and changed comparatively little during the course of their history.

The skull was broad and low, the jaws powerful, the nasals unusually large and expanded behind, the jugal very small in some cases. There were primitively three upper incisors, one of which tended to elongate and meet the single rodent-like lower one. The canines were absent, and the premolars variable, one or more of them being often long, high, striated shearing teeth. The molars were large and had numerous cusps arranged in regular antero-posterior rows, two below and two or three above. These highly characteristic teeth, quite unlike the molars possessed by any other group, were well developed even in the Triassic. The multituberculates were obviously herbivorous types, perhaps living on the fruit and bark of Mesozoic cycads and conifers. The skeleton suggests arboreal habits.

The earliest known form is *Tritylodon* (Fig. 236b), presumably from the upper part of the Triassic of South Africa. The only known specimen, although unfortunately incomplete, is of great interest as the oldest existing mammalian skull. It is more primitive than any other type in certain respects; there are several molars which are not particularly elongated, there is no shearing premolar, and a well-developed lacrimal is present. This form, with which are allied others known only from teeth from the late Triassic and Jurassic of Europe, is much more primitive than later multituberculates, among which are: *Plagiaulax*, a late Jurassic and early Cretaceous form with rather simple molars with two rows of cusps and a series of comb-shaped shearing lower premolars; *Ptilodus* (Fig. 236c, d), of the late Cretaceous and early Paleocene, with one enormously developed lower shearing tooth; and *Taeniolabis* (*Polymastodon*) (Fig. 236a) of the Paleocene, the giant of the group (the size of a beaver), without shearing teeth but with three rows of upper molar cusps. In the later forms there are but two molars, the first of which is much enlarged, and the lacrimal bone is reduced or absent.

The relationships of these ancient and aberrant mammals is a matter of considerable interest. Their teeth are rather similar to those of certain marsupials, and they are often included in that group; while on the other hand, some South American marsupials have been mistakenly called multituberculates. But the marsupials with which they are compared are advanced, not primitive, forms; and even primitive marsupials are not known until the late Cretaceous. It has been suggested that the monotremes have been derived from multituberculates; and such monotreme features as the loss of the lacrimal, reduction of the jugal, and the peculiarly wrinkled embryonic teeth tend to lend plausibility to this idea, which, however, is impossible of proof; that multituberculates were in an egg-laying stage is, however, highly probable from their high antiquity.

The multituberculates were the first herbivorous branch to be developed from the basic mammalian stock; that they were well adapted to their mode of life is shown by their long survival despite severe reptilian competition. In the late Cretaceous and Paleocene they were still abundant. But, seemingly correlated with the development of a varied series of herbivorous placental mammals and with the changed vegetation of the times, they disappeared early in the Eocene.

Jurassic mammals.—The three orders next to be considered are Jurassic groups, known almost entirely from a few English and American localities. All were of small size; and in consequence little is known of them except isolated teeth, occasional jaws, and a few limb bones and skull fragments. Despite the paucity of the remains they are, however, of great interest for the evolutionary history of later mammals.

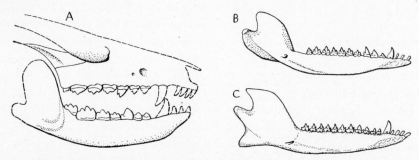

FIG. 237.—Jurassic mammals. *A*, restoration of front part of skull of *Priacodon*, a triconodont (about twice natural size). *B*, inside of jaw of *Spalacotherium*, a symmetrodont (about ⅔ natural size). *C*, inside of jaw of *Amphitherium*, a pantothere (about twice natural size). (After Simpson.)

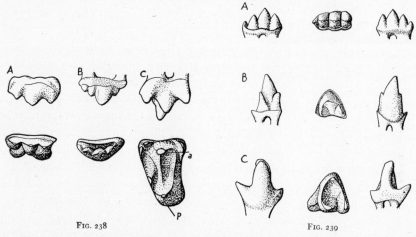

FIG. 238.   FIG. 239.

FIG. 238.—Upper right molars of Jurassic mammals, external and crown views. *A*, *Priacodon*, a *triconodont* (×4½). *B*, *Eurylambda*, a symmetrodont (×6⅔). *C*, *Melanodon*, a pantothere (×7½). In *C*: *a*, amphicone; *p*, probable homologue of placental protocone. (After Simpson.)

FIG. 239.—Lower left molars of Jurassic mammals. Left, internal aspect, center crown view (outside to top), right, external aspect. *A*, *Priacodon*, a triconodont (×⅞ approx.). *B*, *Spalacotherium*, a symmetrodont (×5). *C*, *Dryolestes*, a pantothere (×11). (After Simpson.)

Triconodonts.—The order Triconodonta comprises a series of forms of which the largest, *Triconodon*, was the size of a cat. They very probably were true carnivores rather than insectivorous types. The dental formula reached as high as 4·1·4·5 for the lower jaw. The molars in such forms as *Triconodon* or *Priacodon* (Figs. 237*a*, 238*a*, 239*a*) had three sharp conical cusps of about equal height arranged in a fore-and-aft row. In *Amphilestes*, a more primitive member of the group, the middle cusp was the tallest and the three were not so separate; and it is obvious that these teeth might easily have been derived from a type such as that shown in the protodonts or *Cynognathus*. A natural cast shows the brain to have been very small and primitive. This group was once believed to demonstrate a stage in the development of the type of molars characteristic of higher mammals. But more probably the Triconodonts were a divergent side branch not ancestral to other forms.

Symmetrodonts.—The order Symmetrodonta has been established for the inclusion of a number of Jurassic forms such as *Spalacotherium* (Figs. 237*b*, 239*b*) and *Eurylambda* (Fig. 238*b*), also of comparatively good size and comparatively predaceous habits. These forms also had three separate cusps in each molar tooth and were hence at one time included in the triconodonts, with which group they agree in the absence of an angular process on the jaw. But in the present types the three cusps were arranged in a symmetrical triangle, with the base external above, internal beneath. Early advocates of the tritubercular theory believed that they had arisen from triconodonts by a rotation of the cusps. But there is no evidence of such rotation, and they probably had nothing to do with that group. Although possibly related to the next order, the symmetrodonts seem to have been somewhat off the main evolutionary line.

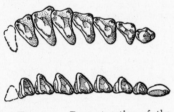

FIG. 240.—Reconstruction of the right upper and left lower rows of cheek teeth of a Jurassic pantothere. (After Gregory and Simpson.)

Pantotheres.—The order Pantotheria (or Trituberculata) includes a comparatively numerous and important series of small Jurassic forms which appear to have been close to the stock from which later mammals are derived. Among the better-known forms were *Amphitherium* (Fig. 237*c*), *Dryolestes* (Fig. 239*c*; cf. Fig. 240), and *Melanodon* (Fig. 238*c*). A typical dental formula for the lower jaw was 4·1·4·8. There was a well-developed but not inflected angular process on the jaw (in contrast with marsupials). The upper molars had a main outer cusp, termed the amphicone, which was in all probability the homologue of the paracone (plus metacone) of placentals. An inner cusp was probably homologous with the protocone of later types, and there were somewhat variable accessory cusps. The lower molars had a trigonid and a low heel comparable with placental structure. It appears highly probable that this was the basic type of tooth from which those of marsupials and placentals may have been derived, and probably the actual ancestor was some member of this varied group.

The early evolution of mammals.—Despite the fragmentary nature of pantothere remains, it is possible from them to gain some general idea of these primitive ancestors of the mammals of later ages. They were small creatures, averaging about the size of rats and mice, and were perhaps somewhat like these forms in their general appearance. Their food must have consisted mainly of insects; they were potential carnivores, but their size limited them to small prey. Other materials, however, as birds, fruit, and eggs, may have made up part of their diet. Whether they were still egg-laying types cannot, of course, be determined, but presumably the nursing habit was already established. Their brains, as far as can be told, were still poor and small by modern mammalian standards, although much better than those of their reptilian ancestors. Presumably they were retiring in habits, possibly nocturnal, and to some extent arboreal. Inconspicuous and small they had to remain, for, as contemporaries of the dinosaurs, the threat of death from the great carnivorous reptiles lay constantly over them.

But this long period of "trial and tribulation" was perhaps not altogether disadvantageous. It was, it would seem, a period of training during which mammalian characteristics were being perfected, wits sharpened, developmental processes improved, and the whole organization undergoing a gradual evolutionary change from reptilian to true mammalian character. As a result, when (at the close of the Cretaceous) the great reptiles finally died out and the world was left bare for newer types of life, higher mammals prepared to take the leading place in the evolutionary drama had already evolved.

Marsupials.—In the late Cretaceous beds we find that, although the multituberculates still flourished, the three typical Jurassic orders had disappeared. The triconodonts and symmetrodonts seem to have left no descendants; but, seemingly developed from the pantothere stock, we find representatives of the two great living groups of mammals—the marsupials and the placentals. The representatives of both groups were still small insectivorous types and again are poorly known. The placentals, which were to dominate the scene in the Cenozoic, were rare. Much more abundant were small opossum-like forms, the earlier marsupials, or pouched mammals.

Today the marsupials constitute a well-defined group including the opossums and a few other New World mammals, together with a large array of types constituting the greater part of the fauna of the Australian region. Certain of their distinctive features are suggested by the name. Almost all have a pouch placed on the belly of the female, which contains the teats and in which the young are carried after birth. This marsupium is rendered necessary because of the fact that birth takes place at a very small and immature stage, and this in turn is due to the fact that an efficient placenta has been evolved in but a few members of the group. The brain is better developed than in monotremes but is nevertheless markedly inferior to that of placental mammals. Among the definite osteological characters that separate them from the monotremes is the fact that (as in higher types) the coracoids are reduced to a single nubbin of bone on the under side of the scapula, a spine is developed on the latter bone, and the interclavicle is lost. Among the more prominent key characters which separate all known forms from higher, placental mammals are the inflected (or inturned) angular process of the jaw (Fig. 241*f*), the usual presence of four molars and but three premolars, and the presence of a pair of marsupial bones articulating with the front of the pubes as in the monotremes (Fig. 211*c*).

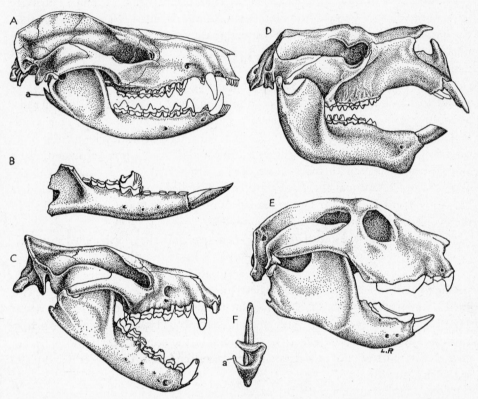

FIG. 241.—Skulls of marsupials. *A*, the living opossum, *Didelphys*. *B*, jaw of *Abderites*, a Miocene South American caenolestid ($\times \frac{7}{8}$). *C*, *Borhyaena*, a South American Miocene carnivore, skull length about 9 inches. *D*, *Diprotodon*, a giant Australian Pleistocene diprotodont, skull length about 40 inches. *E*, *Thylacoleo*, a large Australian Pleistocene type with highly developed shearing teeth; skull length about 1 foot. *F*, opossum jaw (right) from the rear to show inflected angle (*a*). (*B* after Ameghino and Simpson, *C* after Sinclair, *D* after Owen, *E* after Owen and Anderson.)

In the skull of such a marsupial as the opossum (Fig. 241*a*) the braincase is small compared with that of the average placental; sagittal and transverse crests are in consequence usually prominent. There is never any development of a post-orbital bar behind the small orbits. There is never a well-formed auditory bulla of placental type, although the alisphenoid usually sends back a process to protect the middle ear. The peculiar inflected angular process on the jaw has been mentioned.

In the ancestral forms there appear to have been as many as five upper incisors, as is still the case in the opossum; there are seldom more than the conventional three in the lower jaw. Large canines were undoubtedly present in the ancestral forms as they are today in many of the more primitive carnivorous types. In the cheek series there are never more than three premolars and usually four molars. The problem, however, is complicated by the fact that there is almost no tooth replacement, the last premolar being the only one with a predecessor; the more anterior teeth are seemingly permanent milk teeth.

In the more generalized forms (Fig. 242) the teeth are tuberculo-sectorial with triangular upper molars and a trigonid and talonid below. In the upper molars

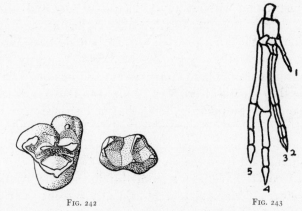

FIG. 242   FIG. 243

FIG. 242.—Upper right and lower left molar teeth of an Upper Cretaceous opossum. In the upper molars there is a well-developed row of outer cusps in addition to the normal trigon. (Much enlarged; after Osborn.)

FIG. 243.—Foot of a living diprotodont marsupial to show syndactylous structure.

there is developed a trigon similar to that of placentals, but in addition an outer row of unnamed cusps. In herbivores the teeth tend to square up with more or less development of a grinding surface.

A clavicle is almost always present in marsupials. There is seldom any reduction of toes in the forefoot. In the hind foot, the hallux appears to have been primitively opposable. There is often (especially in herbivorous types) a curious sort of syndactyly (Fig. 243) in which the fourth toe becomes strong and elongated and the second and third toes are united and balance the fifth toe, while the first digit may be lost. Claws are always present. It has been suggested that the primitive marsupials were arboreal, and many of the structural features tend to bear this out.

The customary division of the order Marsupialia is into the suborders Polyprotodonta and Diprotodonta. The first group is the more primitive, including insectivorous, omnivorous, and carnivorous forms, of which the opossum is typical. The diprotodonts are mainly living Australian herbivores.

American polyprotodonts.—As the name implies, there may be as many as five upper incisors present in the Polyprotodonta. The molars are generally triangular in shape and usually sharp-cusped; there is usually no syndactyly in the foot. There are several families, among which the Didelphiidae are the stem group.

Opossums (*Didelphys*, etc. [Figs. 241*a*, 242]) and their relatives, found today in both Western continents, are in almost every respect ideal ancestors for the whole marsupial group. There are five upper incisors and four lower ones; the upper molars are triangular in shape and rather sharp-cusped (the diet is omnivorous, with a tendency to the carnivorous side). The tail is usually prehensile; the limbs are of normal construction without any reduction of toes and with a well-developed, clawless, opposable hallux used for grasping in the opossum's arboreal mode of locomotion. In the late Cretaceous of the United States and Canada are found forms very similar to the living opossums, and in the early Tertiary these forms are known from not only both Americas but Europe and Asia as well; but since the Miocene they seem to have been confined to the Western Hemisphere. The opossums have lived continuously in South America since then; but in North America there are no fossils of this group in the late Tertiary, and we cannot be sure whether or not our living opossum is really an oldest inhabitant or whether he is a recent re-immigrant from the south.

South America seems to have been separated from the other continents at the beginning of the Eocene. Marsupials were evidently present there at the time, and in addition some placental mammals. But no placental carnivores appear to have gained admission, and there thus came about a good opportunity for the development of purely carnivorous marsupial types. These South American carnivores are separated as a distinct family, the Borhyaenidae. They were terrestrial forms, rather short-legged, with large skulls. The claws were strong and compressed; and the hallux, as in running types generally, was reduced. The teeth, as in true carnivores, tended to the shearing type. These carnivores ranged in size from that of the opossum to that of a bear and were especially abundant in the Miocene, where *Prothylacinus* (Fig. 244) and *Borhyaena* (Fig. 241*c*), a puma-like type, were typical. Following that period, however, there arrived higher ungulate types displacing these beasts' former prey, and placental carnivores displacing these marsupials, which soon became extinct. A curious last survivor in the Pliocene was a form with large stabbing tusks like those of the sabre-toothed tiger.

Somewhat similar forms are found today in Australia. The presence of these carnivores in South America has been used by some as an argument for a direct connection between these continents. But it appears more probable that this is a case of parallel development from the late Cretaceous marsupial stock in two isolated regions.

Australian polyprotodonts.—It is generally believed that Australia became separated from the rest of the world in late Cretaceous days, at so early a time in mammalian evolution that no placentals of any sort gained admission; and, except for bats and some rodents, few or none have entered since except those brought in by man. We know almost nothing of the Tertiary fossil history of Australia, but it seems reasonable to assume that the earliest mammalian fauna was composed of primitive opossum-like marsupials from which have descended the varied living marsupial groups which constitute the great bulk of the Pleistocene and recent mammals of that continent. The most direct descendants of the primitive settlers appear to be carnivorous types which are called "native cats," or (incorrectly) "opossums" (*Dasyurus*), and a number of mouse-like insect-eating forms. Somewhat more advanced is the Tasmanian Devil (*Sarcophilus*), a powerful carnivore

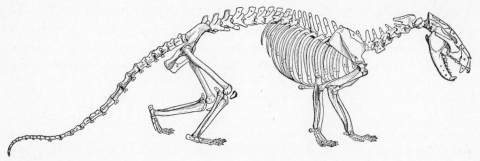

FIG. 244.—*Prothylacinus*, a Miocene carnivorous marsupial from South America. About 4 feet long. (From Sinclair.)

with shearing molars; while the most specialized type is the Tasmanian "wolf" (*Thylacinus*), a very wolf-like type quite similar to some of the South American Miocene marsupials. There are some interesting side branches included in this group, such as a marsupial anteater with typical ant-eating adaptations in the long snout, reduced teeth, and long claws, and a marsupial mole-like type. There are in addition some Australian Pleistocene and recent forms which have diverged farther from the common polyprotodont stock, the bandicoots, such as *Perameles*. These are insectivorous to omnivorous in diet, rabbit-like in size and in appearance except for the long pointed snout. The molars tend to become grinding teeth and assume a square shape with blunter cusps. The hind legs are long, the feet slim with some tendency toward syndactyly and with an emphasis on the fourth toe, very much as in the kangaroos.

Diprotodonts.—A second prominent group of marsupials is that of the Diprotodonta, confined to Australia and almost entirely unknown before the Pleistocene, in which period most of the existing types were represented. Despite our lack of knowledge of earlier fossils from Australia, it is obvious that they are a herbivorous development from the primitive opossum stock. However, many structural changes have occurred. There are never more than three upper incisors, and often there is a development of chisel-like teeth similar to those of rodents. The molars are quadrate in shape. The hind foot is generally syndactylous.

In the great majority of diprotodonts three upper incisors are still present. Seemingly closest to the common ancestors are the phalangers (*Phalanger*, etc.), arboreal types, the marsupial "squirrels," including even flying "squirrels." Somewhat more advanced is *Hypsiprimnodon*, the musk "kangaroo," in which, as in kangaroos, the last premolar is a long, straight-edged cutting tooth similar to that of the multituberculates; the limbs, however, are primitive in structure. The true kangaroos (*Macropus*, etc.) have gone further in the development of long hind legs for hopping with a reduction of the lateral toes and emphasis on the fourth.

Two interesting living forms are characterized by the fact that in the upper jaw as well as the lower there is a large pair of chisel-like teeth, the other upper incisors being small to absent. The living types include: *Phascolarctos*, an arboreal form rather like a large Teddy bear in size and appearance; and *Phascolomys*, the wombat, rather like the woodchuck in habits. Both have large Pleistocene relatives, and in addition there are a number of large extinct Pleistocene marsupials from Australia with a diprotodont dentition. *Diprotodon* (Fig. 241d) is the largest known marsupial and was a form about the size of a large rhinoceros but with a lumbering build suggesting similarity to the living wombat. *Thylacoleo* (Fig. 241e) was even more odd, a form the size of a lion with reduced molars and with the last premolars developed into large shearing teeth. It has been argued that *Thylacoleo* was a carnivore, but it seems more likely that it was really a diprotodont and that the shearing teeth were used in cutting fruit.

Caenolestoids.—The two suborders discussed above are the standard divisions of the marsupials and have been recognized for nearly a century. But certain living and fossil South American forms seem not to fit in well with either group; and for their reception the creation of a third suborder, the Caenolestoidea, is necessary. *Caenolestes* is a small living South American form, mouse-like in size and appearance (and long thought to be a rodent). There are four upper incisors, and the feet are not syndactylous, so that it should be a polyprotodont. But although there are three or four lower incisors, the middle ones are elongate as in diprotodonts, the molars are quadrate, and the last lower premolar in some related fossil types is a cutting type like that of kangaroos. This group goes back in South America to the Eocene; *Abderites* (Fig. 241b) was a typical Miocene representative.

Polydolops and related types from the Eocene of South America are perhaps related to these forms, but go even farther in diprotodont specializations. These small marsupials had but a single upper and lower incisor, as in the more advanced Australian forms. The upper molars were rather like those of multituberculates, and some writers have tended to group them together. This is probably merely convergent evolution. Presumably in the radiation of the marsupials in the late Cretaceous or Paleocene, primitive types which were still polyprotodonts migrated both to Australia and South America. In the former continent some developed into the true diprotodonts. South American forms with the same ancestry, and presumably the same evolutionary tendencies, tended, as the caenolestoids, to parallel them closely and also to parallel the earlier mammalian herbivores, the multituberculates.

Marsupial history.—It is reasonable to think that the marsupials are derived from the pantotheres, although there is no evidence that those Jurassic forms had certain of the peculiarities of the true marsupials. It has often been assumed that the marsupials are the ancestors of the placentals. That the ancestors of the placentals passed through a stage in which the young were born immaturely, as in marsupials, is theoretically probable; but that these ancestors were marsupials in the sense in which we know them (with a pouch, marsupial bones, and inflected jaw angle) is quite doubtful. Indeed, we now know primitive placentals fully as old as the earliest opossum-like forms. It is quite probable that placentals have descended directly and independently from the pantotheres and that the marsupials are a parallel branch of the mammalian stock.

But, while not on the direct line of descent, it seems likely that the more primitive marsupials (such as the opossums and some of the smaller dasyurids) in their mode of life, in their insectivorous-omnivorous diet, and in many structural features give us a good picture of the Mesozoic forms from which the Tertiary mammals have come. It is of interest to note that the opossums and primitive diprotodonts are primitively arboreal types, in agreement with the suggestion that the ancestral mammals were tree-living forms.

It is probable that primitive marsupials had a world-wide distribution in the late Cretaceous. But early in the Tertiary they became almost entirely restricted to two regions—South America and Australia—presumably because they were unable to compete successfully with more highly developed placentals. In South America late Tertiary placental invasions caused the extinction of many types before the end of the Tertiary, and only *Caenolestes* and the opossums have survived. But in Australia the marsupials in the absence of competition radiated out into many different modes of life. A number of forms are still arboreal, but the great majority have become ground-dwellers of many sorts. From the primitive omnivorous-insectivorous diet the living marsupials have branched out into purely carnivorous and herbivorous modes of life. In Australia the marsupials, given their chance for development, have paralleled almost every type which the placentals have produced on the other continents.

CHAPTER XIV

PLACENTAL ORIGINS; INSECTIVORES; BATS

Except for the primitive and aberrant monotremes and the marsupials just considered, all living mammals are members of a single more advanced group which has been dominant since the beginning of Tertiary times—the placentals. In these mammals we find a well-developed placenta formed from the allantois, one of the embryonic membranes; this permits of a long period of prenatal development and of birth at a more advanced stage than was possible in marsupials. The name is somewhat misleading, for some of the living marsupials have paralleled the true placentals to a considerable extent in the development of this structure; but there are many other points of difference between the two groups. There is no pouch in placentals, marsupial bones are absent, there is almost never the inflected angle of the jaw characteristic of marsupials, the brain is considerably advanced over that of the more primitive types, the dental formula was primitively $\frac{3 \cdot 1 \cdot 4 \cdot 3}{3 \cdot 1 \cdot 4 \cdot 3}$ and almost never exceeds that number, and there is typically a complete deciduous dentition for all teeth except the true molars.

Primitive placental structure.—From what we know of living and fossil types it is possible to picture a typical primitive placental at the end of the age of reptiles. Such a type would have been small in size, as had been the ancestral trituberculates of the Jurassic, and the limbs short. The clawed feet would have been applied rather fully to the ground in a semi-plantigrade position, and there presumably would have been a somewhat opposable pollex and hallux. Among technical diagnostic characters in the limbs would have been the presence of a clavicle, of a central bone in the wrist, of an entepicondylar foramen in the humerus, and of a third trochanter on the back of the femur—all characters lost in many later placentals. There would have been about twenty thoracic and lumbar vertebrae between neck and pelvis.

The brain was presumably comparatively small and poorly organized—that is, with the olfactory lobes and olfactory parts large and unreduced and with the neopallium but little developed. The skull, however, would have been fairly large (in correlation with smallness of the beast), with a long facial region and large eyes, and there would have been no development of a postorbital bar. The dentition would have contained the primitive placental number of teeth, and in general appearance would have resembled that of the older pantotheres. The lower molars would have been tuberculo-sectorial in character, with trigonid and talonid; the upper molars, triangular, with an internal protocone and, somewhat in from their

outer edges, not the amphicone present in the older types, but two cusps, the paracone and metacone, derived from the division of the primary reptilian cone.

Quite probably these forms were inconspicuous forest-dwellers, and nocturnal
to some degree at least. Certain characters in their descendants (such as the frequently divergent pollex and hallux) suggest an early arboreal habitat, although
in most placental types terrestrial life seems to have been taken up at an early
date. The diet presumably still consisted essentially of insects but was varied
with other types of soft plant and animal food, such as fruits, worms, and grubs.

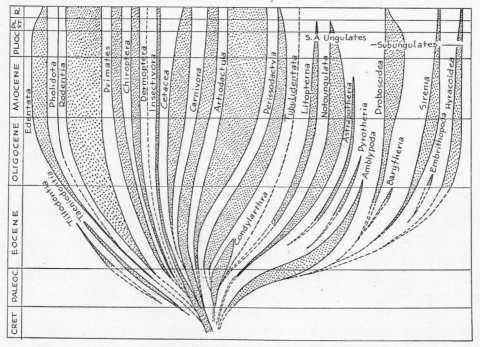

FIG. 245.—The chronologic distribution of the placental mammals.

Such a form as that described above was a purely hypothetical creature a decade
ago. A varied series of placentals were known from the Paleocene; their common
ancestor must have been a Mesozoic form, but no placental had been identified
at any lower stratigraphic level. Today this gap is in great measure filled through
the discovery of Cretaceous mammals in Mongolia and the identification of fragments in the late Cretaceous of America. At the most we know of them only skulls
and teeth, but as far as our knowledge goes they are exceedingly close to the expected ancestral types.

Small and seemingly rare as the earliest placentals were, they were none the
less the most efficiently organized land-dwellers of the times, better in brains and
in mode of development than the marsupials and multituberculates that were

their mammalian contemporaries. With the disappearance of the dinosaurs their spread was rapid. By the beginning of the true Eocene the multituberculates made their last appearance, marsupials had almost disappeared from the Northern Hemisphere, and the placentals had already become differentiated into the ancestors of almost all the known orders of later Tertiary and Recent times.

Insectivores.—As was the case with their Jurassic ancestors, the ancestral placentals were presumably insectivorous in diet. There are still in existence today a number of mammals, such as the shrews, moles, and hedgehogs, which have retained similar feeding habits and which have, despite various specializations, many primitive characters. These forms, grouped with related fossil types as the order Insectivora, are regarded as the most direct descendants of the primitive placentals.

The insectivores are not and probably never have been an abundant group; today they are small in size and few in number. Most of them are highly specialized or are isolated island forms, as is usually the case with surviving members of primitive groups.

As including the supposed stem of the later placental types, insectivores can be characterized for the most part only negatively as lacking the specializations of other derived forms. Many common features were noted above as characteristic of a generalized ancestral placental. The tympanic cavity is usually an open hole, partially surrounded by processes from neighboring bones, with the tympanic an open ring. In many instances the zygomatic arch is incomplete. The teeth are almost always sharp-cusped, and in a majority of cases there is but little departure from primitive placental types of dentition. The incisors are somewhat variable in development, and the canines are often somewhat reduced. There is usually little modification or reduction in the limbs except in burrowers.

Some five suborders of insectivores may be distinguished: (1) Deltatheridioidea, including a few small Cretaceous and early Eocene forms which appear to have been close to the base of the entire placental group; (2) Zalambdodonta, a few rare living and Tertiary types, presumably aberrant descendants of the last; (3) Erinaceomorpha, the more primitive typical insectivores, represented today by the hedgehog; (4) Soricomorpha, somewhat more specialized insectivores, represented by the shrews and moles; (5) Menotyphla, including the living tree and elephant shrews, forms intermediate in many respects between primitive insectivores and primates.

Primitive insectivores.—Of the placental types recently discovered in Mongolia some are typical, although quite primitive, insectivores of the hedgehog group. Another series of forms, however, includes two small forms (*Deltatheridium* [Figs. 246a; 247a, f] and a more imperfectly known relative) which appear to be not far removed from the base of the entire placental stock. The skull of *Deltatheridium* was of a very generalized type; and there were none of the specializations, such as the elongated snout, weak zygomatic arch, or peculiar incisor development, found in later insectivores. Particularly interesting was the development of the upper molars. The paracone and metacone were situated almost in the center of the tooth, and the two cusps were only barely separated at their tips. This is a condition seemingly intermediate between that found in the Jurassic pantotheres, where the original reptilian cone was but a single rather centrally located cusp, and that found in typical placentals, where paracone and metacone are widely separated and placed close to the outer margin. Somewhat similar molars are found in some of the carnivorous placentals and certain insectivores (zalambdodonts) of later

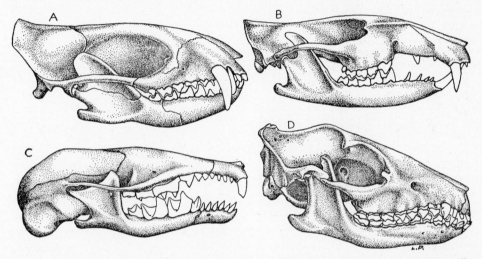

FIG. 246.—Skulls of insectivores. *A*, *Deltatheridium*, a primitive Cretaceous form from Mongolia, skull length about 1¾ inches. *B*, *Zalambdalestes*, a Cretaceous erinaceamorph, skull length about 2 inches. *C*, *Proscalops*, a Miocene soricomorph, skull length about 1 inch. *D*, *Anagale*, an Oligocene menotyphlan, skull length about 2¼ inches. (*A*, *B* after Gregory and Simpson, *C* after Matthew, *D* after Simpson.)

periods. It may be that *Deltatheridium* was on the line leading to one or the other of these later groups, but it was certainly exceedingly close to our ideal of an ancestor for the entire placental stock.

Zalambdodonts.—Highly specialized in many respects, but primitive or even regressive in their molar structure, are a series of curious living insectivores grouped in the suborder Zalambdodonta. The greater number of the living types are often grouped in the family Centetidae, most members of which are found on the isolated island of Madagascar. The smaller members of the group tend to parallel the shrews, moles, and hedgehogs of other regions in their adaptations; the largest form, *Centetes*, the tenrec, is the giant among insectivores, its tailless body measuring about 20 inches in length. Also belonging to this family is *Potomogale*, the otter shrew, a good-sized form from West Africa which is a fish-eater with a strong tail for swimming. Close to the centetids is *Solenodon* of Haiti and Cuba, a fairly large, long-snouted, rather rat-like insectivore. It is probably derived from the last family. More divergent is *Chrysochloris*, the golden mole of South Africa, which superficially resembles the ordinary moles in its adaptations.

The abundance of these curious forms in Madagascar as contrasted with their rarity elsewhere seems to be due to the isolation of that island from early Tertiary times down. (The lemurs, we shall see, offer a similar history.) Fossil types of zalambdodonts are unknown in later Tertiary deposits; but the group was represented in North America in the earlier Tertiary, even in the Paleocene. One form from this period, *Palaeoryctes*, is assigned to the centetidae, which is thus the most long-lived of placental families.

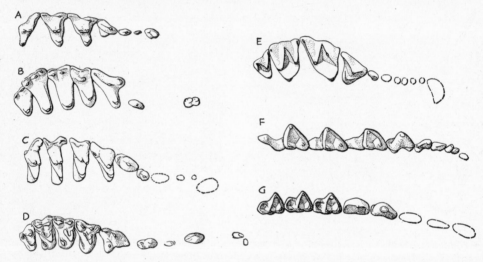

FIG. 247.—Cheek teeth of insectivores. Right upper teeth of *A, Deltatheridium* ($\times 2\frac{1}{2}$), and *B Zalambdalestes* ($\times 3$), primitive Cretaceous forms. *C, Palaeoryctes,* a Paleocene zalambdodont ($\times 3$). *D, Diacodon,* an Eocene erinaceamorph ($\times \frac{5}{4}$). *E, Proscalops,* an Oligocene mole ($\times 4$ approx.). Left lower teeth, *F, Deltatheridium,* and *G, Diacodon.* (*A, B, F* after Gregory and Simpson; *C, D, E, G* after Matthew.)

The group owes its name to the triangular shape of the upper molars (Fig. 247*c*). These have a low cone at the inner apex, accessory tubercles at the outer edge, and, nearly in the center, there is in most cases a high, V-shaped single cusp. This was originally thought to be the protocone; but it is now generally agreed that this represents the original single reptilian cusp, while the protocone is the lower internal structure. The zalambdont tooth has thus a pattern rather resembling that of the pantotheres. This resemblance, however, is quite certainly not due to any direct descent from that Jurassic group. One zalambdodont (*Potomogale*) shows the central cusp partially divided and renders it probable that the suborder represents a series of forms which have passed through a stage represented by *Deltatheridium* and are regressive rather than truly primitive in structure.

Erinaceomorphs.—The suborder Erinaceomorpha is a group of true insectivores, which, as regards the later forms at least, cannot be considered as ancestral to other placental orders. The paracone and metacone are well separated and are close to the outer border of the upper molars in the fashion of most later placentals, and the teeth in the living types are squared up through the development of a hypocone. There may be some enlargement of incisor teeth, but the zygomatic arch is always retained in contrast with most other insectivores.

Living members are confined to the Old World. *Erinaceus*, the hedgehog, is the best known; but more generalized rat-like types, such as *Gymnura*, are found in the Malay region. Members of the hedgehog family are found as far back as the Oligocene of North America and in the Eocene of Europe. The most primitive ancient fossil types are included in the family Leptictidae. Most of the included genera had essentially triangular upper molars; but in all true leptictids, such as *Diacodon* (Fig. 247d, g), there is a weak beginning of a hypocone. The leptictids are characteristic of the Eocene and Oligocene, but an obscure type from the Upper Cretaceous of North America may belong here. That the erinaceomorphs are an exceedingly ancient group is proved by the presence in the Cretaceous of Mongolia, together with the insectivores already mentioned, of *Zalambdalestes* (Figs. 246b, 247b), a small and very primitive form with tritubercular molars of the orthodox placental type and features which suggest that it is ancestral to the hedgehog group, if not also to other types.

Soricomorphs.—The living shrews and moles, the suborder Soricomorpha, are characterized by the para- and metacones forming a W-shaped outer wall on the quadrate upper molars. This feature serves to distinguish them from other insectivores; but otherwise these forms are structurally not far from the hedgehogs and their fossil allies, and presumably have been derived from erinaceomorphs. The shrews (*Sorex*, etc.) are small mouse-like forms which in their habits and general appearance probably closely simulate the ancestral insectivores. They are, however, considerably specialized in internal structure; for example, the zygomatic arch is incomplete, the middle incisors are elongated, and the lower canine and most of the premolars have disappeared. The moles in a broad sense include not only the true moles (such as *Talpa*) with powerful, highly specialized limbs for digging but also some more primitive forms with a more shrew-like appearance. The moles are in some respects more primitive than the shrews, for there are no enlarged incisors and the zygomatic arch is preserved. Members of both the shrew and mole families are known as far back as the Oligocene; *Proscalops* (Figs. 246c, 247e) is a well-known American Miocene member of the latter group. In the Eocene there were a number of poorly known little insectivores which belong to this suborder and which may tend to link it to the older erinaceomorph stock.

Menotyphla.—The suborder Menotyphla, represented today by the tree shrews and jumping shrews of the Old World tropics, may have been derived from the primitive erinaceomorphs, but is an advanced group and one of great antiquity. The tree shrews have a larger brain than do ordinary insectivores, and a well-developed zygomatic arch; and in addition the orbit is inclosed behind by processes from the postorbital and jugal, as in a number of more advanced mammalian types, including all the primates. The teeth are usually four or five cusped with a typical placental trigon.

The more characteristic living menotyphlans are the tree shrews such as *Tupaia* (Fig. 230), rather squirrel-like forms from Southern Asia. A second living group is that of the Macroscelididae, jumping and elephant shrews such as *Macroscelides*, with elongate hind legs and a long flexible snout. These are African types with no known close fossil relatives.

The tree shrews, particularly, seem to be quite divergent from the ordinary insectivores. Their arboreal habits, contrasting with the terrestrial life led by most insect-eaters, the large brain, inclosed orbits, and other morphological features suggest a connection of these forms with the primates. The fossil history of this group is unfortunately none too well known, although some small and poorly known early Eocene forms may be tree shrews and an Oligocene Asiatic form *Anagale* (Fig. 246d) appears to pertain to the Menotyphla. A group of Paleocene and Eocene forms, the plesiadapids, tend to bridge the gap between this group and primates; and while we shall consider them under the heading of primates, they are often included in the present group. Presumably the living Menotyphla are relics of a Paleocene stock from which the primates have been derived.

There are a number of rather obscure early Tertiary types which are assigned to the Insectivora but of dubious relationships. Of them we shall mention only *Pantolestes*, an American Eocene insectivore about the size of an otter, which had started on the road to a water-living type of existence. The braincase was elongate, but the face short and the jaw heavy, the dentition rather carnivorous in character.

The insectivores are of great importance as being the basal stock from which the remaining placental orders have been derived; but like many other stem groups, they have never progressed far in themselves. By the beginning of the true Eocene they had already given origin to all the more progressive stocks, and since then they have been a small and inconspicuous element in the mammalian fauna.

In addition to the insectivores we may well consider here a few mammalian orders presumably derived directly from the insectivorous stock which are not sufficiently important paleontologically to deserve treatment in separate chapters.

The "flying lemur."—Living today in the East Indian islands is *Galeopithecus*, the "flying lemur," only living representative of the order Dermoptera. It is a herbivorous tree-living form, about the size of a large squirrel. The popular name cannot be called appropriate, for the animal is not a lemur, nor does it fly. It is, however, the most highly developed of any of the mammalian gliding forms. A very large membrane stretches from the neck to the hand and foot and onto the tail, enabling the animal to "plane" for a considerable distance. The upper molars are triangular in shape but peculiarly constructed with three outer and two inner cusps, with this arrangement reversed below. *Galeopithecus* does not represent an ancestor of the bats, although it is perhaps not distantly related to them, but may represent morphologically a stage in the development of the bat type of flying apparatus. The fingers are not greatly elongated (although webbed) and retain claws, but the hands are rather large as compared with the animal's bulk.

Through most of the Tertiary there is no record of this interesting type. But in the Lower Eocene of North America have been found several inadequately known forms, such as *Plagiomene* (Fig. 248), with molars of similar structure.

Bats.—Only in the bats, the order Chiroptera, has true flight been developed by mammals. As in the pterosaurs (and in contrast with birds) the wings are formed by webs of skin; but instead of their being supported by a single elongate finger, nearly the whole hand is involved. The thumb, a clutching organ, is free and clawed; the other four fingers are all utilized in support of the wing membrane; claws are lost on these fingers (except the second in fruit bats); and, as would be expected, the end-phalanges are reduced and may be absent. In having the wing expanse broken by the long digits, the

FIG. 248.— Upper molar of *Plagiomene*, a Lower Eocene relative of the "flying lemur" ($\times 3$ approx.). (After Matthew.)

bat has evolved a more flexible and less easily damaged wing than that of the pterosaur. In connection with the bat's habit of hanging by the hind legs, those structures, as well as the pelvis, are peculiarly developed but rather weak.

The orbit is but rarely closed behind. All the teeth (Fig. 249*b, c*) may be present except for an upper incisor and the first premolar, but the anterior teeth may be considerably and variously reduced. The greater number of the bats are insectivorous types, the lower molars being tuberculo-sectorial while the upper molars are often of the old triangular shape or a squared type with a W-shaped ectoloph, a large protocone, and a smaller hypocone. But there is considerable variation in molar structure, for the diet in the various forms ranges from insects and fruit to fish and blood.

The sense of hearing is always highly developed (the auditory region of the skull is greatly swollen), and in many cases grotesque fleshy outgrowths occur about the ears and nose, housing delicate tactile sense organs—adaptations obviously connected with the usually nocturnal flying habits of the group.

The bats are divided into two suborders. The Megachiroptera, the fruit-eating

bats or "flying foxes," are large Old World tropical forms. They are little specialized in most respects, never having the peculiar ear and nose ornaments already
mentioned, and with a long fox-like face. In connection with the fruit-eating
habits, the teeth, especially the molars, are often specialized. Except for a form
from the Oligocene of Italy we have no record of their history.

Vastly larger in the number of contained types is the suborder Microchiroptera,
comprising all other bats. Typically small insect-eaters, as were presumably the
ancestral chiropterans, there is a considerable range of diet in the various families.
The incisors tend to be specialized and reduced; in connection with this and with

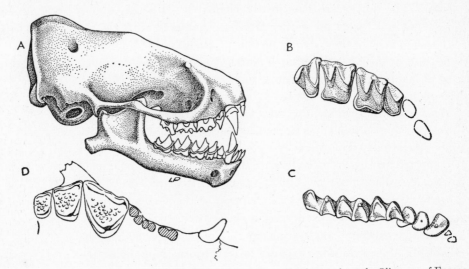

Fig. 249.—Bats. *A*, skull of a member of the existing genus *Nyctinomus* from the Oligocene of Europe;
skull length about ⅝ inches. *B*, *C*, upper and lower teeth of the same, about 6 times natural size. *D*,
upper teeth of the oldest known bat *Zanycteris* (Paleocene). (*A–C* after Revillod, *D* after Matthew.)

the frequent development of nasal excrescences, the premaxilla is usually small or
vestigial, the face is short, and there is a large nasal opening (Fig. 249*a*).

The oldest fossil bat is *Zanycteris* (Fig. 249*d*), from the Paleocene of North
America. Of this form, only an upper jaw has been preserved; this, however, shows
a dentition not unlike that of certain living forms, the Phyllostomatidae, or leaf-
eared bats. These types, now found in South America, are partially frugivorous
as well as insectivorous in some cases, and are rather generalized in structure; they
may be near the dividing line of the two present suborders. While *Zanycteris*
gives us no information as to the remainder of the skeleton, flight must have been
an early development, for complete skeletons (Fig. 250) are found in later European Eocene deposits which have well developed wings. The late Eocene of
Europe contains remains of more than half a dozen kinds of bats, suggesting that
the radiation of the group into the various types had been in great measure ac-

complished by that time. Fossil chiropterans are found here and there throughout the Tertiary, but it is only rarely that much except teeth and jaws is found of these small and delicate forms.

It seems obvious that the bats, essentially insectivorous in their beginnings, have been derived from an arboreal insectivorous group, for in such features as are not connected with flight the bats might well be included in the order Insectivora, and certain anatomical considerations suggest a derivation from the Menotyphla.

Taeniodonts.—An obscure Tertiary group constituting the order Taeniodontia may be considered here for want of a better connection. The order includes but a few forms from the Paleocene and Eocene of North America; they comprise a short-lived archaic outgrowth of the primitive insectivore stock. Such an end-

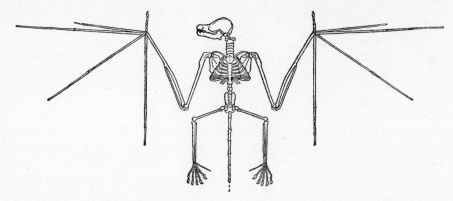

FIG. 250.—Skeleton of a fossil Eocene bat, *Palaeochiropteryx*. (From Revillod.)

type as *Stylinodon* from the Middle Eocene was comparatively large for its day, the skull reaching a foot or so in length. All the teeth had become high-crowned, rootless, simple pegs growing from a persistent pulp, and the enamel covering was limited to bands along the sides of the teeth. Only a single pair of incisors (the lateral) was retained, but the canines were well developed. The skull was short, the jaws deep and powerful; a leaf-eating mode of life has been suggested for these forms. Somewhat earlier forms, such as *Psittacotherium* (Fig. 251b) of the Torrejon and *Camalodon* of the Wasatch, were more primitive in that the teeth (except perhaps the canine) were still rooted and the molars enamel-covered, while the Paleocene *Conoryctes* was so close to the insectivore ancestors that it is difficult to decide in which group to place it. In the early taeniodonts the skull was still of primitive shape, long and low, with long and not particularly deep jaws, while the teeth were not merely rooted and enamel-covered but still retained much of the tuberculosectorial molar pattern of the early insectivores (Fig. 252b). Except for the loss of the central incisors there was little in these forms to show that they were incipient taeniodonts.

Obviously the group constitutes an early "experiment" on the part of the insectivore stock in the creation of a herbivorous form with grinding teeth. Taeniodonts, however, were seemingly never common and soon disappeared when placed in competition with the herbivorous ungulates. They have sometimes been confused with the tillodonts, next to be considered. Some writers have suggested that they are related to the edentates, the so-called "toothless" mammals; but

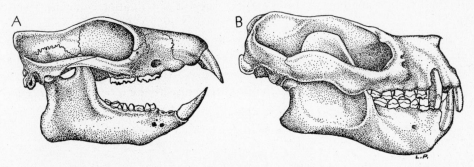

FIG. 251.—Aberrant Eocene placentals. *A, Tillotherium*, a Middle Eocene tillodont; skull about 13 inches long, *B, Psittacotherium*, a Lower Paleocene taeniodont; skull about 9½ inches in length. (*A* after Marsh, *B* after Wortman.)

except for the partial loss of enamel and other adaptive characters (especially in the limbs), the taenoidonts show no particular resemblance to these forms.

Tillodonts.—Here, too, may be mentioned the order Tillodontia, another short-lived archaic offshoot from the base of the placental stem. An end-form, *Tillo-*

FIG. 252.—*A*, upper cheek teeth of *Esthonyx*, a primitive tillodont (×⅔ approx.). *B*, upper molars of *Onychodectes* (×¾), to show the tritubercular origin of the teeth of taeniodonts. (*A* after Cope, *B* after Wortman.)

therium (Fig. 251a), of the Middle Eocene of North America, was the size of a brown bear. The skull, carnivore-like in general proportions, was long and low, the snout slim, the braincase small. The second pair of incisors in both jaws was much enlarged and rootless, much as in rodents; the canines were tiny; and the low crowned molars suggest a herbivorous or omnivorous diet. The beast had plantigrade-clawed five-toed feet and presumably a rather bear-like gait. Lower Eocene forms were much more primitive; *Esthonyx* (Fig. 252a) was less than half as big as the Middle Eocene type, the incisors not so disproportionately large and still rooted. The tillodonts have sometimes been grouped with the rodents, but there is no reason for considering them related except for the large gnawing incisors, a feature which developed in many groups of mammals.

CHAPTER XV

CARNIVORES

Among the varied mammalian groups which arose at the dawn of the Cenozoic, none is more prominent or more clearly derivable from the primitive placental stock than the order Carnivora, the flesh-eating mammals. The development of carnivores is a logical consequence of the insectivorous habits of the ancestral mammals. Once herbivorous mammals had come into existence, it was only to be expected that certain of the early insectivores should tend to prey upon them and take on various adaptations fitting them for a flesh-eating existence.

Carnivore adaptations.—Modifications for this type of life markedly affect the dentition. A good set of incisors for biting off flesh and a pair of piercing canines are essentials which were already present in insectivores and are seldom modified in carnivores. The primitive sharp-cusped cheek teeth may undergo various changes. For flesh-eating some sort of shearing apparatus to slice off the meat and cut tough sinews is a necessity. In insectivores there is some shearing effect between the back edge of each upper cheek tooth and the front edge of the following lower one (cf. Fig. 228). The carnivores have generally tended to emphasize the shear between a pair of highly specialized teeth called the carnassials. In the development of the opposed shearing surfaces, the originally diagonal line of meeting between the teeth tends to swing around to a fore-and-aft position, and the teeth concerned tend to simplify in structure and become high, narrow and elongated. In different carnivore groups the pair of teeth which developed into carnassials has varied. In living types it is always the last premolar above, the first molar below; but in some early types the pair selected was $\frac{M_1}{M_2}$, in others $\frac{M_2}{M_3}$. Some forms never developed carnassial teeth, and others have lost them functionally in correlation with changes in diet.

The teeth behind the carnassials tend to be reduced and lost in the more purely carnivorous types. In forms which have a mixed diet they are less reduced and in some cases have become low-crowned crushing teeth capable of dealing with nuts, fruit, and the like.

A carnivore normally must retain its claws for seizing its prey, and consequently there is but rarely any tendency to develop hoofs. The metacarpals and metatarsals are never greatly elongate, nor is there much reduction in the toes except for the pollex and hallux. Some forms (as the wolves) are rather good running forms; other (as the cats) depend upon a rapid dash and bound to obtain their prey.

Many carnivores are more or less arboreal in habits, while some types have become aquatic forms. The clavicle is reduced or absent.

We may picture a primitive carnivore as a small and perhaps arboreal animal much like the opossum in its general habits. In relation to arboreal life pollex and hallux were somewhat opposable; there was a five-toed semi-plantigrade foot and flexible limbs and body. The teeth would have been of the primitive tuberculo-sectorial type with small shearing surfaces developing between neighboring molar

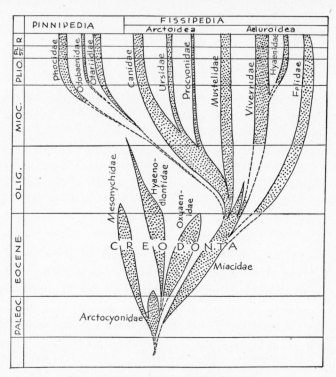

FIG. 253.—The phylogeny of the Carnivora.

teeth. The skull was presumably long; the brain, small. These conditions are approached in some of the known early carnivores.

The general history of the group (Fig. 253) includes: (1) the early development of a group of primitive carnivores (suborder Creodonta) which flourished particularly during the Eocene; (2) the emergence from one progressive family of creodonts of the modernized land carnivores (suborder Fissipedia) at the end of Eocene times; (3) the comparatively late development of marine carnivores (suborder Pinnipedia).

Creodonts.—The creodonts were the earliest and most primitive of carnivores. Appearing at the beginning of the Paleocene, they were very numerous throughout Eocene times. But with the disappearance of the more archaic ungulates upon which most of them presumably preyed they rapidly dwindled in importance and in the Oligocene were almost entirely replaced by the more advanced fissipedes.

The creodonts were in general rather archaic in their build, and their characteristics were mainly negative, primitive ones. The skull was generally rather long and low; the braincase was small with consequently well-developed sagittal and occipital crests. The dentition was usually complete, although exceptionally a small first premolar or the last molar might be lost. The molars were primitively tuberculo-sectorial; but there was considerable variation, especially in the development of carnassials. In contrast with the fissipedes the auditory bulla was unossified; and in the carpus the scaphoid, lunar, and centrale were distinct. There was usually no loss of toes. The claws were usually either fissured or flattened and rather hoof-like (Fig. 256a). In habits there appears to have been considerable variation: some were probably omnivorous, some small types perhaps still mainly insectivorous, others may have been carrion or mollusk-feeders.

The brain of the creodonts was generally of small size and their intelligence presumably low. This may have been a main cause of the early extinction of the group; for with replacement of the slow-footed and stupid herbivores of early Tertiary time by the swifter modernized ungulates, intelligent group pursuit (as the wolf pack) or clever stalking (as in the case of the cats) became necessary for the capture of prey. As will be noted, the only group of creodonts which has survived (by giving rise to the modern carnivore types) was the largest-brained family of the suborder.

The creodonts may be divided into four types: (1) primitive types without specialized carnassials (family Arctocyonidae); (2) forms without carnassials but with heavy crushing teeth (family Mesonychidae); (3) typical creodonts with carnassials $\dfrac{M1}{M2}$ or $\dfrac{M2}{M3}$ (families Oxyaenidae and Hyaenodontidae); (4) the ancestors of the fissipedes, with carnassials $\dfrac{P4}{M1}$ (family Miacidae).

Primitive creodonts.—Most primitive of all creodonts were the Paleocene members of the family Arctocyonidae, such as *Oxyclaenus* and *Tricentes* (Fig. 254a). These forms were of small size, with tuberculo-sectorial molars in which no particular pair was set apart for shearing purposes. Primitive in many other characters, with very small brains, slim bodies, and slender limbs with sharp-clawed feet, they seem unquestionably to represent forms transitional from the primitive Cretaceous insectivores to later carnivores.

Hardly a member of the family survived into the beginning of the true Eocene, but even in the Paleocene divergent lines were beginning to emerge among these earliest of carnivores. Most specialized of the family was the European *Arctocyon*

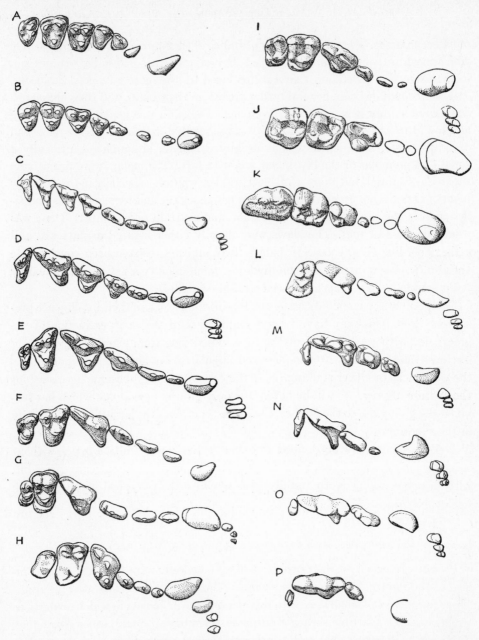

FIG. 254.—Right upper dentition of carnivores. *A, Tricentes* (Arctocyonidae) $\times \frac{3}{2}$ approx. *B, Mesonyx,* $\times \frac{1}{2}$. *C, Sinopa* (Hyaenodontidae), $\times \frac{5}{6}$. *D, Oxayaena,* $\times \frac{1}{2}$. *E, Vulpavus* (Miacidae), $\times \frac{3}{4}$. *F, Cynodictis,* a primitive fissipede, $\times 1$ approx. *G, Temnocyon* (Canidae), $\times \frac{1}{2}$ approx. *H, Phlaocyon,* a primitive procyonid, $\times \frac{5}{4}$. *I, Hemdicyon,* intermediate between dogs and bears, $\times \frac{1}{2}$. *J, Hyaenarctos,* a primitive bear, $\times \frac{5}{8}$. *K, Arctotherium,* a Pleistocene bear, $\times \frac{5}{12}$. *L, Mustela palaeosinensis* (Pliocene, China), $\times \frac{9}{8}$. *M, Hyaena bosei,* from the late Tertiary of India, $\times \frac{5}{12}$. *N, Dinictis,* an Oligocene true cat, $\times \frac{5}{8}$. *O, Metailurus,* a Pliocene true cat, $\times \frac{5}{9}$. *P, Smilodon,* a Pleistocene saber-tooth, $\times \frac{2}{5}$. (*A, B, G, H, M, N, P* after Matthew; *C–E* after Wortman; *F* after Scott; *I* after Gaudry; *J* after Frick; *K* after Merriam and Stock; *L, O* after Zdansky.)

(from which the family name is derived), an early parallel to the bears in size, feet, and dentition.

Blunt-toothed creodonts.—Equally early in appearance was an aberrant group, the family Mesonychidae, destined to survive until Oligocene times and to include among its members the largest of all land-living carnivorous mammals. These forms were primitive in the lack of specialized carnassials, but the early and small Paleocene types such as *Triisodon* show the beginnings of the specializations seen in such Eocene forms as *Mesonyx* (Figs. 254*b*, 255*b*). The cheek teeth had high

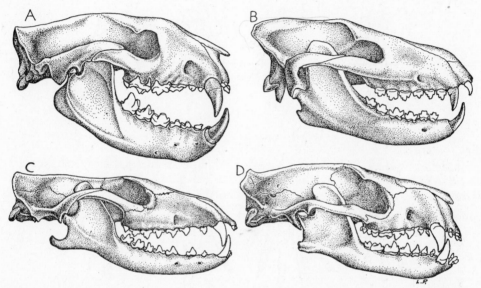

Fig. 255.—Skulls of creodonts. *A, Oxyaena*, skull length 8¼ inches. *B, Mesonyx*, skull length 11 inches. *C, Sinopa* (Hyaenodontidae), skull length about 6 inches. *D, Vulpavus* (Miacidae), skull length about 3 inches. (*A, C* after Wortman, *B* after Scott, *D* after Matthew.)

but blunt cusps which usually show signs of considerable wear, and the lower molars had a curious shearing talonid. In the larger and later forms the feet (Fig. 256*a*) were wolf-like in proportions, but with flattened fissured distal phalanges which presumably bore small hoofs rather than claws. While many early mesony-chids were of small size, some Eocene types grew to the size of a Kadiak bear. The culmination of the group is reached in the last surviving form, *Andrewsarchus*, of the Lower Oligocene of Mongolia, with a skull a full yard in length.

Typical creodonts.—The characteristic carnivores of the true Eocene belong to two families—the Hyaenodontidae and Oxyaenidae—both presumably derived from the Paleocene arctocyonids and both becoming progressively specialized to fit into the various modes of life afforded by the wide array of Eocene herbivorous types which formed their prey. In both families specialized shearing teeth were developed, as was the case in the miacids considered below; but in contrast with miacids the claws of these typical creodonts were inserted into fissured terminal phalanges.

The hyaenodonts begin with *Sinopa* (Figs. 254*c*, 255*c*), of the early Eocene, a rather small lightly built carnivore with comparatively unspecialized teeth, and culminated in *Hyaenodon* and other large and powerful Lower Oligocene types with two-bladed shearing cheek teeth of which $\dfrac{M2}{M3}$ formed the most powerful pair.

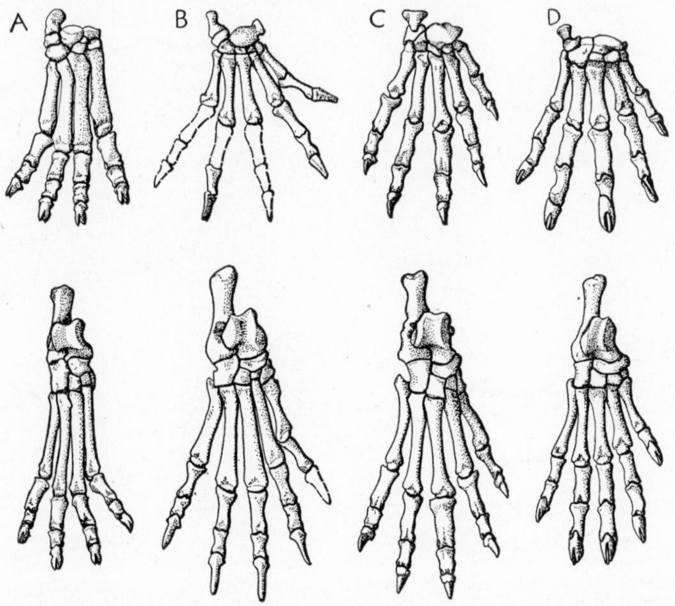

FIG. 256.—Feet of carnivores, manus above, pes below. *A*, *Synoplotheriun*, a mesonychid creodont. *B*, miacid creodonts, manus of *Vulpavus*, pes of *Didymictis*. *C*, the Oligocene canid *Daphoenus*. *D*, *Hoplophoneus*, an *Oligocene saber-tooth cat*. (*A* after Wortman, *B* after Matthew, *C* after Hatcher, *D* after Adams.)

These beasts presumably preyed upon the more archaic ungulates and soon disappeared. The group, however, survived until Miocene times in India and Africa; this is but one of many instances of the persistence in the Old World tropics of forms which had earlier disappeared from the more northerly regions of the world.

More varied in their adaptations were the oxyaenids, in which $\dfrac{M1}{M2}$ became the shearing teeth and in which the post-carnassial molars tended to disappear. The oxyaenids were generally rather long-bodied short-legged types with spreading plantigrade feet. Although tending to grow to large size in some cases, they seem to have been somewhat comparable to the modern mustelids in habits. *Oxyaena* (Figs. 254*d*, 255*a*, 257), of the Lower Eocene, was a powerful wolverine-like animal which appears to be ancestral to the Middle Eocene *Patriofelis*, of bear-like size, and to a still larger late Eocene Mongolian form. *Limnocyon* and its relatives were smaller mink-like flesh-eaters, while *Palaeonictis* was a rather cat-like type. Common in the Eocene, the oxyaenids disappear from the fossil record at the end of that period and were replaced by the developing fissipede families.

Progressive creodonts.—Although the creodonts previously considered were the dominant forms of the early Tertiary, the family Miacidae is more important from the point of view of later carnivore history, for it is this group which gave rise to the fissipedes of later ages. The first miacid appeared in the Paleocene; and there was a considerable number of Eocene genera, such as *Didymictis* and *Vulpavus*

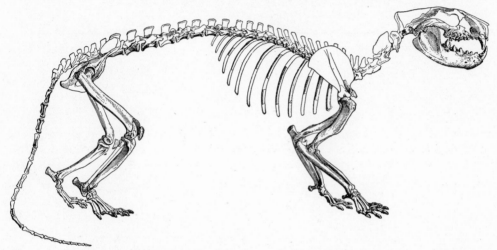

FIG. 257.—*Oxyaena*, an Eocene creodont (Oxyaenidae). Original about 39 inches long. (From Wortman.)

(Figs. 254*e*, 255*d*). In general they are comparatively poorly known, for almost all were of small size; and there is considerable evidence that they were rather persistently arboreal forest-dwellers—types which are usually infrequently fossilized. As in primitive carnivores generally, the body and tail were long, the limbs short but flexible, the pollex and hallux somewhat opposable (Fig. 256*b*). The tympanic bulla was unossified, and there was no fusion of carpal bones in cases where the skeleton is adequately known. In contrast with other creodonts the carnassial teeth were $\dfrac{P4}{M1}$, and the claw phalanges were unfissured.

These last characters are, of course, features in which the miacids resembled the later fissipedes; and it is generally agreed that these forms are the ancestors of the later carnivores. We have here followed the prevailing custom of including them (as being primitive and early carnivores) among the creodonts, but we might with equal propriety include the miacids with their descendants in the Fissipedia.

Judging by skeletal features alone, it is not clear why these small miacids, rather than the more flourishing Eocene families last considered, should have survived to give rise to later successful types. But it may be noted that they alone among the

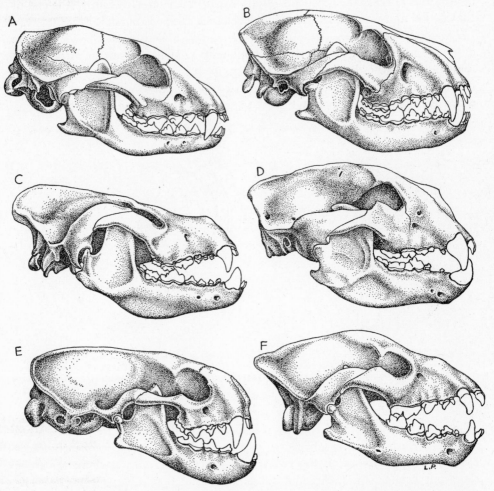

FIG. 258.—The skull in fissipede carnivores. *A*, *Cynodictis*, a primitive Oligocene fissipede, length of original about $3\frac{1}{4}$ inches. *B*, *Cynodesmus*, an Oligocene canid, length of original about $5\frac{1}{4}$ inches. *C*, *Hemicyon*, a Miocene form intermediate between dogs and bears, skull length about 13 inches. *D*, *Arctotheriun*, an American Pleistocene bear, skull length about 13 inches. *E*, *Mustela robusta*, an English Pleistocene weasel, skull length about $2\frac{2}{3}$ inches. *F*, *Hyaena variabilis*, a late Tertiary fossil hyaena from China, skull length about 9 inches. (*A* after Scott, *B* after Matthew, *C* after Frick, *D* after Merriam and Stock, *E* after Reynolds, *F* after Zdansky.)

older carnivores seem to have tended toward an increase in size of brain; and the rapid evolution of modernized ungulates may have placed a premium on brain, rather than dental or skeletal features, as an important factor in survival.

Within the Miacidae several types seem to have been more or less clearly distinguished. In some very primitive types the postcarnassial teeth were rather similar to the carnassials in structure, but in most they were flattened crushing teeth. In a number of types, of which *Miacis* is typical, all the molars were retained. These forms are thought to be possibly directly ancestral to the dog group; while in *Viverravus*, in which but two upper molars remained, we have a representative of forms possibly ancestral to the civets. In the late Eocene are found a number of genera, poorly known for the most part, which seem to lead almost imperceptibly into many of the primitive fissipede stocks of Oligocene times.

Fissipedes.—From these small but large-brained creodonts have thus been derived the Fissipedia, the dominant carnivores of the Oligocene and later periods. From most creodonts fissipedes may be easily distinguished in that the carnassials

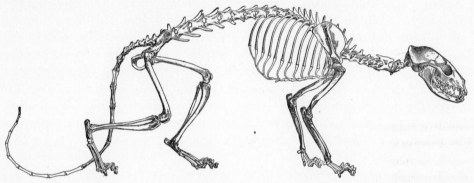

Fig. 259.—*Cynodictis*, a small primitive Oligocene fissipede carnivore. Original about 20 inches long. (From Matthew.)

are always $\dfrac{P4}{M1}$, the claw-bearing phalanges are never fissured or flattened, the auditory bulla is usually ossified, and in the hand the scaphoid, lunar, and centrale are fused into a single bone. But from the ancestral miacids they may be distinguished only by the last two characteristics.

The majority of late Eocene and early Oligocene fissipedes were still small and rather generalized types, perhaps rather civet-like in appearance and habits. *Cynodictis* (Figs. 254f, 258a, 259), found in the early Oligocene of both Europe and North America, was a typical primitive form. The skeleton was much like that of a civet or weasel. The body was long and flexible; the limbs, short. All five toes were present on the short and spreading feet, which appear to have been armed with retractile claws. As in most later carnivores the last upper molar had already disappeared. This form and most of its contemporaries were probably forest-dwellers and partly arboreal. *Cynodictis* is customarily considered a primitive dog but in most respects seems not far from an ideal ancestor of the whole fissipede group.

Before the end of the Oligocene several of the major groups of carnivores had already become distinct, and by the latter part of the Tertiary the carnivores had become divided into the seven or more families still existing at the present time.

It has long been recognized that living fissipedes may be conveniently divided into two great groups; one, the Arctoidea, including such types as dogs, raccoons, bears, and weasels; the other, the Aeluroidea, including civets, hyaenas, and felids. The fossils tend to support this division, although the distinctions are none too clear cut. The arctoids, which we shall first consider, may be distinguished in that the claws are almost never retractile, the tympanic bulla is formed entirely by the tympanic bone itself, and there is a long canal running fore and aft beneath the bulla for the artery (carotid) which supplies blood to the skull region and brain (cf. Fig. 224).

Dogs.—The basic stock of the arctoid group is to be found in the family Canidae. Represented today by a considerable number of dogs, wolves, and foxes, the group goes back to the very beginning of fissipede history, and fossil types are very numerous, presumably because the canids have been in great measure dwellers in open plains country. They are essentially cursorial terrestrial types with four digits well developed but with the pollex and hallux reduced, the toes close together, the claws blunt. The skull is long; the bulla, typically large. The shearing function of the carnassials is well developed; but there is some grinding surface on the molars, two of which are normally retained.

In the Oligocene and Lower Miocene of North America and Eurasia there were several dogs, such as *Cynodesmus* (Fig. 258b) and *Temnocyon* (Fig. 254g), which seem to have been on the main line of evolution toward the living canids; they were still small and generalized types which tended to lose the last upper molar. The limbs were elongating, pollex and hallux were reduced, and the running gait was evolving. It is probable that at about this stage there diverged a number of types leading to odd living forms, such as *Cuon*, the hunting dog of India, and *Otocyon*, the "large-eared fox" of South Africa. This last is of interest in that the number of molar teeth has secondarily increased so that there are often $\frac{4}{5}$ molars— one of the few cases in which the primitive placental number of teeth has been exceeded.

Tomarctus and other canids were common carnivores on the plains of the Northern Temperate Zone in later Tertiary times and lead to the dog and wolf (*Canis*) (Fig. 224), foxes (*Vulpes*), and other living types. Although now present in the three southern continents, canids were unknown in the Southern Hemisphere before Pleistocene times; and the dingo of Australia is quite possibly a type introduced by man. Dogs appear to have been the oldest animals domesticated by man, and remains of this camp-follower are common in Neolithic sites; probably the original dog was a wolf type, although the jackal has been advocated as an ancestor.

An extinct branch of the main dog stem is that of the Hyaena-like dogs of the Pliocene and Pleistocene, such as *Borophagus* and *Hyaenognathus*. These were large animals with a massive head and heavy teeth suggesting a carrion-feeding habit similar to that of the hyaenas of the Old World.

Bear dogs.—*Daphoenus* of the Lower Oligocene of America is of interest as the earliest representative of the group of "bear dogs" of Middle Tertiary times. This form was already about the size of a coyote. The early Miocene *Daphoenodon* (Fig. 260), possibly a direct descendant, had grown to the size of a wolf; while some of the later bear dogs of the Upper Miocene and Pliocene, as *Amphicyon*, rivaled the bears in size. The build was heavy, the tail long and massive, the limbs short and powerful, the feet five-toed and rather spreading; unlike the bears, however,

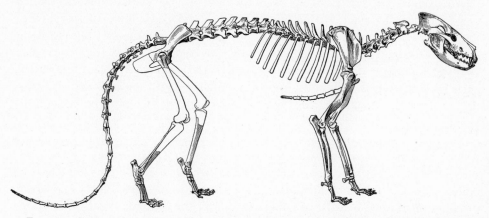

FIG. 260.—*Daphoenodon*, a Lower Miocene bear-dog. Original about 5 feet long. (From Peterson.)

they were digitigrade types. The complete set of molars was preserved and highly developed, while the shearing function of the carnassials was reduced. Obviously these big forms were far from being pure carnivores. While the later members of this group were merely parallel in development to the bears, *Daphoenus* was probably close to the true bear stock as well.

Raccoons.—Fairly closely related to the canids are the Procyonidae, of which the raccoon, *Procyon*, is the type. This and most other members of the family are small tree-living forms with semi-plantigrade feet and a full complement of toes. The procyonids have a mixed diet; and while there are only two molars, these have a good grinding surface. The carnassials have lost their shearing function, and the upper one has developed a hypocone. This obviously seems to be a reversion from the primitive carnivorous canid adaptations. In other respects, however, the procyonids are seemingly merely a series of persistently primitive relicts of the arboreal ancestors of the dogs. There are several other forms from central and South America, such as the kinkajou and coati, which are customarily included in the Procyonidae. A bit farther from the typical dogs is the Asiatic panda, *Ailurus*, a larger terrestrial form somewhat more bear-like, with a better development of the grinding teeth.

Phlaocyon (Fig. 254*h*), of the Lower Miocene of North America, is perhaps close to the ancestry of the raccoons. This animal was quite similar to the smaller dogs of the period except that the carnassial was losing its character with the development of the hypocone.

Bears.—The bears, constituting the family Ursidae, are a further development of the arctoid "dog" group away from a carnivorous mode of life to a mixed and mainly herbivorous diet. Their ancestors had lost the last molar before giving up flesh-eating; but in compensation the remaining molars are much elongated, with a wrinkled grinding surface. Here, as in the raccoons, the carnassial has lost much of its shearing character, but no hypocone has developed and the protocone has migrated backward. All the digits are retained in the plantigrade feet. While in diet and certain structural features the bears show some similarity to the raccoons, they differ in many others, such as, for example, the notably large size of the bears, their generally terrestrial habits, and (as a minor feature) the stub tail. Presumably their similarities are due merely to the descent of both groups from the primitive dog stock of the Oligocene.

Most living bears—the brown, grizzly, and black bears—form a closely related group, the genus *Ursus*, with which the polar bear is closely associated; while certain forms from Southern Asia, such as the Malay sun bear and the honey bear of India, are somewhat more distantly related; and the spectacled bear *Tremarctos* of South America is a still wider departure from the common ursid type. Bears are not uncommon in the Pleistocene of Eurasia and North America: in Europe a giant race of the brown bear was a cave-dweller contemporary with early man, while in the Americas *Arctotherium* (Figs. 254*k*, 258*d*), a short-faced relative of the spectacled bear, was present in both continents.

The early history of the bears has been a subject of much debate. A clew is given by the rare and poorly known living genus *Ailuropus* of Thibet. Sometimes called the "parti-colored bear," sometimes the "greater panda," this beast seems to be in many respects morphologically ancestral to the bears. It is considerably smaller than any true bear; and the teeth have not assumed the full bear characters, the molars being of a simpler pattern and less expanded than in more "orthodox" living types. Very similar to this living form and probably ancestral to the true bears was *Hyaenarctos* (Fig. 254*j*) of the Pliocene of Eurasia. This in turn is probably derived from *Hemicyon* (Figs. 254*i*, 258*c*) of the late Miocene of North America, which appears to be a descendant of the primitive Oligocene *Daphoenus*.

Mustelids.—Much more distantly related to the dogs, although also classed as arctoids, are the Mustelidae, a family including many familiar forms such as the skunk, weasel, badger, wolverine, and otter. Superficially at least, they appear more primitive than many of the arctoids just discussed; they tend to remain comparatively small in size, with short, stocky limbs and a full complement of toes; a majority have remained forest-dwellers, and many are still more or less arboreal; almost universally the mustelids have remained good carnivorous types. Continued emphasis on a flesh-eating diet has not only resulted in the retention of well-developed shearing teeth in the greater number of mustelids but also in the reduction of the molars; no living mustelid has more than a single post-carnassial molar in either jaw. In most forms the upper molar has a characteristic expansion of the inner portion with a "waist" between the two halves. The reduction in the molars (and often in the anterior premolars as well) has been accompanied by a shortening of the facial region of the skull.

The taxonomy of the numerous modern forms is somewhat unsettled (some have proposed to divide them into as many as thirteen subfamilies); and the fossil history of mustelids is comparatively poorly known, for apparently most of them were forest-dwelling types.

The ancestral Oligocene forms were small sharp-toothed carnivores. The two upper molars were usually still present, while the peculiar shape of the first molar had not been developed. These early types seem to have been very close to the more primitive dogs and even to the contemporary civet ancestors. Three main groups appear to have become established by Miocene times: (1) A group including the weasels (*Mustela* [Figs. 254e, 258e]), martens, fishers, etc. These are the typical small, short-limbed bloodthirsty carnivores of the group and have retained a sharp cutting type of dentition. (2) The wolverine (*Gulo*) and the "honey badger" of the Old World, large forms with robust teeth but predaceous habits. (3) A large group in which the dentition somewhat parallels the raccoons in that the carnassials have lost much of their shear while the molars tend to take on a grinding character. The skunks (*Mephitis*, etc.) are the more generalized members of this group; the otters (*Lutra*, etc.) are related forms which have taken up an aquatic fish-eating life, one even becoming a marine type, paralleling the seals. The badgers (*Taxidea*, etc.) are types in which the dentition is still less carnivorous, a hypocone being developed on the carnassial.

Civets.—The second major subdivision of the fissipede carnivores is that of the Aeluroidea, including the civet family, the hyaenas, and the felids. While it is generally recognized that this is a natural group, diagnostic characters common to all types are difficult to find. One technical key character lies in the fact that in this group, in contrast to the arctoids, the tympanic bone forms only the outer margin of the bulla, which is a double structure, the major portion being formed by a separate ossification, the entotympanic.

The basal stock of the group appears to lie in the family Viverridae, including civets, genets, the mongoose, and a number of other Old World types. The civet,

Viverra, is a representative form. It is a small carnivore with a long skull, a slim body, long tail, and short legs. All the premolars are present in this genus, but the first is tiny and is lost in many relatives. The carnassial is a good shearing tooth. Only two molars are present in either jaw; the upper ones are triangular and never develop a hypocone; the second is considerably smaller than the first.

In dentition and many other respects the typical civets are very similar to the viverravine subfamily of miacid creodonts of the late Eocene from which it is generally believed they have descended, and it is difficult in many cases to decide whether late Eocene or early Oligocene civet-like forms are true viverrids or their ancestors, and it is also difficult to distinguish them from primitive arctoids. Since the Oligocene, viverrid types have ranged widely in the Old World, although their history is not completely known, and they are absent from America, perhaps because their tropical habits have been a bar to migration.

Hyaenas.—A side branch of the civets which has progressed so far as to rank as an independent family is that constituting the Hyaenidae (Figs. 254m, 258f). The living hyaenas of the Old World tropics are large scavengers with heavy and blunt teeth for bone-crushing. The carnassials are powerful, but of the post-carnassial teeth there remains only a tiny upper molar. The hyaena is a digitigrade running type which has lost hallux and pollex and has blunt nails rather than claws.

There are two living types, the spotted hyaena of South and Central Africa, and the striped hyaena of North Africa and Southern Asia; both were present in Europe in the Pleistocene. The hyaenas can be traced back with ease to the viverrids, from which they are a late offshoot. *Ictitherium* of the Upper Miocene and early Pliocene is intermediate in character, for, although tending in the hyaena direction, it has the complete viverrid dentition and the teeth are not as heavy as in the modern types.

Conventionally grouped with this family is the "aard wolf," *Proteles*, of South Africa, which superficially has the appearance of a small, slim hyaena. It is, however, an insect-eater, and in relation to this fact the jaws are (in marked contrast to the hyaena type) slim in build and the teeth tiny and uniform in character. Like the hyaenas the "earth wolf" is obviously a specialized offshoot of the civet group, but no connecting fossil forms are known.

Cats.—The most interesting of the aeluroids and in many ways the most specialized of all carnivores are the "cats," comprising the family Felidae. All modern felids, from the domestic form to the lion and tiger, may be included in the genus *Felis* in a broad sense. In contrast to the dogs, for example, the cats, although digitigrade, are not good running types, but depend for success in catching prey on a sudden leap onto their victim; the skeleton is hence of a more flexible type than that of the dog, the claws are sharper and are retractile. The pollex is lost in modern forms, although the hallux is retained. The skull is comparatively short and high. The canines are powerful. The premolars partake somewhat of the carnassial pattern, and one upper and two lower ones are functional (there are one or two additional small ones in the upper jaw). The carnassials are well developed

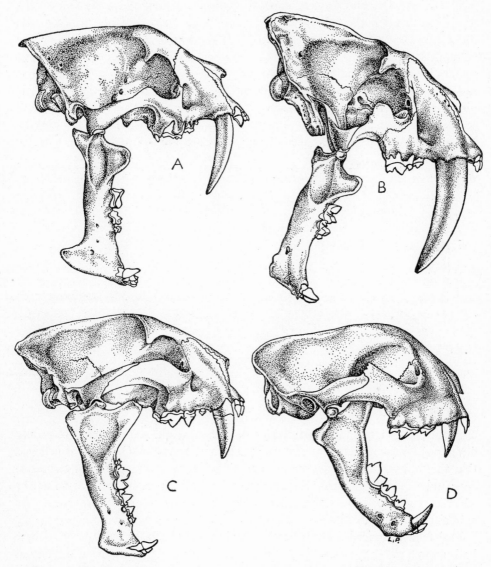

FIG. 261.—Skulls of saber-tooths and true cats. *A, Hoplophoneus,* an Oligocene saber-tooth. Skull length about $6\frac{1}{4}$ inches. *B, Smilodon,* Pleistocene. Skull length about 12 inches. *C, Dinictis,* an Oligocene ancestor of the true cats. Skull length about $6\frac{1}{8}$ inches. *D, Metailurus minor,* a Pliocene true cat. Skull length about $5\frac{3}{4}$ inches. (*A–C* after Matthew, *D* after Zdansky.)

as purely shearing structures of two blades, paracone and metastyle above, paraconid and metaconid below (the heel is lost). The cats are almost pure carnivores, and there is no grinding surface left in their dental battery; as in the hyaenas, only a tiny first upper molar remains behind the carnassials.

The living felids may be considered as typical of a subfamily, the Felinae. In sharp contrast are the saber-toothed "cats," Machaerodontinae, of which the Pleistocene *Smilodon* (Figs. 254*p*, 261*b*) is a good example. In the saber-tooths the upper canines were exceedingly long stabbing and slicing structures; the lower canines were correspondingly reduced, and there was often a flange at the front end of the lower jaw serving as a guide for the upper teeth. Connected with this specialization were many related ones. The jaw was so constructed that it could be opened to about a right angle; the reduced ascending ramus of the jaw and the high-crested V-shaped back part of the skull are related to the consequently

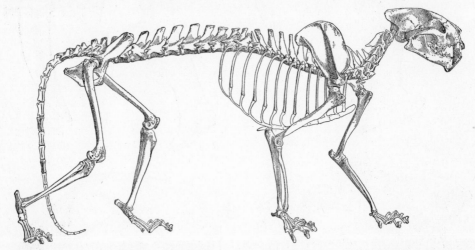

Fig. 262.—*Dinictis*, an Oligocene ancestor of the cats. Original about $3\frac{1}{4}$ feet long. (From Matthew.)

changed position of the temporal muscle. The mastoid process was powerfully developed for the attachment of muscles which pull down the head. It is believed that the saber-tooths preyed mainly upon thick-skinned animals such as mastodons and elephants, in which the cat method of biting into the neck would not be effective, and operated by stabbing and slicing with the mouth open, causing the animal to bleed to death.

Both felines proper and saber-tooths may be traced back to the Oligocene, where both groups were represented by forms somewhat more primitive but already of fairly good size. In *Hoplophoneus* (Fig. 261*a*) we see all the essential characters of the later saber-tooths, although they were here not so highly developed; the skull was not so high posteriorly, the saber not quite so long (although the jaw flange was even more prominent), and the premolars were less reduced than in later forms. The probable Oligocene ancestor of the true felines was *Dinictis* (Figs. 254*n*, 261*c*, 262). This animal was more primitive than later cats in such respects as the comparatively unreduced cheek teeth; but the upper canine was considerably larger than in modern cats (although not as large as in *Hoplophoneus*), the lower canine smaller, and there was a distinct flange alongside the lower jaw. *Dinictis* was thus a saber-tooth to some extent and by some has been thought really to belong to that group. But there is a good series of forms connecting *Dinictis* with the modern felines (Figs. 254*o*, 261*d*). It appears that in the true cats there has been a reversal of evolution, that their ancestors passed through a primitive saber-tooth stage, but that since the Oligocene they have tended to reduce the upper canines again to normal proportions and redevelop the lower ones.

The extinction of saber-tooths, plentiful all through the Tertiary, may perhaps be associated with the increasing rarity of large thick-skinned ungulates, "pachyderms," such as elephants and mastodons, upon which they preyed and the comparative increase of smaller types, as horses and antelopes, on which the true cat type of biting attack was more effective. It is possible that the mastodon was a favorite victim of the later saber-tooths. In North America these primitive proboscideans persisted until the end of Pleistocene times, and so did *Smilodon*. In Europe, however, mastodons disappeared at the beginning of the Ice Age, and the saber-tooths also disappeared early.

The great majority of living felids are inhabitants of the Eastern Hemisphere. This is perhaps to be associated with the comparative absence of large game animals in the Americas; in the Pleistocene, when large herbivores were more abundant in North America, a large lion-like type was present, as well as the contemporary saber-tooths.

The ancestry of the felids cannot be followed back of the beginning of the Oligocene. The group, however, must have originated well back in Eocene times, for, while the other fissipede carnivores of the early Oligocene were almost universally still small and primitive in structure, the contemporary cats had not only become rather large and highly specialized but had already split into these two divergent groups.

Pinnipeds.—A final subdivision of the order is that including the aquatic carnivores, the Pinnepedia. In the seals and walruses, in contrast with all other aquatic vertebrates, swimming is entirely accomplished by means of the limbs, for the tail apparently had become so reduced in the terrestrial ancestors of the seals that it was incapable of redevelopment into a propulsive organ. The two hind legs in the seals have been turned backward to form a substitute for the tail, while the front legs are well-developed steering organs. In the limbs the upper segments are short and lie inside the surface of the trunk. The hand and foot are long, although there is no increase in the number of phalanges. All five toes are retained with webs of skin between them, the first digit often being quite strong and acting as a cutwater. Scaphoid, lunar, and centrale are fused in the hand, as in fissipedes (suggesting descent from that group). The dentition, for fish or mollusk-eating, is regressive. The incisors tend to disappear, although the canines are usually well developed. The molars are usually reduced in number, but the premolars are preserved. There is no specialization of carnassials, and the cheek teeth form a uniform series of simple structure.

Most primitive in many ways are the eared seals (family Otariidae) in which group are included the fur seal and sea lion. External ears are present, and the hind legs are still flexible enough to be brought around forward again from the swimming position for locomotion on land. The cheek teeth have but a single cusp and usually but a single root. The family goes back to Lower Miocene strata in which *Allodesmus* is a rather primitive type. Practically all known fossils are from the shores of the Pacific, which thus appears to have been the ancestral home of the family.

An offshoot of this group is *Odobaenus*, the walrus of northern seas, placed in a distinct family. It appears to be structurally related to the eared seals but is larger and clumsier, earless, and with a dentition adapted to mollusk-eating. There are huge rootless upper canines, but most of the other teeth are small and tend to drop out early, leaving a few heavy pegs of premolars for shell crushing. The oldest forms, such as *Prorosmarus*, of the Upper Miocene, were somewhat more primitive and closer to the eared seals.

The Phocidae, earless seals, are the most abundant pinnipeds today. These forms are more completely adapted for water-living; the hind legs cannot be turned forward at all. In contrast with the eared seals, however, the cheek teeth are usually two-rooted and have accessory cusps.

As with the two other types, the earless seals may be traced back to the Miocene. Beyond this date, however, our record of pinniped ancestry cannot be traced. It has been suggested that they have descended directly from Eocene creodonts. But a number of features suggest that they have been derived from primitive fissipedes, probably of the arctoid group. Perhaps a better knowledge of Oligocene coastal deposits may some day yield specimens of the intermediate forms in which the transition from terrestrial life to a fish-eating aquatic existence was under way.

CHAPTER XVI
ARCHAIC UNGULATE GROUPS

Under the head of "ungulates," or hoofed mammals, may be ranged almost all the larger herbivorous members of the class. The name, however, is not entirely a distinctive one, for while typical forms, such as the horse and cow, have hoofs, there are included in the ungulate orders a number of animals with well-developed claws and even such types as the purely aquatic sea cows. Nor do the ungulates form a single natural group, for the hoofed condition has undoubtedly been attained independently by various lines; and, strange as it may seem, a cow is, for example, probably as closely related to a lion as to a horse.

Despite the artificial nature of the assemblage, there are certain structural changes which have been generally undergone in the transformation of a primitive placental of whatsoever group into a large herbivore—changes having chiefly to do with dentition and the locomotor apparatus.

Ungulate teeth.—The generalized dentition of primitive placentals was unfitted for a purely herbivorous diet; low-crowned sharp-cusped molars are not suitable organs for undertaking the thorough mastication which leaves, grain, or grass must undergo before passing into the digestive tract; and the development of a large grinding area is an obvious necessity for a herbivore. The primitively triangular upper molars have tended to square up, usually by the development of a hypocone at the back, giving essentially a four-cusped tooth in which the two intermediate conules have played a varying rôle (Fig. 227*b*, etc.). In the lower molars the paraconid has disappeared and the heel is built up to give a type of tooth with the talonid and trigonid of equal height and each contributing two of the four principal cusps—protoconid, metaconid, hypoconid, and entoconid.

The originally sharp tubercles generally softened down to low swellings, giving a bunodont condition found in many early ungulates (Fig. 268*a*, *b*, etc.) and still present in an exaggerated form in the swine. Further changes have taken place in most groups. There may be an elongation of the individual cusps into curved ridges, most characteristically seen in the selenodont (crescent moon-shaped) pattern of many even-toed ungulates, such as camels, deer, and cattle (cf. Fig. 304*a*, *b*, *c*, etc.). More common, however, has been the development of connections between adjacent cusps, forming varied patterns of ridges (lophs) on the tooth. In a lophodont upper molar (Fig. 229) three lophs are most common: (1) an ectoloph, forming the outer wall of the tooth, connecting paracone and metacone and often (if the styles external to the cusps develop) with a W-shaped contour; (2) a protoloph, including the protocone and protoconule; and (3) a metaloph, similarly

297

formed from hypocone and metaconule. There are sometimes varied secondary connections of these crests, and in some cases additional spurs and ridges may develop. The cross crests may develop but not the ectoloph (primitive proboscideans, etc.); conversely, only the ectoloph may develop, leaving isolated rounded cusps internally, a bunolophodont tooth (as in titanotheres, chalicotheres [Fig. 288g, h]). In the lower teeth a common development has been the retention and emphasis of the two V's of the original triangular pattern (Fig. 289). These ridges undergo various modifications; they may become crescentic in shape or develop into two hook-shaped ridges which may eventually become two cross-lophs very similar to those sometimes found in the upper teeth.

Food-grinding, with the passage of one tooth across the surface of its opponent, implies considerable wear; this wear is greatly increased when an animal takes up highly abrasive silicious food such as grass; further, increased size of the individual only squares the grinding surface available while cubing the amount of food required. It is not surprising, therefore, to find that, although many early types had low-crowned (brachyodont) molars, many ungulates develop a high-crowned prism-shaped type of cheek tooth which will stand a very considerable amount of grinding before being worn down to the roots and exhausted.

In this process of development of hypsodont teeth we find that the cement, originally confined to the roots of the teeth, plays a prominent part. If nature were to construct a high-crowned tooth merely by greatly elongating the original ridges and cusps, the product would be a series of thin parallel columns, easily broken and full of crannies. One alternative "solution" would seem to be that of enormously thickening the block of dentine above the root, leaving the cusps as superficial structures. This, however, is seldom seen except in some archaic and comparatively unsuccessful mammals. Instead, in a number of groups, there has been a development of the cement so that it completely covers the tooth before eruption and fills all the interstices between the ridges. This results in a solid structure which, upon wear, exhibits all three tooth-forming substances on the crown—dentine in the center of the ridges, an enamel layer at their boundaries, and cement outside and filling all vacant spaces.

Increased surface may also be attained by elongation of the row of grinding teeth. This may be accomplished by the increase in size of individual teeth, and in many cases (as in the horses) molars in later types are longer than in earlier ones. But a more common process by which this end has been attained is by expanding the premolars (usually of comparatively small size to begin with) and adding them functionally to the molar grinding series. Independently in a large number of groups may be traced a progressive increase in the surface area of the premolars, and in some cases (horses, for example) all except the first of these teeth have become almost identical in structure with the molars (cf. Fig. 288a, b).

The cropping of food is the function of the anterior portion of the dentition. For this duty the incisors are commonly retained, as in the horse. But the upper ones may be lost (as in the cow), the upper lip or a horny pad taking their place; and we find here and there various other specializations, such as the much enlarged chisel-like incisors of South American ungulates. The canines are often functionless and reduced or absent; and in most ungulate groups we find a gap, or diastema, developing between the front group of cropping teeth and the grinding series in the cheeks.

The ungulates have always been the main source of food for the larger contemporary flesh-eaters. In connection with defense, horns or horn-like structures

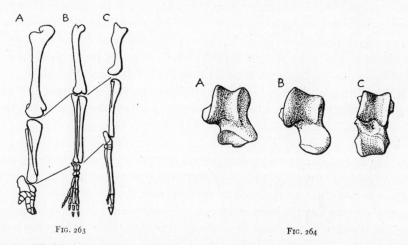

FIG. 263

FIG. 264

FIG. 263.—Hind limbs of elephant, opossum, and horse, to show changes in limb proportions from a primitive condition (B) to (C) that of a fast-running ungulate with short femur and long metapodials, and (A) a graviportal type with a long femur and short broad foot. (Mainly after Gregory.)

FIG. 264.—Astraguli of Eocene ungulates: A, *Heptodon*, a perissodactyl. B, *Phenacodus*, a condylarth. C, *Homacodon*, an artiodactyl. (A, B after Osborn, C after Marsh.)

have developed in many groups. Sometimes (especially in early types) there may be large stabbing canines. In general, however, the best defense is flight; and rapid locomotion, both for escape from enemies and for migration from one feeding ground to another, is characteristic of ungulates.

Ungulate limbs.—In the more typical ungulates the limbs are elongated and the limb bones typically slim. In fast-running forms the humerus and femur are short, resulting in a speedier muscle action, and the second segment of the limb is much elongated (Fig. 263). With this elongation there is often a tendency toward the reduction of the ulna and fibula and the placing of the entire weight on radius or tibia. There is never, however, a complete loss of these bones, for they carry important muscle attachments and articulations, and the ends are usually present but fused with the remaining bone. There is practically no capability of rotating the limb segments; motion tends to be restricted to a highly efficient fore-and-aft drive. Most ungulates have an alternating type of carpus (and tarsus)—one, that is, in which the connections between the elements and with the metapodials are so arranged that each functional toe helps support at least two of the three proximal carpal elements. The astragalus (Fig. 264) usually develops a rounded and deeply grooved upper surface over which the tibia glides without danger of turning or twisting.

The primitive placental was presumably more or less plantigrade. With faster locomotion, the metapodials (and thus the palm and sole) tend to be lifted off the ground, giving a digitigrade gait. With further development of speed the digits themselves are lifted, until the animal may only touch the ground with the tips of the toes—the unguligrade condition. With the result of attaining solid stance, hoofs are developed; the terminal phalanx of the toes broadens and is surrounded on the front and sides by a thick nail-like modification of the original claw, while a horny layer padded by elastic tissues protects the flat lower surface.

With the lifting of the hand and foot into an unguligrade position, it is obvious that there would have been a tendency for the shorter lateral toes to fail to reach the ground and become non-functional. This was, in most groups, followed quite naturally by a reduction of these side toes and increasing strengthening of the central ones. The hallux and pollex, which are not only short but originally diverged at an angle from the other toes, were the first to go. Beyond this stage reduction has taken place according to two schemes. In the majority of ungulates (as in the ancestors of the horses, for example) the third toe was the longest, and the axis of symmetry of the foot lies through this digit (mesaxonic). In such forms the fifth toe has usually been lost, giving a three-toed condition, and further emphasis of the central toe and reduction of lateral ones has led in the modern horses to the development of a one-toed form (Figs. 287, 296, 297). In other ungulates, such as the ancestors of the cow and pig, the third and fourth toes were primitively equal in length, and the axis of symmetry passed between them (the paraxonic type). As in mesaxonic ungulates, pollex and hallux usually disappear, and many forms are found to be in a four-toed state. Frequently, however, the two central toes have enlarged and the lateral ones have dwindled or vanished to leave a two-toed form; the cloven hoof of the cow or deer is, of course, really two appressed digits (Figs. 307, 309, 312).

Simultaneously with toe reduction, changes have usually occurred in the metapodials. In fast-running forms there has been a great lengthening of these elements, giving a third functional segment to the limb through which an additional upward and forward drive may be imparted to the body. With the reduction of the toes, metapodial reduction usually takes place as well. Splints of bone often represent the metapodials of lost digits, as in the horse; while, on the other hand, the metapodials may be incomplete, although small non-functional toes may remain as dew claws. In paraxonic forms the two main metapodials may fuse in advanced types into a single element, the cannon bone.

In typical ungulate running, the forward spring is given chiefly by the hind legs; the fore limbs bear the main impact on landing. The clavicle is usually absent, thus releasing the body from any solid connection with the front limbs and allowing the shock to be taken up by the elastic give of the muscles slinging the body between the shoulder blades.

The heavy ungulates, such as the elephants, have a different locomotor "problem" somewhat comparable with that of the dinosaurs. In an animal of this sort, the graviportal type, the limbs tend to be large straight columns, with the femur and humerus longer than the second segments (Fig. 263c), giving a powerful rather than a speedy muscular action. There is little elongation of the metapodials, and all the digits tend to be retained to form a semicircular clump presumably inclosed, in fossil forms as in the living elephant, in a thick pad. The pelvis tends to be so shaped that the head of the femur lies beneath it rather than at the side, and the ilia are typically expanded laterally into broad wings in relation to the changed position of the muscles.

Ungulate classification.—The term "ungulate" covers, as we have noted, a vast and varied assemblage. Most living forms are included in two orders—the mesaxonic (odd-toed) perissodactyls and the paraxonic (even-toed) artiodactyls—which have flourished in the northern continents since the beginning of the Eocene, while the elephants, conies, and sea cows are surviving members of an ancient African group of subungulates. There are, in addition, a number of entirely extinct groups which will be treated later in the present chapter.

Ungulates are unknown in any Cretaceous deposits but presumably must have been developing from the primitive placental stock at the end of the Mesozoic. For in the Paleocene three distinct types of archaic ungulates were already present and widespread in Eurasia and America. These ancient forms are ranged in three orders: (1) the Condylarthra, a Paleocene and Eocene group which includes a number of generalized and primitive types and may be close to the ancestry of many later hoofed forms; (2) the Amblypoda, a group which did not survive the Eocene but was for a time the most prominent of ungulate orders; (3) the Notoungulata, rare and early extinct in northern regions but attaining a striking development in the Cenozoic of South America.

Condylarths.—The order Condylarthra includes a number of Paleocene and Eocene ungulates of primitive character. Best known of the group is *Phenacodus* of the Lower Eocene of North America and Europe (Figs. 265, 266, 268a, b, 269). This ungulate reached a size rather considerable for the times, the largest species attaining the dimensions of a tapir. Its general appearance was that of a carnivore rather than an ungulate, for the tail was long and the limbs short and quite primitive in structure. The radius and tibia were only about the same length as femur and humerus, and ulna and fibula were unreduced. There was little elongation of the metapodials; and all five toes were present, although (in mesaxonic fashion) the third toe was somewhat the longest and strongest. The carpus was serial in nature, each distal element lying directly beneath a proximal one, without the sharing of support characteristic of the alternating carpus of most ungulates. The

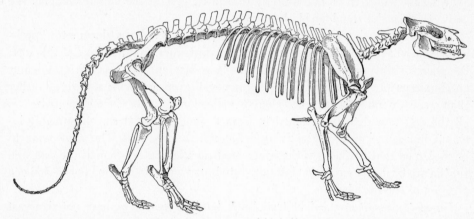

FIG. 265.—*Phenacodus*, a primitive ungulate (Condylarthra). Original about $5\frac{1}{2}$ feet long. (From Osborn.)

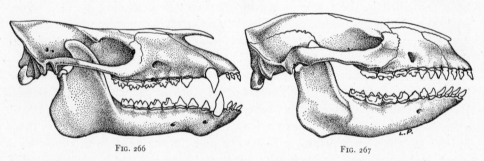

FIG. 266

FIG. 267

FIG. 266.—Skull of the condylarth, *Phenacodus*, length about 9 inches. (After Cope.)
FIG. 267.—Skull of *Hyopsodus*, length about $2\frac{3}{4}$ inches. (After Matthew.)

clavicle, however, had already disappeared; and one certain ungulate character was present in that hoofs obviously were present on the stumpy end phalanges.

The skull, again, was much like that of the creodonts—long and low, with orbits open behind and with a sagittal crest in correlation with the very small brain. The dentition was complete, the canines were still large, and there was only a slight diastema. However, the cheek teeth were already partially adapted for a herbivorous rather than a flesh-eating mode of life. The molars were in the bunodont stage. Six cusps were present above and below, for a hypocone had already developed in the upper molars, while the paraconid was still present in the lower teeth. The premolars were still comparatively simple; the last lower one had attained a molar-like appearance, but none of the upper ones had passed beyond a tritubercular stage.

This interesting form was once believed by some to be the ancestor of the later ungulates, particularly the perissodactyls. But it is rather late in occurrence and much too large to occupy such an ancestral position, and some of its characters (as the serial carpus) are not those expected in an ancestor of the later groups. In the Paleocene of North America occurs *Tetraclaenodon*, which appears to have been a direct ancestor of *Phenacodus*. In this somewhat smaller form the dentition

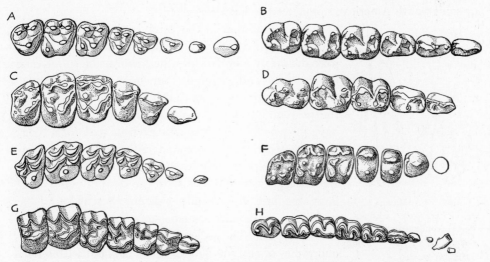

Fig. 268.—The cheek teeth of condylarths and litopterns. *A, B*, right upper and left lower cheek teeth of the condylarth *Phenacodus*, $\times\frac{5}{6}$ approx. *C, D*, of *Hyopsodus*, $\times\frac{3}{2}$ approx. *E*, right upper teeth of *Meniscotherium*, $\times\frac{5}{4}$ approx. *F*, right upper teeth of *Didolodus*, a primitive litoptern, $\times\frac{5}{4}$ approx. *G, H*, right upper and left lower teeth of *Diadaphorus*, an advanced litoptern, $\times 1$ approx. (*A–E* after Matthew, *F–H* after Ameghino.)

was more primitive in nature, and the feet were apparently terminated by rather broad claws instead of hoofs. *Ectocion*, of the Lower Eocene, had teeth of a type similar to those of perissodactyls, although not itself an ancestor of the odd-toed forms.

Very different in many respects was *Hyopsodus* (Figs. 267, 268c, d), a form about the size of a hedgehog which was common throughout the Eocene of North America. In skull and dentition *Hyopsodus* was rather primitive and not unlike certain insectivores or lemurs. There was no diastema; but the canine was reduced and the teeth were of uniform height, while the molars were of the bunodont type of many primitive ungulates. Primitive, again, were the clawed phalanges and the short and spreading feet; it is not improbable that *Hyopsodus* was a semi-arboreal type. Despite these facts it is to be regarded as a condylarth rather than as an insectivore or primate, with which groups some would place it. *Mioclaenus*, a Paleocene relative, is mainly known from cheek teeth which are quite sharp-cusped and similar to those of early creodonts.

Little *Meniscotherium* (Fig. 268e), of the late Paleocene and Lower Eocene of North America, represents a third type of condylarth, with a peculiar combination of characters. The molars were advanced in structure, with a selenodont pattern. The limbs were short and stout, as in *Phenacodus;* but the feet (as in *Hyopsodus*) appear to have had claw-like structures rather than hoofs. The relationships of this odd form are none too clear. A connection with the Old World conies or some South American ungulates has been suggested.

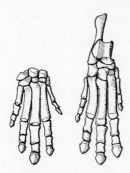

FIG. 269.—Manus and pes of *Phenacodus*, a Lower Eocene condylarth. (After Cope.)

It is obvious that in the condylarths we are dealing with a group of very primitive ungulates. In all the teeth were distinctly adapted for a herbivorous diet, but their low-crowned and generally bunodont condition shows them to have been very primitive herbivores indeed. In the postcranial skeleton *Phenacodus* alone appears to have possessed true hoofs, but even in that form there were few other ungulate characteristics. It is not improbable that the more primitive condylarths (although not *Phenacodus*) were quite close to the stem of many of the later ungulate groups, although our present knowledge permits of no definite statement.

Amblypods.—The order Amblypoda constitutes a second group of early ungulates which contains within itself some highly specialized types, including the largest land mammals of the Eocene. Hoofs were developed, but five toes were always present and the limbs were never elongated. The teeth were usually lophodont in nature, and of peculiar (although varied) structure. As in the condylarths (and, indeed, most early mammals) the brain was small and primitive in structure.

A rather characteristic primitive form was *Pantolambda* (Figs. 270a, 271a, 272a, 273a, *b*) of the Upper Paleocene of North America. This form was already surprisingly large for the times, being nearly the size of a sheep. The skull was long and low; all the teeth were present and the canines large, presumably serving as defensive weapons. In the triangular upper molars the three main cusps were V-shaped, while two V-shaped crests were present in the lower molars. The tail was long, the limbs short and stout, the toes stubby and spreading, and the skeleton in general retains many primitive features.

Periptychus, also from the North American Paleocene, was as large as *Pantolambda* and related to that form. The dentition, however, was quite different, for, while the molars were more primitive in that they were bunodont, *Periptychus* had expanded the inner side of the upper molars by adding to the protocone not only a hypocone behind but a large protostyle in front (Fig. 274). Smaller and earlier members of the family to which *Periptychus* belonged were often no larger

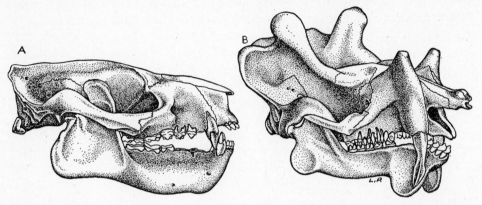

FIG. 270.—Skulls of amblypods. *A, Pantolambda bathmodon* of the Paleocene; skull about 6 inches long. *B, Uintatherium* of the Upper Eocene; skull about 2½ feet in length. (*A* after Osborn, *B* after Marsh.)

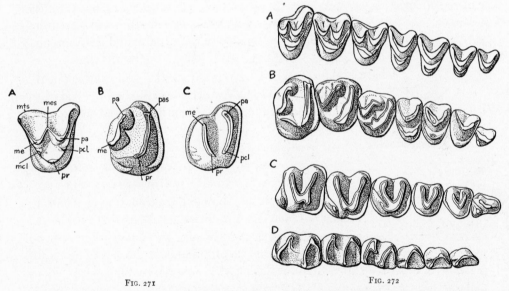

FIG. 271   FIG. 272

FIG. 271.—Right upper molars of three amblypods. *A*, the Paleocene *Pantolambda*. *B*, the Lower Eocene *Coryphodon*. *C*, the Late Eocene *Uintatherium*. In *Pantolambda* the tooth is of a simple trituber-cular pattern. The homologies in *B* and *C* are disputed; the interpretation here adopted is that of Simpson. For abbreviations see Figure 290.

FIG. 272.—Amblypod teeth. Right upper cheek teeth of *A, Pantolambda*, about ¾ natural size, *B, Coryphodon*, about ⅓ natural size, *C, Uintatherium*, about 5/12 natural size. *D*, left lower cheek teeth of *Coryphodon*, about ⅓ natural size. (*A, B, D* after Osborn, *C* after Matthew.)

than a rat in size; they are poorly known but may lie near the base of the amblypod stock.

A stage beyond *Pantolambda* is found in *Coryphodon* (Figs. 271*b*, 272*b*, *d*, 275), which appeared in the late Paleocene and was common in the Lower Eocene of North America and Europe. *Coryphodon* resembled the later hippopotamus in

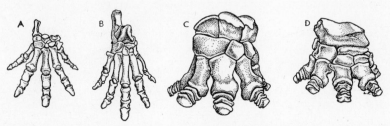

FIG. 273.—Feet of amblypods. *A, B*, manus and pes of the Paleocene *Pantolambda. C, D, Uintatherium* of the Upper Eocene. (*A, B* after Osborn, *C, D* after Marsh.)

size and build. The limbs were short and massive with a columnar structure and an elephant-like type of foot.

The skull was (again) low with a high sagittal crest, and very large. The premolars and lower molars were very similar to those of *Pantolambda*, but the structure of the upper molars was quite different. According to a current interpretation, the para- and metacones had swung toward the back half of the tooth, while a great ridge extended outward from the protocone along the front edge. *Coryphodon* became extinct at the end of the Lower Eocene, although a relative lingered on for a time in Mongolia.

FIG. 274.—Right upper molar of *Periptychus*, an Eocene amblypod. The protocone (*pr*) is centrally situated on the inside of the tooth, bounded posteriorly by a small hypocone (*hy*) and anteriorly by a protostyle (*prs*). (After Osborn.)

More advanced amblypods were the uintatheres, which ranged through the entire Eocene. In most respects the later and larger forms, such as *Uintatherium* (Figs. 270*b*, 271*c*, 272*c*, 273*c, d*), showed a continuation of the evolutionary tendencies exhibited in *Pantolambda* and *Coryphodon*. The bulk was that of a rhinoceros, the limbs still more massive. Three pairs of bony, horn-like protuberances developed on nasals, maxillae, and parietals; these and the dagger-like canines were much larger in the males. There was considerable reduction in the front teeth; the upper incisors and the first premolar were usually absent, and the lower incisors small; here, as in a number of other later ungulates, the lips were presumably replacing the teeth as cropping organs.

The upper molars were of a peculiar construction, with two converging crests occupying most of the surface of the tooth. The nature of this structure has been

much debated. If, as seems likely, one ridge is formed by protoconule and paracone, the other of protocone and metacone, it is obvious that the uintatheres were
not descended from *Coryphodon* but represent a parallel development from the
primitive amblypod stock.

The uintatheres appeared in the shape of comparatively small and primitive
forms at the close of the Paleocene and continued to grow in size and become increasingly bizarre and specialized during the course of Eocene. At the close of the
period they disappeared, giving place to more progressive ungulates. Neither they
nor any other well-known amblypods appear to have been the progenitors of later

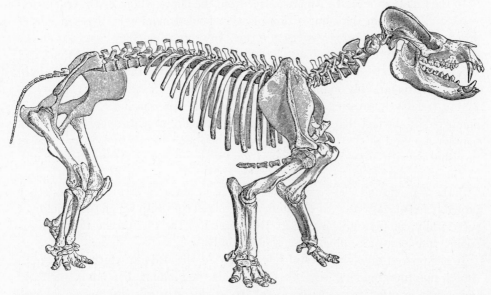

FIG. 275.—*Coryphodon*, a large Lower Eocene amblypod. Original about 8 feet long. (From Osborn.)

ungulate types. They seem merely to have been a sterile, but for the times a most
successful, experiment in ungulate development. Comparatively crude and in-
adaptive limb and tooth structure and a small brain seem to have been among
the factors which led to their extinction.

South American ungulates.—A third archaic group of Paleocene and Eocene ungulates is that of the Notoungulata. But, while this order was early present in the
northern continents and seems to have been one of the earliest of ungulate groups,
it is better known from the later deposits in South America. The other ungulates
of that continent in Tertiary times also seem to be survivors of archaic types, and
the evolution of South American ungulates may not inappropriately be considered
here.

The few perissodactyls and artiodactyls which ever penetrated into South
America did so only in Pleistocene times. But at that time the continent was al-

ready the home of a great and varied assemblage of ungulate types quite unrelated to those of other continents which had flourished there since the Eocene but
which are now entirely extinct.

That South America was cut off from the other continents at a very early Tertiary date seems to be indicated by the fact that but few placental mammals appear
to have been present at the time of severance of continental connections. In the
Eocene deposits of that continent have been found (in addition to the marsupials
previously discussed) only a few edentates and a number of primitive ungulates of
types almost unknown in other regions of the world.

In the isolation of South America, free from the depredations of the true carnivores and free from the competition of other hoofed mammals, these ungulates
developed into an amazing variety of forms. In proportions they ranged from the
size of a rat to that of an elephant. Some simulated the rodents in appearance and
habits; others were analogous to the hippopotamus and the rhinoceroses; still
others were remarkably similar to horses and elephants in structure. These types
were extremely interesting and often bizarre. But our consideration of them is
hampered by the fact that, in the absence of existing representatives, we lack both
popular names and that mental picture of the living form which in most cases
furnishes us with a good starting-point for the discussion of mammalian groups.

These ungulate groups reached the climax of their development in the Miocene;
with the Pliocene and Pleistocene came the advent of the carnivores, to which they
probably fell an easy prey, and of higher ungulate types with which they could not
successfully compete for pasturage. By the end of the Pleistocene this once extremely numerous assemblage vanished entirely.

It has proved difficult to establish the age of the beds in which these South
American forms are found, since they differed in their mammalian fauna so greatly
from those in other parts of the world. By some early workers most were supposed to be considerably earlier in date than is now believed to be the case. In consequence of that belief it seemed that forms which simulated the horses, elephants,
and various other groups appeared in that continent considerably earlier than did
these types themselves in other regions. Mistaking these parallelisms for real relationships, a patriotic Argentinian, to whom we owe much of our knowledge of these
forms, laid claim to the origin of many mammalian groups for South America, a
viewpoint which is frequently reflected in the names given to the various genera
and groups.

Notoungulates.—By far the greater number of forms from South America are
included in the order Notoungulata (or Toxodontia). The members of this group
varied much in size and adaptive features, but many general structural similarities
run through the three subdivisions of the order. The skull was typically rather
short, flattened above, with a broad braincase and forehead, the nasals broad, the
nostrils usually terminal. The zygomatic arches were broad and heavy, and there

was never a postorbital bar. Seldom was there a reduction in the dentition or a development of a diastema; and while there were often strong chisel-like incisors, the rest of the teeth formed a series in which there was often a gradual transition from the small canine to the molars. Primitively brachyodont, the cheek teeth (Fig. 279) in many lines tended to become high prisms, often with persistently growing roots. Even in the earliest forms there was seldom any trace of the bunodont stage through which the ancestral forms presumably passed, and lophodont and selenodont types of teeth were rapidly developed. An upper tooth had typically a straight or curved ectoloph, a long protoloph running back from this at an angle, and a short metaloph projecting in at a right angle. There were often various complications in pattern, such as a cross-connection between lophs and an additional posterior ridge formed from the cingulum. In the lower molars there was considerable resemblance to the perissodactyls in the development of two typically crescentic ridges; the front one was usually much the smaller. The most characteristic feature of the notoungulate dentition is the fact that the entoconid primitively lay isolated inside the curve of the posterior crescent.

Although there is great variation, the feet were essentially mesaxonic in structure in a majority of cases, the number of toes tending to reduce from five to three. But there was never any great acquisition of true ungulate characters in the feet and never an attainment of the unguligrade position. A number of types may have had hoofs, but claws were retained in many cases; the feet in general rather resembled those of rodents or the hyrax.

Entylonychians.—The oldest known, the earliest to disappear, and in many respects the least specialized of the notoungulate groups is the suborder Entylonychia. An end-form is *Homalodontotherium* (Figs. 276, 277a, 278a) of the Miocene. The skull, which reached about 2 feet in length, was broad and flat with heavy arches; the nasal opening was farther back on the top of the skull than would primitively have been the case, suggesting a tapir-like snout. The teeth were comparatively primitive for the order, with rather high crowns but closed roots and a very gradual transition in shape from incisors to molars. The molars had a very simple, rather rhinoceros-like, pattern, with three main lophs above and two crescents (the front one short) below. As is usually the case in the notoungulates, the pattern tended to become obscure with wear; and in the lower teeth the originally isolated entoconid merged into the outer crescent.

The limbs of this large end-form were of an odd type. Five toes were present on each foot and terminated not in hoofs but in blunt heavy claws. The hind feet were short and plantigrade, but the front legs were long and powerful. This suggests that *Homalodontotherium* was a large root-digger, analogous to the chalicotheres of the Northern Hemisphere.

This Miocene form was the largest, and one of the last, of the group. But in the earlier Tertiary of Patagonia entylonychians were very numerous, and in the

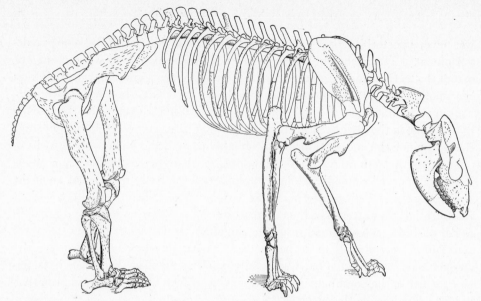

FIG. 276.—*Homalodontotherium*, a Miocene entylonychian notoungulate, about 6 feet in length. (From Scott.)

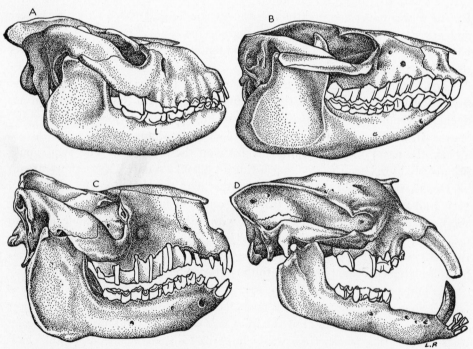

FIG. 277.—Skulls of Miocene South American ungulates. *A, Homalodontotherium*, an entylonychian; skull length about 15 inches. *B, Protypotherium*, a typothere; skull length about 4 inches. *C, Nesodon*, a toxodont; skull length about 16 inches. *D, Astrapotherium;* skull length about 27 inches. (*B* after Sinclair, others after Scott.)

Eocene comparatively small types with simple low-crowned teeth such as *Noto-stylops* and *Pleurostylodon* (Fig. 279c, d) were the commonest of South American mammals. It is probable that these little early forms had much the place in nature occupied by the rodents in other times or places.

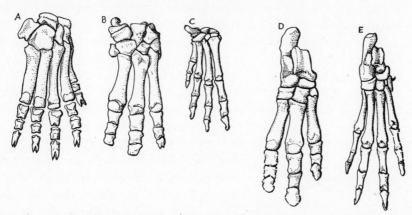

FIG. 278.—Feet of notoungulates. *A*, manus of *Homalodontotherium*, a Miocene entylonychian. *B*, manus of *Nesodon*, a Miocene toxodont. *C*, manus of *Protypotherium*, a Miocene typothere. *D*, pes of *Nesodon*. *E*, pes of *Protypotherium*. (*A, B, D* after Scott; *C, E* after Sinclair.)

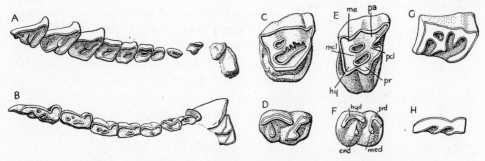

FIG. 279.—Teeth of notoungulates. *A*, upper right, and *B*, lower left tooth rows of the Miocene toxodont *Nesodon* ($\times\frac{1}{4}$). *C*, upper right and *D*, lower left molars of *Pleurostylodon*, an Eocene entylonychian ($\times 1$). *E, F*, same of *Oldfieldthomasia*, an Eocene typothere ($\times 3$), *G, H*, of *Proadinotherium*, an Oligocene toxodont ($\times\frac{1}{3}$). Upper molar: *hy*, hypocone; *mcl*, metaconule; *me*, metacone; *pa*, paracone; *pcl*, protoconule; *pr*, protocone. Lower molar: *end*, entoconid; *hyd*, hypoconid; *med*, metaconid; *prd*, protoconid. (*A, B* after Scott, *C–F* after Schlosser, *G, H* after Loomis.)

Back of this we had, until a few years ago, no knowledge of the history of any of the notoungulates. It was assumed that they must have reached South America from the north, but no representatives had been found in any other part of the world. A decade or so ago, however, a jaw of a small primitive entylonychid, *Arctostylops* (Fig. 280), was found in the Lower Eocene of North America, presumably a straggler along the road of emigration.

It was hoped that recent work in Mongolia would solve the question of the

Paleocene home of many mammalian groups (including the more advanced ungulates, artiodactyls, and perissodactyls) which suddenly appear in Europe and
North America at the beginning of the true Eocene. This hope has, for the most
part, so far met with disappointment; but curiously enough, another small primitive entylonychid, *Palaeostylops*, has been found to be the commonest of mammals
in the Asiatic Paleocene. We can thus trace the migration of the notoungulates
from an ancestral home in the Old World through North America to their definitive habitat in South America.

Toxodonts.—Much more specialized in many respects, and more orthodoxly
ungulate in adaptations, were the members of the suborder Toxodontia, a group
which is common in all stages of the South American Tertiary from Oligocene to
Pleistocene times. Later members of the group were large, heavily built forms.
Among the ungulate features of the skeleton may be mentioned the presence of

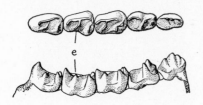

FIG. 280.—Fragment of lower jaw of
Arctostylops, only known notoungulate
from North America, left p_3–m_3, showing
the characteristic development of the
entoconid (*e*), crown and lateral views.
(After Matthew.)

but three hoofed toes on each foot and the
absence of the clavicle (which may have been
retained in entylonychians). But the ulna and
fibula were always complete and heavy, although the latter sometimes fused with the
tibia.

The teeth remained in a nearly closed row,
seldom developing a diastema; and there was
little loss except that the canines were weak
or absent. The incisors were often expanded
into chisel-like cropping structures, while the
primitively low-crowned molars tended to be-
come high crowned and rootless and sometimes were covered by a cement sheath.
The upper molars curved in strongly toward each other, a feature to which the
term "toxodont" (bow-tooth) refers.

Toxodon (Fig. 281) of the Pliocene and Pleistocene is the largest and one of the
latest members of the group, built like a short-legged rhinoceros. The dorsal position of the nasal opening suggests the presence of a large snout; the general appearance may have been that of a gigantic guinea pig. A diastema, absent in
earlier types, had developed in the dentition. *Toxodon* appears to have been the
commonest large ungulate of the South American Pleistocene. The Miocene *Nesodon* (Figs. 277c, 278b, d, 279a) was a smaller and more slimly built toxodont the
size of a tapir. The dentition was comparatively primitive, for the tooth row was
a closed one, although the intermediate teeth (canines and anterior premolars)
were small, and the molars finally became rooted late in life. *Adinotherium* was
another Miocene form of still smaller size, with a small horn on the frontal bones.
Ancestral toxodonts, such as *Proadinotherium* (Fig. 279g, h), are present in the
Oligocene; but the group is not known in the Eocene.

The Oligocene *Leontinia* represents a separate family close to the toxodonts proper in many respects. The nostrils, however, had a very peculiar shape with a peculiar swelling of the premaxilla in front and a long projecting nasal above; there must have been some odd type of proboscis present.

Notohippus and its relatives (mainly Oligocene, although surviving into the Miocene) are a poorly known, early side branch of the toxodonts. The complex teeth had some superficial resemblance to those of horses, and it was once claimed that they were members of the Equidae; they were, however, true toxodonts and quite unrelated to the horses.

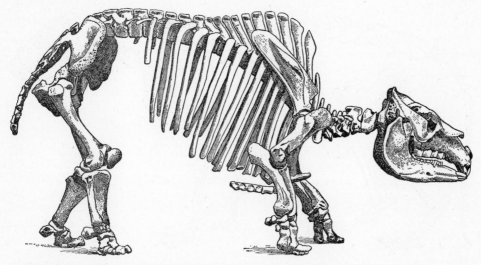

FIG. 281.—*Toxodon*, a large Pleistocene South American notoungulate, about 9 feet in length. (From Lydekker.)

Typotheres.—Closely related to the toxodonts, but very different in their superficial aspects, were the abundant typotheres. We have seen rather rodent-like adaptations in the teeth of the toxodonts; the small, lightly-built typotheres were much more rabbit-like in structure and in their probable appearance and mode of life.

The dentition was basically similar to that of the toxodonts and entylonychians; the teeth were high crowned, cement covered, and usually rootless in the later forms; and the lophodont molars usually wore down to a flat surface early in life. The first upper incisor was usually enlarged in rodent fashion, as were one or two of the lower ones. The skull (Fig. 277*b*) was often rather long, while the snout was unusually high and thin; the tympanic bulla was sometimes enormously inflated. The feet (Fig. 278) ranged from plantigrade to digitigrade. Usually there were four toes; in some cases the third and fourth digits tended to be larger than the lateral ones. In contrast with the toxodonts, the clavicle was still present. The pointed but flat-based terminal phalanges appear to have been covered with some structure intermediate between hoof and claw.

Pachyrukhos, which ranged from the Miocene to Pleistocene, was one of the smaller members of the group. Of about rabbit size, this typothere resembled that rodent in the development of a stub tail and long hind legs, and presumably had a hopping gait. In the front part of the mouth there remained but a single enlarged upper incisor and two lower ones. *Typotherium* was another Pleistocene form with a somewhat similar dentition, but it was the size of a brown bear and lacked the disproportionate development of the hind legs.

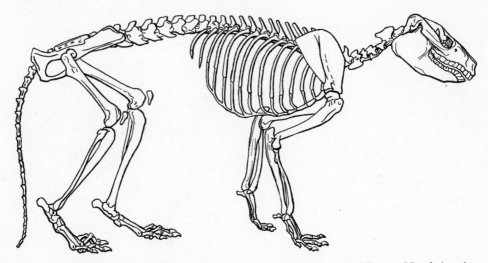

Fig. 282.—*Protypotherium*, a Miocene typotherian notoungulate from the Miocene of South America, about 20 inches in length. (After Sinclair.)

The Miocene and Oligocene typotheres were numerous and varied and in general slightly more primitive in structure. In such forms as *Hegetotherium, Interatherium,* and *Protypotherium* (Fig. 282) all the teeth were still present, although the teeth (lateral incisors, canines, and anterior premolars) lost in later forms were already much reduced. The teeth were high-crowned and generally persistently growing, but in some cases roots were still formed. The typotheres were already abundant in the Eocene, but forms of that age (such as *Oldfieldthomasia,* Fig. 279e, f) were usually of quite small size and with a complete dentition of low-crowned, rooted teeth.

True rodents, as will be seen, were not present in the Eocene of South America; and the typotheres of the Oligocene seem to have fitted into the ecological niche occupied by that group in other continents, as had the entylonychians in the Eocene. Relatives of the modern guinea pigs and porcupines did reach the southern continent in Oligocene times; but the typotheres, having reached their full specialization by that time, seem to have been able to withstand this competition re-markably well, for there were numerous Miocene types, and several genera were still common in Pleistocene days.

Notoungulate history.—The history of the notoungulates is indeed a remarkable one. Their presence in the Paleocene of Asia suggests that they must have been one of the very earliest groups to split off from the basic placental stock. Seeming-ly they constituted a first wave of ungulate development, possibly even older and more primitive than the archaic condylarths and amblypods already considered. Their almost utter absence from the Eocene deposits of the Northern Hemisphere suggests that they were unable to withstand the competition of even those archaic groups, to say nothing of that of the more modernized perissodactyls and artio-dactyls.

But to their early development is due their fortunate inclusion among the few placental groups which had reached South America before the isolation of the continent in earliest Eocene times. For more than half of the Tertiary they flour-ished there in the comparative absence of herbivore competition or carnivore menace. The peak of their development was reached in the Miocene, when a great many of the notoungulates flourished in Patagonia and presumably in other regions as well. But beyond this time dissolution set in. In the Pliocene many types of these ungulates disappeared. The irruption into the continent in the Pleistocene of the saber-tooths and other carnivores and of competing ungulates of northern types may have caused havoc among the reduced notoungulate stocks. Today not a single form survives to give us any conception of the appearance, life, or habits of the notoungulates.

Astrapotheres.—The three notoungulate groups all appear to have been fairly closely related and are fundamentally similar in structure, although varying wide-ly in adaptive features. *Astrapotherium* (Fig. 277d) and its relatives form a much more divergent group, which is sometimes included in the notoungulates but is perhaps better regarded as a separate order, the Astrapotheria. The group did not persist beyond the Miocene but had become remarkably specialized by that time. *Astrapotherium*, the last of the line, was about the size of a rhinoceros, with an elephantine limb construction. The skull was exceedingly peculiar. At first sight it would seem that its whole front end had been cut off, for the upper incisors had been lost and the premaxilla reduced to a nubbin between the huge curved and persistently growing canines. The lower incisors were present, however, while the lower canines were also rather large. Following a marked diastema were rudi-mentary posterior premolars and large molars, the last two of enormous size. The slit-like nasal opening was placed on the upper surface of the skull and was only partially roofed by the short nasals. The presence of large air sinuses in the frontal bones gave the forehead a swollen, dome-like appearance.

The situation of the nostrils renders it probable that an elephant-like proboscis was present; the well-developed lower incisors indicate the presence of a tough upper lip to form a cow-like cropping mechanism. What peculiar habits were responsible for the presence of the great canines of this remarkable animal is not at all clear.

Albertogaudrya of the Eocene was a somewhat more primitive genus without the huge molars of later forms. But the development of the canines was already under way. This astrapothere was tending to gigantism; already of tapir size, *Alberto-gaudrya* was the largest member of the Eocene assemblage, and an Oligocene form was even larger than *Astrapotherium* itself. The Eocene and Oligocene beds contain, in addition, smaller and more primitive genera such as *Trigonostylops*. Possibly the astrapotheres have come from some primitive notoungulate type; but this is uncertain, and they may have arisen independently from some other archaic ungulate stock.

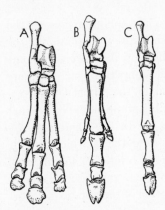

FIG. 283.—The pes of litopterns. *A, Macrauchenia. B, Diadiaphorus. C, Thoatherium.* (After Scott.)

The litopterns.—Also peculiar to South America is the order Litopterna. This stock never developed into the multiplicity of types found in the notoungulates but was more orthodoxly ungulate in character. Hoofs were always present, and toe reduction took place on the mesaxonic plan with the development of three-toed types and even a one-toed horse-like form. Except for occasional reductions in the incisors a complete dentition and a closed tooth row were usual features in the order. The cheek teeth were usually low crowned, with six-cusped upper molars in which the protocone was large and rather centrally placed. In contrast to the notoungulates the later types built up a postorbital bar.

Small litopterns, such as *Didolodus* (Fig. 268f), present in the oldest known Tertiary beds of South America, had primitive bunodont cheek teeth and simple premolars. In the Eocene there also appeared more progressive forms with lophodont teeth, which in the Oligocene are clearly separable into two distinct families. One, the proterotheres, developed into horse-like types. *Diadiaphorus*, of the Miocene (Figs. 268g, h, 283b), was a three-toed form; but in the contemporary *Thoatherium* (Figs. 283c, 284a) we have an ungulate, about the size of *Mesohippus*, which seems more horse-like than any true horse, for it was single-toed with splints more reduced than those of modern equids. This pseudo-horse was, however, comparatively unprogressive in other respects, for the cheek teeth were low crowned and the carpus was poorly adapted for monodactyl running. Parallel to the typotheres was the development of chisel-like incisors (one above and two below). This one-toed proterothere became extinct in the Miocene, and only some of the more conservative three-toed types lingered on into Pliocene times.

Macrauchenia (Figs. 283*a*, 284*b*, *c*) of the Pleistocene was the last surviving member of the order and the most highly developed of a second group of litopterns. The limbs and neck were elongated, and three functional toes persisted. The skull was peculiarly constructed. There was a very long snout which accommodated a well-developed battery of cheek teeth, high crowned, in contrast to other litopterns. The nasal opening was very far back on the top of the skull, much as in some sauropod dinosaurs; and the nasals were rudimentary. Some writers have suggested that a proboscis was present, but a more probable explanation is that *Macrauchenia* was a swamp-dweller with nostrils dorsally situated for breathing in the water. This form was about the size of a camel and with rather camel-like

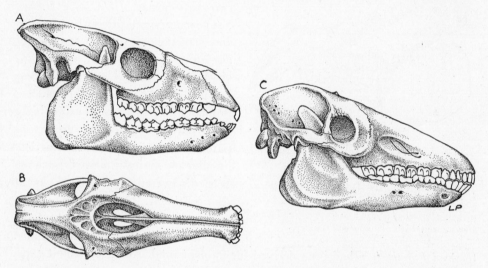

Fig. 284.—Skulls of litopterns. *A*, *Thoatherium*, skull length about 7 inches. *B*, *C*, *Macrauchenia*, dorsal and lateral views, skull length about 18 inches. (*A* after Scott, *B*, *C* after Burmeister.)

proportions. Older members of this series, such as *Theosodon*, of the Miocene, had lower-crowned teeth and rather longer nasal bones.

The ancestry of the litopterns is still obscure; no remains of the group have been found outside of South America. There are, however, some indications of relationship to the condylarths, and it is possible that they were descended from early members of that archaic ungulate group which had found a haven in South America. As was the case with the notoungulates, the litopterns declined in the Pliocene and Pleistocene and have now vanished completely.

Pyrotheres.—*Pyrotherium* (Fig. 285), of the Oligocene of Patagonia, is a member of a small, short-lived, and isolated group, the order Pyrotheria, which completes the roster of the South American ungulates. This beast had not only grown at that early time in the Tertiary to the size of an elephant but had anatomically paralleled the proboscideans to a very remarkable degree. The dorsal nasal openings indicate the presence of a proboscis; the facial region was turned upward (rather than downward) on the cranial axis. Above the broad zygomatic arches lay small orbits, behind which no postorbital bar had developed. A heavy transverse crest lay along the top of the occiput for the attachment of strong neck muscles necessary to support the heavy head.

The dentition was strikingly like that of the early proboscideans. Tusks were developing out of the incisors, of which but two were retained above and one below. Behind a long diastema lay the cheek teeth, six above and five below. As in the earliest proboscideans, these low-crowned teeth were each composed of two cross-crests.

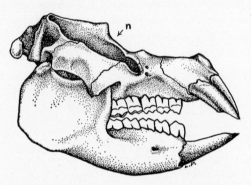

FIG. 285.—The skull of *Pyrotherium*, a South American ungulate paralleling the proboscideans. There is a tusk-like development of the incisors, and the nostrils (*n*) are situated above the orbits, suggesting development of a proboscis. Skull length about 2 feet. (After Loomis and Gaudry.)

The many similarities in body, skull, and dentition all suggest that *Pyrotherium* was really related to the proboscideans, then developing to the east in Africa. But these resemblances are probably merely a case of exceedingly close parallelism, for the group apparently had arisen in South America. Smaller and more primitive types have been discovered in Eocene rocks of that continent. The dentition of these earlier forms shows, as might have been expected, that the cross-lophed teeth of *Pyrotherium* had been derived (as in elephants) from a bunodont type. But beyond this fact we have no clue as to the origins of the pyrotheres, although obviously they come from some early ungulate stock.

With the pyrotheres we conclude our survey of the native ungulates of South America. These forms owed their successful Tertiary career to their comparative freedom from competing ungulate types and from carnivores, for the advent of these forms is unmistakably associated with the disappearance of notoungulates and litopterns. A curious fact, however, is that, despite the disappearance of the native types, few northern ungulates have installed themselves in their places. Mastodons, mammoths, and horses all reached South America, but failed to survive. Only the llama group, the peccary, the tapir, and a few deer still exist there. South America is a continent almost devoid of ungulates.

CHAPTER XVII

PERISSODACTYLS

Among all vertebrates there is perhaps no group whose fossil history is better known than that of the order Perissodactyla, the "odd-toed" ungulates. Although represented at the present day by but a few species of tapirs, rhinoceroses, and horses, perissodactyls were numerous throughout the Tertiary and included not only the ancestors of these living groups but also such interesting extinct types as the huge horned titanotheres and the grotesque clawed chalicotheres.

Limbs.—As usual with ungulates, the locomotor apparatus has been of importance in the evolutionary history. In most perissodactyls the limbs have tended to become long and slim, with a lengthening of the distal segments as compared with the proximal ones, while the ulna and fibula may be reduced. There is, as usual in ungulates, no clavicle; but in contrast with the artiodactyls (or even-toed ungulates) the femur has a well-developed third trochanter. The carpus is of the alternating type. The upper end of the astragalus has a well-keeled surface for the tibia; but, unlike the artiodactyls, this is not duplicated at the lower end, which is, at the most, rounded (Fig. 264).

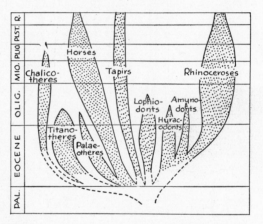

FIG. 286.—The phylogeny of the perissodactyls.

The feet (Figs. 287, 296, 297) are of the mesaxonic type, with reduction usually taking place to three toes or even to one in late horse types. In the hind foot the earliest known forms had already reduced the number to three, with only metatarsal splints representing the first and fifth digits. But the first stage in reduction in the front foot led to a four-toed condition common in the Eocene, for, while no trace of the thumb has been found in even the earliest of perissodactyls (except in a chalicothere), typical early forms had retained all the other toes, although the outer one was somewhat weak. This stage in toe reduction, with four digits in front and three behind, is retained to this day by the tapirs. But beyond the Lower Oligocene other surviving types had no more than three toes on each foot.

Teeth. Equally characteristic of the group is the tooth development (Figs. 288, 289). The full complement is found in many early forms, but there may be various

319

losses and specializations in the insicors and canines, and a diastema almost always develops, the first premolar being sometimes lost in the process.

The upper molars in the most primitive known forms had already gained a hypocone and (as seen in a very primitive horse [Fig. 227*b*]) showed six bunodont cusps, the intermediate conules being primitively well developed. Typically, a lophodont condition arises from this (Fig. 229). An ectoloph, often W-shaped through the development of the external row of styles, occurs in most forms. Transverse protoloph and metaloph are found in three of the five main groups; but, on the other hand (in titanotheres and chalicotheres), the inner cusps may retain a bunodont condition. In the lower molars a pair of V's usually develops

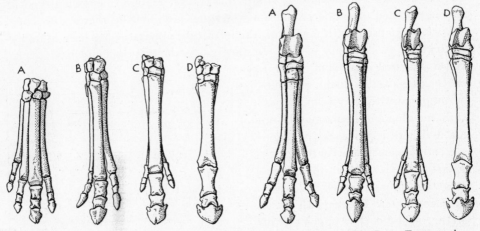

FIG. 287.—Feet of horses. Manus at left, pes at right. *A, Eohippus,* a primitive Lower Eocene perissodactyl with four toes in front, three behind. *B, Miohippus,* an Oligocene three-toed horse. *C, Merychippus,* a late Miocene form with reduced lateral toes. *D, Equus.* (*A* after Cope, *B, C* after Osborn.)

from the original trigonid and talonid and may become a W-shaped structure through union of their adjacent ends or have their main posterior limbs changed into transverse crests. The teeth may remain low crowned, as in the early forms, while in others (especially in the horses) the teeth may become markedly hypsodont.

Complete molarization of most of the premolars is general among later members of the group. In some cases, as in the horses, the process has been carried so far that there is almost complete identity in appearance. These highly developed teeth contrast to the small and undeveloped premolars found in artiodactyls.

The facial part of the skull (Fig. 291) is usually rather long in connection with the development of a long series of grinding teeth. A postorbital bar is developed only in the later horses. The nasals are broad posteriorly and usually extend freely well forward over the nasal opening. Horn-like structures have developed in the titanotheres and many rhinoceroses.

Horses.—The order may be divided into subordinal groups, of which we shall

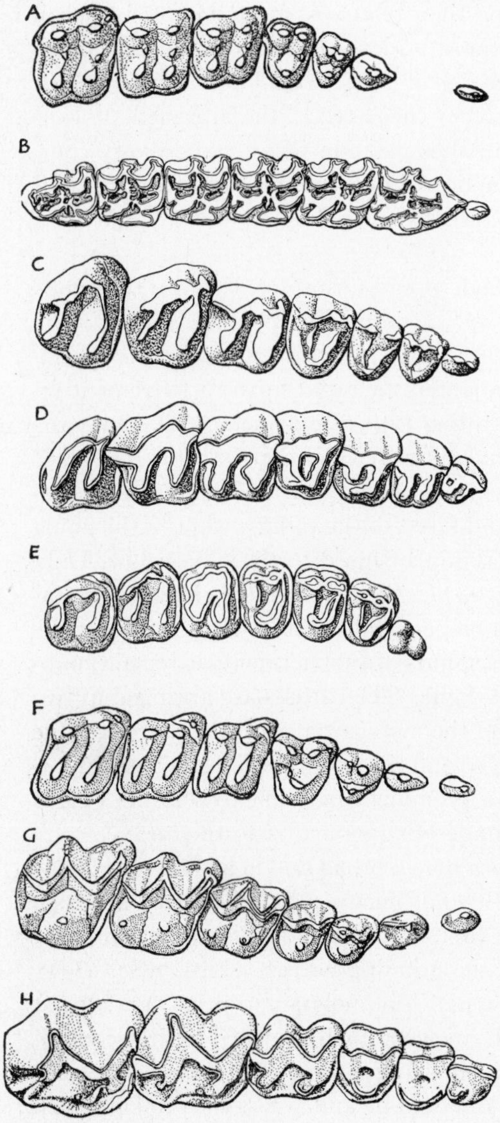

FIG. 288

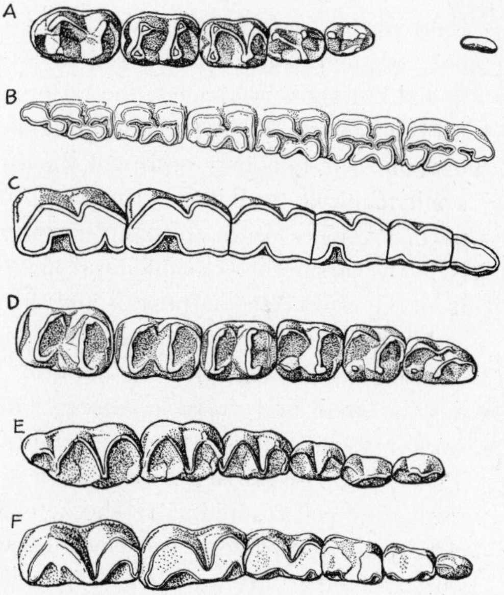

FIG. 289

FIG. 288.—Right upper cheek teeth of perissodactyls. *A*, *Eohippus*, $\times 1$ approx. *B*, *Equus occidentalis* (Pleistocene) $\times \frac{1}{2}$ approx. *C*, *Hyrachyus*, $\times \frac{5}{8}$ approx. *D*, *Caenopus*, $\times \frac{2}{5}$ approx. *E*, *Tapirus validus*, $\times \frac{5}{9}$ approx. *F*, *Homogalax*, an Eocene tapiroid, $\times 1$. *G*, *Palaeosyops*, $\times \frac{5}{12}$ approx. *H*, *Moropus*, $\times \frac{1}{3}$. (*A*, *B*, *F* after Matthew, *C*, *D*, *G* after Osborn, *E* after Hatcher, *H* after Peterson.)

FIG. 289.—Left lower cheek teeth of perissodactyls. *A*, *Eohippus*, $\times 1$ approx. *B*, *Equus leidyi* (Pleistocene) $\times \frac{1}{2}$ approx. *C*, *Diceratherium*, $\times \frac{2}{7}$ approx. *D*, *Tapirus validus* (Oligocene) $\times \frac{5}{9}$ approx. *E*, *Limnohyops*, $\times \frac{5}{12}$ approx. *F*, *Moropus*, $\times \frac{1}{3}$. (*A* after Wortman, *B* after Simpson, *C*, *F* after Peterson, *D* after Hatcher, *E* after Osborn.)

first consider the Equoidea, the horses and their relatives, most progressive of all perissodactyls. In these forms there is almost no loss of teeth, the incisors being retained and forming chisel-shaped cropping organs. Cross-lophs slanting back from the ectoloph are developed on the upper cheek teeth; the intermediate conules tend to retain their individuality and thus make in many cases a very complicated pattern. There was an early reduction of toes to three in the front as well as the hind foot, and in later types a progressive reduction toward and to a monodactyl condition.

A discussion of the structure of the modern end-forms constituting the genus *Equus* (horses, asses, zebras) gives a good introduction to horse history. The modern horse has the most highly specialized limb structure of any perissodactyl. In its mechanism it is almost perfectly adapted for rapid forward movement on hard ground and almost incapable of any other type of movement. The humerus and femur are short, powerful, driving segments from which depend the much longer radius and tibia, the main supporting elements of the front and hind feet respectively. The shaft of the ulna is reduced and fused to the radius; while of the fibula there remains only a splint above and a rudiment fused to the tibia below. Only one toe, the third, is well developed (Fig. 287d); this has a much elongated metapodial but short phalanges, the terminal one expanded into a semicircular structure supporting the hoof. Of the side toes splints of the metapodials remain; nubbins on their ends may represent the lost digits. The carpals are arranged in two semicircular layers between the radius and the metacarpal with the magnum (the normal support for the third finger) enlarged and the first carpal vestigial. Similarly in the tarsus the ectocuneiform plays a prominent part in carrying the weight from the well-keeled astragalus and the underlying navicular to the toe.

All the incisors are present in the modern horse; broad and in a closed row, they form an efficient cropping mechanism. Behind them is a long diastema in which lies the small and variable canine. The first lower premolar is absent, but the small upper one lies at the front end of the grinding battery (Figs. 288b, 289b). This is composed of six teeth in each jaw half, the molars and premolars almost identically constructed. The cheek teeth are very high crowned with a complicated prismatic pattern, the aspect of which changes somewhat with wear as the siliceous food grinds down across enamel and dentine and across the cement which fills the interstices and covers the tooth. The pattern, though complicated, can be identified with the primitive bunodont and lophodont conditions found in early equids (Fig. 290). In the upper molars the ectoloph is represented by two crescents for the paracone and metacone, with projections formed by the parastyle and mesostyle. Anteriorly a crescent swings inward as the protoconule. Internal to this is the nearly isolated protocone; while the posterior end of the protoconule connects with the metaloph, developed internally into a crescentic hypocone. From this last, in turn, a ridge representing the hypostyle runs outward toward the posterior end of the ectoloph. This much folded pattern, presenting alternating layers of three different substances, forms a highly effective grinding organ. The lower teeth have had a similar history, but the pattern is obviously derivable from a primitive pattern in which a connecting link between the two V's is afforded by a metastylid adjacent to the metaconid.

The facial part of the skull (Fig. 291b) is elongated in relation to the long set of cheek teeth and the diastema. In the modern horses there is a postorbital bar.

Eocene horses.—The modern horses and their relatives in both limbs and dentition are almost perfectly adapted for a grazing, plains-dwelling life. Far different in structure and probable habits were the earliest horses, such as *Eohippus* (Figs. 287a, 288a, 289a, 290a, 291a, 292), of the Lower Eocene of North America, a small form no larger than a fox terrier. The skull had but a short facial region, the

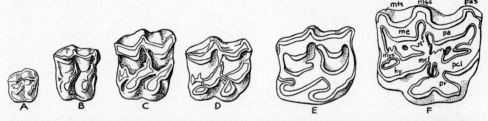

FIG. 290.—Right upper molar teeth of various horse types, all natural size. *A, Eohippus* (L. Eocene). *B, Mesohippus* (Oligocene). *C, Parahippus* (L. Miocene). *D, Merychippus* (U. Miocene). *E, Pliohippus* (Pliocene). *F, Equus complicatus* (Pleistocene). The complicated cusp pattern of the modern horse tooth may be traced back to the comparatively primitive condition in *Eohippus. hy*, hypocone; *hys*, hypostyle; *mcl*, metaconule; *me*, metacone; *mss*, mesostyle; *mts*, metastyle; *pa*, paracone; *pas*, parastyle; *pcl*, protoconule; *pr*, protocone. (After Matthew.)

orbits (lacking, of course, a postorbital bar) lying in the middle of its length. All the teeth were present, and there was but a short diastema. The low-crowned molars were already squared up with six cusps present above and four below. There was here just the beginning of a tendency toward loph formation; but a contemporary European horse, *Hyracotherium* (Fig. 227b), was still definitely bunodont. The premolars were still comparatively simple, none of the upper ones having progressed beyond a triangular shape. The limbs were moderately long and slim, with the metapodials rather elongated and with definite hoofs on the end-phalanges. The toes were already reduced in number. In the front foot all traces of the thumb had disappeared; but the other four toes were all functional, although the outer one was comparatively small. In the hind foot only three toes were present; but there were traces of the missing digits in the form of metatarsal splint bones. This small forest-dwelling browser is of great interest. Unquestionably, it stands at the base of the horse series. But even more than that, it exhibits many features to be expected in the ancestors of other perissodactyl families and, without doubt, was very close to the roots of the whole perissodactyl stock.

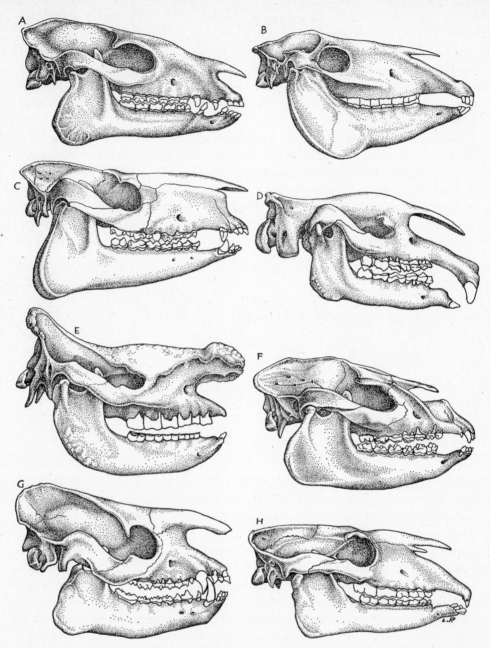

Fig. 291.—Skulls of perissodactyls. *A, Eohippus*, skull length about 5¼ inches. *B, Equus niobrarensis*, a Pleistocene American horse, skull length about 23 inches. *C, Hyrachyus*, an Eocene hyracodont, skull length about 11½ inches. *D, Baluchitherium*, a giant hornless Oligocene rhinoceros, skull length about 4½ feet. *E, Diceros pachygnathus*, a Pliocene horned rhinoceros, skull length about 2 feet. *F, Tapirus validus*, an Oligocene American tapir, skull length about 1 foot. *G, Limnohyops*, an Eocene hornless titanothere, skull length about 15 inches. *H, Moropus*, an American Lower Miocene chalicothere, skull length about 2 feet. (*A* after Cope, *B* after Hay, *C* after Scott, *D, G* after Osborn, *E* after Gaudry, *F* after Hatcher, *H* after Peterson.)

In the Middle and Upper Eocene of North America we find, in *Orohippus* and *Epihippus*, descendants of this primitive equid in which the structure was essentially the same and in all of which four toes were retained in the front foot. A few advances, however, did take place: there was some increase in size, the splints disappeared in the hind foot, and the last two premolars took on the molar pattern.

Mesohippus and related types.—The next main stage in horse evolution begins in the Lower Oligocene, again in North America. There, in *Mesohippus* (Figs. 290b, 293), typically the size of a collie, and the somewhat larger *Miohippus* (Fig. 287b) we find the beginning of a series of functionally three-toed horses. In the front foot the outer toe has gone, although a rudiment of its metatarsal persisted

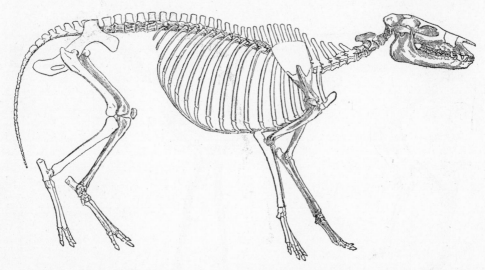

Fig. 292.—*Eohippus*, the "dawn horse" of the Lower Eocene, probably close to the stem of the perissodactyls. Length about 18 inches. (After Cope, from Smith Woodward.)

in many later equids. The metapodials of the three remaining toes were much more elongated than in Eocene types; but while the central toe was somewhat larger, all three undoubtedly reached the ground.

The diastema had continued its development; and, while the cheek teeth were still low crowned, all the premolars except the small first one had become completely converted to the molar pattern. This pattern was now definitely lophodont, with a typical W-shaped ectoloph above but with the cusps constituting the cross-lophs retaining their individuality. At the back edge of the upper molars the hypostyle was beginning to be prominent. In the lower jaw there were two crescents with a distinct double cusp (metaconid and metastylid) at their junction.

The teeth and feet of these typical Oligocene horses suggest that, like their ancestors (and the tapirs today), they were essentially browsing forms, living on soft vegetation in forests and glades where their spreading three-toed feet would enable them to go over soft ground difficult for the later single-toed horse. A tendency in

some members of this stock to grow to larger size without much change in structure led, at the end of the Oligocene and beginning of the Miocene, to the development of *Anchitherium*, about the size of a pony but with persistently primitive three-toed feet and low-crowned teeth. This type migrated to Europe (where
true horses had been absent since the earliest Eocene) and was common there in
the early Miocene. The related *Hypohippus* persisted as a forest form in North
America and China until the Pliocene, and one species the size of a rhinoceros was
the largest known horse of all times.

Miocene horses.—The beginning of a third main structural stage is found in
Parahippus of the Miocene of North America. In this horse the diastema was

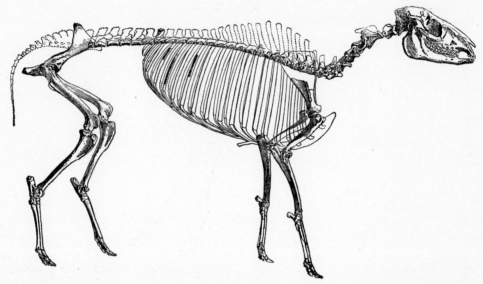

FIG. 293.—*Mesohippus*, a small three-toed Oligocene horse, about 40 inches long. (From Scott.)

well developed, and the molar teeth were lengthening. The face was consequently
considerably elongated, the orbit being considerably back of the middle of the
skull length. The eye was partly inclosed behind by a developing process from the
frontal; this formed a complete bar in all later types. While the molar teeth (Fig.
290c) were still fairly low crowned, cement was beginning to make its appearance
on their surfaces. In the feet the side toes were somewhat reduced; so that they
would probably not have touched the ground during rapid locomotion. Thus, it
would seem that in *Parahippus* we have a form transitional from the old forest-
dwellers to modern plains-dwelling grazing horses.

Directly descended from this genus was *Merychippus* (Figs. 287c, 290d), characteristic of the later Miocene of North America and the undoubted ancestor of the
later horse types. Here the teeth were definitely high crowned and prismatic, with
a good cement covering and a molar pattern quite comparable to that of living

horses. In the upper molars the hypostyle joined with the hypocone to inclose a posterior cement "lake," and a similar anterior lake was inclosed between proto-loph and metaloph. From *Merychippus* were derived several closely related types found in the late Miocene and Pliocene of North America. One of them, *Hipparion*, a form about the size of a pony and rather lightly built, spread to Eurasia (in which area *Anchitherium* had already disappeared) and is characteristic of the Lower Pliocene fauna there. A second genus, *Protohippus*, includes a number of small forms, some of which appear to have reached South America, giving rise there to several Pleistocene genera, such as *Hippidium* (Fig. 294) and *Onohippidi-*

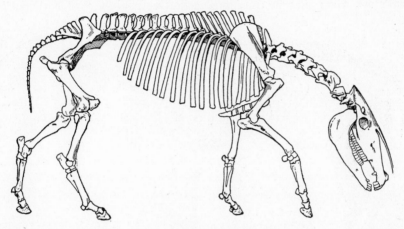

Fig. 294.—*Hippidium*, a South American Pleistocene horse. (From Scott, *Land Mammals of the Western Hemisphere*, by permission of the Macmillan Company, publishers.)

um. In these small but heavily built South American types, as in the true modern horses, the side toes were reduced to splints, but the limbs were short (suggesting a mountain habitat); and they differed in the excessively long and slim nasal bones. These forms did not survive the Pleistocene.

Later horse evolution.—The main line of equid evolution appears to have continued in North America during the Pliocene. *Pliohippus* is a genus derived from *Merychippus*, which tended to somewhat larger size and a somewhat heavier build than the contemporary *Hipparion*. The cheek teeth had become quite high crowned, as in *Hipparion*, but had retained a rather simpler pattern (Fig. 290e). The feet were very advanced in structure, for, while there were still complete lateral toes in some species assigned to this genus, others had already become mono-dactyl with but splints remaining of the side toes. *Plesippus*, another American Pliocene type, had molars with some folding of the enamel bands and appears to have been transitional to the existing genus *Equus*. This final type appeared in the Pleistocene and has spread to every continent (except, of course, Australia). In the Old World minor differentiations led to the development of the zebras (characteristically African), the asses still found wild in some of the more barren tropical regions, and the true horses, of which a wild species still exists in central Asia. Strangely enough, while North America had been, all through the Tertiary, the center of horse evolution with only a few occasional migrants reaching Eurasia, the group became extinct in the New World by the end of the Pleistocene. The American plains and pampas, which proved to be perfectly suitable for horses when reintroduced by man, were barren of equid life when first seen by Europeans.

Palaeotheres.—True horses, as we have noted, were absent in the later Eocene of Europe. Instead, we find developing various short-lived side branches of the equoid stock which may be considered collectively as the "palaeotheres." These

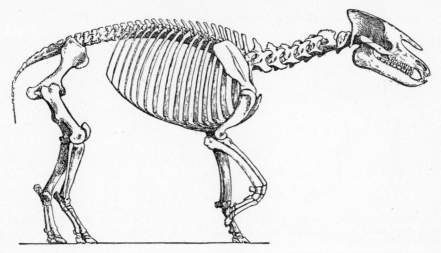

Fig. 295.—*Palaeotherium magnum*, a late Eocene giant horse-like mammal. Much reduced. (From Abel.)

forms tended to become prematurely large and advanced in structure. *Palaeotherium* (Fig. 295), which survived to the beginning of the Oligocene, may be taken as characteristic of the group. The last of the palaeotheres reached the size of a rhinoceros. The toes were reduced to three in both front and hind feet, but the legs were rather short and stout. Three premolars had become somewhat precociously molarized in the course of development of the genus; and the cheek teeth became markedly lophodont, although differing in details from those of the true horses. Other forms of Middle to Upper Eocene age were generally smaller, with somewhat more primitive teeth and less premolar development. One form, however, had already acquired cement on the molar crowns and had very slim lateral metapodials—features which were not attained in the true horses until the beginning of the Miocene. Despite these progressive features, the palaeotheres did not survive; the characteristic ungulates of the Oligocene and later Tertiary of Europe were artiodactyls, not perissodactyls.

Tapirs.—The tapirs, only living members of the suborder Tapiroidea, are in many respects still very close in structure and habits to the oldest perissodactyls. Living in forest regions and on comparatively soft ground, they have persistently retained the primitive limb structure of their Eocene ancestors; the legs and feet (Figs. 296e, 297c) are short, ulna and fibula are still complete and unfused, and, as

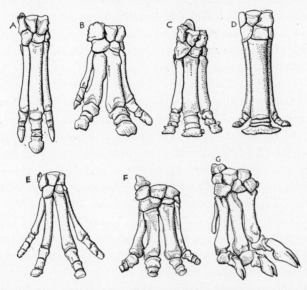

FIG. 296.—Manus of various perissodactyls. *A, Hydracodon,* an Oligocene running rhinoceros. *B, Trigonias,* an Oligocene four-toed true rhinoceros. *C, Diceratherium,* a three-toed primitive rhinoceros. *D, Baluchitherium,* a large Oligocene Asiatic rhinoceros with a pillar-like limb. *E, Tapirus validus. F, Menodus,* an Oligocene titanthere. *G, Moropus,* a chalicothere. (*A* after Scott, *B* after Hatcher, *C* after Peterson, *D, F* after Osborn, *E* after Wortman and Earle, *G* after Holland and Peterson.)

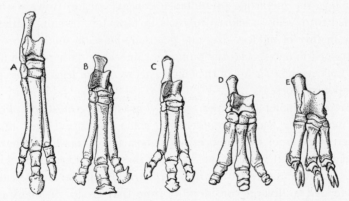

FIG. 297.—The pes of various perissodactyls. *A, Hyracodon,* an Oligocene running rhinoceros. *B, Diceratherium,* a Miocene rhinoceros. *C, Tapirus. D, Menodus,* an Oligocene titanothere. *E,* the chalicothere *Moropus.* (*A* after Scott, *B* after Peterson, *D* after Osborn, *E* after Holland and Peterson.)

in the Eocene, there are four toes in the front foot and three behind. The tapirs are still browsers, with low-crowned teeth which have no cement covering. The canines are well developed; and there has been no loss of teeth, although a moderate diastema is developed. The modern forms have molarized three premolars, as have the horses. All the cheek teeth (Figs. 288*e*, 289*d*) have a very simple pattern, the upper molars having a pattern of simple lophs while the lower teeth have developed two cross-crests. The one considerable specialization of the modern tapir is the presence of a short proboscis, with the accompanying backward migration of the bony opening of the nose and shortening of the nasal bones found in all forms which have developed a trunk (Fig. 291*b*).

A primitive perissodactyl which was close to the ancestry of the Tapiridae, if not the actual ancestor of that family, is found in *Homogalax* (*Systemodon*) (Fig. 288*f*) of the Lower Eocene of North America. The premolars were, of course, not yet molarized; and the molars were quite similar to those of *Eohippus* but showing the beginning of the tapir cross-crests. The proboscis appears to have been undeveloped in this and other Eocene types. True members of the modern genus *Tapirus*, in which the molarization of the premolars and the development of the proboscis had been initiated, appear in the Oligocene of Old and New worlds. Further forms are found in the later Tertiary of Eurasia. In the Pleistocene tapirs were present in both Americas and are still found in the tropics of the New World. In the Old they had left Europe by the end of the Pliocene and become restricted to their present home in southeastern Asia.

In addition to the true tapir ancestors, there developed, in both North America and Eurasia in Eocene and early Oligocene times, a number of forms similar to the tapirs in many features which may be conveniently grouped as the "lophiodonts." Relationship to the tapirs is shown by the development of simple lophodont teeth, which, however, were often distinguishable by the fact that in the upper molars the crest along the metacone presented a concave surface toward the outside. Some tended to develop a short proboscis in tapir-like fashion. Although these forms were mainly of modest size, one genus, *Lophiodon*, of the European later Eocene, attained in one species the bulk of a rhinoceros. Others, such as *Helaletes* of the late Eocene and *Colodon* of the Oligocene, were slim-legged types paralleling the contemporary horses.

Rhinoceroses.—Among all the perissodactyl groups, the most complicated fossil history is that of the Rhinocerotoidea, the rhinoceroses and their relatives. At present there survive of the rhinoceroses only a few forms from the Old World tropics, but throughout most of the Tertiary they were exceedingly numerous in the northern continents. Starting from forms rather similar to the early horses, they have tended to diverge considerably from that group. In many cases there have developed horn-like structures which, however, are composed, not of bone or horn, but of a fused mass of modified hair. As contrasted with most equids, rhinoceroses have tended to grow to large size, usually with comparatively short stout limbs in which digital reduction has proceeded at a slow pace, for the fifth digit in the hand was present in some Oligocene forms, and a monodactyl stage has never been attained. The premolars have tended to molarize, but the row of cheek teeth does not greatly lengthen and the face is usually comparatively short. The molars have a comparatively simple π shaped pattern above, and in all later forms the last molar is reduced; the lower molars develop two V-shaped cross-crests. The cheek teeth seldom tend to become very high crowned, and cement is almost never present. The incisors and canines, however, are variable, and there are frequent losses and specializations.

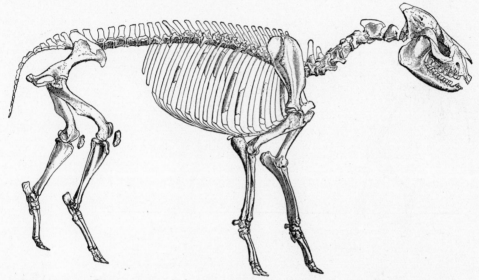

FIG. 298.—*Hyracodon*, an Oligocene running rhinoceros. About 5 feet in length. (From Osborn.)

Running rhinoceroses.—Most primitive of the three families into which the group may be divided are the hyracodonts, the running rhinoceroses of the Eocene and Oligocene. Earliest of rhinoceroses was *Hyrachyus* (Figs. 291*c*, 288*c*), of the Middle Eocene of North America. Although already definitely a rhinoceros in diagnostic dental features, this form (about the size of a wolf) was rather similar in build to the early equids and may well have come from a form almost identical with *Eohippus*. The complete dentition was present; but, while the essential features of the rhinoceros molar pattern were developed, the premolars were still simple and not molarized; the incisors were unspecialized and canines were well developed. The legs were slim and rather like those of *Eohippus*, with four toes in front and three behind; the neck, in contrast with most later rhinoceroses, was long. These running rhinoceroses were common in the later Eocene of America and Asia but did not reach Europe. An end-form was *Hyracodon* (Figs. 296*a*, 297*a*, 298), of the Oligocene, of considerably larger size but still a good running form, with long slim legs and but three toes in front, and with the three back premolars already molarized. These evolutionary advances were very similar to those found in the contemporary horses, but were not continued, for the group disappeared before the close of the period.

Amynodonts.—An early side branch, presumably derived from the primitive hyracodonts, was that of the family Amynodontidae. These forms are found in the late Eocene and Oligocene only. They had about the general size and proportions of a hippopotamus, and the conditions under which their remains are found suggest that they were river-living forms. *Metamynodon* (Fig. 299), of the American Oligocene, had short massive limbs, still retaining four short toes in front and

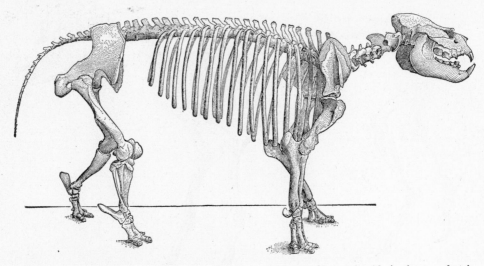

Fig. 299.—*Metamynodon*, an Oligocene amphibious rhinoceros (Amynodontidae), about 14 feet in length. (From Osborn.)

three behind. In the massive skull the premolars had failed to molarize, several had been lost, and the incisors were also reduced; here too, the canines were powerful.

Early true rhinoceroses.—All remaining forms are commonly placed in a third family as true rhinoceroses, the Rhinocerotidae, known only from rare fragments in the later Eocene. These types first became prominent in the Oligocene and (in contrast with the contemporary running rhinoceros) tended to large size and stout limbs, while (in contrast with the amynodonts) the premolars became rapidly molarized. The cropping mechanism of true rhinoceroses is peculiar: A pair of incisors, the first upper and second lower, are always enlarged cutting teeth (in some late forms they may be secondarily lost), and a narrow muzzle with a pointed lip develops. The last upper molar is always simpler than the others, with ectoloph and metaloph forming a single continuous crest (Fig. 288*d*).

Trigonias (Fig. 296*b*), *Caenopus* (Fig. 300), and their relatives of the American Oligocene appear to represent the central stock of the true rhinoceroses. *Caenopus* had already attained fairly large size (the skull averaged well over a foot in length), and the limbs supporting the stocky body were stouter and shorter than in the hyracodonts and comparable to those of modern tapirs. Four toes were still present in front in *Trigonias*, but the fifth toe was already small and had disappeared in *Caenopus*. All later types retained a three-toed foot. Incisor tusks were developed; and most of the other front teeth were retained, in contrast with later forms. The premolar teeth were at first simple but during the Oligocene tended to

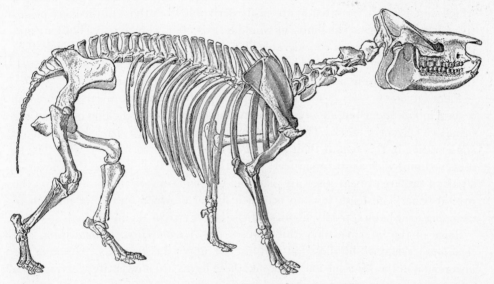

Fig. 300.—*Caenopus tridactylus*, an Oligocene hornless rhinoceros, about 8 feet in length. (From Osborn.)

assume the molar pattern. The primitive Oligocene rhinoceroses were hornless (the matted hair of the "horn" does not fossilize, and our evidence for the presence of horns consists in a rough area of the bone at its base).

The center of rhinoceros distribution appears to have been in North America, although some early Old World types are known. One very intimately related descendant of the early caenopids was *Diceratherium* (Figs. 289*c*, 296*c*, 297*b*), a small rhinoceros common in the Lower Miocene of North America and found somewhat later in Eurasia. This type was quite similar to its Oligocene ancestors except for the fact that the males possessed small horns; but unlike other later rhinoceroses, these were placed side by side at the tip of the nose.

The origin of the true rhinoceroses was long in doubt. But present evidence tends to show that they were derived from some of the smaller and more primitive running rhinoceroses of the Eocene and through them trace back to the primitive perissodactyl stock.

Giant rhinoceroses.—Also directly descended from the *Caenopus* stock were *Baluchitherium* (Fig. 291*d*) and other huge hornless forms recently discovered in the Oligocene and early Miocene of Asia. These were the largest of known land mammals. The head of *Baluchitherium* was about 4 feet in length, but even so was small in proportion to the body size. This great beast must have stood about 18 feet high at the shoulders, with a long neck which, combined with long front legs, enabled him to browse on the higher branches of the trees. The grinding teeth were quite like those of *Caenopus;* while the single pair of blunt incisors, which were his only front teeth, are easily derivable from those of the more primitive Oligocene forms. The limbs, as would be expected, were massive but long and pillar-like. There is even considerable elongation of the metapodials, which were stout and placed close together in a pillar above the three stubby toes (Fig. 295*d*); the lateral digits were more reduced than in any other rhinoceroses.

Later rhinoceros types.—The remaining, later, rhinoceroses appear to represent several independent but closely related evolutionary lines branching out from the primitive Oligocene stock. These later forms tended to large size (although more conservative in this regard than *Baluchitherium*) and, in correlation with this, to massive limbs with short broad feet. Horns have usually developed, but never as a pair; if two are present, they are placed in tandem—one on the nasal, one on the frontal bone. The teeth tend to be much higher crowned, partly in relation to changing food habits, partly because of the larger size of the individuals.

Some of the later Tertiary rhinoceroses—as *Aceratherium, Chilotherium,* and *Aphelops*—remained hornless but had lost the upper incisor tusks. Although not uncommon in the Miocene and Pliocene, these forms are now entirely extinct; the later types of rhinoceroses are horned forms.

A prominent side branch of the horned rhinoceroses in late Miocene and Pliocene times included *Teleoceras* and its relatives. *Teleoceras* was a short-legged, broad-footed, round-bodied beast with a build like that of a hippopotamus. These short-legged rhinoceroses were presumably marsh- and river-dwellers. Technically they were horned, for the nasals exhibit a roughened area showing the presence of at least the rudiment of this structure.

The center of rhinoceros evolution seems to have shifted to Eurasia in the later Miocene and Pliocene, with only hornless types and *Teleoceras* representing the family in North America. Since the Pliocene there have been no rhinoceroses in the Western Hemisphere. In the late Miocene and Pliocene of the Old World we find an abundance of types which, although poorly known in many cases, seem to point the way to the varied groups of Pleistocene and Recent times. These forms are mainly distinguished by the variable development of the horns and incisors.

The term *Rhinoceros* is, in a narrow sense, applicable only to the large living

Indian "unicorn" and a smaller relative from Java in which there is a single massive horn on the nasal bones and both incisor tusks have been retained. Members of this group can be traced back to the Miocene of Asia.

A large and important group of later Tertiary and living rhinoceroses includes those in which both nasal and frontal horns are present. *Dicerorhinus* of Sumatra is a surviving primitive form with but rudimentary horns, low-crowned teeth, and with the incisor tusks retained. The remaining two-horned rhinoceroses, including both living types and fossils dating back to the Miocene, are much more advanced, in that the teeth are much higher crowned and that the incisors are absent, making them entirely dependent on their lips for cropping vegetation. They include the living African rhinoceroses, both black and "white" (really gray) (*Diceros* [Fig. 291e] and *Ceratotherium*), as well as a number of Pleistocene beasts, of which the most interesting was *Coelodonta*, a wooly rhinoceros adapted to a cold climate, which survived in Europe to the close of the Pleistocene. This form, related to the living white rhinoceros, was a favorite subject for old Stone Age cave artists, while specimens "pickled" in an oil seep have been found entire in Galicia.

Like these two-horned forms in the loss of the front teeth but highly specialized in other respects was a small group of forms which culminated in *Elasmotherium* of the Pleistocene of Russia and Siberia. This rhinoceros had no nasal horn but a truly enormous frontal one indicated by a basal rugosity nearly a foot in diameter. The name refers to the fact that the teeth, although with the characteristic rhinoceros pattern, had a wavy strap-like outline of the enamel.

The history of the rhinoceroses has, in general, run a course parallel to that of the related horses but with emphasis on bulk rather than on speed. Eocene and early Oligocene members of both groups tended to vary widely, producing in the case of the rhinoceroses not only running types but the large amynodonts. In the Oligocene the rhinoceroses in the main settled down to become a group of forms characteristically much larger than the horses but more conservative in that most remained browsing forms. Like the horses, they were abundant in late Tertiary times but are now limited to a few Old World types.

Titanotheres.—There remains for consideration among the perissodactyls two extinct groups—the titanotheres and chalicotheres—both spectacularly specialized but both with an unprogressive dental equipment to which their extinction may be at least partially due. Of these two the earliest to reach a climax and earliest to become extinct were the titanotheres, an interesting series of which North America seems to have been the evolutionary center. The end-forms of this line are found in such genera as *Brontops* (Fig. 301), *Brontotherium*, *Menodus*, and *Megacerops*, of the early Oligocene. These creatures were of great size, the height at the shoulder reaching 8 feet in one type. The skull (as in almost all titanotheres) was long and low; the brain was very small; and the braincase had a characteristic sag on top rather than any expansion of the skull. A striking feature was the development at the front of a pair of large rugose horn-like processes.   These horns were always of fairly good size in these end-forms (although smaller in the females); but they varied enormously in the different genera, sometimes being long diverging structures, sometimes (in *Embolotherium*, of the Oligocene of Mongolia) rising up sharply as a single broad, fused mass dividing at the top. The teeth (Figs. 288g, 289e), on the other hand, were strangely unprogressive. The incisors, as well as a premolar, might be lost entirely. The premolars were only partially molarized in pattern and small in size. The molars were large in surface area but crowned with a bunolophodont pattern. In the upper molars there was a W-shaped

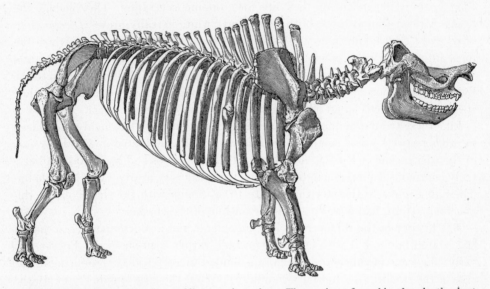

Fig. 301.—*Brontops*, a large Lower Oligocene titanothere. The specimen figured is a female; the short horns a sex difference. Original about 14 feet long. (From Osborn.)

ectoloph, on the inner side of which lay the main grinding surface, and isolated internal cones representing protostyle, protocone, and hypocone. Below was a double V of somewhat the same pattern as that of the horses but without the reduplication of the cusp at the union of the V's found in most equids. The limbs, in correlation with the huge bulk, were of the graviportal type, short and massive with the conservative number of four and three toes, respectively, in the stubby front and hind feet (Figs. 296f, 297d).

In the Upper Eocene of America and Asia were somewhat more primitive types, such as *Dolichorhinus*, in which there were never more than slight traces of horns on the long nasal bones. In size the Upper Eocene types averaged but about two-thirds that of the end forms; and the body was, in consequence, less massive in its proportions. All the teeth were present, the upper molars still possessed the two primitive intermediate cusps lost later, and the premolars were all simple and un-molarized. A further stage back is found in *Palaeosyops* and *Limnohyops* (Fig. 291*g*), of the Middle Eocene of North America, which had reached only the size of a tapir and were hornless. In the late Lower Eocene there was present in North America not only a primitive true titanothere (*Eotitanops*) but also a small form, *Lambdotherium*, intermediate between titanotheres and the primitive equoid types.

The main evolutionary trends seen in this series of forms seem to be pointed toward the rapid attainment of large size. The development of horns seems to have been a somewhat ineffective "attempt" at protection against the larger contemporary carnivores; it is to be noted that in Upper Eocene times rudimentary horns were developing independently in a number of separate lines of titanotheres. Lack of good brains and of good teeth seem to have been the main factors in their failure to succeed. Their diet must have consisted of extremely soft vegetation, for, despite the large amounts of food which must have been required for the sustenance of the huge body, the teeth could not undergo any great amount of wear. Any slight change in the vegetation and the curtailment of soft food would readily have destroyed their hold on existence.

Chalicotheres.—A final perissodactyl group is that of the chalicotheres. The characteristic features of these most curious forms are, for the most part, well illustrated in *Moropus* (Figs. 291*h*), of the American Lower Miocene. In general appearance (as well as in size) *Moropus* was probably rather horse-like, although the front legs were somewhat longer than the hind. The perissodactyl nature of this beast is indicated by many features of the skull and skeleton. In the slim skull the general proportions were those of the horses of that age; the long slender nasals were a perissodactyl character. The cropping teeth were weak to absent in chalicotheres. Unlike the typical perissodactyls, the premolars had remained comparatively small and simple; but the molars (which tended to remain low crowned) were rather similar to those of the titanotheres, with a double V in the lower molars and a W-shaped ectoloph above (Figs. 288*h*, 289*f*).

In the feet (Figs. 296*g*, 297*e*) we have quite another story. There were in this genus three toes in each foot, and the manus was primitive in retaining a well-developed metacarpal for a small fifth digit (lost in other perissodactyl groups by that date). So far all is still orthodoxly perissodactyl. But the digits, instead of bearing hoofs, were terminated by large fissured ungual phalanges, undoubtedly bearing not hoofs but stout claws.

Such a feature is one quite unlooked for in a form which otherwise agrees so well with the hoofed groups considered in this chapter; for half a century or so after the first fragmentary remains of chalicotheres were discovered it was not imagined that skull and feet could possibly have pertained to the same form. Because of the claws, some are even inclined today to place these chalicotheres in a separate order.

But the rest of the skeleton is so typically perissodactyl that we cannot refuse them admittance to this group. We must regard them as a specialized side branch of the perissodactyls in which the high development of claws is associated with some specialized habit of these forms. The long front legs of *Moropus* and other members of the group have suggested to some a browsing habit in which the front feet may have been used in dragging down branches. But a more probable explanation is that the food consisted of roots and tubers and that the claws were used as digging organs.

Older forms were present in the Oligocene of the Old World and in the Eocene of North America. The Eocene *Eomoropus* had attained only the size of a sheep and had (as usual in Eocene perissodactyls) a well-developed fifth finger and even had rudiments of a pollex, unknown in other perissodactyls. The ungual phalanges show little of the later compression into claw-bearing organs, and the dentition was unreduced and quite primitive. This form was not far from the primitive perissodactyl stock.

While the Middle Miocene saw the extinction of this group in America, chalicotheres persisted much later in Eurasia, with forms in the Miocene and Pliocene, such as *Chalicotherium*, in which the front legs were much longer than the hind. A related form straggled on into the Pleistocene in China and India; with this the group came to an end.

With the chalicotheres we terminate our account of the perissodactyls. All five main groups had appeared early in the Eocene, and during the early part of the Tertiary they flourished greatly. By the Miocene, however, they were beginning to lose somewhat in relative importance. In Pleistocene times horses and rhinoceroses still flourished. Today the perissodactyls are but an insignificant part of the world's ungulate population.

CHAPTER XVIII

ARTIODACTYLS

The order Artiodactyla, the even-toed ungulates, includes a great variety of living hoofed mammals, such as the pigs and peccaries, hippopotamus, camels, deer, cows, sheep, goats, antelopes, and their relatives, together with many important extinct types. Exceeded in numbers in many early horizons by the perissodactyls, they have succeeded in far outdistancing their early rivals and are the dominant hoofed mammals of later Tertiary and Recent times.

Structure.—The most obvious and characteristic feature of the group is the type of toe reduction, for, whereas almost all other ungulates tend to have a mesaxonic foot with the axis through the third toe, the artiodactyls are paraxonic with the axis between the third and fourth toes. Pollex and hallux are rarely found even in early forms. Four-toed types are common in the earlier part of the Tertiary; the pigs and hippopotami are still four-toed, and rudimentary lateral "dew claws" are present in many other forms. The higher types tended early to reduce the toes to two on each foot, the typical "cloven hoof" in which the two principal metapodials fuse together into a cannon bone.

In contrast with perissodactyls there is no third trochanter on the femur. The ulna is reduced and in higher forms fuses with the radius; and the fibula, too, is usually incomplete or fused with the tibia. In the carpus the three proximal elements are always separate, but in the distal row the magnum and trapezoid fuse in some advanced types to support the third metacarpal, while the unciform supports the fourth. The astragalus (Fig. 264c) is the most characteristic bone in the skeleton, for it has not only a rolling surface above but an equally developed lower pulley surface, giving very great freedom of motion to the ankle. The astragalus rests equally on the navicular and the cuboid (these two elements are fused in many types [cf. Fig. 312]). The cuboid lies above the fourth toe, the outer of the two principal digits, while the navicular transmits half the weight to the third toe through the ectocuneiform (the other cuneiform bones tend to be reduced).

The dentition was complete in many of the early types, as it is still in the pigs. The most primitive known forms had normal incisors and rather large, carnivore-like canines. The premolars were simple, and the molars in the simplest forms were of the primitive tritubercular pattern with rather bunodont cusps. From this primitive pattern, not so different from that of primitive carnivores, there have been great variations.

The incisors are often reduced; and the upper ones are absent in the more advanced types, their place as a cropping organ being taken functionally by the calloused upper lip. The upper canines often form defensive tusks; the lower ones sometimes take on the aspect of incisors. A diastema has usually developed, and the first premolar is frequently absent. The premolars, in contrast with those of perissodactyls, do not usually assume the full molar pattern but remain comparatively simple (cf. Fig. 304). The cheek teeth, primitively low crowned, have become hypsodont in many forms. As in other herbivores the molars (Fig. 305) almost always take on a four-cusped pattern. The rather bunodont primitive condition may be emphasized, as in the pigs; but usually each cusp develops into a crescent, giving the typical selenodont pattern of the higher artiodactyls. In this process the outer cusps tended to become crescentic before the inner ones, giving a buno-selenodont condition in some fossil forms.

One peculiar feature, however, is found in the upper molars. In most mammals the postero-internal cusp of a four-cusped molar is obviously the hypocone. This is true in a few artiodactyls (Fig. 305b), but in the great majority of the group (including all living forms) it seems probable that the postero-internal cusp is not the hypocone but an enlarged metaconule and that the hypocone has never developed (Fig. 305c, e–h, j–p).

There are typically nineteen thoracic and lumbar vertebrae. The clavicle is, as might be expected, universally absent.

Many forms have a postorbital bar, and there is always at least a postorbital process. The front part of the skull is sharply bent down on the braincase in the more advanced forms; and the frontals tend to be large; the parietals, on the contrary, reduced.

Classification (cf. Fig. 302).—The artiodactyls appear in the fossil record at the beginning of true Eocene times. These earliest types were quite primitive in many respects, with simple teeth implying a mixed diet and with features which suggest a relationship to the primitive carnivores. Nevertheless, such distinctive artiodactyl features as the double-pulleyed astragalus were already developed, and it is obvious that the ancestral forms must have been undergoing development in some unknown area in Paleocene times. Inconspicuous at the beginning of the Eocene, the artiodactyls had developed into a great variety of types by the end of that period. Many of these have since become extinct, but others are indicative of the lines of descent leading to the existing forms.

The classification of living artiodactyls is simple. They comprise: (1) the suborder Suina, or swine in a broad sense—pigs, peccaries, and hippopotamus; (2) the suborder Ruminantia, cud-chewers, which include (a) the Tylopoda, or camels, (b) the Tragulina, or chevrotains, and (c) the Pecora, the deer-giraffe-antelope-cattle group. The "swine" have bunodont molar teeth, canine tusks, four-toed feet with separate metapodials, and a simple stomach; the ruminants have selenodont molars, the upper incisors are small or absent, the feet are usually two-toed, with a cannon bone, and there is a compound ruminating stomach.

But when the fossil forms are included, such an easy separation is impossible; we are confronted with a large array of families which are intermediate in many respects between existing types or belong to extinct side branches. One attempt

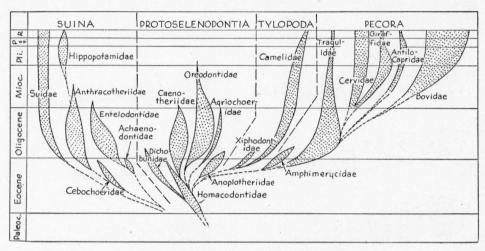

FIG. 302.—Provision phylogeny of the artiodactyl groups.

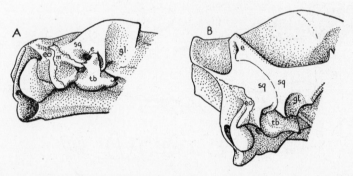

FIG. 303.—Lateral (and somewhat ventral) views of the posterior part of the skull in *A*, the anoplothere *Diplobune* and *B*, the peccary *Dicotyles*, to show the contrast between mastoid and amastoid artiodactyls. In *A* the mastoid is widely exposed on the surface of the skull between the squamosal and exoccipital, in *B* this area is occupied by an extension of the squamosal. *e*, external auditory opening; *eo*, exoccipital; *gl*, glenoid cavity; *m*, mastoid; *sq*, squamosal; *tb*, tympanic bulla. (After Pearson.)

at classification has been made on the basis of the types of cusps of the molar teeth, with a division into bunodonts, buno-selenodonts, and selenodonts. The arrangement of the molar cusps and the presence or absence of a hypocone has served as the basis for another type of subdivision. A third attempt at classification is based on the degree of development of the mastoid bone (Fig. 303). In primitive mammals this element of the ear region appears to have been well exposed on the surface of the skull at the postero-lateral corner of the braincase, between the exoccipital and squamosal. This is still the case in living ruminants; but in the "swine" the squamosal has grown back to meet the exoccipital over the area once occupied by the mastoid, and this last bone no longer reaches the surface.

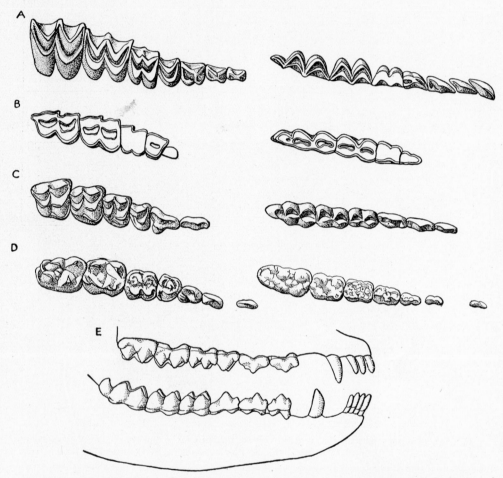

FIG. 304.—The cheek teeth of artiodactyls. Left, teeth of upper right side; right, teeth of lower left side. *A, Merycochoerus*, a Miocene oreodon, $\times\frac{1}{3}$ approx. *B, Camelops*, a Pleistocene camelid, $\times\frac{2}{3}$. *C, Archaeomeryx*, a primitive fossil pecoran, $\times\frac{3}{2}$ approx. *D, Cheleuasto choerus*, a Pliocene pig, $\times\frac{5}{8}$. *E*, side view of upper and lower dentitions of *Archaeomeryx* to show the unreduced upper incisors. (*A* after Loomis, *B* after Merriam, *C, E* after Matthew, *D* after Pearson.)

The investigation of the mastoid region in fossil forms shows that a definite division may be made on this basis. The forms which have the mastoid visible include some very primitive types but are mainly those which developed selenodont molars and lead in the direction of the living ruminants. All these may be provisionally grouped as Ruminantia, although it is doubtful if cud-chewing had developed in the early forms. Fossil artiodactyls in which the mastoid is absent are generally bunodont types which appear to be related to the swine or hippopotami and thus may be properly included in the Suina.

Of these two groups we shall first consider the ruminants, not only because these forms include the most numerous and progressive artiodactyl types but also for the reason that the oldest known and most primitive of artiodactyls may be assigned to this group.

Primitive artiodactyls.—Earliest of known artiodactyls, and probably close to the stem of the whole group, are a number of forms such as *Diacodexis* and *Homa-*

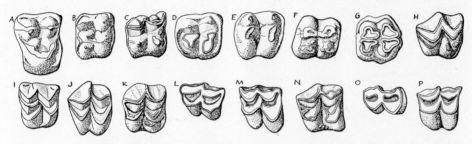

FIG. 305.—Right upper molar teeth of artiodactyls. *A, Diacodexis,* a Lower Eocene form with tritubercular molars. *B, Dichobune,* a hypocone present, in contrast with most members of the order. *C, Anthracotheriun,* a bunoselenodont five-cusped molar. *D, Archaeotherium,* an entelodont with a pig-like tooth with developed hypocone. *E, Platygonus,* a peccary. *F, Sus erymanthus,* a Pliocene pig. *G,* a Pleistocene *Hippopotamus. H, Anoplotherium,* a bunoselenodont type with protoconule still present. *I, Caenotherium,* with protocone migrated to back half of tooth. *J, Oreodon,* a simple four-cusped selenodont tooth. *K, Xiphodon. L, Alticamelus,* a Pliocene camel. *M, Samotherium,* a Pliocene giraffe. *N, Dicrocerus,* a primitive deer. *O, Tetrameryx,* a Pleistocene prongbuck. *P, Tragocerus,* a Pliocene bovid. (*A* after Sinclair, *B, I* after Stehlin, *C, F, H, P* after Gaudry, *E* after Osborn, *G* after Cuvier, *K, N* after Schlosser, *L* after Cook, *M* after Ringström, *O* after Lull.)

codon from the Lower and Middle Eocene mainly in North America. These forms are sometimes associated with a group (dichobunids) mentioned later, but their primitive features seem to warrant their separation as a family Homacodontidae. The dentition was of an exceedingly primitive character. The molar teeth were low crowned, with rounded, non-crescentic cusps, and in *Diacodexis* (Fig. 305*a*) had a simple tritubercular pattern. In others, as *Homacodon,* there was an incipient hypocone, a feature rarely met with in later artiodactyls. The canine teeth were large, and the incisors normally developed.

The skull (Fig. 306*a*) was of primitive shape, rather long and low; and as in primitive artiodactyls generally, there was no postorbital bar. The mastoid was well developed, and for this reason we may range these forms among the Ruminantia. They are, however, far more primitive than any other members of this group; and their dentition suggests a mixed, rather than a purely herbivorous, diet.

There is little in the skull or dentition to prove that these forms are artiodactyls at all. Fortunately in a few cases remains of the limbs have been discovered. Here we find that the typical artiodactyl astragalus was present and that the feet (although none too well known) were paraxonic in nature, each with two large toes and smaller lateral ones.

Primitive selenodonts.—These oldest artiodactyls were rare members of the early Eocene faunas. During the later Eocene, however, there appeared numerous

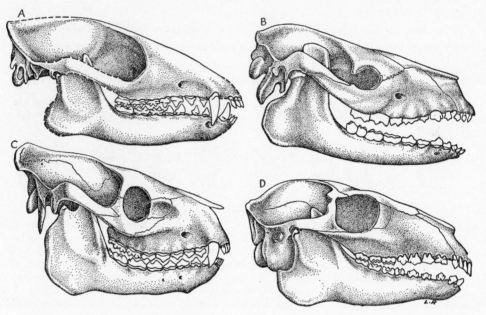

Fig. 306.—Skulls of some early "mastoid" artiodactyls. *A, Homacodon*, a primitive Eocene type (jaw restored from a contemporary form), length of skull about 3 inches. *B, Anoplotherium*, a late Eocene anoplothere, skull length about 14 inches. *C, Oreodon culbertsoni*, an Oligocene oreodont, length of skull about 5 inches. *D, Caenotherium*, length of skull about 3 inches. (*A* after Sinclair, *B* after de Blainville, *C* after Leidy, *D* after Schlosser.)

artiodactyl types which were, for the most part, unprogressive in skeletal features but were advancing rapidly toward the selenodont type in their dentition. These forms include representatives of a number of families, most of them destined to be short-lived. We may provisionally group them as an infraorder Protoselenodontia and, despite the incongruity of the name, include with them their probable ancestors, the early Eocene forms just described.

In general these primitive selenodonts were comparatively short-limbed forms with four well developed toes (Fig. 307*e, f*). In the molar teeth the outer cusps were crescentic in all cases, but in many Upper Eocene members of the group the inner cusps were still bunodont. In the lower teeth four cusps were invariably present, representing protoconid, metaconid, mypoconid, and entoconid. In the upper molars there was some variation; but in most Upper Eocene selenodonts there were five crescents, the protocone, protoconule, and paracone being usually ranged in the front half of the tooth and the metaconule and metacone in the posterior half (cf. Fig. 305h). The premolars remained comparatively simple in con-

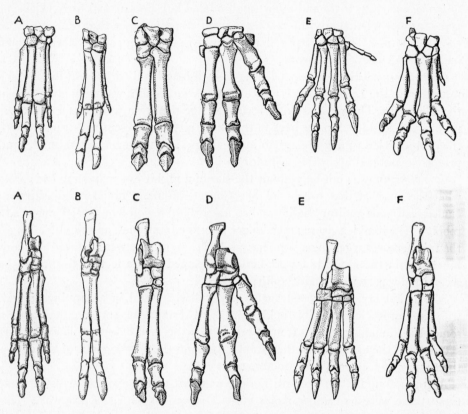

FIG. 307.—Feet of various artiodactyls. Manus above, pes below. A, Ancodus, an anthracothere. B, Mylohyus, an advanced Pleistocene type of peccary, with side toes reduced in front, lost behind and a cannon bone formed in the pes. C, Dinohyus, a Lower Miocene entelodont. D, Diplobune, an aberrant three-toed anoplothere. E, Agriochoerus, a clawed Oligocene American selenodont. In this and in F, Oreodon, the pollex is preserved. (A after Kowalevsky, B after Brown, C after Peterson, D after Schlosser, E after Wortman, F after Osborn.)

struction but were elongated so that often no diastema developed. Usually all the incisors were retained; but the canines were frequently reduced to the size of the adjacent teeth, giving a rather uniform tooth row; in some cases the first premolar was enlarged to function as a canine.

Primitive European selenodonts.—Early ruminant evolution seems to have pursued somewhat different lines in Europe and North America. In the former continent there appeared a wide diversity of types. Most of them soon vanished, but among them were presumably the ancestors of the Pecora. In North America the late Eocene assemblage was a more restricted one but included the first oreodonts and seemingly the ancestors of the camels. We shall first consider the diverse European forms.

Dichobune (Fig. 305*b*) and a few small related late Eocene and early Oligocene types are not particularly interesting in most respects, since they do not lead to any later forms. They were peculiar, however, in that they, alone of selenodonts, had a well-developed hypocone.

Caenotherium (Figs. 305*i*, 306*d*) was a small long-lived Old World form which ranged from the Upper Eocene to the Lower Miocene and was very abundant in the Oligocene. The most striking feature of the dentition was the fact that the protocone had shifted to the back of the tooth, giving a five-cusped structure with the protoconule forming the antero-internal cusp and metacone, metaconule, and protocone all lined up in the posterior half.

Caenotherium was not only about the size of a rabbit but may have had somewhat the place of that rodent in the Oligocene fauna. Cranial peculiarities included enormous auditory bullae and an anteorbital region fenestrated much as in rabbits. The hind legs were much longer than the front ones, and the tibia longer than the femur, suggesting a hopping gait. The lateral toes were reduced and nonfunctional in the hand, but were better developed in the feet (incidentally the second toe was shorter than the fifth).

The artiodactyl type of astragalus is peculiarly useful in a hopping animal, which requires a very flexible ankle joint; and certain rodents have developed a somewhat similar structure. It may well be that this type of locomotion was characteristic of the ancestors of the artiodactyls, and the hopping gait of the caenotheres may be a primitive characteristic.

A group abundant in the late Eocene was that of the anoplotheres. In these types there were five upper molar cusps (Fig. 305*h*) with the protocone (persistently bunodont) in the anterior half of the tooth. In general there appear to have been four rather short toes present, the lateral ones moderately reduced. Some of the members of the family were obviously aberrant. *Anoplotherium* (Fig. 306*b*) was a large form, reaching the proportions of a tapir; *Diplobune* (Fig. 307*d*) was characterized by an odd three-toed foot in which the fifth digit but not the second had been lost. The molar structure of the family is of a type expected in the ancestors of the later selenodonts, and it is not improbable that some of the smaller and less specialized Eocene anoplotheres were ancestral to more advanced types.

Oreodonts.—The ruminant assemblage of North America in the late Eocene and later periods was of quite a different nature. There were no known representatives of the caenotheres, anoplotheres, or true dichobunids. Instead are found ancestors of the oreodonts and related types—rather pig-like forms which were the common herbivores in North America during the Middle Tertiary. In time oreodonts ranged from the Upper Eocene to the Lower Pliocene and were especially abundant in the Oligocene and early Miocene; in strata of those ages their remains outnumber those of all other forms together. There were about thirty oreodont genera, most of them very conservative in tooth and foot structure. They were good selenodonts with four rather V-shaped cusps in the molar teeth (Fig. 305j); and while generally brachyodont, there were some hypsodont types. The dentition was usually complete (Fig. 304a). The lower canine was taken over into the incisor series (as in ruminants) and was replaced functionally by the first premolar. The skull was large, the body rather long, and the legs short. The orbit was usually closed; there was often an anteorbital pit or opening, presumably containing, as in

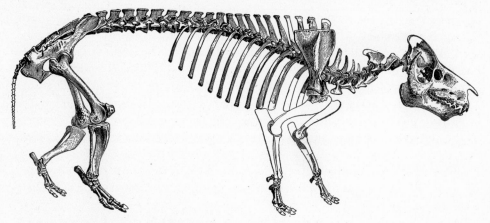

FIG. 308.—*Promerycochoerus*, a Lower Miocene oreodon. Original about 5½ feet long. (From Peterson.)

later ruminants, a facial gland. In a few forms, such as *Pronomotherium*, the nasals were short and the nostrils far back, indicating the development of a proboscis. There were always four complete toes (Fig. 307f) and in one early genus even a pollex, a remarkably primitive character for an artiodactyl. There was never any fusion of limb elements.

In the oldest known true oreodont from the Upper Eocene, *Protooreodon*, the orbit was still open, in contrast with all other members of the group; and there was still a separate protoconule in the front half of the upper molars, as in many other primitive selenodonts of that date. *Oreodon* (Fig. 306c), the common Oligocene genus, was still a rather generalized type; but later forms—*Promerycochoerus* (Fig. 308), *Merychyus*, and numerous others—specialized in various ways, such as increase in size, formation of a proboscis, development of hypsodont teeth, and loss of incisors.

Differing in a number of respects from the typical oreodonts (and often placed in a separate family) were *Agriochoerus* and a few relatives from the late Eocene and early Oligocene. Striking features were present in the fact that the feet (Fig. 307e) bore claws instead of hoofs and that the tail was elongated. These forms were persistently primitive in the retention of a pollex. In *Agriochoerus* the upper incisors were lost, and the biting mechanism was presumably similar to that of the higher ruminants. It is difficult to be sure of their mode of life. Perhaps, like the chalicotheres, they ate tubers, while the normal oreodonts may have lived upon soft riverside vegetation, and some of them were probably amphibious.

Camels.—The primitive selenodont groups considered above were the common artiodactyls in the late Eocene and were, for the most part, still abundant in Oligocene and early Miocene times. But in the Upper Eocene appeared the forerunners of two higher ruminant groups, the tylopods and pecorans, which were destined to supplant them as the dominant herbivores.

Principal members of the Tylopoda are the Camelidae, represented today by the Old World camels and the llamas of South America. The family may be traced back to the beginning of the Oligocene or the end of the Eocene, the major part of camelid development having taken place in North America.

Despite their dissimilarity in superficial appearance, the camel and llama are essentially alike in structure, the hump of the camel (probably absent in most older camels) and the heavier hairy covering of the South American llamas being probably recently acquired features associated with the habitats of these modern forms. Unlike the majority of the pecora, members of the camel group are never horned. There is a postorbital bar in the living forms; the tympanic bulla is filled with spongy bone.

Modern camelids have a cropping mechanism similar to that of the Pecora, in which the lower incisors extend forward and the herbage is pressed between these and a stout upper lip. The reduction of the upper incisors has been taken at a slower tempo than in the other living ruminants, however; and the lateral one is still retained. A small canine is present, and the premolars have been much reduced with the development of the diastema.

The neck is elongated, and the limbs are long. Radius and fibula are, of course, much reduced; and there are no traces of lateral toes. As in the Pecora, the trapezium has gone from the carpus, and the meso- and ectocuneiform have fused in the tarsus; but the other elements are still separate. The feet (Fig. 309b) are exceedingly characteristic, for, unlike normal ungulates, the living camelids are digitigrade, with spreading toes set nearly flat on the ground; and instead of a hoof, there is a small nail and a heavy pad beneath the toes.

The division of the stomach into chambers has not proceeded as far in camels as in the Pecora, but the development of stomach pockets for water storage is peculiar to this group.

An early camelid is *Poëbrotherium* (Fig. 310a), of the North American Oligocene,

somewhat smaller than a sheep. The dentition was complete with canines and incisors of similar build and grading over into the elongated premolars with almost
no trace of a diastema, a construction similar to that of many primitive selenodonts. The orbit was still open behind, al-
though the two processes which were to bridge
the gap were already long. The side toes had
been lost already at this early date, but the
two remaining metapodials were still separate
and did not diverge at the ends; and the animal
presumably had a hoof rather than the modern
padded camel foot (Fig. 309a). It is obvious
that these forms must have had a separate
history well back into the Eocene, for they
were at this time more advanced in limb construction than the contemporary Pecora. *Protylopus*, an Upper Eocene ruminant about the
size of a jackrabbit, has been suggested as a
possible ancestor; in this form lateral toes were
still present in the front foot.

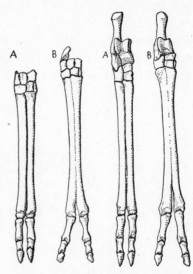

FIG. 309.—Manus (at left) and pes (at
right) of camels. *A*, the Oligocene *Poëbrotherium*. *B*, the Pliocene *Procamelus*.
(After Wortman.)

There was a large number of camelid genera
in the later Tertiary, almost all of them until
near the end of that period exclusively North
American. Along the main evolutionary line
there was a gradual increase in size in Miocene and Pliocene forms such as *Procamelus* and *Pliauchenia*, the orbit became inclosed by bone, a diastema developed, the two inner upper incisors dropped out, and the metapodials fused to

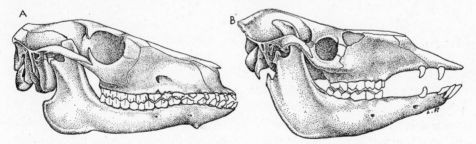

FIG. 310.—The skull of camelids. *A*, *Poëbrotherium*, a primitive Oligocene form, skull length about
6¼ inches. *B*, *Camelops*, a Pleistocene American type, skull length about 22½ inches. (*A* after Wortman,
B after Merriam.)

form a cannon bone. During the later half of the Tertiary, when camels were
numerous in North America, there were many side branches, including such forms
as the "gazelle camel," *Stenomylus*, a small and graceful type from the Lower

Miocene, and the group of "giraffe camels," such as *Oxydactylus* (Fig. 311) and *Alticamelus* (Fig. 304*e*) with very long neck and legs.

In the Pliocene appeared forms much closer to the living camelids in which the true ungulate type of hoof was abandoned and the flat spreading type of toe was developed. The differentiation of modern types was then well under way. Llama-like forms were present in North America, while forms ancestral to the true camels not only were present in North America but had also for the first time migrated westward to Asia. *Camelus* spread widely in the Old World in the Pleistocene;

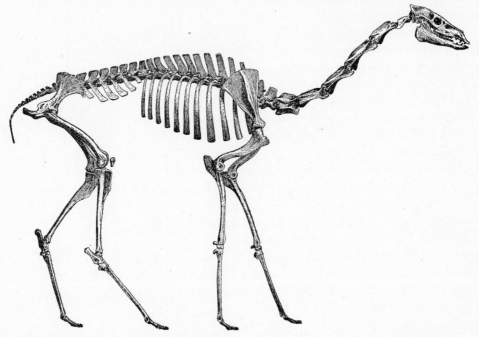

FIG. 311.—*Oxydactylus*, a long-limbed Miocene camel. Original about $7\frac{1}{2}$ feet long. (From Peterson.)

while relatives of the llama, *Auchenia*, reached their present South American home at that time. In North America *Camelops* (Fig. 310*b*) and other forms not only persisted into the Pleistocene but apparently lived in the Southwest until comparatively recent times. As in the case of the horses, the cause of the extinction of this group in the region which had been so long their home is not obvious, for, when reintroduced during the last century, camels were well able to survive in a wild state in the Western deserts.

Xiphodonts.—Bracketed with the camels in the Tylopoda are *Xiphodon* and a few related forms which were very common in Europe on the Eocene-Oligocene boundary. They resembled closely the early camels in both limbs and teeth. They, too, were precociously didactyl, with long slim limbs retaining only small splints of the side metapodials. As in the ancestral camels, the dentition was complete and without a diastema and the teeth graded evenly over from incisors into the cheek teeth. The upper molars (Fig. 305k) still had the primitive five-cusped pattern, the protoconule remaining distinct.

The Pecora.—All remaining artiodactyls, including the vast majority of the living members of the order, may be included in the Pecora in a broad use of that term. The modern forms are readily grouped in five families: (1) Tragulidae, or chevrotains; (2) Cervidae, the deer; (3) Giraffidae, the giraffe and okapi; (4) Antilocapridae, the American "antelope"; (5) Bovidae, including cattle, sheep, goats, and antelopes.

In these specialized and very successful ungulates the stomach is complicated in structure and the ruminating habit highly developed. The build is, in general, a graceful one; and the limbs are long and slender. All are functionally two-toed types; but reduction of the side digits has gone on at a slower pace than in the tylopods, for small lateral toes are present in a number of living pecorans as well as in many fossil forms. The two principal metapodials have usually fused into an elongated cannon bone. There has been considerable fusion in carpal and tarsal elements, and the union of navicular and cuboid in the ankle is a feature diagnostic of the group. The ulna is reduced, and of the fibula there remains in typical living forms only a nubbin of bone in the ankle region.

Most living pecorans possess weapons in the shape of horns or similar bony outgrowths from the skull. In many primitive types, both living and extinct, these are absent; but long stabbing upper canines are frequently present in their place. The upper incisors have given way to a horny lip pad as part of the cropping mechanism. There appear, at first glance, to be four lower incisors, for the canine has (as in oreodonts) been taken over into the incisor group. One premolar early disappeared with the development of a diastema. The molars have, since the earliest times, been selenodont in pattern with but four cusps—the proto-, para-, and metacone, and metaconule—in the upper molars.

The oldest pecorans.—Members of this group are not present in the earlier Eocene deposits and first appear at the end of that period. Best known of these ancestral forms was *Archaeomeryx* (Fig. 304c, e), of Mongolia, a small ungulate about the size of a fox. This type was already a pecoran, as indicated by such features as the fused navicular and cuboid. But it was in many respects more primitive than any of its descendants in later periods. The side toes were still complete and functional, the middle metapodials had not fused to form a cannon bone, and ulna and fibula were much less reduced than in later pecorans. Neither horns nor enlarged tusks were present. The most noteworthy feature of all lay in the fact that, in contrast with all later members of the group, the full complement of upper incisors was still present and functional. The low-crowned molars had already attained a four-cusped selenodont pattern, but the premolars had acquired almost no grinding surface as yet.

Tragulids.—The Oligocene was a time when the protoselenodonts were the most flourishing of artiodactyls. But in that period we find in addition a large series of small and rather primitive pecorans which bridge the gap between the early Eocene ancestors of the group and the more progressive families which appeared in later Tertiary times. The chevrotains, living inhabitants of the Old World tropics, have preserved for us many of the features of the archaic Oligocene types. *Tragu-*

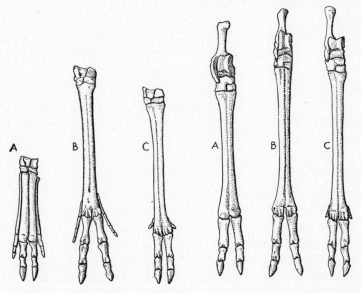

FIG. 312.—Manus (left) and pes (right) in various Pecora. *A*, the primitive Oligocene *Leptomeryx*. *B*, the Miocene cervid *Blastomeryx*. *C*, the Miocene antilocaprid *Merycodus*. (*B* after Scott, *C* after Matthew.)

lus, of Southern Asia, is a tiny ungulate rather like some of the larger rodents in size and habits. The upper incisors are absent, but in other respects this little animal is quite primitive in structure. There are no horns or antlers; but large upper canines are developed, particularly in the males. The limbs are much more primitive in nature than in other pecorans, for the side toes and metapodials are quite complete, although small and slim, and the ulna and fibula are comparatively unreduced. *Hyaemoschus*, the water chevrotain of tropical Africa, is somewhat larger but even more primitive in some respects, for the middle metapodials in these forms have failed to fuse into a cannon bone.

These small modern inhabitants of forest glades and river banks give us some idea of the nature of the varied Oligocene pecoran assemblage of which they are persistently primitive survivors. These early types were varied in size and in adaptive features and are often ranged in a number of families (Hypertragulidae, Protocerotidae, etc.). We shall here consider them as members of the family Tragulidae, using that term in a broad sense. The early forms, like the chevrotains, were generally small and lightly built, seldom with any horn development and sometimes possessing canine tusks. In the front feet (Fig. 312a) there was little tendency for the formation of a cannon bone, and the side toes and their metacarpals were usually well developed. In the hind feet, however, the side toes were rudimentary or absent, and the lateral metapodials were reduced and a cannon bone formed in most cases.

Many of the Oligocene types are suggestive of the ancestry of deer, giraffes, and bovids; others, however, appear to represent sterile "experiments." *Hypertragulus*, of late Oligocene and early Miocene times, appears to represent a stock ancestral to the living chevrotains. *Hypisodus* had a skull but 2 inches in length and was the smallest of all known artiodactyls. A curious feature was the enormous swollen auditory bullae. An odd side branch is represented in the late Oligocene of North America by *Protoceras*, with three pairs of bony swellings, incipient "horns," on the skull. These peculiar structures found further development in *Syndyoceras*, of the Lower Miocene, in which the front and hind pair were developed into long horns, giving the beast a grotesque appearance; and a final stage is reached in the Pliocene *Synthetoceras* (Fig. 313b). *Leptomeryx* (Figs. 312a, 313a, 314) is representative of a group which in many features is suggestive of the ancestry of the deer and the giraffes, while other rather poorly known Eurasian forms may lead in the direction of the cattle family. *Gelocus*, of the Oligocene of Europe, although probably not ancestral to later types, was precociously advanced in foot construction, for the side toes had disappeared and only small splints remained of the lateral metapodials.

These and many other tragulid types flourished in the Oligocene. By Miocene times the group had become insignificant in numbers, although *Dorcatherium*, much like the African water chevrotain, persisted in Europe until the Pliocene.

Deer.—Succeeding the tragulids in the Miocene were the earlier members of the higher pecoran types—the deer, giraffes, prongbucks, and bovids—to which the term Pecora is often narrowly restricted. In these forms the feet (Fig. 310b, c) were progressive, for there were never more than tiny "dew claws" and incomplete metapodial splints remaining of the side toes, and a stout cannon bone was always formed. In addition some type of horn or antler was almost always present.

The most striking feature of the modern forms of the deer family, the Cervidae, is the presence in the males of antlers, branching structures of solid bone which project from the skull posterior to the orbits. There is no horny covering; during growth they are surrounded by skin covered with downy hair, the velvet, which dries up and is rubbed off when the antler reaches full growth. Yearly the antler is shed (the place of resorption of bone at its base is marked by a roughened burr)

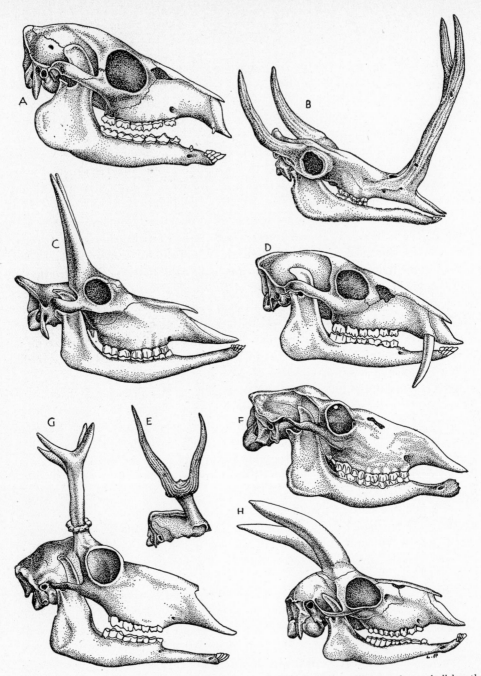

Fig. 313.—Skulls of pecorans. *A, Leptomeryx*, a primitive American Oligocene form, skull length about 4½ inches. *B, Synthetoceras*, a grotesque American Pliocene form, skull length about 18 inches. *C, Samotherium*, a Pliocene giraffe (a male; the "horns" shorter in the female), skull length about 2 feet. *D, Blastomeryx*, a Miocene hornless cervid, skull length about 14 inches. *E,* horns of *Dicrocerus*, a European late Miocene cervid. *F,* female of *Megaceros*, the "Irish elk," skull length 20 inches. *G, Merycodus*, a Miocene antilocaprid (young form, larger horns in older individuals), skull length about 7 inches. *H, Gazella brevicornis*, a Pliocene antelope, skull length about 6 inches. (*A, D, G* after Matthew; *B* after Stirton; *C* after Bohlin; *E, H* after Gaudry; *F* after Owen.)

and a new and usually more complex antler developed. This type of structure is in marked contrast to the hollow, horn-covered, unbranched, and permanent true horn of the bovids. The molars are low crowned, for the deer are mainly browsers rather than grazers and have remained forest-dwellers. In the front foot the lateral toes are small but complete, but only small and variable rudiments remain of the metapodials.

Except for most of Africa (and, of course, Australia) the deer are widespread today. The modern New World forms are probably late emigrants from Eurasia, but some of the early stages in the evolution of the group appear to be represented

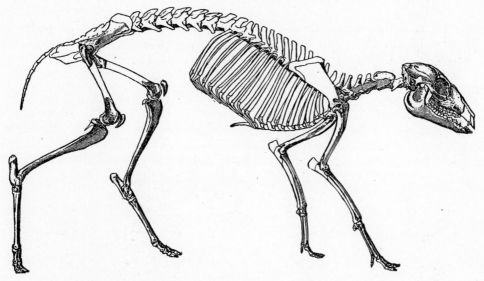

FIG. 314.—*Leptomeryx*, a primitive Oligocene pecoran about 2 feet in length. (From Scott.)

in North America. *Leptomeryx*, as has been noted, was a probable cervid ancestor. A first stage in the evolution of the deer is that represented by *Blastomeryx* (Figs. 312b, 313d, 315), of the American Miocene, as well as various European forms (*Amphitragulus*, etc.) of similar age. These were small ungulates, averaging but a foot or two high at the shoulder but already quite deer-like in structure. There was, as yet no trace of antlers but in their stead large canine tusks like those of chevrotains. This primitive stage is still represented today by such forms as *Moschus*, the musk deer of Southeastern Asia which still lacks horns and retains tusks.

By the late Miocene antlers were already making their appearance in Eurasian types; and in the Pliocene, forms such as *Dicrocerus* (Figs. 305n, 313e), with small antlers, often with but a single branch, were common. A number of small existing deer, such as the muntjacs of Southeastern Asia, with small and simple antlers and persistently large canines, are still of this Pliocene type.

But in the deer, as in other ungulates, "horns" are much more prominently developed in animals of large size. The late Pliocene and Pleistocene cervids continued to increase in bulk, and among them forms with many-tined antlers had become common. Among the more interesting forms was the gigantic "Irish elk,"

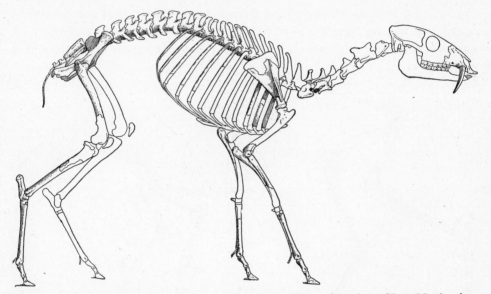

FIG. 315.—*Blastomeryx*, a Miocene ancestral deer. Original about 2½ feet long. (From Matthew.)

Megaceros (Figs. 313*f*, 316), with the largest antlers of any known deer, found throughout most of the Pleistocene in Europe.

Giraffes.—The Giraffidae today include only the giraffes and okapi of Africa. Like most living pecorans, they are "horned," having small skin-covered bony protuberances which are never shed. The long neck and legs are the most obvious specialization of the modern giraffe and are clearly associated with the tree-browsing habits of the animal. *Samotherium* (Figs. 305*m*, 313*c*) and other forms with a more normal build have long been known from the early Pliocene of Europe and Southern Asia. It was hence of great interest when, about thirty years ago, there was discovered in the forests of the Congo the okapi, a comparatively short-legged, short-necked giraffid, almost indistinguishable from such ancestral Tertiary types.

As a side branch of the family may be included *Sivatherium* and other forms from the Pliocene of India. These were quite large and heavily built and had developed two pairs of short but massive "horns" of rather irregular shape.

The earlier history of the giraffes seems to show that they are closely related to the deer and may represent an offshoot from the primitive cervid stock in about the Miocene *Blastomeryx* stage of development. While the deer are forms characteristic of temperate regions, the giraffe group attempted less successfully to follow a similar browsing life in the tropics.

Prongbucks.—*Antilocapra*, the prongbuck of the Western plains, usually but erroneously called an "antelope," is an isolated and interesting type. While in many features, such as the high-crowned cheek teeth, this form is quite similar to the antelopes, the horns are radically different in character. These structures are, it is true, covered with horn, as in bovids; and the bony core is never shed. But the horn is somewhat forked, much as in primitive deer; and, curiously, the horny covering is shed yearly. This suggests that the prongbuck has been long separated from the bovid stock, and it would seem that the living form is a survivor of a North American evolutionary series parallel to the bovids of the Old World.

An early ancestor appears to be *Merycodus* (Figs. 312c, 313g), of the Upper Miocene. This form at first sight would appear to be a deer rather than a prongbuck, for the bony outgrowths from the skull were long, forked (sometimes with several tines), and have a burr at the base. But these structures were present and complete in all known specimens; it thus seems obvious that, in contrast with the deer, there were horns in both sexes and that these were never shed. The burr may

FIG. 316.—*Megaceros*, a giant deer ("Irish elk") from Pleistocene of Europe. About $\frac{1}{38}$ natural size. (From Reynolds.)

be explained as the point at which an annual shedding of the horny covering occurred. The small horn of the modern prongbuck is probably due to reduction; a Pleistocene type from the Southwest had a larger two-pronged horn.

Bovids.—By far the largest group of living artiodactyls is that included in the family Bovidae, where are placed such forms as the cattle, bison, musk ox, sheep, and goats, and that great and varied assemblage of forms termed "antelopes." As in the giraffes and prongbuck, there are at the most only nodules left to represent the lateral digits. The teeth are usually hypsodont (in contrast with deer and giraffes), for the bovids are in general grazers rather than browsing forms. In contrast with the deer, the upper canines are reduced or absent. In all bovids there are present (usually in both sexes) true horns consisting of a simple unbranched core of bone covered with a conical sheath of horn; no part of this structure is ever shed.

The bovids have been not only the most successful and numerous of artiodactyls but of ungulates in general in late Tertiary and Recent times; and, as this fact might suggest, their development has taken place at a comparatively late date. They have undoubtedly been derived from the tragulids of the Oligocene, but the first representatives of the family appear in Europe only toward the end of the Miocene. Eurasia appears to have been the center of dispersal of the bovids; in the Pliocene of that region there appeared ancestors of many of the living types of antelopes. By the Pleistocene most of them had disappeared from Europe; but in this case, as in many others, Africa and Southern Asia have been havens of refuge for forms which increasing cold had forced from the North Temperate region; Africa alone contains some twenty genera of living antelopes.

But few members of this group have reached the New World. The dispersal of the group seems to have taken place at such a late date that the cold climate heralding the approach of the Pleistocene glaciation seems to have rendered the passage through Siberia and Alaska difficult. Only the buffalo, the mountain sheep, and the mountain "goat," all of which seem to be able to withstand rigorous climatic conditions, have successfully invaded this region; and no bovid has ever reached South America.

The oldest and most primitive members of the family from the late Miocene and early Pliocene are typified by *Tragoceras*, a form in which the horns were directed upward and backward and were straight, or at the most but slightly curved. Probably rather directly descended from them are a number of large types which have very long but nearly straight horns also directed backward. First present in the Pliocene, there are still a number of African survivors, such as the oryx and addax antelopes. Side branches of the primitive antelope stock, of which the fossil history is almost unknown, include a number of tiny African forms, some no larger than rabbits, such as the duikerboks and klippspringers. In these forms the horns, still small and backwardly directed, are present only in the males.

The gazelles and related antelopes from Northern Africa and Southern Asia are steppe and desert forms of moderate size and graceful build, with horns slightly curved but still of a simple primitive type. *Gazella* (Fig. 313h) can be traced back to the early Pliocene. Related to the gazelles is the saiga antelope, with a heavier build and peculiar swollen muzzle; now confined to the arid regions of Asia, it penetrated Europe in the Pleistocene, where its presence is indicative of steppe conditions.

Two further lines of bovid evolution have led to the development of more familiar types—to the sheep and goats on the one hand, and to the cattle, bison, and musk ox on the other. Pointing out the evolutionary road to the sheep and goats are the types often called "goat antelopes," such as the chamois (*Rupicapra*) of Europe and the Rocky Mountain "goat" (*Oreamnus*), with short but sharply curved horns. In the sheep (*Ovis*) and goats (*Capra*) there has been a great development of the horns, which tend to become very large and often spirally coiled in the males (those of the females are much smaller). These forms are upland-dwellers (which may account for the fact that their fossil history is little know), inhabitants of the mountain chains from the Mediterranean region eastward through Asia, and have, as we have noted, even penetrated to the Rocky Mountains.

The evolution of ox-like bovids appears to have begun well back in Pliocene times with the appearance of large antelopes with teeth rather resembling those of modern cattle and with horns which (although still directed backward) had developed a lyre-shaped form with spiral twist. Living representatives are the eland of Africa and the nilghai of India. A type still more cow-like and also dating from the early Pliocene is that now represented by the large gnus and hartebeests of Africa, in which the lyrate horns spread sidewise and are, in the former, directed forward rather than backward.

From these cow-like antelopes the development of the cattle has been but a short step. A rather slim and antelope-like ox, *Leptobos*, is found in the late Pliocene of Eurasia; and cattle, most of which may be included in the genus *Bos*, were widespread in the Pleistocene. Common domesticated cattle are but one of several members of this group which have been utilized by man. A large wild ox survived in Europe from the Pleistocene into medieval times. Closely related to the cattle are the true buffaloes of Southern Asia and Africa, now including domesticated types, as well as wild forms.

Bison (Fig. 317) is a genus closely related to the true cattle whose members were dwellers in the temperate regions of the Old World and which, alone of plains-dwelling bovids, has successfully invaded North America. The Old World bison has persisted in a wild state, and a few herds are still preserved in Eastern Europe. In America the bisons became exceedingly numerous in the Pleistocene and seemingly branched out into a number of types, to judge by the varied types of fossil horn cores discovered (one specimen had a spread of horns of some 10 feet). Although essentially dwellers in the plains region, Pleistocene bisons were present from the Atlantic to the Pacific.

Northern representatives of the bovids are the forms now represented by the musk ox, *Ovibos*, heavily built with massive laterally directed horns (much smaller in the females). The musk ox is now confined to the Arctic Zone; but in the Pleistocene musk oxen penetrated as far south as France and Kentucky, and in North America there were also several extinct related genera.

Primitive "swine."—All the artiodactyls so far considered have been classed as ruminants, in a broad sense of that term. Except for some of the earliest forms a selenodont dentition has developed, and all the living members of the group are purely herbivorous with the development of cud-chewing habits.

In contrast are the living members of the Suina—the pigs, peccaries, and hippopotami—and a number of fossil groups which we shall here associate with them. In almost none of these forms is there any development of a selenodont pattern; on the contrary, there is usually a highly developed bunodont condition. The limbs are generally quite primitive in nature. Most forms have remained four-toed, no cannon bone is formed, and the lower leg bones almost always remain

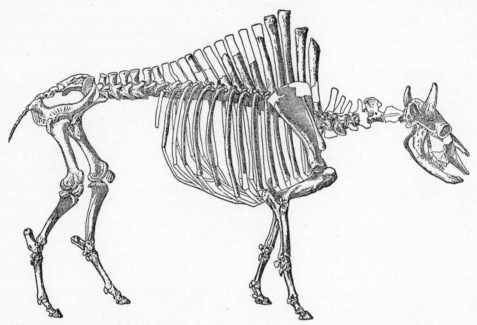

FIG. 317.—*Bison occidentalis*, a Western Pleistocene species, about 7 feet in length. (From Hay.)

separate. The stomach is always simple, and the diet of the swine is a mixed one. Further, as a key character, we have noted that in these forms the mastoid bone has been reduced and no longer appears on the surface of the skull. Using especially this last characteristic to guide us, we find that in the Suina, in a broad sense, may be included not only the living forms mentioned but also the entelodonts or "giant pigs" and the Anthracotheres, both prominent in Middle Tertiary faunas.

The swine were somewhat more tardy in development than the ruminant group. There are no representatives of the suborder in the Lower Eocene, although quite possibly their ancestors lay among the homacodonts mentioned earlier. Even in later Eocene deposits there are but a comparatively small number of forms pertaining to this group. Among them may be mentioned *Achaenodon* (Fig. 318a) of North America, a "short-faced pig" which may possibly be related to the ancestry of entelodonts, and *Cebochoerus* of Europe, possibly ancestral to the anthraco-theres. These forms show considerable variation but agree in possessing four-cusped bunodont molars, stout canine tusks, a deep lower jaw, and a reduced

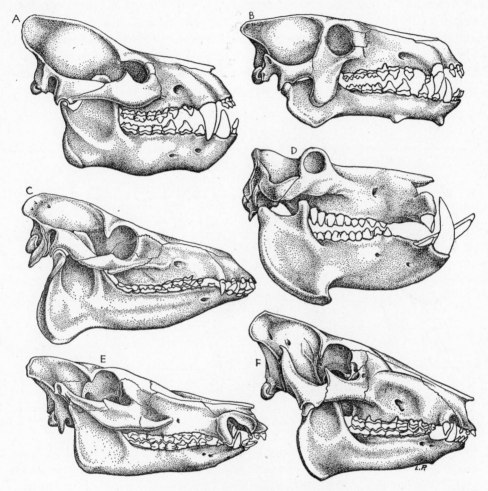

FIG. 318.—Skulls of pig-like artiodactyls. *A, Achaenodon*, an upper Eocene "short-faced pig," skull length about 15 inches. *B, Archaeotherium*, an Oligocene entolodont, average skull length about 18 inches. *C, Ancodus*, an Oligocene anthracothere, length of skull about 17 inches. *D*, a Pleistocene European *Hippopotamus*, skull length about 2 feet. *E, Cheleuastochoerus*, a late Tertiary pig from China (boar), skull length about 12 inches. *F, Perchoerus*, an Oligocene and Miocene peccary, skull length about 10½ inches. (*A, F* after Peterson, *B, C* after Scott, *D* after Reynolds, *E* after Pearson.)

mastoid—characters differentiating them sharply from the contemporary rumi-nants.

Entelodonts.—One offshoot of the primitive "swine" stock which early rose to prominence and early disappeared was the family Entelodontidae, the "giant pigs" which flourished in Oligocene times. Common Oligocene genera were *Entelodon* in Europe, and the similar *Archaeotherium* (Figs. 305*d*, 318*b*) in America. Last and largest of the group was *Dinohys* (Figs. 307*c*, 319) of the early Miocene of America. The entelodonts were large forms with huge skulls often reaching nearly a yard in length. The incisors were long and pointed; the canines, heavy and showing wear-grooves suggesting a root-eating diet. The premolars were simple; the molars were relatively small, with bunodont cusps. In the upper molars there is thought to be a true hypocone, in contrast with all artiodactyl groups except the dichobunids. The skull was much elongated, especially the facial region,

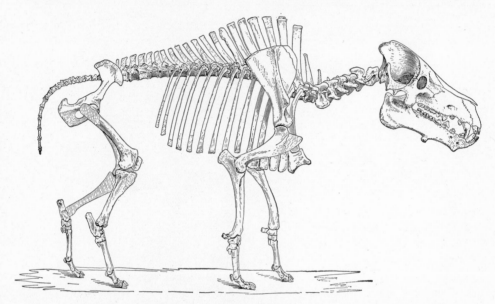

Fig. 319.—*Dinohyus*, a giant pig-like artiodactyl (Entelodontidae) from the Lower Miocene of America. Original about 10½ feet long. (From Peterson.)

while the braincase was small; a postorbital bar had already developed. A large flange was developed on the zygomatic arch and two tuberosities on the lower jaw. Their functions are uncertain; perhaps they were for muscle attachments. The neck was short; and there were high spines in the anterior thoracic region for the support of the heavy head, giving the back a humped appearance. Radius and ulna were fused; and, although no cannon bone was formed, the lateral toes were reduced to vestiges. These large beasts were not closely related to the true swine but resembled them in many features and may have been similar in habits.

Anthracotheres.—*Anthracotherium* and *Ancodus* (Figs. 307*a*, 318*c*, 320) were typical members of a group of rather large but primitive artiodactyls common in the Middle Tertiary of the Old World. The general impression is that of a rather pig-like form, and certain structural features suggest that the early anthracotheres were related to the swine. The limbs were short, with four functional toes, the skull low and with a long facial region. The dentition was complete, although a diastema was developed in some members of the group. The molars were low crowned; here alone in the present suborder there is some tendency toward a selenodont condition. There are (as in many primitive selenodonts) five upper molar cusps, the protoconule having been retained (Fig. 305c). The anthracotheres were very probably amphibious forms comparable in habits to the later hippopotami.

Anthracotherium was widespread and common in Europe in the Oligocene, as was *Ancodus*, a very long-jawed genus. Both forms reached North America but were

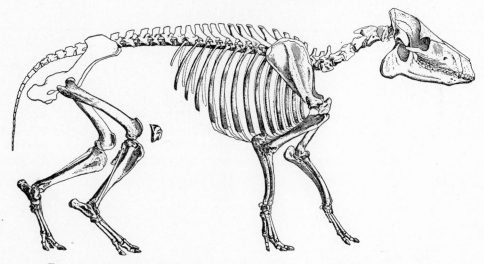

Fig. 320.—*Ancodus*, an Oligocene anthracothere, about 5 feet in length. (From Scott.)

not common there; presumably they could not compete successfully with the native oreodonts, whose habits may have been similar. *Brachyodus*, a giant form, survived in the Old World tropics until Miocene times.

Hippopotami.—The hippopotamus is the only living amphibious artiodactyl. All known forms, living or fossil, may be included in the single genus *Hippopotamus* (Figs. 305g, 318d) and have been confined to the Old World. The hippopotamus lives on soft, water vegetation which is cropped with the heavy anterior teeth and lips. The incisors, flanked by the canines, are set in a transverse row in the broad snout. All the teeth are present in the hippopotamus except the outer incisors, and even these were present in some fossil types. The eyes are small and, in relation to the amphibious habits, are set high up on the skull; there is the beginning of a postorbital bar. The plump body is supported by short stout legs; four toes, all functional, are present in the broad foot. Today the hippopotami are confined to Africa, but in the Pleistocene they were widespread in the warmer regions of the

Old World. A form similar to the larger African races was widespread in Europe, while pigmy types were present on some of the Mediterranean islands and in Madagascar (a pigmy is found today in Liberia). In the Pliocene hippopotami were present in the Mediterranean area and India, those from the last region being the more primitive in the possession of the complete set of incisors. Back of this their history is uncertain. There is, however, considerable evidence that they are descendants of the anthracotheres, which they resemble in their mode of life and in some structural features.

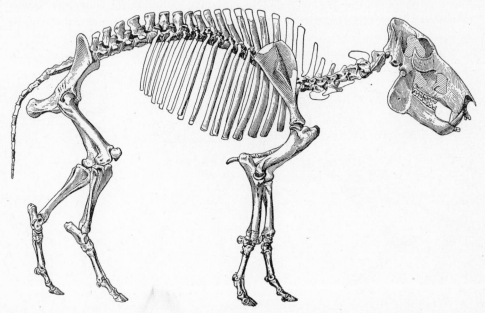

FIG. 321.—*Platygonus*, a Pleistocene peccary, about 3½ feet long. (From Hay.)

Pigs and peccaries.—The most widespread of later Tertiary Suina in late Tertiary times and, except for the hippopotamus, the only survivors of the group are the pigs and peccaries. In these forms the skull (Fig. 318e, f), low in front, ascends steeply toward the back of the head. The orbits are open behind. The canines have a persistent growth and are especially powerful in the males. The dentition (Fig. 304d) is often complete, but an incisor or the first premolar may drop out. The lateral toes, although complete, are small and function only on soft ground.

The typical pigs are Old World forms and have never penetrated America. A characteristic pig feature is that the upper canines curve outward and upward, a character which reaches its extreme in the babirussa of the East Indies, in which these teeth coil upward in horn-like fashion over the forehead. Besides the typical wild boar and the domesticated varieties (*Sus*), various specialized types are present in the Old World tropics. There were numerous genera of fossil pigs in the

Pliocene, Miocene, and Oligocene of Eurasia. There were, however, no pigs in the Eocene, and none of the known forms of that period pertaining to the suborder seem to be directly on the line of pig ancestry.

The living peccaries of the New World (*Dicotyles*) are obviously related to the pigs but have had a long separate history. A key character is found in the fact that the upper canines have remained in the normal vertical position. The molars (Fig. 305*e*) are comparatively short and are simple in appearance in contrast with the wrinkled teeth of the Old World hogs (Fig. 305*f*). In some peccaries the side toes are much reduced (Fig. 307*b*). There is the beginning of the formation of a cannon bone, and radius and ulna become fused. In these features the peccaries are much more progressive than their Old World relatives.

The modern peccary ranges through South America, which continent it presumably reached only in the Pleistocene, and as far north as Texas. In the Pleistocene *Platygonus* (Fig. 321) and several other forms were widespread in temperate North America. The oldest known American peccary is *Perchoerus* (*Thinohyus*) (Fig. 318*f*), of the Oligocene. It is probable that the group first reached this continent at that time, as migrants from Eurasia; and certain Oligocene Old World suids seem to be closer to the peccaries than the true pigs.

CHAPTER XIX

SUBUNGULATES

Often grouped as subungulates are several types of animals which at first sight appear to be quite unrelated. These include: (1) the hyraces or conies, small Old World hoofed mammals quite rodent-like in appearance and habits; (2) *Arsinoitherium*, a huge horned fossil mammal from Egypt; (3) the proboscideans, the elephants and their extinct relatives; (4) the sirenians, or sea cows. It appears incongruous to place together a seeming jumble of land and sea forms, large and small types; but early representatives of these varied groups show fundamental similarities which strongly suggest a common origin; and the fact that the earliest fossil forms are found in Africa suggests that that continent was their common ancestral home.

Because of the great diversity in adaptations which these forms have undergone, it is difficult to find many distinguishing features which hold true of all subungulates. There is usually a greatly enlarged pair of incisors in either jaw, while other front teeth are often reduced; the grinding teeth tend to develop cross-lophs, the premolars become molarized. There is never a clavicle. Usually the land types retain most or all of the digits, with a mesaxonic symmetry, while the primitive claws have developed into structures more like nails than hoofs.

By many these groups are included in an order (or superorder) Subungulata. We shall treat of them as a number of distinct orders, recognizing however, their close relationship.

Conies.—Most primitive of subungulates in many respects are the Hyracoidea, represented today in Africa and Syria by *Hyrax* and related small forms, the conies of the Scriptures. They resemble the rabbits not only in size, general appearance, and habits but also in many adaptive skeletal features. All are herbivores; some are dwellers in rocky country, while others are somewhat arboreal. The tail is short, the legs but moderately long. The gait is plantigrade, with the toes (four in front and three behind) bound together with a pad beneath. There is a centrale in the carpus, unusual in living ungulates.

The skull is of a rather normal construction. Alone among subungulates the living hyraces have a complete postorbital bar. The lower jaw is very deep posteriorly. In living forms there is a considerable amount of reduction in the permanent teeth. In most there is a single large rootless upper incisor which meets two enlarged lower ones in rather rodent-like fashion. Behind this the lateral incisors and canines have been lost, leaving a diastema in front of the cheek teeth. The molars tend to be high-crowned, and rather resemble those of the earlier rhinoceroses in pattern, the upper ones having an ectoloph and two cross-lophs, and the lower teeth a double **V**. The posterior premolars are molarized; the anterior ones, simpler.

Although none too common today, the hyracoids appear to have played an important rôle in Africa in earlier times, for the group is represented by a consider-

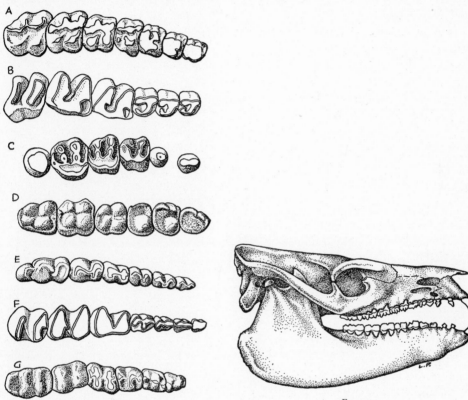

FIG. 322   FIG. 323

FIG. 322.—Dentition of subungulates. *A–D*, right upper cheek teeth, *E–G*, left lower cheek teeth. *A*, *E*, *Saghatherium*, a hyracoid, ×⅝. *B*, *F*, *Arsinoëtherium*, ×⅛ approx. *C*, *Miosirin*, an Oligocene sirenian. *D*, *G*, *Moeritheriun*, a primitive probosciden, ×⅓ approx. (*A*, *B*, *D–G* after Andrews, *C* after Abel.)

FIG. 323.—*Megalohyrax*, a Lower Oligocene hyracoid from Egypt. Skull length about 12 inches. (After Gregory and Schlosser.)

able variety of forms, such as *Saghatherium* (Fig. 322*a*, *e*) and *Megalohyrax* (Fig. 323) in the Lower Oligocene beds of Egypt. These animals were not only already definitely hyracoid in structure but had even diverged considerably along various adaptive lines. They ranged in size from modest proportions to those of a lion; the teeth varied from brachyodont to high-crowned types, from bunodont to seleno-dont in pattern. However, they were all more primitive than the living forms, for the postorbital bar was incomplete, the brain small, and the dentition complete (although the teeth later lost were already reduced in size). The later Tertiary history of Africa is poorly known, but conies have been reported from most of the later deposits there and one even from Greece. The fossil types, as well as the living forms, are found exclusively around the eastern Mediterranean and in Africa; the group thus appears to have been characteristically African in origin and development.

Arsinoitherium.—A separate order, the Embrithopoda, is necessary for the reception of *Arsinoitherium* (Figs. 322b, f, 324), a peculiar form from the Lower

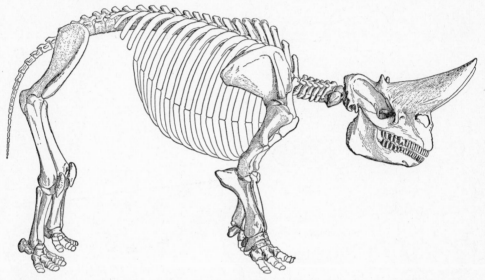

Fig. 324.—*Arsinoetherium,* a large horned subungulate from the Lower Oligocene of Egypt; about 11 feet in length. (From Andrews.)

Oligocene of Egypt. This great beast was of rhinoceros size. The limbs were graviportal in structure with long and massive humerus and femur, short lower segments, and a broad spreading five-toed foot. The most striking feature of the animal was the presence of a huge pair of horns on the nasal bones, together with small ones on the frontals. The two great horns were fused at their bases, while, much as in some rhinoceroses, an ossification of the partition between the nostrils below aided in their support. The structure of the front part of the skull suggests that there were movable cropping lips, but the tooth row was complete and there was not the enlargement of incisors seen in other subungulates. The molars were hypsodont (an usual feature at that early Tertiary date), the upper ones having heavy protoloph and metaloph, while the lower ones had cross-crests showing distinct traces of derivation from the double-V pattern.

This curious creature is quite isolated; we know nothing of its ancestors or any

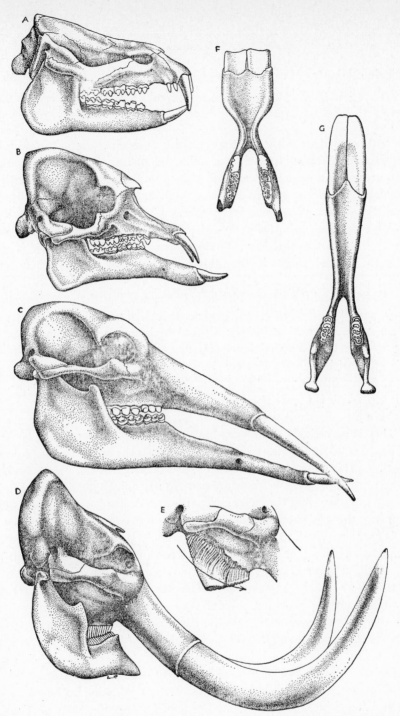

FIG. 325.—The skull and jaws of proboscideans. *A*, *Moeritherium*, from the late Eocene and early Oligocene of Egypt, ×¼. *B*, *Phiomia wintoni*, a primitive bunomastodont from the Lower Oligocene of Egypt, ×⅟₁₄. *C*, "*Mastodon*" (*Trilophodon*) *angustidens*, from the Miocene of Europe, ×⅟₁₀. *D*, *Mammonteus primigenius*, the wooly mammoth, ×⅟₂₀. *E*, Diagram of cheek region of the last, with the bone over the molars removed to show direction of tooth replacement. *F*, dorsal view of lower jaw of the mastodon *Platybelodon* from the Pliocene of Asia, ×⅟₂₅. *G*, the low jaws of *Amebelodon*, from the Pliocene of North America, ×⅟₂₈. (*A*, *B* after Andrews, *C*, *D*, *E* composite, *F* after Osborn, *G* after Barbour.)

possible descendants. Many points, especially the molar pattern, suggest a common origin with the hyracoids; but the relationship must be a distant one, for the development of the peculiar features of this form must have taken considerable time.

Proboscideans.—One of the most spectacular stories in mammalian evolution is that of the order Proboscidea—the mastodons, elephants, and related types. Like the two preceding groups they were of African origin but, in contrast with other subungulates, succeeded in invading the other continents and in middle and later Cenozoic times were widespread in Eurasia and North America and even reached South America. Today, however, only two living forms survive. We may perhaps best treat of this interesting group by describing the highly specialized structures found in the later elephants before taking up the earlier stages in their development.

The elephants and the related Pleistocene mammoths include the largest of late Cenozoic and living land mammals and as such have typical graviportal adaptations: an expanded ilium, columnar legs, a long humerus and femur, short lower limb segments retaining a well-developed ulna and fibula, and broad five-toed feet (cf. Fig. 329) with nail-like structures on the outer side of the digits and a pad beneath. The skull (Fig. 325d) is of huge size and roughly rounded shape, with a swollen top which is highly pneumatic. The brain, although reaching 11 pounds in weight in the Indian elephant, is, of course, small compared with the size of the skull. The comparatively small eyes have no bar behind them. The bony nasal orifice lies high up on the front of the skull between the eyes; from it projects the long flexible trunk. Below this opening the premaxillae descend vertically, bearing the roots of the huge tusks. These are enormously enlarged second incisors. On emergence from the skull the tusks curve forward, upward, and outward. On the short palate, the posterior development of the maxillae (in which the teeth develop) is notable. The lower jaw is correspondingly short; in front is a projecting chin superficially like that of man but developed in quite another fashion.

The dentition is remarkable. There are no anterior teeth other than the large upper tusks. In the cheek region the elephants have met the requirement of a large grinding surface in unique fashion. Six teeth develop in each jaw half; these consist of three milk premolars and the three molars (the permanent premolars never make their appearance). Each tooth (Fig. 326d) is elongate and exceedingly hypsodont and is formed of a large number of high thin crosswise ridges. The spaces between these "leaves" is filled by cement, so that with wear all three elements of the tooth are exposed in a regular pattern—dentine in the center of the ridges, an enamel band about this, and cement forming the outer portions. The number of ridges increases considerably from front to back, the milk premolars being much simpler in structure.

Instead of having all the teeth in place at once, as is usually the case in mammals, the elephants normally have exposed at any given time only four teeth in all, one in each half of each jaw. As these four teeth are worn down, they are pushed forward and the next group of teeth, which meantime has been forming in the maxilla or dentary, takes their place (Fig. 325e). This process is repeated until all six members of a series are utilized. Since the teeth push into the tooth row at an angle, the grinding surface is at an angle to the rather flat crown; and elephant teeth, when isolated, show a diagonally beveled wearing surface.

Parenthetically, it may be noted that, while teeth are the most common remains of fossil elephants, their interpretation presents difficulties, for the number of plates not only differs from form to form but even more widely from tooth to tooth of the same individual, while the appearance of the ridges varies with the degree of wear.

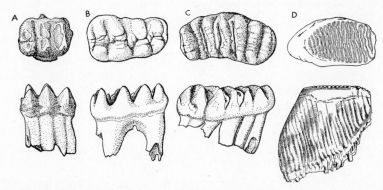

FIG. 326.—Crown views (above) and lateral views (below) of molar teeth of A, American *Mastodon;* B, "*Mastodon*" (*Tetralophodon*) *longirostris; C, Stegodon; D, Mammonteus primigenius.* (A, ⅛ natural size B and C about ¼, D about ½.) (A after Hay, B after Vacek, C after Matsumoto, D after Osborn.)

Moeritherium.—Very different in character from the living elephants, but already definitely proboscidean in tendencies, was *Moeritherium* (Figs. 322d, g, 325a), of the Upper Eocene and early Oligocene of Egypt, the earliest known member of the order. Although by far the smallest known proboscidean, it had already reached the size of a tapir. The skull was still fairly long, with the eyes far forward. The nasal opening was somewhat to the top: but the developing trunk was probably little more than a flexible, tapir-like snout.

The dentition already shows the beginnings of the proboscidean specializations. The formation of tusks had already begun, for the second incisors were much enlarged, the upper one pointing down, the lower one projecting forward to meet it. A diastema was in process of development; and in connection with this the first premolars, the lower canine, and lateral lower incisors had been lost. The molars were low crowned with two cross-lophs. The limbs were comparatively primitive but already somewhat heavy in build. We have in *Moeritherium* the beginnings of the specializations which led to the later mastodons and elephants. The skull shows many interesting points of resemblance to that of the conies and sirenians; but those groups were already in existence at that time, and their common ancestor must be looked for far back in the Eocene of Africa.

There is considerable evidence that a number of types branched off early from the primitive proboscidean stock. For example, *Barytherium*, a contemporary of the last form, known only from a jaw and a few other fragments, possessed similar bilophodont molars and an enlarged lower incisor. But the jaw was quite peculiar in other respects, and it is quite possible that this genus was but distantly related to the proboscideans.

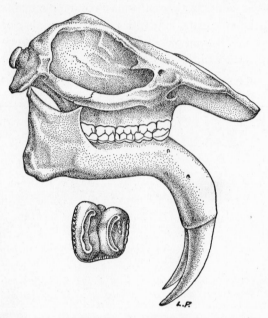

FIG. 327.—Skull of *Dinotherium*, a Miocene proboscidean, length about 47 inches. Molar tooth, ×⅕ approx. (After Gaudry and Andrews.)

Dinotherium.—Certainly a proboscidean, but obviously far off the main evolutionary path of the group as a whole, was *Dinotherium* (Fig. 327), a large form found fairly commonly in the Miocene of Eurasia and Africa. The general build was elephantine; and, although the earlier forms were of modest size, later types exceeded most of the true elephants in bulk. The cheek teeth (with but two premolars) were quite primitive, low crowned, and with but two cross-ridges in the back two molars (the first had three). The nostrils were high up on the face, suggesting a long proboscis. While the premaxilla extended well forward, there was, in contrast with all other proboscidians, no trace of an upper tusk. The lower tusk was, however, well developed and curved sharply downward and even backward. What purpose this curious structure could have served is a matter for speculation. *Dinotherium* disappeared from most of Eurasia at the end of the Miocene but, like many other primitive forms, survived much later in the tropics and appears to have been present in the Pleistocene in Africa.

Mastodons.—Leaving these divergent forms, we may now return to the consideration of the evolutionary main line represented by the mastodons. These proboscideans, although now extinct, were very numerous and diversified throughout the greater part of the Tertiary. From elephants the mastodons may be generally distinguished by the fact that the teeth were low crowned with few ridges, and many or all of the cheek teeth were usually in place simultaneously. Almost always there was a lower, as well as an upper, pair of tusks.

In Egypt, again, appeared the earliest and most primitive of known mastodons, *Palaeomastodon* (Fig. 328a) and *Phiomia* (Figs. 325b, 328b). These Lower Oligocene forms were of larger size than *Moeritherium;* the largest had already reached the proportions of a modern elephant, although the average was much smaller. Structurally, too, they had progressed considerably beyond *Moeritherium*. The braincase was much shorter and higher; the nostrils were placed quite far up and back on the skull; and the snout must have been long. Of the anterior teeth there remained but a single pair of incisors. These, however, were already

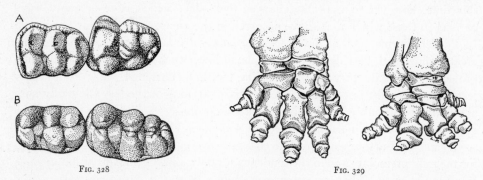

Fig. 328.—*A*, right, M^2–M^3 of *Palaeomastodon beadnelli; B*, left, M_2–M_3 of *Phiomia wintoni;* $\times \frac{3}{8}$ approx. (After Andrews.)

Fig. 329.—Front and hind feet of the American *Mastodon*. (After Warren.)

definite tusks. The upper tusk was borne on the elongated premaxilla and curved downward and outward. The short lower tusks formed a somewhat scoop-shaped affair at the end of the elongated jaw. Premolars (three above, but only two below) and molars were again lophodont, low crowned, and all in place simultaneously.

In *Phiomia*, the molars had advanced over those of *Moeritherium* in that three cross-crests were usually present instead of two; and accessory cusps (in addition to the two which normally formed a crest) had begun to make their appearance, tending to make a somewhat bunodont and pig-like tooth.

From *Phiomia* appear to have descended most of the later mastodons, characterized by teeth in which a multiplicity of accessory cusps tended to make their appearance. These forms with suid teeth, often grouped as bunomastodonts, appear to have early invaded the northern continents, for a member of the group was present in the Oligocene of India. In the Miocene and Pliocene these forms were widespread and numerous in Eurasia; their taxonomy and mutual relationships are none too well understood. In the earlier Miocene forms, such as *Trilophodon angustidens* (Fig. 325*c*), the lower jaw was enormously long, bearing short broad tusks at the end, while the premaxilla was also elongated for the fairly long and slightly decurved upper tusks. The nostrils were high on the skull, but the free portion of the trunk (which presumably began at the end of the premaxilla) must have been comparatively short. Six cheek teeth were present above and five below, all in the jaw at one time, with permanent premolars still replacing the milk premolars. The pattern was becoming more pig-like, with an increasing number of irregular cusps; and the number of ridges was increased slightly over *Phiomia*, for, although three were typical, four or five cross-crests were present in the last molar.

Members of the bunomastodont group persisted in the Old World until fairly late in the Pliocene and are even found in the early Pleistocene in Africa. During this time, however, remarkable changes took place which were in many ways parallel to those which must have occurred in the ancestry of the true elephants. In Pliocene forms such as *Tetralophodon longirostris* the lower jaw had become greatly shortened, leaving only a very small lower tusk in the end of a chin-like projection of the dentary; the premaxilla, too, had shortened, while from it projected long straight upper tusks. With this shortening of the face the fleshy nose above was presumably freed to become a long proboscis such as that found in the modern elephant. The teeth had become somewhat high crowned and had gained some cement. Further elephant-like changes are seen in the loss of replacing teeth for the milk premolars and in the tendency for only a part of the dentition to come into play at once. There was, however, only a gain of a molar crest or so (Fig. 326*b*), four typically and five in the last molars; and the pig-like multiplicity of cusps in the cheek teeth shows that we are dealing with a line that was not ancestral but parallel to that of the true elephants.

Members of the bunomastodont group were the first proboscideans to invade the New World, appearing in the Upper Miocene in North America and lasting through the Pliocene into the earliest Pleistocene, while mastodons found in the Pleistocene of South America appear also to have been of this type. In North America in the late Miocene and Pliocene a peculiar development was that found in *Rhynchotherium*, in which the long lower tusk was turned downward somewhat as in *Dinotherium;* another curious specialization was represented in *Amebelodon* (Fig. 325*g*) of the American Pliocene and *Platybelodon* (Fig. 325*f*) of Asia—forms which had a lower jaw and symphysis even more elongated than in the primitive bunomastodonts and tusks broadened to a huge shovel.

While *Phiomia* had three-lobed teeth which tended to a complicated pattern, the contemporary *Palaeomastodon* retained rather simple, tapir-like, two-lobed molars. From this genus descended a line of mastodons in which the teeth had a persistently simple pattern always with low crowns and simple ridges and without cement. Such forms are found in the Miocene (*Mastodon tapiroides*) and Pliocene (*Mastodon borsoni*) of Eurasia, although more rarely than the bunomastodonts, and had as an end-form *Mastodon* proper (Figs. 326*a*, 330) which persisted in North America throughout the Pleistocene and (as frequent skeletons from postglacial swamps show) probably lived until not many thousands of years ago. In these forms the skull must have changed in a fashion similar to that of the bunolopho-donts, for the American mastodon had never more than a rudiment of the lower incisor in the short jaw, the skull was high and short, there were huge upper tusks curving upward and outward, and there were never more than two teeth at a time in each jaw half.

Elephants.—The family Elephantidae, in which the recent forms are included, is easily distinguished from a majority of the mastodons through the much

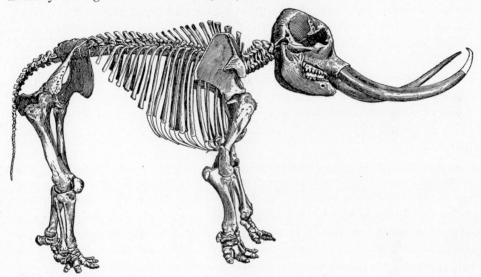

FIG. 330.—The American Pleistocene *Mastodon;* length about 10 feet. (From Hay.)

higher, shorter head, the huge curved upper tusks, the short tuskless lower jaw, and especially by the cheek teeth with their high cement-covered rows of numer-ous lamellae and peculiar mode of succession. The elephants are not descendants of any of the well-known mastodon types but appear to have had a long inde-pendent history. Seemingly Asia was the home of the group, and the oldest ele-phant types are found in the late Miocene and Pliocene Siwalik beds of India. In *Stegodon*, of the Pliocene and early Pleistocene of Asia, the skull was somewhat longer than in true elephants; but the teeth (Fig. 326*c*), while still low crowned, had sometimes as many as fourteen simple ridges with some traces of cement. While there were still traces of the permanent premolars which have been lost in later elephants, the type of tooth succession was changing, for no more than two were present in a jaw half at one time. Further, the lower jaw symphysis had been reduced to a chin in which there were only tiny rudiments of the lower tusks, while the upper tusks were long and somewhat spirally curved.

By the end of the Pliocene the first of the typical elephants with short head, tuskless lower jaws, and high-crowned cement-covered teeth had appeared in Southern Asia and Europe; and in the Pleistocene various elephant types usually referred to as "mammoths" were abundant in all the northern continents. All these forms are often included in the genus *Elephas*, using that term in a broad sense; but recent workers have tended to divide the group into a number of separate genera. Close to the base of the group appears to be the genus *Archidiskodon*, with comparatively low-crowned and broad teeth with primitively a small number of ridges (ten to fourteen as a maximum in early types). *Archidiskodon planifrons*, of the late Pliocene of Asia, is one of the oldest and most primitive of elephants. *Archidiskodon meridionalis*, the southern mammoth, was a primitive type common in the Mediterranean region in the Pleistocene. *Archidiskodon imperator*, the imperial mammoth of southern North America in the Pleistocene, was a large and somewhat progressive member of this group; and *Parelephas*, usually termed the "Columbian mammoth," was a closely related form characteristic of temperate climates in North America. In these American archidiskodonts the number of molar crests tended to increase very considerably and reached as high a count as thirty in the last molars of the Columbian mammoth, thus paralleling the woolly mammoths.

A second type of elephants includes forms with high-crowned narrow teeth with much thinner leaf-like tooth plates which reach a maximum number of twenty-seven. The living Indian elephant, *Elephas* proper, is a form which has persisted in the probable original homeland of this group. *Mammonteus primigenius* (Figs. 325d, 326d), the woolly mammoth, was a form adapted to cold climates, common throughout the Pleistocene in the northern parts of both Eurasia and North America. It is known not only from skeletal remains but also through the many figures made by paleolithic man on cave walls and through complete cadavers unearthed in the frozen tundras of Siberia.

A third group of elephants had narrow but rather low-crowned molars with a comparatively small number of ridges which, with wear, tend to show a rhomboidal pattern. *Palaeoloxodon antiquus*, the straight-tusked "ancient elephant," was an inhabitant of Southern Europe and Northern Africa in the Pleistocene. Some specimens reached a height of 14 feet at the shoulder; on the other hand, dwarf races of this form, some no larger than a pig, have been found as fossils on Mediterranean islands. *Loxodonta africana*, the living African elephant, is a derivative of this stock.

Sirenians.—A final order, the Sirenia, includes the most aberrant of subungulates. These forms, manatees and dugongs, or sea cows, are not ungulates in any sense of the term but purely aquatic animals found along the coasts and river mouths of various parts of the world. The skin of living sirenians is nearly naked, tough and leathery. The body has assumed the torpedo-like shape characteristic of many water vertebrates with no distinct neck and with a laterally expanded tail. Here, as in other groups, the front legs have been transformed into flippers, while there is no surface indication of the rudimentary hind limbs and pelvis. A characteristic feature of the skeleton of manatees is that much of the bone has a compact structure—pachyostosis—seen in certain other aquatic vertebrates (the mesosaurs, for example).

The brain (and consequently the cranial cavity) is small. Only in the case of one living form is the postorbital bar developed. The premaxilla forms a long "bill," usually curved downward, with the nostrils placed above and well to the rear; the nasals are rudimentary. The lower jaw is heavy and has a long symphysis in front.

A peculiarity of the backbone lies in the fact that the short cervicals may vary from six to eight in number, which, apart from the edentates, is the only vari-

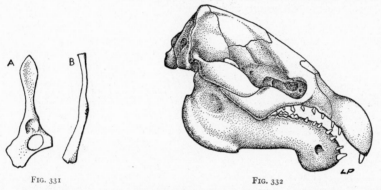

FIG. 331   FIG. 332

FIG. 331.—Pelvis of *A*, an early sirenian, *Eotheroides*, and *B*, the modern *Dugong*. (After Abel.)

FIG. 332.—Restored skull of a primitive Eocene sirenian, essentially *Eotheroides;* length of original about 13 inches. (Data from Abel and Andrews.)

ation of this sort in any group of mammals. The short front legs are transformed into fins, but the modifications are not so great as in the whales, for there is still considerable freedom of movement at the elbow and wrist and in the fingers. There tends to be considerable fusion of carpal elements, however. The thumb is reduced; but, while the other fingers may have but two joints, the number may increase to four.

Living forms possess a pelvis (Fig. 331*a*) which is only a solid plate or rod without subdivisions and without bony connection with a sacral rib. In some cases nothing remains of the hind limb; in others, there is a tiny rudiment of the femur.

Like their terrestrial subungulate relatives and in contrast with other types of aquatic mammals, the sea cows are purely herbivorous. The dentition of living forms is quite specialized and reduced anteriorly. The dugong has but a pair of upper incisor tusks, while the manatee has no front teeth at all as an adult; in both types horny plates form a substitute cropping organ. The back teeth of manatees have two cross-crests after the fashion of a primitive proboscidean.

Primitive sirenians.—Remains of sea cows are not uncommon in the Eocene beds of Egypt. While this fact suggests an African origin, their migrations must have begun at an early date, for an Eocene sirenian is also reported from Jamaica. Typical of early sirenians was *Eotheroides* (Fig. 332), of North Africa. Sirenian features are shown in the elongate snout (here nearly straight and not bent down as in dugongs), somewhat enlarged incisors, the two-ridged molars, and the beginning of the development of pachyostosis.

But in many respects *Eotheroides* was much more primitive than the living sea cows and much closer to their terrestrial ancestors. All the primitive forty-four placental teeth were still retained. The nostrils were still well forward; and nasals and lacrimals, rudimentary in later sirenians, were unreduced. The pelvis was quite well developed (Fig. 331*a*), while the hind leg appears to have been complete and still functioning, although of small size.

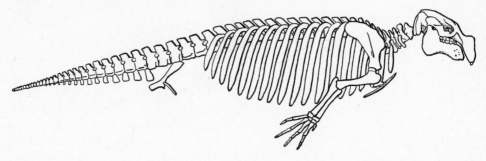

FIG. 333.—*Halitherium*, an Oligocene sirenian, about 9 feet in length. (Simplified from E. v. Stromer, *Lehrbuch der Palaeozoologie*, Vol. II, B. Tuebner, Leipzig.)

Dugongs.—The dugong (*Halicore* or *Dugong*), the "mermaid" of the Red Sea and Indian Ocean, is the sole survivor of a group very common as fossils throughout the Tertiary. There is a massive beak bent down above the heavy lower jaw. Of the front teeth, which are mainly replaced by a heavy horny rubbing pad, there remain only vestiges except for upper incisor tusks. The premolars are degenerate and the permanent set never develops; while the molars are large and, with a wrinkled surface and many bunodont cusps, superficially resemble those of the pigs or the bunomastodonts.

A tendency in the dugong direction was already apparent in some of the Eocene sirenians, such as *Eosiren.* The beak was already slightly tilted, nearly the full complement of teeth was still present, but the first incisors were somewhat enlarged; the number of cusps in the molars was already tending to increase, and the intermediate teeth were much reduced in size. In later Tertiary deposits, especially in Europe, have been found a considerable number of forms leading toward the living type. Some, such as *Halitherium* (Fig. 333) of the Oligocene and early Miocene, *Metaxytherium* and *Miosiren* (Fig. 322*c*) of the late Miocene, and the

Pliocene *Felsinotherium*, are quite well known. In them a lower incisor tusk persisted for some time but finally disappeared along with the smaller remaining front teeth. The beak was bent downward in dugong fashion, the pelvis was reduced, and the hind legs dwindled and vanished.

Through most of the Tertiary various side lines of this family are known, of which perhaps the strangest was that which ended with Stellar's sea cow, *Rhytina*, found by the Russians in the Bering Sea and exterminated by them nearly a century ago. Here both the tusks and the entire set of cheek teeth had disappeared, to be replaced by rubbing plates.

Manatees.—A second living group is that of the manatees, *Manatus*, inhabiting the Atlantic shores of Africa and America. The beak, while long, is not decurved. All the front teeth have disappeared. The cheek teeth have undergone a curious development. As individuals they retain a simple structure of two cross-lophs. But the number in each jaw half has increased to twenty or more, of which five or six may function at one time. The method of replacement is quite peculiar; the teeth form at the back of the jaw, and as they function, push forward until they are worn down and disappear at the forward end of the tooth row. This type of tooth replacement is reminiscent of that of the later mastodons and elephants. Almost nothing is known of the history of the manatees.

FIG. 334.—Crown and lateral views of a molar tooth of the aberrant Miocene sirenian *Desmostylus*, ×⅓. (After Matsumoto.)

Desmostylus.—We know little of the marine life of the Pacific except for a glimpse in the Miocene. At that time (besides a normal dugong) there was present on both shores of the North Pacific an aquatic animal, *Desmostylus*, so peculiar in structure that, while it may provisionally be assigned to the sirenians, its true nature is doubtful. The skull was certainly unlike that of a sea cow in many respects, for the nostrils (with well-developed nasals) were at the end of the snout; and, contrary to the usual condition, there was an incisor tusk below while the upper tusk was a canine. The cheek teeth (Fig. 334) were peculiar in structure, the large back ones consisting of a large number of irregularly placed cusps developed as closely packed cylinders. The temporal arch was also quite unlike that of the normal sirenian, for the jugal was very small and the maxilla ran far back toward the jaw articulation. It has been suggested that the creature was a peculiar aquatic monotreme, the argument being based chiefly on the fact that the teeth were somewhat like the embryonic teeth of the Australian duckbill, while that form also has a small jugal. Multicuspidate teeth of somewhat the same type, however, are found in other fossil sea cows and other mammalian groups; while the jugal is reduced in some other mammals, although not in sirenians. It may be that the form was an early offshoot of the primitive sirenian stock.

The earliest sirenians, as we have seen, showed very clearly their derivation from land forms; and the fact that so many early remains are from Egypt suggests Africa as the continent of origin. The primitive complete dentition, with large incisors and molars with cross-lophs, is suggestive of that of the early elephants, while many details of skull structure are highly comparable with those of both elephants and conies. The evolutionary tendencies shown in later members of the order are also similar to those of the proboscideans in such respects as the development of a single pair of incisor tusks, the tendency toward a polybunodont type of cheek tooth, and the tooth replacement of the manatee, essentially similar to that of the modern elephant.

All in all, our study of the various groups discussed in this chapter tends to confirm the seemingly odd assumption of the relationship of the diversified subungulate forms. But, although the early Egyptian fossils seem to be approaching the common type from which the subungulates have been derived, conies, proboscideans, and sirenians were already distinct groups at that time. It is only through some future discovery of very early Tertiary deposits in Africa that we may hope to find the common ancestor of the later subungulate orders.

CHAPTER XX

EDENTATES

Grouped as edentates in many of the older natural histories is a heterogeneous assemblage of forms from the tropics of both New and Old worlds—the tree sloths, armadillos, and anteaters of South America, the aard vark of Africa, and the scaly pangolins of Africa and Southern Asia. In great measure the bonds which were supposed to unite these varied types lay in the nature of the dentition. Some, as the pangolins and the American anteaters, are toothless; in the others teeth are practically confined to the cheek region and lack the hard enamel covering found in other mammals.

But many of these edentates are anteaters, and the reduction or loss of teeth in such types is obviously a functional adaptation and is no argument for their relationship to one another; we have seen that in the aard wolf, an anteating marsupial, and the monotreme Echidna similar habits have been associated with a similar reduction of the teeth. The aard vark is, it is now generally agreed, quite unrelated to the other edentates. The pangolins, as well, seem to occupy an isolated position; and, aside from specializations for a diet of ants, there is little to connect them with other forms.

True edentates.—As regards the other living "edentates," however, a different situation exists. Comprising, as they do, the South American anteaters, the armadillos, and the tree sloths, as well as the extinct armored glyptodons and giant ground sloths, these New World tropical types exhibit striking superficial differences. But in internal structure there are many features which tend to show that these varied forms really constitute a natural group to which the ordinal name Edentata may be restricted.

A striking feature common to all living and most fossil members of the group and not found in any other mammals is the presence of extra (xenarthrous) articulations between the successive arches of the posterior trunk vertebrae in addition to the normal zygapophyses (Fig. 335c). Here, too, are found the only cases (apart from sirenians) in which there is variation from the normal mammalian number of cervical vertebrae; from six to nine may be present. A fusion of the cervical vertebrae may occur.

There are many peculiarities in the limb skeleton of South American edentates. In the shoulder the acromion and coracoid process are generally much more developed than in other placentals. The ischium articulates with the proximal caudal vertebrae to form a peculiarly elongated sacrum (Fig. 335b). The limb bones are usually short, stout, and massive with strong muscular processes. Radius and ulna remain separate, but tibia and fibula have fused in armadillos and ground sloths. Claws are often excessively developed, and in several groups there is a tendency to walk on the outer side of the front foot.

The cranial region is characteristic. The brain is small and on a low plane of organization; the braincase is a long cylindrical tube. The premaxilla is usually reduced, although there is sometimes a supernumerary prenasal bone strengthening the snout. The palate is elongate and may even be bridged over between the pterygoids. Except in armadillos and some glyptodons, the zygomatic arch is incomplete, the jugal often ending posteriorly in a fan-shaped expansion but failing to reach the squamosal.

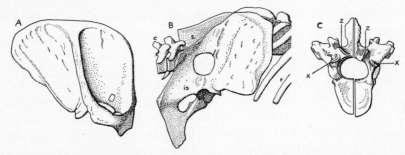

FIG. 335.—*Mylodon.* *A*, scapula, to show bridge from acromion to coracoid. *B*, pelvic region, showing upward growth of ischium (*is*) to join with sacrum (*s*). *r*, ribs; *c*, caudal vertebrae. *C*, a posterior dorsal vertebra, to show "xenarthral" articulations (*x*) in addition to the normal zygapophyses (*z*). On the left side the anterior view, posterior on the right. (After Stock.)

Only in anteaters have the teeth been altogether lost. But they are usually absent from the front of the mouth, while in the cheek roots are never formed and there is no enamel covering.

A tendency toward the development of protective armor in the skin appears to have been inherent in the group. In the armadillos and the extinct glyptodons we find a bony carapace covered by horny scales. No bones are present in the skin of tree sloths and anteaters, but in some of the extinct ground sloths the skin was reinforced by numerous bony nodules lodged in the thick hide.

The center of evolution of these types is unquestionably South America, the present home of practically all members of the group. Ground sloths, glyptodons, and armadillos are known as fossils from the late Cenozoic of the United States; but it is generally agreed that these forms were immigrants from the south. It seems highly probable that the ancestral edentates, like the peculiar ungulates of that region, had reached South America at the very beginning of the Age of Mammals and there underwent an isolated development during most of the Tertiary.

Palaeanodonts.—If, as in the case of the notoungulates, the edentates are presumed to have reached their southern home by way of North America, it might be expected that some trace of the group would be found in the early Tertiary of the north; and, ranging from late Palaeocene to Middle Eocene, we find two North American genera—*Palaeanodon* and *Metacheiromys* (Fig. 336)—which appear to represent the primitive edentate stock.

In many ways these forms were much more primitive and generalized than any of the later South American edentates. There is no indication of the presence of dermal armor, and the skull and backbone were primitive in character. But the limbs seem to have been in many ways intermediate between the primitive placental type and the typical edentate condition and had much of the stocky clumsy edentate build. Long compressed claws were present in the front feet, somewhat shorter and broader ones behind, and even here there was already some tendency for a twist in the wrist.

The teeth show many of the characteristics to be expected in the ancestral edentates, for the incisors had disappeared except for one small lower tooth, the cheek teeth were at the most pegs, and nearly all of the enamel covering had been

Fig. 336.—*Metacheiromys*, a small Eocene edentate about 18 inches long. (From Simpson.)

lost. There were, however, some specializations. The canines were powerful cutting organs; and while the earlier *Palaeanodon* still had four cheek teeth, these had nearly completely disappeared in *Metacheiromys* and may have been functionally replaced by horny pads.

The clawed feet and peculiar dental apparatus of the palaeanodonts suggest that they may have fed upon small terrestrial invertebrates, digging for grubs, insects, and worms much as do modern armadillos.

These North American genera appear to represent in most of their features the ancestral edentate type from which the South American forms have sprung. It is obvious, however, that they are too late in time to have been the actual ancestors, for South America was presumably already separated by the time of their appearance. They were merely wayside stragglers, destined not to survive in competition with the numerous other orders already appearing in North America. Except for a single Oligocene skull which may pertain to this group, nothing further is known of their history; seemingly they soon disappeared.

Xenarthrans.—The continuation of the story of edentate development is to be sought in South America. There edentates were already present in the oldest known Eocene beds. Although the remains from the earlier deposits are fragmentary, it is probable that the oldest forms possessed many of the features absent in the palaeanodonts but characteristic of later groups, such as the additional vertebral articulations, union of ischium and backbone, and peculiar skull type. Because of these common features, all later types may be grouped as the Xenarthra, which we shall here consider as a suborder contrasting with the more primitive early North American forms.

Among the xenarthrans there have evolved five distinct types which may be placed in two infraorders. One group, the Loricata (armored), comprises the "shelled" forms, the living armadillos and the extinct glyptodons; the other, which may be termed the Pilosa (hairy), includes the anteaters, the tree sloths, and the extinct ground sloths, all hair-covered, unarmored forms.

Loricates.—The great development of dermal armor is the most obvious feature uniting the armadillos and the now extinct glyptodons. A large number of bony plates covered with horny scutes form a protective carapace over the trunk, while plates may develop on the head and tail as well. The teeth tend to be more numerous than in the sloths; there are always as many as seven cheek teeth, often a higher number. The zygomatic arch is usually complete. There is a tendency for a fusion of vertebrae under the shield; and some of the cervicals, at least, are fused in all forms.

In the armadillos, the family Dasypodidae, the carapace never becomes a single solid shield, as in glyptodons. Instead, the bony plates usually tend to form solid plates over the shoulder and pelvis, between which are transverse movable bands. Beneath the pelvic plates is a long heavy sacrum, while fused neck vertebrae lie beneath the shoulder plate. The cheek teeth of these insect and carrion feeders are simple pegs, usually about eight to ten in number in each jaw half. There is thus a tendency to exceed the normal placental number, an extreme being reached in one living form with as many as twenty-five.

These armored types at first sight would seem to be very aberrant. But curiously enough, they are the oldest known of South American edentates, for they are the only types represented in the Upper Eocene beds of that continent. Furthermore, the structural tendencies seen in palaeanodonts seem to lead more directly to the armadillos than to other edentates. It thus appears probable that the armadillos represent the main stem of the xenarthrans. The Eocene forms are but little known, except for isolated plates. By the Miocene armadillos, such as *Proeutatus* (Figs. 337a, 338a) and *Stegotherium*, were abundant and varied. With the reestablishment of continental connections the armadillos pushed north, reaching the Gulf Coast region in Pleistocene time; and one form still persists in southern Texas. In the Pleistocene of both continents there were present giant armadillos, now extinct, one as large as a rhinoceros.

The extinct glyptodons (*Glyptodon* [Figs. 337c, 339], *Panochthus* [Fig. 338b],

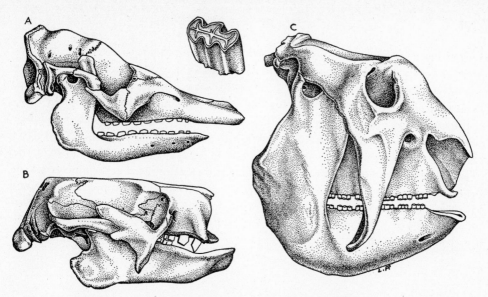

Fig. 337.—Skulls of edentates. A, *Proeutatus*, a Miocene armadillo, skull length about 5 inches. B, *Mylodon*, a ground sloth, skull length about 20 inches. C, *Glyptodon*, skull length about 11 inches. Above, in center, a glyptodont tooth. (A after Scott, B after Stock, C after Burmeister.)

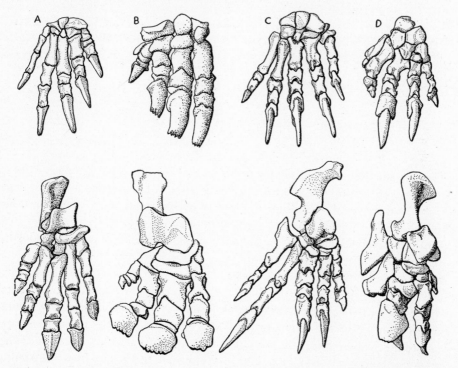

Fig. 338.—Feet of edentates, manus above, pes below. A, *Proeutatus*, a Miocene armadillo. B, *Panochthus*, a Pleistocene glyptodont. C, *Hapalops*, a primitive Miocene ground sloth. D, Pleistocene ground sloths, manus of *Mylodon*, pes of *Nothrotherium*. (A, C after Scott, B after Burmeister, D after Stock.)

etc.) were a group related to the armadillos and, like them, had developed a protective armor, but in a different fashion. Originally it would seem the bony plates on the back may have been placed in cross-rows, as in the primitive armadillos. But typical glyptodons tended to fuse the entire mass into a solid, turtle-like carapace composed of a mosaic of countless small polygonal plates. There was much fusion of the vertebrae, mainly in relation to support of the shield. Most of the cervicals, except the first, were fused; a second solid mass included most of the dorsals; while the last dorsals, lumbars, and sacrals were fused and connected with the posterior part of the carapace. The tail was sheathed in armor plates sometimes with projecting spikes. Like the armadillos these forms were generally five-toed and clawed; but the toes were short and stubby, the claws broad and rather hoof-like.

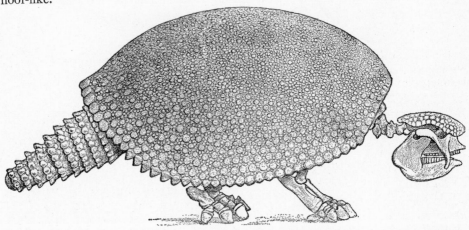

FIG. 339.—*Glyptodon*, from the Pleistocene of South America, length about 9 feet. (From Lydekker.)

The face and jaw were excessively deep. In these forms, alone among edentates, there was a postorbital bar and the zygomatic arch had a long downward projecting process of the jugal. There was no clavicle, in contrast to most other edentates. Although the teeth did not exceed eight in number, they were typically very high crowned; and some, if not all of them, had a peculiar three-lobed pattern analogous to that of some of the rat-like rodents.

It seems certain that the glyptodons have been derived from the primitive armadillos. They first appeared in the Oligocene and were well represented in the Miocene beds of South America. These earlier forms were small compared to the later members of the group but were already of larger size than most of the contemporary armadillos. There were still present many primitive armadillo-like characters such as the comparatively long skull, low-crowned teeth, and the persistently primitive arrangement of some anterior plates in more or less transverse rows. By the Pliocene large size and characteristic glyptodon structure had been attained.

These huge armored forms early migrated northward, and one genus had reached Texas before the end of the Pliocene. In the Pleistocene the glyptodons were numerous from Florida to Argentina. Here again, however, as in the case of most large land mammals in the Western Hemisphere, the end of the Pleistocene witnessed the extinction of the group.

Living "hairy" edentates.—The remaining South American edentates may be grouped as the infraorder Pilosa, the name referring to the hairy covering of these animals and the absence of a carapace. The zygomatic arch is always incomplete, although the jugal is usually much expanded posteriorly. There are never more than four or five simple cheek teeth. Among the peculiar features in the skeleton may be noted the fact that the expanded acromion arches forward to unite with the coracoid region (Fig. 335a). Included in this group are the anteaters and tree sloths inhabiting the tropical forests of South America, and the extinct ground sloths.

The anteaters, *Myrmecophagus* and related forms, exhibit specializations which seem but a logical outcome of the insect-eating habits of the palaeanodonts. In the front feet are developed large claws (particularly on the middle toe) which are used for digging into termite nests; the lateral toes are reduced. With the presence of these large excavating tools it has become impossible for the foot to be placed flat upon the ground, and the weight rests on a pad on the outer side of the knuckles with the toes turned inward. In the hind foot the claws are smaller and the foot plantigrade in the more primitive types.

The postcranial skeleton of the anteaters seems to be of the type which would be expected in the ancestors of the remaining groups of edentates. But the highly developed termite-eating habit has been associated with great modification in the head region. There is a very long tubular snout containing a protrusible whip-like tongue, the jaw is weak, and these forms, alone among true edentates, have entirely lost their teeth.

The living tree sloths of South America included in the family Bradypodidae are among the most curious of mammals. They are small arboreal nocturnal forms with a lichenous growth which often gives a green tinge to their gray hair. They are very slow and clumsy, spending much of their time hanging upside down from branches and holding on by their long curved claws, two or three in number. The front legs are longer than the hind; the body is elongated, but the tail is rudimentary. These leaf-eating types have but four or five cylindrical cheek teeth, one of which is anteriorly placed and may be a canine. The skull is very short in the facial region, and there is only a tiny premaxilla. The jugal ends posteriorly in a flaring termination.

Except for a Pleistocene skull, nothing is known of the early history of anteaters or tree sloths; remains of these forest-dwellers are not to be expected in the deposits of the Argentinian plains from which most of the older South American fossils are obtained. But even in default of fossil evidence it is not impossible to gain some idea of the nature of the primitive stock of the Pilosa from which these two types have been derived. Very probably this ancestral form would have had a rather omnivorous diet (as is still the case in armadillos) with a dentition comprising a small number of peg-like cheek teeth in a moderately elongate skull. Presumably the ancestor would have been a long-clawed terrestrial grubbing form with much the proportions and foot pose of the terrestrial anteaters. From this type the ant-eaters have departed mainly in cranial features connected with their food habits; the tree sloths, in body changes related to their specialized arboreal life.

The requirements for this hypothetical primitive ancestor are very closely ap-proached in some of the more primitive ground sloths.

Ground sloths.—The large and numerous forms of the ground sloth group in the Pleistocene of both North and South America are among the most interesting of extinct mammals. A majority of the group is included in the family Megatherii-dae, which is known as far back as the Oligocene in South America. The oldest forms are poorly known. In the Miocene, however, the comparatively primitive and small ground sloths of the times are known from complete skeletal material. *Hapalops*, the best-known form was (for a ground sloth), small in size, with a length of but 4 feet or so, including the elongate tail. The body was moderately elongate and rather slim in its build. A full complement of clawed toes was present (Fig. 338c). The claws were particularly well developed on the front foot, which was twisted over to rest the weight on the outer knuckles, while the stocky hind foot was plantigrade in pose with a backwardly directed prop formed by the cal-caneum. The skull was moderately elongated; slim premaxillae above and a spout-process from the jaws presumably supported horny cropping plates; in the cheek there were present five simple teeth above and four below, the first seemingly a canine. The zygomatic arch was incomplete; but the huge jugal, which splays out into a number of projections posteriorly, came close to the anterior end of the squamosal.

Hapalops was seemingly not far from the ancestral stock of the Pilosa and in many features was close to the hypothetical ancestor of the tree sloths and ant-eaters described above. True ancestral types may some day be discovered among the poorly known Oligocene sloths. But by the Miocene *Hapalops* and his known contemporaries appear to have already become terrestrial herbivores, true ground sloths ancestral to the later giant types.

During the Pliocene and Pleistocene there occurred a rapid increase in bulk in most ground-sloth types. This was accompanied by many structural changes. The body became much more massively built in relation to the requirements for weight support. These large types appear to have reared up on their hind legs in bear-like fashion to crop leaves from the branches of trees. The hind legs which must then support the entire weight of the body were short but extremely massive, the flattened hind feet presenting a broad surface to the ground; the front legs were more flexible digging and grasping organs (Fig. 338d). The skull (Fig. 337b) usually was shortened considerably from the originally elongated type. We shall mention but a few of the numerous ground sloths which were not only abundant in the late Cenozoic of South America but invaded North America in Pliocene and Pleistocene times.

Megalonyx, of the North American Pleistocene, was about the size of an ox with a skull about a foot in length. It seems to have been nearly a direct descendant of *Hapalops* and, while much more heavily built, resembled that form in many features, such as the retention of an anterior tusk-like tooth absent in *Megatherium* and *Mylodon*. The skull, however, was shortened; and in both hand and foot the two outer toes upon which the greater part of the weight rested had become clawless. Relatives of this form appear to have been abundant and migratory in habits, for they alone of ground sloths had reached North America in Pliocene times, and a number of related genera have been found in Pleistocene deposits in the West Indies. How these forms, which ranged from cat to bear in size, reached those islands is an interesting problem in geographical distribution.

Nothrotherium (Fig. 340) was a small relative of Megalonyx present in both North and South America in Pleistocene times. It persisted to a very late date in the Southwestern United States, for not only has a skeleton been found with much of the skin and tendons still preserved but it also appears that this form was a contemporary of early man.

Megatherium, which gives its name to the family, including all types mentioned thus far, ranged from South America to the Southeastern United States in the Pleistocene. This largest of ground sloths reached the size of an elephant, with a total length of 18 feet, and both skull and skeleton were massive in build. Complete skeletons have been preserved; and plaster casts, at least, are a common feature of the larger museums. Only one toe, the third, was clawed in the hind foot.

A second ground-sloth family later in appearance was that of the Mylodontidae. Members of this group are found in the Miocene of South America but are rare. In the Pleistocene, however, *Mylodon* (Fig. 337b), a creature half again as big as *Megalonyx*, was widespread in both Americas. In the mylodonts round ossicles deeply embedded in the skin seem to have afforded a defense against enemies. The jaws were weak and short. The front foot was rather similar to that of *Megalonyx*, but the inner toe had disappeared from the hind foot. *Mylodon* appears to have survived until a late date in the Southwestern United States, and in Patagonia a specimen of a related form (*Glossotherium*) appears to have been confined in a cave and killed by man.

Ground sloths were exceedingly abundant in the Pleistocene. But at the close of that period they were utterly wiped out. Why, we cannot say. Unlike the South American ungulates, which seem to have disappeared when faced by progressive competitors, the ground sloths had not only held their ground but had successfully invaded North America. The factors causing their extinction are as mysterious as those which destroyed most of the other larger mammals of the Western World.

Pangolins.—The Old World "edentates," the pangolins and aard vark, may be considered here for want of a better connection.

The scaly anteaters or pangolins of tropical Asia and Africa constituting the genus *Manis* are the sole representatives of the order Pholidota. The horny overlapping scales completely covering the body form the most notable peculiarity of these animals. This covering is probably a secondary protective device and not due to direct inheritance from reptilian ancestors. With the adoption of an ant-

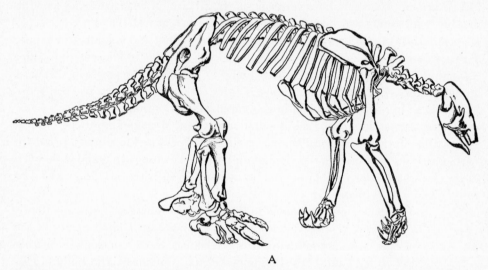

A

FIG. 340.—The skeleton of *Nothrotherium*, a small Pleistocene ground sloth. Length about $7\frac{1}{2}$ feet. (From Stock.)

eating diet there have developed many cranial adaptations similar to those of American termite-eaters. Teeth are completely absent; there is a long snout, a slim jaw, and a long tongue. The temporal arch is incomplete, and the jugal lost; the eyes are much reduced. The tail is usually long, sometimes prehensile. All toes are present; but the hand is functionally tridactyl, with the development of powerful digging claws.

Representatives of the living genus have been found in the Pliocene and Pleistocene of Southern Asia. A few bones from the Miocene and Oligocene of Europe have been thought to pertain to this group; but this is quite doubtful, and we know nothing of the earlier history. Relationship with American edentates has been often suggested, but the similarities are such as are obviously related to digging and to eating ants; there are no positive resemblances to the xenarthrans. The pangolins may have evolved quite independently from some early primitive placental stock.

The aard vark.—Quite isolated, too, is the "earth pig," *Orycteropus*, sole living representative of its own order, the Tubulidentata. This is an uncouth looking African mammal which lives on termites. There is a long snout, a small mouth, and a long tongue, as in other ant-eating mammalian types; but there is comparatively little reduction of the jaws, and the temporal arch is well developed in contrast to other anteaters. In the embryo teeth are numerous, exceeding the usual placental number; but in the adult only four or five peg-like cheek teeth remain. These lack enamel but have cement on the outside; while, instead of a pulp cavity, the dentine is traversed by a large number of small tubules, a feature to which the group owes its name.

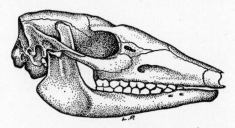

There are a number of primitive skeletal features. Tibia and fibula, however, are fused proximally; and the pollex has disappeared. The feet are semiplantigrade; and there are stout "nails" intermediate between claws and hoofs in nature, inserted in fissured end-phalanges much as in some early carnivores.

FIG. 341.—*Orycteropus gaudryi*, a fossil aard vark from the Lower Pliocene of Samos. Snout restored. Skull length about 6¼ inches. (After Andrews.)

Fossil aard varks (Fig. 341) ranged through Eurasia in the Pliocene in company with the ancestors of many other living African types. Back of that there are in Europe but a few doubtful fragments from the Oligocene and Miocene. In the Lower Eocene of North America have been recently found fragmentary remains of *Tubulidon*, a form which shows the beginning of the characteristic tubular structure of the teeth of the aard varks. It would seem that the group has had a long, if unimportant, history; whatever its origin, it has no apparent connection with the true edentates.

CHAPTER XXI
WHALES

Among mammals which have turned to an aquatic life, the whales, the order Cetacea, constitute the largest and most important group and that best adapted to an existence in the water. Both structurally and functionally they have become completely divorced from their former land life and are helpless if stranded. Only in their need for air breathing do they exhibit any functional reminiscence of their former terrestrial existence.

Modern whales have reassumed the torpedo-like streamline shape of primitive aquatic vertebrates, partly through a shortening of the cervical vertebrae and the consequent absence of a neck. However, the body is thick and rounded in section, and hence (unlike the typically slimmer fish) the main propulsive force is confined to the tail fin alone. As in other aquatic mammals, the tail has failed to resume its original fin structure, and (as in the sirenians) horizontal flukes supported by fibrous tissue supply the locomotive power. A dorsal fin has usually redeveloped. The hind limbs are lost completely, as far as any superficial indication goes, although rudiments may be present internally. The front legs have been transformed into short broad steering flippers. Although there are no extra digits, as many as a dozen extra phalanges may be present. Hair has been abandoned and may be absolutely lacking on the skin of the adult whale; a thick layer of blubber affords protection against cold.

Marine life has been accompanied by many internal modifications. The original whales appear to have been fish-eating carnivores. The majority of modern whales are still toothed types, but in them (as in the seals) the teeth have been simplified usually into simple pegs. The number has in many cases increased greatly over the primitive placental forty-four; in others teeth have been reduced in number or entirely abandoned for a straining apparatus of whalebone. The anterior portion of the skull has been elongated from the first. But in relation to the breathing problem in diving types, the nostrils have moved backward in the skull and in living whales are placed, as the blowhole, on the top of the head (Fig. 342b–d). In this process the premaxillary and maxillary bones have been dragged back over the more posterior elements, often in an asymmetrical fashion. This results in a peculiar telescoped effect, heightened by the fact that usually the occipital bones have pushed forward over the top of the skull. Apparently there is no top to the skull; it is all front and back.

The braincase has been much modified in shape in relation to these odd modifications, and is short but broad and high. The orbit is always open behind, al-

though typically covered by a broad supraorbital process of the frontal; and the
jugal is small. The premaxilla of modern whales is usually toothless and, although

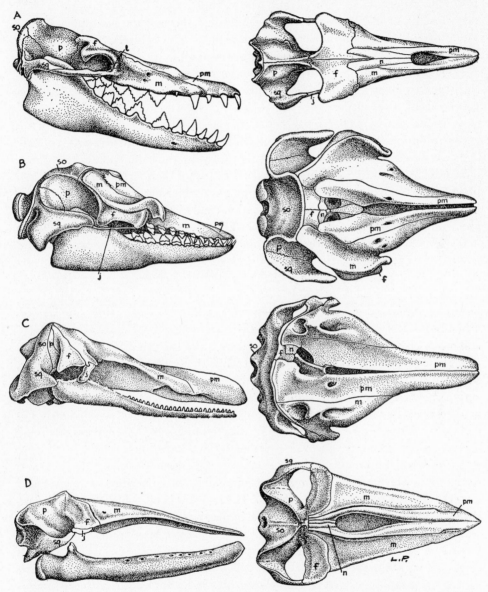

FIG. 342.—Skulls of cetaceans, lateral and dorsal views. *A, Prozeuglodon atrox*, an Eocene archaeocete,
skull length about 2 feet. *B, Prosqualodon*, a Miocene squalodont porpoise, skull length about 18 inches.
C, Aulophyseter, a Miocene sperm whale, skull length about 4 feet. Jaw restored. *D, Cetotherium samari-
nense*, a Miocene whalebone whale, skull length about 22 inches. *f*, frontal; *j*, jugal; *m*, maxilla; *n*,
nasal; *o*, occipital; *p*, parietal; *pm*, premaxilla; *s*, squamosal. (*A* after Andrews, *B* after Abel, *C* after
Kellogg, *D* after Capellini.)

well developed on the skull roof, has no expansion in the mouth. The ears are much changed for use in such "submarine" forms; the external tube and drum tend to be modified and reduced; and hearing, apparently acute (in contrast to the lost sense of smell), appears to be accomplished through the instrumentality of vibrations set up within the heavy shell-like bulla, which, fused with the periotic, is but loosely attached to the remainder of the skull.

Whales may be divided into three suborders: the Archaeoceti, of the early Tertiary; and two living groups—the Odontoceti, or toothed whales, and the Mystacoceti, or whalebone whales (Fig. 345).

Primitive whales.—The archaeocetes are the oldest and most primitive of the cetacean groups, first appearing in the Middle Eocene. All known types of that age are from Northern Africa, suggesting that (like the subungulates) they may have originated on that continent. Many features of their structure suggest their origin as a branch of the primitive creodont stock which had taken up a fish-eating life, but a number of important modifications had already occurred in *Protocetus* and *Prozeuglodon* (Fig. 342a) of the Upper Eocene. The snout was elongate (as in many fish-eating reptiles before them), and the nostrils had already accomplished half of their migration backward onto the top of the skull. In other respects, however, the skull was still much like that of a primitive creodont; there was a long low braincase, and there was no trace of the telescoping of elements which was to be the most marked peculiarity of later whale skulls. The dentition, too, was essentially primitive, for, while the front teeth were peg-like, the cheek teeth were still much like those of creodonts in appearance and the primitive placental tooth count of forty-four was not exceeded. But while the skull was still quite primitive, the body skeleton seems already to have advanced far in aquatic adaptations. Skeletal remains are rare; but by Upper Eocene times, if not earlier, the hind legs had been reduced to rudiments which did not project from the body. Obviously the earliest whales were already more highly adapted to marine life than are the living seals, although the story of whale specialization was far from finished.

The peak of archaeocete development was reached in *Zeuglodon* (Fig. 343) and its relatives, which were widespread and common in the Upper Eocene seas. These were the giants among primitive whales. The long low skull (which reached a maximum length of 5 feet) was still primitive in many features, but the teeth were already tending to increase in number, and the much compressed and serrated cheek teeth were departing farther from the primitive carnivore type. While modern cetaceans are comparatively short and stockily built, some of the zeuglodonts were slim and elongate types and reached as much as 70 feet in length, with the proportions which modern imagination ascribes to sea serpents.

Zeuglodon and other primitive types did not, in general, survive the end of the Eocene. Only some comparatively small short-bodied members of the archaeocetes (*Dorudon* and its relatives) persisted in lessening numbers through the Oligocene and into the beginning of Miocene times.

Primitive toothed whales.—Odontocetes, or toothed whales, comprise the great majority of living cetaceans, ranging from small porpoises and dolphins to the huge sperm whale. The body is short and stocky, in contrast with the elongation in *Zeuglodon*. The teeth are usually simple pegs or wedges, are not differentiated into incisors, canines, and cheek teeth, and usually far exceed the primitive placental number (as many as three hundred in one porpoise). Most marked feature of specialization, however, is the extreme telescoping of the skull roof mentioned above. The nostrils have moved far back over the top of the skull, forming a single vertically placed blowhole unroofed by the reduced nasals. A backward elongation of the premaxillae and maxillae has accompanied this process. The maxilla has spread out sidewise over the frontals in a great shelf over the orbits and temporal region and, pushing the parietals entirely out of the mid-line of the skull roof, often comes in contact with the supra-occipital.

No trace of this telescoping process is seen in the known archaeocetes. The toothed whales are presumably not derived from the elongate and temporarily successful zeuglodonts but may well have been derived from the earlier members of

FIG. 343.—*Zeuglodon*, an archaic Eocene cetacean. Original about 55 feet long. (From Gidley.)

the archaeocete group. The development of the modern whale type proceeded rapidly. Two ancestral forms, of which *Agorophius* is the better known, appeared in Upper Eocene seas as contemporaries of *Zeuglodon*. The skeleton is unknown, but in their skulls they show definitely an early stage in the telescoping process, for, while there was little shifting of the occipital bones and the temporal region was still open above, the nostrils were already in position above the orbits and the maxilla was beginning to extend back and cover over the frontals.

These primitive forms appear to have been ancestral to the squalodonts which, first appearing in the late Oligocene, became the characteristic world-wide cetaceans of early Miocene times. Such forms as *Squalodon* and *Prosqualodon* (Fig. 342*b*) probably resembled greatly the modern porpoises in habits and appearance. These types owe their name to the triangular shark-like teeth found in the posterior part of the beak (which was often much elongated). The squalodonts were much more modernized than their Eocene relatives, for the telescoping process in them had been completed, the parietals eliminated from the top of the skull, the maxillae had formed a contact with the supra-occipital, and the blowhole had reached its most posterior position above and behind the eyes. The temporal opening, however, had not yet been roofed over, as in many later odontocete types.

The squalodonts were not long destined to retain their importance, for only a single survivor lingered on into the Pliocene; and even by Middle Miocene times they had been largely replaced by other porpoise-like types.

Perhaps most closely related of living whales to the squalodonts are the long-beaked river porpoises of South America (*Inia*) and China (*Lipotes*). Here, as in most later odontocetes (and in contrast with squalodonts), all the teeth are simple peg-like structures, and the premaxilla has tended to become toothless. But a primitive feature is found in the fact that in these porpoises, as in the squalodonts, the temporal opening is still unroofed. The living types are confined to the lower reaches of rivers, but their ancestors were undoubtedly sea-dwellers; a number of presumed relatives were present in the Pliocene, and one even in early Miocene times.

Beaked whales.—While the squalodonts were the first toothed whales to attain prominence, other porpoise-like odontocetes became increasingly important during the Miocene. Among these forms are found the ancestors of the modern beaked whales, the Ziphiidae. In a modern beaked type, such as *Mesoplodon*, the "cow fish," the teeth have been lost except for one or two tusks in the lower jaw and non-functional rudiments in the maxilla. There are deep pockets on the top of the skull at either side of the blowhole. The temporal opening is roofed over by the maxilla in this family and in the remaining odontocete types considered; and in addition there is some asymmetry of the skull, a twisting of the elements about the blow-hole. In modern members of this family, too, we find the beginnings of a fusion of the cervical vertebrae characteristic of the larger whale types.

The beginnings of the beaked whales are to be found as far back as the beginning of the Miocene in the shape of a small dolphin, *Diochotichus*, which showed the be-ginnings of xiphioid characters in many respects but still resembled the squalodonts in the retention of a good set of teeth and in other primitive characters. True but primitive beaked types (such as *Choneziphius*) with a much reduced dentition were also developed during the Miocene, and by the end of that period the existing genus *Mesoplodon* had already appeared.

Porpoises.—The most numerous of living small cetaceans are those included in the family Delphinidae, the living oceanic porpoises and dolphins and their rela-tives. They are quite advanced in such structural features as the completely tele-scoped skull and the temporal region. But in contrast to most other living whales, most delphinids have retained an efficient battery of teeth in both upper and lower jaws. The dolphins must have developed rapidly out of the primitive toothed whale stock, for forms essentially modern in build were not uncommon in the early Miocene when the squalodonts still flourished, and the family had become the most abundant group of odontocetes by Middle Miocene times. Commonest of Miocene types were long-snouted forms such as *Eurhinodelphis*, in which the ros-trum made up four-fifths or more of the skull length. More modern porpoise types, such as *Kentriodon* (Fig. 344), appeared toward the close of the Miocene and in the

Pliocene. Apart from the more typical porpoises and dolphins, the family includes
a considerable number of more aberrant types, such as the killer whales, which
prey upon seals, penguins, and even larger cetaceans, and the narwhal, with its
"horn" formed from a sole remaining tooth. The slim-snouted *Platanista* of the
Ganges River is probably a distant offshoot of the dolphins rather than a relative
of the other river porpoises mentioned previously. It may have had a long separate history, however, for a type possibly related is known well back in the Miocene.

Sperm whales.—Largest of all odontocetes, and exceeded among all animals only
by certain whalebone whales, is the living sperm whale, *Physeter*, type of the family Physeteridae. *Kogia*, the pigmy sperm whale, is a much smaller form. The
huge snout of these whales is mainly occupied by a great reservoir of sperm oil; the
upper jaws are slender and depressed, but farther back the skull rises to a great

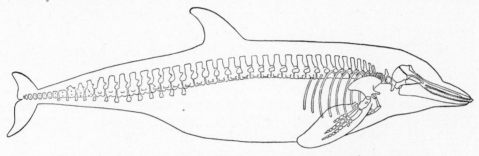

FIG. 344.—*Kentriodon*, a Miocene porpoise about 5½ feet long. (From Kellogg.)

cross-crest cupping the hinder end of the sperm pocket. The asymmetrical twisting of the bone about the blowhole is especially noticeable in these forms, particularly in the greater backward expansion of the right premaxilla. In the upper jaw
there are only a few functionless rudiments of teeth in the gums, but the lower jaw
retains a complete and well-developed battery of teeth. In the postaxial skeleton
a specialization lies in the fact that all the short cervical vertebrae are fused (with
the exception of the atlas) into a solid mass. This feature is seemingly associated
with the enormous head and repeated in some large-skulled whalebone whales.
The living sperm whale had already appeared before the end of the Miocene times.
In earlier Miocene strata, however, are found remains of ancestral types. These
were smaller, more primitive, and closer to the primitive porpoise stock, still retaining teeth in the upper jaw but with distinct evidences of the development of
the pocket for the sperm-oil reservoir. *Aulophyseter* (Fig. 341c) of the Middle Miocene is transitional between the older and younger types.

Whalebone whales.—The Mysticeti, the whalebone whales, include but a small
number of types almost all of which, however, are of enormous size, including the
largest of vertebrates, living or extinct. These greatest of cetaceans live on the

smallest of prey, tiny floating invertebrates; it is impossible for such a whale to swallow any large object, for the gullet does not exceed 9 inches in width. Whale-bone consists of ridges of hardened skin which extend down from the roof of the mouth in parallel crosswise rows like the leaves of a book. They are fringed at the edge with "hairs" upon which food particles catch, to be promptly licked off by the huge tongue. The teeth have been lost with the development of this peculiar apparatus; the mouth is enormously enlarged, the jaws bent out and down (and failing to meet in a symphysis), and the rostrum sometimes arched up. Telescoping of the skull has taken place in this group also, but in a somewhat different fashion from that of the toothed whales; for, while even in modern types the blow-

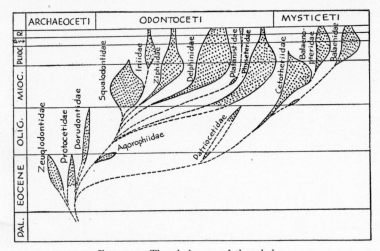

FIG. 345.—The phylogeny of the whales.

holes (here double) are still situated in front of the orbits, the normal roofing elements have been almost excluded from dorsal view by a forward migration of the supra-occipital region. The maxilla is braced against the frontal bone but does not override that element, although sending a finger-like process back over the skull roof. There is, in contrast with toothed whales, no trace of asymmetry.

It is obvious that these, now toothless, forms have descended from primitive toothed whales of some sort. One fragmentary late Eocene specimen, together with one or two Oligocene types such as *Patriocetus*, appear to show the beginnings of the type of skull telescoping which occurs in modern mysticetes. At all events, the history of the group had begun in the Oligocene with the first appearance of the cetotheres, primitive whalebone whales which were common forms in the Miocene and survived into Pliocene times. *Cetotherium* (Fig. 342d) and its relatives were already toothless types in which telescoping was well under way. This process, however, had not progressed as far as in living types, for dorsally a considerable gap still existed between the backward finger-like process of the maxilla and the supra-occipital.

Representatives of the two living families were in existence by Miocene times. Of these families one includes the rorquals (*Balenoptera*) and their relatives—types with small skulls, free cervical vertebrae, and a low and broad rostrum. The other family includes the right whales (*Balaena*) now confined to Arctic and Antarctic regions, forms with large skulls, fused cervicals, a curved rostrum, and a deep jaw. Of the rorquals, the blue or sulphur-bottom whale is estimated to reach a maximum weight of 150 tons or more, being thus far larger than any dinosaur.

CHAPTER XXII

RODENTS

Among the gnawing animals, the order Rodentia, are included the squirrels, beavers, rats and mice, porcupines, guinea pigs, hares and rabbits, and hosts of less familiar forms. The rodents are, without question, the most successful of all living mammals. In the number of genera and species they exceed all other orders combined; they are found in almost every habitable land area of the globe, and seem to thrive under almost any conditions, flourishing even in man-made towns and cities. The range of adaptations is a wide one. A majority of rodents are terrestrial and often burrowing types. No purely aquatic forms have developed, but such forms as the beaver and muskrat have progressed far in this direction. Others, as the squirrels, are arboreal; and while there are no flying rodents, the "flying" squirrels have tended in this direction.

In size the rodents are a modest group. Most forms are small, and the rat or squirrel may be taken as an average; the capybara of South America, the size of a small pig, is the giant of the group.

Dentition.—The rodents are essentially herbivores, although certain of them, as the rats, will accept a wide variety of food; the peculiar gnawing and grinding dentition and adaptations related to its use are highly characteristic of the group. A single pair of incisors is present in the lower jaw, and it is opposed by a principal pair above. In the hares and rabbits there is in addition a small second upper pair, a feature which separates these types, as the suborder Duplicidentata, from the remaining rodents, the Simplicidentata. These huge incisors never form roots, and have bases which curve far back inside the bones of the upper and lower jaws; their continual growth counterbalances the wear to which they are subjected in gnawing. The other incisors, the canines, and a number of premolars have been lost in all known rodents, leaving a long diastema between the gnawing teeth and the grinding series. The number of premolars tends to be decreased in many of the more advanced types, and in many of the modern rat-like forms only the molars remain in the cheek region. The most primitive known rodents, like most other herbivorous mammals, had an essentially four-cusped molar pattern. The pattern in many later types, however, has been much modified by the development of high-crowned prismatic grinders in which the primitive cusps have become obscured and fused. Not only do the cheek teeth often become high crowned; but in many cases they, too, fail to close their roots, and continue to grow throughout life.

Skeleton.—With these adaptations for grinding and gnawing has come a series of peculiar adaptations in the skull and jaws. In most rodents there occur both fore-and-aft and transverse grinding movements of the lower jaws on the skull. In consequence the glenoid fossa of the skull (in which the lower jaw condyle is received) is long and shallow, permitting considerable freedom of motion. The principal muscle concerned in pulling the jaw forward on the skull is the masseter, and the position of the origin of this muscle on the skull is an important key to the classification of the order (Fig. 347). The rodent skull is usually long and low, the orbit always open behind.

There are comparatively few specializations in the postcranical skeleton. The clavicle is usually retained; claws are always present. The front leg is usually flexible and often used as an aid in bringing food to the mouth, and there is little tend-

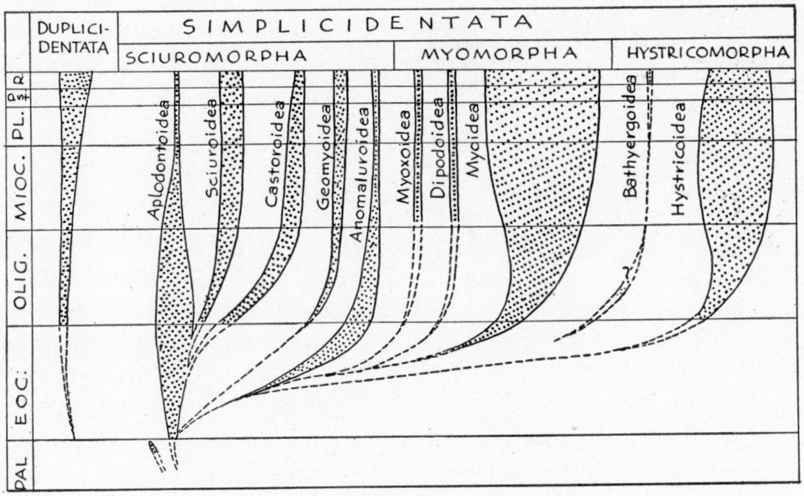

Fig. 346.—The phylogeny of the rodents.

ency toward loss of digits in the manus except for the occasional reduction of the pollex. The hind leg, however, is less flexible in its movements and confined to a fore-and-aft motion; tibia and fibula often fuse distally, and there are varying degrees of reduction of the toes with the development of a hopping or springing type of locomotion.

The primary division of the group, as has been said, is into the Simplicidentata, comprising the great majority of all rodents, and the Duplicidentata, the hares and their relatives. The two groups were already quite distinct at the time of their appearance in the fossil record; and, although it is quite probable that they have sprung from a common ancestor, no connecting form has ever been found.

Simplicidentates.—The primary diagnostic feature of the suborder Simplicidentata is the presence of but one pair of incisors in both upper and lower jaws. The cheek teeth are also characteristic. While in the hares three upper and two lower premolars are present, no simplicidentate, even the earliest, has more than two upper premolars and one lower one. Further, simplicidentates differ not only from the hares but from nearly all other mammals in that the two upper series of grinders are much closer together than the lower ones, and the grinding surface of the upper and lower teeth meet in a plane tilted at an angle.

So great is the number of types of rodents that a rather complicated system of classification is necessary to bring some sort of order out of chaos. That which is adopted here is a system long used by which all simplicidentates are arranged in three infraorders—the Sciuromorpha, the Myomorpha, and the Hystricomorpha—typified by the squirrel, the mouse, and the porcupine, respectively (Fig. 346).

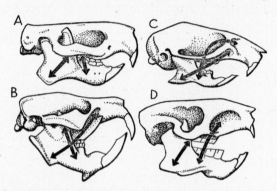

FIG. 347.—Diagrams to show the development of the superficial and deep portions of the masseteric muscle in various rodent types. *A*, a primitive sciuromorph; the masseter originates mainly from the lower edge of the zygomatic arch. *B*, an advanced sciuromorph; the superficial masseter originates from the outer side of the skull in front of the orbit. *C*, a myomorph; the superficial masseter is similar, but the deeper portion has pushed up through the orbit and arises in a pocket on the face formed from the infraorbital foramen. *D*, a hystricomorph; the superficial masseter is unspecialized but the foramen is enormously developed to accommodate the deeper portion.

Sciuromorphs.—It is generally agreed that the Sciuromorpha is the most primitive of the three groups and that the other two have probably been derived from primitive squirrel-like forms. Only in the sciuromorphs are two upper premolars and a lower premolar present, and even here the anterior upper one is small and often lost. A characteristic feature is the comparatively primitive position of the masseteric muscle. Primitively both major parts of this muscle attached to the skull mainly along the lower edge of the zygomatic arch (Fig. 347*a*). This position appears to have been retained in primitive sciuromorphs. In other members of the group (Fig. 347*b*) a superficial portion passes upward and forward from the lower jaw to take origin from a pocket or groove cut into the side of the muzzle in front of the orbit; no part of it (as in the other two groups) passes through the orbit.

In this infraorder are many of the more primitive of the living rodents, including the squirrels, beavers, and pocket gophers, which may be arranged in five superfamilies—the Aplodontoidea, Sciuroidea, Castoroidea, Geomyoidea, and Anomaluroidea.

Aplodontoidea.—Perhaps the most primitive of living rodents is *Aplodontia*, the sewellel, or "mountain beaver," of the American Northwest. This small grounddwelling rodent is more primitive than any other living type in many respects; the skull is long and low, the brain small, and the braincase is not swollen. There is not even a trace of a postorbital process of the frontal bone, and the masseter attaches to the lower edge of the zygomatic arch in primitive fashion.

Related to this form are the most primitive of known rodents, *Paramys* (Figs. 348a, 350, 351), *Ischyromys* (Fig. 349a), and similar types which flourished in the

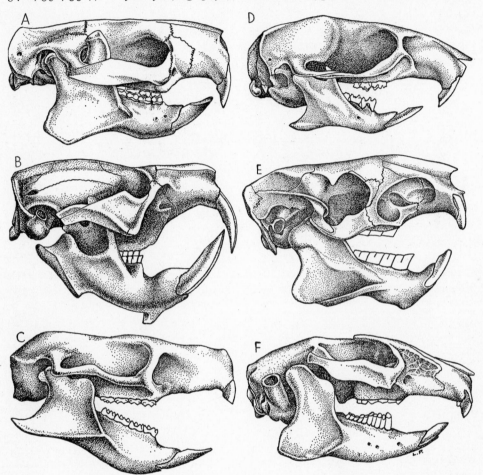

FIG. 348.—Skulls of rodents. *A, Paramys*, a primitive Eocene sciuromorph, skull length about $3\frac{1}{2}$ inches. *B, Palaeocastor*, a Lower Miocene castoroid, skull length about $2\frac{3}{4}$ inches. *C, Pseudosciurus*, an Oligocene anomaluroid, skull length about $2\frac{1}{2}$ inches. *D, Cricetops*, a Tertiary myoid, skull length about 1 inch. *E, Neoreomys*, a Miocene South American hystricomorph, skull length about 4 inches. *F, Palaeolagus*, an Oligocene hare, skull length about 2 inches. (*A* after Matthew, *B* after Peterson, *C* after Schlosser, *D* after Schaube, *E* after Scott, *F* after Troxell.)

northern continents throughout the Eocene and Oligocene. They were rather squirrel-like in size and proportions, and very possibly appearance and habits as well. The cheek teeth were still low crowned and had a quadritubercular pattern readily derivable from that of generalized primitive placentals. Except for a poorly known Paleocene type from Asia of dubious relationship, these forms are the oldest known rodents. But, although primitive in many ways, they were already definitely true rodents and give us little indication of the early stages by which the group arose from the primitive placental stock.

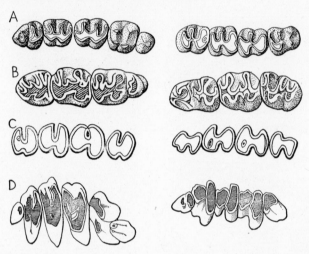

FIG. 349.—Teeth of rodents. At left, upper cheek teeth of right side; at right, lower cheek teeth of left side. *A*, *Ischyromys*, a primitive Oligocene sciuromorph ($\times\frac{7}{2}$). *B*, *Eumys*, an Oligocene myomorph ($\times$5 approx.) *C*, *Sciamys*, a Miocene South American hystricomorph ($\times\frac{9}{2}$). *D*, *Desmolagus*, an Oligocene duplicidentate ($\times$4 approx.) (*A, B, D* after Matthew and Granger, *C* after Scott.)

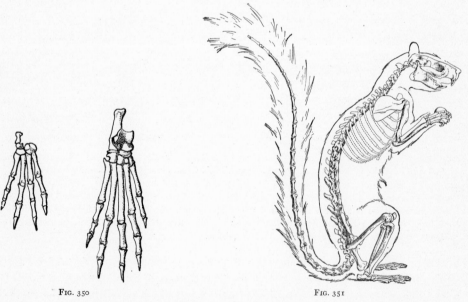

FIG. 350

FIG. 351

FIG. 350.—Right manus and pes of *Paramys*, an Eocene sciuromorph rodent. (After Matthew.)

FIG. 351.—*Paramys*, a primitive Eocene squirrel-like rodent. Original about 16 inches high in sitting pose. (From Matthew.)

These primitive forms gave rise to a varied series of types in addition to ancestors of the existing sewellel. An early specialized side branch includes some Middle Tertiary American forms such as *Mylagaulus*, in which the last premolar became enormous and the cheek teeth reduced, and *Ceratogaulus* and its relatives, which alone among rodents had horns (in the male at least).

Squirrels.—The squirrels and their relatives constitute a second group, the Sciuroidea, but little changed from the primitive stock. The skull is somewhat arched, and the brain larger; a postorbital process is present, and in squirrels and the remaining sciuromorph group there is a well-developed groove up the front of the zygomatic process in front of the orbit for an important division of the masseteric muscle (Fig. 347b). Otherwise, these forms are quite primitive rodents; the teeth are almost always low crowned and of primitive pattern, and the small third upper premolar is usually retained. The main group of squirrels are arboreal forms, with the "flying" squirrels of the Northern Hemisphere as an offshoot. Others, as ground squirrels, have become primarily terrestrial, including such forms as the "gophers" and chipmunk, while a group of large, short-tailed burrowing forms includes the marmot, woodchuck, and the prairie dog common on the western American plains. The squirrel ancestry may be traced back through intermediate Oligocene types to *Paramys* and its relatives.

Beavers.—A third superfamily of sciuromorphs is that of the Castoroidea, represented today only by the beavers. These forms tend to grow to rather large size. The third premolar has disappeared in castoroids and all remaining simplicidentates and the grinding teeth have become hypsodont, as in many rodents considered later. In contrast to the squirrels, the skull is low and the postorbital process is not developed. Here, as in a large number of types later considered, the tibia and fibula fuse.

While the beaver, *Castor*, is an aquatic type, the older members of the group were probably burrowing forms. *Palaeocastor* (Fig. 348b), *Steneofiber*, and its relatives are common Miocene fossil rodents in both Europe and North America; in western Nebraska peculiar upright "devil's corkscrews" found in the Lower Miocene beds have been thought to be their mud-filled burrows. Giant beaver types were found in both northern continents in the Pleistocene; *Castoroides* (Fig. 352) of North America attained the size of a half-grown bear; and *Trogontherium* was a large European form.

Geomyoids.—Also included in the sciuromorphs is the superfamily Geomyoidea, a purely American assemblage containing the mouse-like kangaroo rats (*Heteromys*) and the larger burrowing pocket gophers (*Geomys*), both of which occur in that continent from Oligocene times on. From a low-crowned condition in the Oligocene ancestors, the teeth have gradually become high crowned and in the pocket gophers rootless. Here, again, tibia and fibula are fused. The pocket gophers are burrowing types owing their name to the large cheek pouches; the kangaroo rats are small hopping desert rodents with elongate hind legs. This is the first of several similar hopping types of rodents which have evolved independently in various groups.

Anomaluroids.—A final offshoot of the primitive sciuromorph stock is that of the superfamily Anomaluroidea. Living members of the group include only two specialized African types—*Anomalurus*, resembling a flying squirrel, and *Pedetes*, a jumping "hare." Little is known of either type as fossils. But in these forms is to be found a structural feature of great interest. In all mammals a small infraorbital foramen leads from the front of the orbit forward onto the face carrying nerves and blood vessels to the region of the upper lip. In the myomorphs and hystricomorphs this opening is much enlarged, and the deeper portion of the masseter muscle has almost always pushed forward into it. In the present types an intermediate condition is to be found, for the opening is large but no muscle penetrates it.

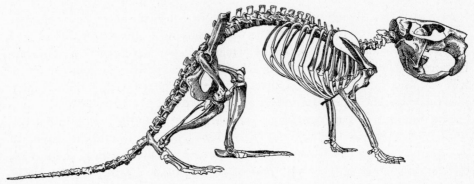

FIG. 352.—*Castoroides*, a giant beaver, about 7½ feet in length, from the Pleistocene of North America. (From Hay.)

It appears probable that, although these living African forms are themselves too specialized to be truly ancestral, they are representatives of a group intermediate between the primitive rodents and the more "advanced" groups. In agreement with this suggestion is the fact that in the late Eocene of Europe and the Oligocene of both Europe and Africa are found a considerable number of small rodents presumably lacking the specializations of the living anomaluroids but with the same type of construction of the interorbital canal. These forms, such as *Pseudosciurus* (Fig. 348c) and *Theridomys* appear to be transitional in character between the primitive *Paramys* type and the myomorphs and hystricomorphs. It seems probable that the Eastern Hemisphere had been the center of higher rodent evolution, and the presence in the Lower Oligocene of Africa of types which appear to be transitional to the porcupine-like rodents suggests that the hystricomorph group may have been developed in that continent in early Tertiary times.

Myomorphs.—The second of the three major groups of the simplicidentates is that of the Myomorpha, the rats and their allies. In all of them the superficial division of the masseteric muscle passes forward in front of the orbit, while a deeper division enters the orbit and runs forward from there through a much enlarged infraorbital canal into a pocket in the side of the face (Fig. 347c). In all members of the group tibia and fibula are fused together at both ends. The great majority of the rat-like forms appear to have been of Old World origin; Eurasia appears to have been the center of myomorph distribution.

Doormice.—Three superfamilies of myomorphs may be distinguished, of which perhaps the most primitive is that of Myoxoidea, the doormice or sleepers, of which *Myoxus* is the type. These small arboreal fruit-eaters are rather like squirrels in general appearance. The teeth are low crowned and rooted with three cross-crests. In most cases (and unlike the typical myoids) the last premolar is still present. The living forms are found exclusively in the Old World; and the only known fossil types are from Europe, where a doormouse is found as far back as the Miocene and possibly late Eocene. It is probable that these living forms are fairly representative of the primitive stock from which have come the rats.

Jerboas.—An interesting side branch of the myomorphs is that of the Dipodoidea, the typical members of which are hopping rat-like types such as *Dipus*, the jerboas, almost all of which are confined to the Old World. Their chief peculiarities are the elongate hind legs with fused metatarsals and a frequent reduction in the number of toes. The teeth are low crowned and rooted, and the premolar still persists in most cases. Little is known of the history of these desert forms, although one member of the group is found in the Miocene of Africa, which continent may have been the center of their dispersal. One living form has hind legs of normal length and thus obviously is a transitional type from the primitive myomorphs to the jerboas.

Rats and mice.—The main myomorph group is that of the superfamily Myoidea, containing the mice, rats, and their relatives, the most successful and abundant of rodent types (Figs. 348d, 349b). The last premolar has disappeared, the molars taking over the entire burden of grinding; the first is usually larger than the others. In the more primitive forms the teeth are low crowned and rooted; in others there is a development of high-crowned rootless teeth.

The rats and mice are probably mainly a group which has centered in the Old World, although numerous types have invaded other regions. Forms which apparently are ancestral mice are found not only in Eurasia but also in North America as far back as late Eocene and Oligocene times; some of these early types still retained a small premolar. The members of the group are, in the main, terrestrial woods and meadow types. Some, as the American muskrat (*Fiber*) have tended to an aquatic life; a few Old World types have become burrowing and mole-like; and some are hopping types. The common rats (*Epimys*) and mice (*Mus*) have become followers of man and have journeyed with him into all parts of the globe. The myoids are the most ubiquitous of mammals. They are probably the only land mammals which have succeeded in reaching Australia, unaided by man, since that continent became separated at the end of Mesozoic times, and are the only rodents except the rabbits which have reached South America to dispute the ascendancy of the hystricomorph types.

Hystricomorphs.—Last of the three great simplicidentate divisions is that of the Hystricomorpha (Figs. 348e, 349c). The name is taken from the widely distributed porcupines; the guinea pig, however, is a more typical representative. One feature which separates these forms from all other rodents is the fact that the angle of the lower jaw arises from the outer wall of the incisor socket rather than the lower border of the bone. We have noted that the infraorbital canal was enlarged in the myomorphs. Here, however, the enlargement for the deep masseteric muscle is extreme; while the superficial masseter (in contrast to the rats) does not extend forward onto the face. In contrast with many of the rat-like types, the last premolar is always present and the teeth are usually high crowned. Tibia and fibula, fused in the myomorphs, have here remained separate.

The present distribution of these forms, coupled with their known geological history, suggests some interesting problems in ancient geography. Most widespread of living hystricomorphs are various porcupines, such as the European *Hystrix* and the American *Erethizon;* they are found in all continents except Australia. Apart from these, hystricomorphs are confined to Africa and tropical America. The African forms are not numerous; they include the large cane rat (*Thryonomys*), widely distributed in the more fertile part of that continent, the rock rat, *Petromys*, and a number of digging desert types, such as *Ctenodactylus*.

On the other hand, the South American types are extremely numerous and, except for a few Pleistocene invaders, are the sole rodents of that region. The guinea pig, *Cavia*, is a fairly typical hystricomorph; but there is a wide range of other types from that continent, ranged in half a dozen families. Among the more interesting and conspicuous types may be mentioned the "water pig" *Myopotamus*, with hoof-like feet, largest of living rodents, reaching the size of a hog; the silky-furred chinchillas; a water-living beaver-like form, *Myocastor*. This radiation of South American hystricomorph rodents is in many respects comparable to that of the South American ungulates or edentates and suggests a long isolation of the group on that continent.

The geological history of the group is a peculiar one. We have already noted the presence in Europe and Africa of a number of late Eocene and Oligocene types which appear to be transitional between the primitive sciuromorphs and the hystricomorphs; the Old World thus seems to have been their region of origin. Porcupines appeared in the European Oligocene and presumably have been present in the Old World since that time (the North American porcupines are probably Pleistocene invaders from South America).

In South America the hystricomorphs appeared suddenly in the Oligocene, at which time primitive ancestors of the porcupines, guinea pigs, and chinchillas are present in the fossil record. These forms were newcomers, as there were no rodents present in the Eocene. But we believe the land bridge from North America to have been closed at the very beginning of the Eocene, and, further, hystricomorphs are quite unknown in North America until the Pleistocene. Seemingly these rodents must have come from Africa, and a transatlantic bridge has been suggested to account for their entrance. But there is no evidence of intermigration of other mammal groups, and a bridge seems out of the question. A plausible suggestion is that some stray rodents may have been transported across the narrows of the Atlantic on a mass of floating vegetation, a natural raft such as may sometimes be found today hundreds of miles from the mouths of great rivers. Such a stray may have been the ancestor of the South American rodents; once landed on that continent, the hystricomorphs have found a wide-open field for rodent exploitation. The varied types now present in South America were widespread in that region as well as in Central America and the West Indies during later geological periods, and in the last-mentioned region produced a number of curious Pleistocene insular types.

Possible relatives of the hystricomorphs are *Bathyergus* and its relatives, aberrant burrowing types from Africa whose fossil history is obscure; they resemble the porcupine group in the position of the angular process of the jaw but are not otherwise particularly close to any of the common rodent types.

Duplicidentates.—All the previous types discussed have been members of the suborder Simplicidentata; we may conclude by a consideration of the suborder Duplicidentata, the hares and their relatives, sometimes even placed in a distinct order, since they are widely separated from the other rodents in structure and resemble them little except in the presence of gnawing incisors and grinding cheek teeth.

As in other rodents, the functionally important gnawing teeth are a single pair of incisors above and below, but in the duplicidentates an accessory pair of small upper incisors is present behind the principal ones. There is, as before, a long diastema; the outer incisors, canines, and some premolars have been lost in its development. The number of cheek teeth present is higher than in any simplicidentate, for there are always three upper premolars and two lower ones in addition to three molars. The cheek teeth (Fig. 349d) are high crowned and rootless, with two prominent cross-crests presumably derived from the typical primitive herbivorous four-cusped pattern. In contrast with other rodents, the two upper tooth rows are farther apart than the lower ones, and the teeth have more of a chopping than a grinding motion. There is never any enlargement or muscular invasion of the infraorbital canal. A peculiar lattice-work fenestration of the side of the snout is a noticeable feature of the duplicidentate skull. The tail is short or absent in all known forms.

Best known of the group are the leporids, including the living hares (*Lepus*) and rabbits (*Oryctolagus*) and their relatives, leaping forms with much elongated hind legs. A less prominent type is that represented today by the pika, *Ochotona*, of the mountains of Western America and Asia, with short legs and short ears. Both types may be traced back to the Oligocene, the former (as *Palaeolagus* [Fig. 347*f*]) in North America, the latter in Europe. But even in the oldest genera the typical duplicidentate characteristics were well developed, and there are no intermediate forms known between them and the primitive simplicidentate rodents. The question of the region in which duplicidentate types were undergoing development during the Eocene is an unsolved one. If a common ancestor for the two suborders once existed, the time of their separation must certainly have been no later than the very beginning of Tertiary times in order for the hares to have advanced so far by the Oligocene.

The hares and rabbits are a flourishing group, although their history has been confined almost entirely to the northern continents. Like most other rodent types, they never reached Australia; but their all-too-successful career there since their artificial introduction is a well-known story.

CHAPTER XXIII

PRIMATES

The order Primates is of especial interest since its members include not only the lemurs, monkeys, and apes but man himself. Unfortunately, however, fossil remains of this group are more rare than is the case in any other large group of mammals. The reasons for this paucity of material are fairly obvious. Primates are, for the most part, tree-dwellers; deposits in which fossil vertebrates are to be found are not normally formed in forested regions. Again, primates are mostly dwellers in the tropics, whereas most of the known Tertiary fossil beds are in what are to-day zones of temperate climate. It is only in Eocene times, when these regions (as shown by the vegetation) knew tropical conditions, that primates are found to any extent in the fossiliferous deposits of Europe and North America.

The primates may be divided primarily into three groups: (1) the lemurs (sub-order Lemuroidea), typically small four-footed forms of rather squirrel-like appearance, found today in the Old World tropics but present in the Eocene in Eurasia and North America; (2) the suborder Tarsioidea, which includes *Tarsius*, a curious, small, hopping, rat-like creature from the East Indies and its fossil Eocene relatives, occupying an intermediate position between lemurs and higher primates; (3) the suborder Anthropoidea, comprising the South American monkeys, the more advanced monkeys of the Old World, the great man-like apes, and man.

Primates are essentially arboreal, only a few forms (such as the baboons and man) having returned to a life on the ground. There is considerable evidence suggesting that the primitive placentals were tree-dwellers to begin with and that the primates have merely continued on in this ancestral track. Arboreal life is apparently responsible for much of the progressive development of primate characteristics; and, although man is not a tree-dweller, this life of his ancestors has left its mark deeply upon him and is perhaps in great measure responsible for his attainment of his present estate.

Arboreal adaptations—limbs.—Locomotion in the trees has left the postcranial skeleton of the primates in a condition much closer to that of the primitive placentals than is the case in most groups. Flexibility is necessary for climbing trees, and there is none of the restriction of limb movement to one plane found in ungulate groups and in many carnivores and rodents. Very rarely is there any reduction or fusion of bones in the lower segment of the limbs. The clavicle is retained, in contrast with running forms, its connection of shoulder and trunk relieving the strain on the muscles when the animal is suspended from a limb.

In contrast with such arboreal types as the squirrels, in which climbing is accomplished by digging the claws into the bark, the primate hold is generally accomplished by grasping bough or twigs. The primitive claws have been transformed into flat nails serving as a protection to the finger tips, although in many cases (particularly in lemurs and marmosets) there is a return to a claw-like structure.

In primitive placentals the pollex and hallux were presumably somewhat divergent. This grasping characteristic has in general been retained and emphasized in primates (Fig. 234). In most cases it is the hallux which is the most highly developed and divergent. In contrast, the thumb is sometimes reduced, or even absent, in forms which habitually progress by swinging from branch to branch, the other four fingers here hooking over the bough and the thumb not only being useless but actually in the way. Otherwise, there has been but little reduction of digits; the primates are in this respect more conservative than most mammalian groups.

Quadrupedal locomotion is the rule among primates, bipedal tendencies becoming apparent for the most part only among the higher members of the order. The hands, however, while primarily possessing their grasping adaptation in relation to locomotion, are well adapted (almost alone among mammals) for grasping food and other objects; and even among the lemurs there is a tendency toward a sitting posture and the release of the front feet from supporting the body.

The primitively long tail is retained in almost all the lower primates and is apparently of considerable use in balancing. In many South American monkeys it has developed into a prehensile "fifth hand." In a number of cases, however, the tail is reduced or absent, and there is no external tail in the man-like apes and man.

Teeth.—An omnivorous diet appears to have been general in early primates, and similar food habits characterize many living types (although there has been a strong herbivorous trend). The dentition (Figs. 353, 354) is hence usually less specialized than in most mammalian groups. One incisor had already been lost in the earliest known primates; the other two are retained in all monkeys and apes but are variously modified and reduced in lemurs. The canines are usually unreduced, projecting moderately above the other teeth, and are often larger in the males.

While four premolars are present in a few primitive fossil forms, no living primate possesses more than three; and the higher members of the order have but two. Related to this is a shortening of the tooth row evident in the group as a whole, although (as in the baboons) there may be a secondary lengthening brought about by elongation of the molars. The premolars are never molarized and are typically bicuspid.

The molars of the most primitive forms (Fig. 227a) are often very similar to those of the primitive placentals, showing clear traces of the primitive triangular pattern; but the originally sharp cusps have tended to soften down to a bunodont condition. A hypocone is usually added above. Below, as in many other groups, the paraconid disappears to give an essentially four-cusped tooth; but a hypoconulid on the back margin is persistent in many cases, and even in man this fifth cusp is often present. There is little tendency toward a hypsodont condition, since the food is mainly of the softer kinds such as fruit and buds.

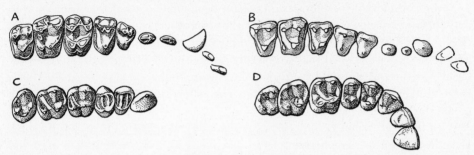

FIG. 353.—Upper right dentitions of primates. *A*, *Notharctus*, an American Eocene lemur; hypocone split off from protocone ($\times\frac{3}{2}$ approx.). *B*, *Pronycticebus*, a European Eocene tarsioid; hypocone derived from cingulum ($\times\frac{5}{2}$ approx.) *C*, *Dryopithecus*, a late Tertiary anthropoid ($\times\frac{2}{3}$ approx.). *D*, Mousterian youth ($\times\frac{1}{3}$ approx.). (Mostly after Gregory.)

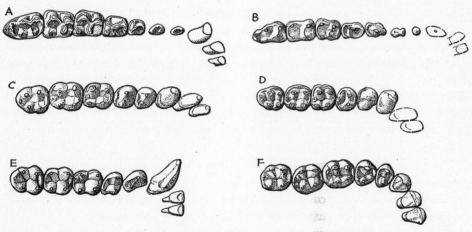

FIG. 354.—Lower left dentitions of primates. *A*, *Notharctus*, an Eocene lemur ($\times\frac{3}{2}$ approx.). *B*, *Pronycticebus* ($\times\frac{5}{2}$ approx.). *C*, *Parapithecus*, an Oligocene Old World monkey $\times\frac{5}{3}$ approx.). *D*, *Propliopithecus*, an ancestral Oligocene anthropoid ($\times\frac{3}{2}$ approx.). *E*, *Dryopithecus*, a late Tertiary anthropoid ($\times\frac{2}{3}$ approx.). *F*, Mousterian youth ($\times\frac{1}{3}$ approx.). (Mainly after Gregory; *C*, *D* after Schlosser.)

Sense organs.—Arboreal life has had a profound effect upon the sense organs. A ground-dwelling mammal is in great measure dependent upon smell for his knowledge of things about him, and his olfactory organs are highly developed while sight is usually comparatively poor. The reverse is true in these arboreal types. For locomotion in the trees good eyesight is essential, and throughout the primate group there has been a progressive series of advances in the visual apparatus. Even in the lemurs the eyes are large, and there is a tendency to rotate them forward from their primitive lateral position. This results, in such forms as *Tarsius*, in a condition in which the two fields of vision are identical. Here, however, while the vision is technically binocular, it is still not stereoscopic, for it is probable that a separate mental picture is formed by each eye. In even the lowest of the monkeys, however, considerable further advances have been made, so that the vision is probably similar to our own. A sorting-out of the nerve fibers running from eye to brain takes place, so that the brain pictures formed by the two eyes coincide, and the minute variation between the two pictures gives the effect of depth; stereoscopic vision has been attained. In addition the Anthropoidea possess in each retina a specialized central region, the macula lutea or yellow spot, in which detail is much more clearly seen.

With this increase in vision goes a corresponding decrease in the sense of smell. Even in the lemurs the olfactory sense is reduced, and in the man-like apes and man it is probably in the most rudimentary state to be found in any land-dwelling placental.

Brain.—The brain, as well, has been profoundly influenced by arboreal life. Locomotion in the trees requires great agility and muscular co-ordination, which in itself demands development of the brain centers; and it is of interest that much of the higher mental faculties is apparently developed in an area alongside the motor centers of the brain. Again, the development of good eyesight rendered possible for primates a far wider acquisition of knowledge of their environment than is possible for forms which depend upon smell. Perhaps still more important in the development of primate mentality has been the development of a grasping hand. This is not only an advantage in feeding but undoubtedly has contributed materially to primate mental development through the knowledge gained by the examination of objects.

A constantly increasing brain size has been a characteristic feature of primate development. The cerebral hemispheres have grown in size and in all the higher anthropoidea completely cover the cerebellum. Among the smaller monkeys are to be found the highest relative weights of brain to body in mammals.

Skull.—These changes in dentition, sense organs, and brain have been associated with great changes in the primate skull. The fossil lemurs and some of the living types have an elongate skull of primitive appearance with a long facial region and a long low braincase. But with the reduction of the sense of smell and the concurrent abbreviating of the tooth row, the muzzle in most primates has shortened considerably, the face sloping downward toward the mouth at a considerable angle. The orbits were rather large in even the most primitive of the lemurs, and in the early Eocene already had a bar behind them—a feature in which they were in advance of almost all known forms of that period. In the higher lemurs the orbits tend to turn forward, their median boundaries crowding close together above the nostrils—a position in which they are found in all higher primates. The originally superficial bar separating orbit and temporal opening becomes in the higher forms a solid partition. In many forms the upper margin of the orbits is above the level of the braincase, projecting as a supraorbital ridge.

The expanding brain naturally requires an enlarged braincase; and, except for some primitive types, the primate braincase tends to be high vaulted and rounded. Sagittal and occipital crests, present in the early lemurs, are rare in later and higher types, for with expansion of the braincase the temporal muscles between which the crests form fail to meet. These crests are only met with in the larger forms and in the more heavily muscled herbivorous types. The occipital condyles are usually shifted in a varying degree from the back to the under side of the skull, perhaps partially due to the development of a sitting pose or erect posture, but primarily, apparently, to an actual posterior expansion of the skull above them. The two halves of the lower jaw, primitively loosely connected, become fused in higher types.

Lemurs.—Most primitive of primates are the lemurs, found today in tropical Asia and Africa, more especially on the island of Madagascar, but known also from early Tertiary deposits. A typical Madagascar lemur of today is a fairly small arboreal animal, nocturnal in habits, with a bushy hairy covering which contrasts with the rather sparse coat of most higher primates. The limbs are moderately long, the ears pointed, and the eyes are directed more laterally than forward. Their superficial appearance is quite different from that of the higher primates, and they differ as well in certain more important characters, so that some writers have held that they are not really members of the order.

The lemur tail, usually long, is never a grasping organ. Pollex and hallux are always widely separable from the other fingers; the big toe is especially well developed and has a flat nail in all forms, whereas the other digits are variable in their covering. Typical lemurs have a claw-like nail on the second toe but normal nails on the other digits.

In living lemurs the upper incisors are often small or absent, while the lower ones, together with an incisor-like canine, slant forward as a fur-combing organ. The upper molars vary from the triangular to the quadrangular pattern.

The lemur face may undergo some shortening, but it is in most cases a comparatively long and fox-like muzzle. The braincase is long and low in the more primitive living types, but is somewhat more expanded in the more advanced lemurs.

Eocene lemurs.—The earliest lemurs are found in the Eocene of the northern continents, the more typical forms being included in the family Adapidae of which *Notharctus* of North America, and *Adapis* and *Pronycticebus* of Europe, are among the better-known types (Figs. 234, 353*a, b,* 354*a, b,* 355*a*). *Notharctus* was a small mammal with a skull about 2 inches long which probably resembled the ordinary lemurs of today in general appearance. It was already quite lemur-like in its proportions and many structural features. The dentition, however, was more primitive in a number of respects. Although some members of the family had but three premolars, *Notharctus* still retained the full complement of four. Further, the upper incisors were comparatively normal; the canines were of primitive type; and the lower incisors little, if at all, procumbent. In *Notharctus* a hypocone had already developed in the upper molars, but some Eocene relatives had but slight traces of this structure. In the European forms a hypocone was developed as well; but a curious feature is that, while the two forms were closely related and had both acquired this same new cusp, *Adapis* and *Pronycticebus* had obtained it by an upgrowth of the cingulum, *Notharctus* by a budding-off from the protocone.

The adapids are obviously proper ancestors for the typical lemurs. In many features they seem close to the probable ancestors of all the primates. The known

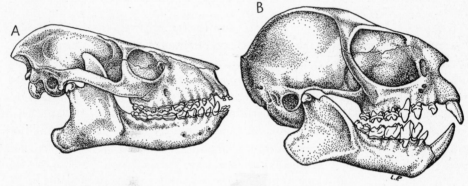

FIG. 355.—Skulls of Eocene primates. *A, Notharctus*, an Eocene lemur; length of skull about 3 inches. *B, Tetonius*, an Eocene tarsioid; length of skull about $1\frac{1}{8}$ inches. (After Gregory.)

forms, however, are somewhat too late in time to have been the actual ancestors of higher primates, for members of the higher tarsioid group are found at an even earlier date.

It is usually agreed that the primates have been derived from the arboreal insectivores represented today by the tree shrews. In the Paleocene and Eocene there were a number of forms which lay close to the boundary between the two groups. Some may eventually prove to be actual intermediate types (the gap is not great). Others, however, represent early side branches of this arboreal stock which obviously lay far off the main line of primate development. *Plesiadapis* and related types from the Paleocene and Eocene of the northern continents form the most conspicuous of these aberrant groups. In these forms the cheek teeth were much like those of lemurs; but the anterior part of the dentition was rather like that of rodents, for a diastema was developed and a pair of incisors was enlarged into chisel-like cutting organs.

Madagascar lemurs.—By the close of the Eocene the lemurs had disappeared from the fossil record in the North Temperate Zone, and we know nothing of their further history until Pleistocene and Recent times. Here we find them present in Old World tropical regions, where conditions today are probably not dissimilar to those prevailing farther north in the Eocene. The main center of the group is the island of Madagascar. This region presumably has been cut off from the mainland during most of the Tertiary; and there are but few carnivores—a fact which may have been responsible for the survival of these primitive primates (as well as of many insectivores). The Madagascar lemurs may all be included in the family Lemuridae, using this term in a broad sense. A majority of these types are rather typical lemurs (*Lemur*, etc.), with the long low skull and general body build of their Eocene ancestors and a normal type of limb structure. These forms are of interest as giving us today as near an approach as we can obtain to the general appearance and habits of our earliest primate ancestors.

There are, however, various divergent types within the family, including a small hopping form, and *Indris* and a few other types of rather large size.

Most of the living lemur types have been discovered in Pleistocene bog deposits on the island, some of them quite large. In addition there were other forms now extinct. *Megaladapis* was the largest known lemur, attaining the size of a pig, with a skull a foot long, peculiarly long and decurved nasal bones, and small eyes; it seems to have resembled the Eocene lemurs closely in many features. A second extinct group was represented by *Archaeolemur*, also large for a lemur (a 5-inch skull) but with large eyes turned remarkably far forward, and a large brain, there being no sagittal crest. The face was considerably shortened. This extinct form paralleled in a number of respects the higher primates and is one of several abortive "efforts" of the lemur group to reach a monkey status.

A final member of the Madagascar primate fauna is the aye-aye, *Chiromys*. It is a nocturnal form about the size of a small cat, with a short high skull of the shape found in the higher lemurs and monkeys. All the digits except the big toe have claw-like structures rather than nails; the middle finger is very long and slim and is said to be used to extract grubs from their holes in the wood. The single remaining pair of incisors is enlarged in rodent fashion and is used in gnawing through bark in search of insect food. The aye-aye has been thought to have descended from the plesiadapids but may well represent merely a parallel evolution among the Madagascar lemur group.

Higher lemurs.—All the living non-Madagascar lemurs are included in a higher group, the family Lorisidae, of which the loris of the Indian region is typical. The muzzle is rather short, the braincase high, the eyes turned somewhat forward, and the premolars reduced to two; the lower front teeth, however, have the typical arrangement of the Madagascar lemurs. The index finger is reduced, giving a better grasp between the thumb and the remaining fingers. In Africa the group is represented by the potto and *Galago*, the "bush baby."

The loris group is obviously on a higher level of organization than the primitive fossil lemurs and their comparatively unmodified Madagascar descendants. It is possible that these living types are the descendants of very early types transitional from the lowest lemurs to the higher primates; but unfortunately we have not a single certain fossil representative of these interesting forms.

Tarsius.—A small but very interesting primate group is that which includes a single living animal, *Tarsius*, in addition to Eocene fossil types. These forms have often been classed as lemurs but are quite advanced in structure and may be appropriately placed in a separate suborder, the Tarsioidea, intermediate between the true lemurs and the Anthropoidea.

Tarsius is a small nocturnal tree-living form from the East Indies. The tail is very long, and the hind legs are adapted for a hopping gait. The brain case is large and rounded, and the foramen magnum is pushed somewhat forward onto the under side of the skull in contrast to the usual lemur condition. The visual apparatus is much more advanced than that of the lemurs. The eyes are exceptionally large and are turned completely forward from the primitive lateral position, with the orbits very close together above the nose. In ordinary lemurs there is only a superficial bar separating orbit and temporal fossa; but in *Tarsius* the alisphenoid extends outward below the frontal and jugal and closes off the greater part of this opening much as in the Anthropoidea.

While vision has thus advanced, the sense of smell has been proportionately reduced. The fox-like snout of the typical lemur has disappeared, and the nose is reduced to a small nubbin tucked in beneath and between the eyes. There is little projection of the muzzle (the tooth row is rather short); and we have here the beginning of the type of face found in monkeys, apes, and man.

There are some specializations of the front teeth, but the cheek teeth are of primitive pattern with fairly typical tritubercular and tuberculo-sectorial molars.

The hind limbs are specialized for a hopping gait. Alone among primates we find in *Tarsius* a partial fusion of tibia and fibula. A third segment is introduced into the limb by means of an elongation not of the metatarsals but of the calcaneum and navicular (a similar development has occurred in a Madagascar lemur and in *Galago*). This seemingly odd fashion of developing a third joint is readily understandable when we consider the situation. The ordinary animal which introduces an extra segment for hopping, or indeed fast locomotion of any sort (as the kangaroo, jumping mice, or any typical ungulate), has no grasp to its thumb and is usually a ground-living type. The primate, however, is in great measure dependent for security in the trees on the powers of opposibility of the great toe. If the metatarsals were to elongate, his grasp would be lost; elongation must take place proximal to the origin of the big toe, and the proximal tarsal bones give the only possibility for this development.

Apart from this peculiar limb specialization, *Tarsius* is close to the higher primates in most features. An additional suggestion that this form is a relic of a primitive group transitional to the Anthropoidea lies in the structure of the placenta. In the lemurs this structure was of a type probably present in primitive placentals. But in *Tarsius* the placental connections between mother and young are concentrated into a pancake-shaped structure which is shed at birth as in the higher primates.

Eocene tarsioids.—Back of Recent times there is a gap in the history of the group extending to the Eocene. But in deposits of that period we find in Europe and North America numerous remains of small forms unquestionably related to *Tarsius.*

A number of them are known merely by the dentition. This was often as in *Tarsius*, close to the primitive placental type in molar construction, the hypocone appearing only rarely. In two genera the first lower premolar was still present as a small tooth; but normally there were, as in *Tarsius*, but three premolars, and in one case there were but two. The anterior teeth, however, were quite variable in structure. In such forms as the best-known genera, *Tetonius* (Fig. 355b), of the American Lower Eocene, and *Necrolemur*, of the Upper Eocene of Europe, there was an enlarged and rather rodent-like pair of front teeth much as in some lemurs (but here the lower tusk was probably the canine).

In *Tetonius* the general structure of the skull is quite similar to that of the living *Tarsius*, with a very short face and huge forwardly turned orbits with a developing partition behind them. Some of the others, as *Necrolemur*, appear to have been rather more lemur-like, with a somewhat less reduced snout.

In most cases nothing is known of the postcranial skeleton. But in one or two Eocene types we know that the peculiar specializations of the hind legs found in the living forms were already present.

These fossil forms first appeared in the Middle Paleocene of North America and were already quite specialized—in some cases, at least. It is obvious that the earliest tarsioids must have come into existence at a much earlier time, possibly well back in the Cretaceous.

Anthropoids.—All the remaining primates—monkeys, apes, and man—may be placed in the suborder Anthropoidea, the man-like primates. In all of them we have a very distinct advance upon the types already discussed. The eyes are large and placed facing forward, as in *Tarsius;* but in addition there is true stereoscopic vision, while the yellow spot, with its central clear area making for better color perception and the distinguishing of details, is developed in even the lowest of monkeys. The orbits are completely separated from the temporal fossa. The sense of smell is unimportant, and the snout is greatly reduced.

The monkey normally is a four-footed walker, but there is a great tendency for an upright sitting posture and the freeing of the hands for the manipulation of food and other objects. The tail is variable; in some South American types it is prehensile, but in the higher forms it is frequently reduced.

There are never more than three bicuspid premolar teeth, and the higher Old

World forms have but two. The last molar tends toward reduction and actually is lost in one monkey family. The upper molars are still tritubercular in a few of the more primitive forms, but generally the typical quadrate pattern is developed in both jaws.

The brain is comparatively large in all the members of the group. The brain-case is typically much expanded, and crests are only exceptionally developed. The foramen magnum tends to be under, rather than at the back, of the skull, with the face turned forward almost at right angles to the backbone. The two halves of the jaw are fused.

The suborder may be divided into two groups, isolated geographically both at the present day and in the past, as far as our knowledge goes. The more primitive infraorder, the Platyrrhini, are the monkeys of South America; the Catarrhini include the more advanced monkeys, apes, and man, all of which have their home in the Old World.

South American monkeys.—The Platyrrhini comprise two families of monkeys now living and found as fossils only in South and Central America. Superficially, many are quite similar in appearance to Old World monkeys but seem to be more primitive in a number of respects. They are, on the average, much smaller than their Old World relatives. Almost never is there any reduction of the primitively long tail. The thumb is but little opposable to the other fingers. Three premolars are still present in all cases, whereas the oldest fossil representatives of the Old World apes had already lost the second premolar. The group name ("flat nose") refers to the fact that the nostrils are usually far apart and face outward.

Marmosets.—Of the two families the smallest both in number of forms and in the size of the individuals is that of the marmosets, the Hapalidae. *Hapale*, the common marmoset, is a small creature, squirrel-like in size and general appearance, with thick fur and a bushy tail. Squirrel-like, too, is the fact that the toes (except the hallux) have the nails compressed and claw-like, so that the progression is mainly by digging the claws into the bark; the hallux has lost much of its opposability. A peculiar feature is the fact that the last molar has been lost, the only case of its complete reduction among primates (although man is approaching this condition). The incisors, and the lower canine with them, are rather procumbent and lemur-like. Unfortunately, we know no fossil marmosets back of the Pleistocene. Some have believed that these creatures are the most primitive of anthropoids, but such features as the molar loss suggest that they are specialized rather than primitive.

Cebids.—A more important and larger group is that of the Cebidae, the typical South American monkeys. Here the size is somewhat larger; the hairy covering somewhat thinner (a tendency carried much farther in Old World types,) and the teeth are little specialized and with the full anthropoid complement of three premolars and three molars. In some cebids, alone among primates, is a prehensile tail developed.

Most primitive of living cebids is the group represented by *Aotus* (*Nyctipithecus*), the owl monkey or dourocouli, a small form with a presumably primitive thick wooly covering and a small brain. It is a nocturnal form, while most monkeys are active in the daytime. (Parenthetically, this raises the question as to whether the primitive primates were not nocturnal, for this is the case in *Tarsius* and almost all of the lemurs.) The owl monkey is quite similar to the marmosets and may be close to the base of the platyrrhines. This belief is strengthened by the fact that the only fossil South American monkey of any antiquity, *Homunculus* of the Miocene, belongs to this group.

The owl monkeys and several other fairly primitive forms lack a prehensile tail. This "fifth limb" is developed in the remaining cebids. Of these the commonest group is that best known through the capuchin monkey, *Cebus*, usually to be found accompanying the organ-grinder. Closely related are the spider monkeys, *Ateles*. Here the limbs are very long and slender, the thumb reduced or absent, the nails rather claw-like. These monkeys are clever acrobats, swinging from the branches by any one or more of their five useful appendages.

A final group is that of the howling monkeys, *Alouatta*. These are the largest of the New World forms, some as large as a good-sized dog, and are leaf-eaters with heavy molar teeth. The larynx is expanded into a huge ossified shell, with a resonating chamber within by means of which night is made mournful in the South American forests.

Little is known, unfortunately, of the fossil history of the South American monkeys. Beyond the fact that most of them were present in the Pleistocene, we know only that *Homunculus*, a member of a primitive group within the family, was present in that continent in the Miocene. South America, as we have noted, seems to have been an isolated area from early Eocene times. Perhaps the ancestral platyrrhines entered South America at the dawn of the Tertiary; such forest-dwelling forms of this sort might have been present, and even abundant, in the Eocene and Oligocene and yet fail to be preserved in the plains deposits of Patagonia. On the other hand, it is possible that, like the hystricomorph rodents, they managed to gain access to the continent at a later date.

Catarrhines.—The catarrhines of the Old World form a well-defined group including the living monkeys of Asia and Africa, the anthropoid apes and man, and their fossil representatives. The name indicates one of the many features in which they are more advanced than the South American monkeys, in that the nostrils are closer together and open forward and down with a smaller bony opening. There is a rather general tendency toward an increase in size which culminates in the chimpanzee, man, and gorilla. Although primitively arboreal, some of the higher or more specialized types, as man and the baboons, tend toward a terrestrial life. The

tail is often shortened or absent. Primitively four-footed, some have tended to an
arm-swinging type of locomotion in which the body is held erect; man has attained
an erect posture. Although progression on the ground is usually on all fours, the
long arms bring the back into a slanting position, while sitting is the common
catarrhine pose when not in motion. The thumb is usually well developed and
opposable, and the big toe universally so except where secondarily reduced in man.
The hairy covering is always thin and the face naked.

The brain is large; but since the forms are, on the average, larger, sagittal and
occipital crests are more common than in South American monkeys. The face,
primitively short, tends to elongate in many instances in correlation with a tendency toward a vegetable diet and a consequent increase in tooth size. The second
premolar is always absent, the tooth formula being invariably $\frac{2 \cdot 1 \cdot 2 \cdot 3}{2 \cdot 1 \cdot 2 \cdot 3}$. The molars are quadrangular and essentially four-cusped.

Old World monkeys.—The most primitive known member of the group was
Parapithecus (Figs. 354c, 356b), from the Lower Oligocene of Egypt. Known only
from one jaw, there is yet enough information to be derived from this to tell us that
we are dealing with a small ancestor of the monkeys. The canine was quite small;
and the first premolar was still simple, in contrast with its usual bicuspid condition in catarrhines. There were four main cusps on the molars, but these were not
connected by cross-crests, as in the living monkeys; and a fifth cusp, the hypoconulid, was present on all three molars, whereas it only appeared on the last in the existing Old World monkeys. The two halves of the jaw met at a sharp angle, a
primitive feature contrasting with the more rounded contour of the "chin" in all
living Old World forms. The jaw proportions suggest that the skull, if found,
would reveal the presence of large eyes and a large brain. As far as our knowledge
goes, this small monkey may well have been the common ancestor of all the later
catarrhines. In appearance it might have been similar to the more generalized
African monkeys of the present day.

The living members of the Old World monkeys constituting the family Cercopithecidae include a large number of forms with a wide range of structure. They are,
in terrestrial locomotion, four-footed forms, walking flat on palm and sole. The
more primitive forms are arboreal, but the baboons and their relatives show a progressive tendency toward a ground-dwelling life. Toughened skin areas, the ischial
callosities, are present on the buttocks. As noted above, the molars are four-
cusped, the hypoconulid being present only on the last lower molar; and characteristically two cross-crests are developed.

Two great groups may be distinguished, the larger being that of the subfamily
Cercopithecinae. This includes many primitive African and Asiatic arboreal monkeys and a series of forms leading structurally to the baboons. The primitive types
are short faced, but the baboons have a long muzzle due to the vegetable diet and

the correlated long tooth row. There are well-developed cheek pouches for the stowing-away of food, while the stomach (in contrast to the other subfamily) is simple.

The genus *Cercopithecus* includes most of the African monkeys commonly found in zoölogical gardens (as the green monkey, vervet monkey, and diana monkey).

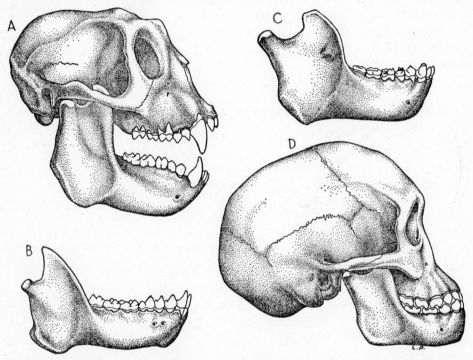

FIG. 356.—*A*, the skull of *Mesopithecus*, a Pliocene Old World langur. Length of original about 3 inches. *B*, the jaw of *Parapithecus*, oldest known Old World monkey from the Lower Oligocene of Egypt. Original about $1\frac{1}{2}$ inches long. *C*, the jaw of *Propliopithecus*, oldest anthropoid ape, from the same deposits, original about $2\frac{3}{4}$ inches long. *D*, Restored skull of *Australopithecus*, a young individual of an extinct anthropoid ape type from South Africa. (*A* after Gaudry, *B*, *C* after Schlosser, *D* after Dart and Broom.)

Typical arboreal forms with a short face, they probably stand near the base of the monkey stock. The macaques (*Macacus*) are monkeys of fairly large size and mostly Asiatic in distribution but with a representative, the barbary "ape" in North Africa and Gibraltar; there are fossil forms from the Pliocene of Eurasia. The tooth row is considerably elongated, and the snout consequently projecting. These forms are only partially arboreal, some species living in great measure on the ground. From this, several intermediate types lead to the baboons (*Papio*). These forms have become completely terrestrial, with a four-footed plantigrade gait. The tooth row of these exclusively herbivorous types is much elongated, and a dog-like muzzle is developed. The tail is short and in some of the related types may be practically absent. Baboons are found in both Pliocene and Pleistocene of Northern Africa and Asia.

The second subfamily of the modern Old World monkeys is the Semnopithecinae, a comparatively small group including *Semnopithecus*, the sacred monkey of India and its relatives (mostly Asiatic, with one African genus). There is never any facial elongation, the body is slim, the hind legs especially long, the tail usually well developed. Instead of cheek pouches, there is a complicated stomach for food storage. Cross-crests on the molars are highly developed. All the members of the

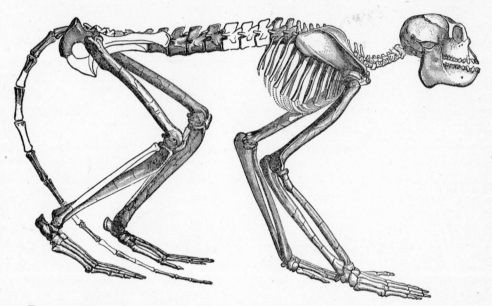

Fig. 357.—*Mesopithecus*, a Pliocene relative of the living langurs. About ⅓ natural size. (From Gaudry.)

group are good arboreal types. Remains of ancestral forms are widespread in the Pliocene of the Old World; *Mesopithecus* (Figs. 356a, 357) is known from the complete skeleton. While much like the living forms, the body was stouter and the legs shorter, pointing the way back to the ancestral cercopithecids.

Man-like apes.—These later Old World monkeys constitute two specialized lines neither of which can be considered as ancestral to the anthropoid apes or man. To follow this history we must return again to the Lower Oligocene beds of Egypt, in which has been found *Propliopithecus* (Figs. 354d, 356c), the oldest known ancestor of these more highly developed primates. Here, again, we have only a jaw to deal with; but, again, one that is quite characteristic. It is not more than an inch and a half in length, indicating a form much smaller than any living man-like ape. The lower molars are definitely five-cusped, in agreement with the great apes and in contrast with the living monkeys, and the jaw has the relatively great depth of the higher forms.

The family Simiidae, of which this is the earliest representative, includes four living types: the gibbon, the orang-utan, the chimpanzee, and the gorilla. They are of large size, ranging from the comparatively small gibbon to gorillas several times as heavy as a man. In the quadrangular molars a fifth cusp (hypoconulid) is well developed below, while in the upper teeth the hypocone is comparatively small, the old trigon still being apparent. The molars tend to be rather long, and there is some lengthening of the face. The skeleton is rather close to the human type. The chest is broad in contrast to that of the monkeys; the ilia tend to broaden, as in man. The hands are rather similar to those of man, but the fingers are very long as compared with the thumb, and the arms much lengthened. The legs, on the contrary, are short; and the hallux, as well as the remaining toes, are much better developed and more finger-like than in man. These skeletal characteristics have seemingly developed in relation to the anthropoid-ape type of locomotion. With increasing size, normal four-footed progression in the trees has become increasingly impossible; and the members of the group normally progress by swinging from bough to bough with the body suspended from the hands. The feet are used more than ever as grasping organs and have so much lost their primitive mammalian character that most great apes cannot walk flat on their soles but must support their weight on the outer side of the foot.

It will be noted that in swinging by the arms the body is necessarily erect. Further, the front legs of all forms being much longer than the hind legs, the body is necessarily tilted up considerably in front in quadrupedal progression. Bipedal locomotion has thus begun among the arboreal types.

The brain is large, especially in the gorilla. But, in these large forms its growth, as might be expected, has hardly kept up with the increasing body weight. Since the braincase is comparatively small, sagittal and occipital crests may develop and the upper margins of the orbits project in most forms as supraorbital ridges above the front edge of the braincase. There is, as in most mammals, no projecting chin, the jaw sloping away under the symphysis.

Gibbons.—Smallest and most primitive of the living anthropoids are the gibbons (*Hylobates*) of the Malay region. The average gibbon stands about 3 feet high in the erect position. Alone among the living anthropoids he customarily walks erect with the arms used as balancers. The gibbon, however, is almost entirely a tree-dweller and with his long arms, which can reach the ground in erect position, is a very clever acrobat. The bulk of the gibbon brain averages about 90 cubic centimeters. This seems a small figure compared with that of man but is far above the average for a mammal of that size. The braincase of the gibbon is practically smooth, and the supraorbital ridges small. Rudimentary ischial callosities are still present.

Pliopithecus, of the late Miocene of Europe, was very similar to the living gibbon in almost all known respects; and from this in turn it is a short step back to *Propliopithecus*, from which it is generally agreed that the gibbon is derived.

Orang-utan.—The orang-utan, *Simia*, the "man of the woods" of Sumatra and Borneo, stands next above the gibbon in the scale of living primates. Considerably larger in size (adult males reaching nearly 5 feet), the orang is still a true arboreal type and is but a clumsy four-footed performer on the ground; the arms are somewhat shorter, reaching only to the ankles. The brain here is vastly larger than that of the gibbon, reaching 550 cubic centimeters in capacity. The braincase is expanded, crests rarely develop, and the supraorbital ridges are negligible. The tooth row, however, is long and the snout projecting, with a characteristic concave lateral profile to the face. The only fossil remains which can be associated with the orang ancestry are some molar teeth from the Upper Miocene of India, known as *Palaeosimia*, which exhibit a wrinkling of the surface similar to that of the living form.

Higher anthropoid apes.—The highest living members of the anthropoid group are the chimpanzee (*Anthropopithecus* or *Pan*) and the *Gorilla*, both inhabitants of tropical Africa. It is generally agreed that these two forms are closely related. Both are less pronounced in their arboreal adaptations than the lower apes and monkeys; the gorillas spend most of their time on the ground, although walking as quadrupeds rather than bipeds. Both are large, the chimpanzee exceeding 5 feet in height and old male gorillas more than 6 feet with a weight of 600 pounds. The arms are short as compared with those of the lower anthropoids. Those of the chimpanzee reach a bit below the knee and those of the gorilla not quite so far. In both the brain is large, that of the gorilla having in some cases a capacity of 500 to 600 cubic centimeters, or at least half that found in some human races. Nevertheless, sagittal and occipital crests and supraorbital ridges tend to develop, being especially heavy in the old male gorillas. Associated with the long tooth row there is considerable development of a muzzle. The canines are enlarged, and the dental arcade is U-shaped with the molars in two parallel rows, in contrast with the hyperbolic-shaped tooth row of man. Among interesting details in which these forms agree with man is the absence of the centrale in the hand, a bone otherwise almost universally present in the order.

In the Miocene and Pliocene of Europe and India there is a considerable number of specimens seemingly representative of the higher anthropoids but of somewhat smaller size than the living chimpanzee or gorilla. Unfortunately, all are fragmentary; and even in the best-known form, *Dryopithecus* (Figs. 353c, 354e), we have little more than most of the lower jaw and the upper cheek teeth. These creatures were certainly anthropoid apes and not men, for the canines, where known, are enlarged and the dental arcade has the ape U-shape. Their characters, as far as known, would permit of their being ancestral to the chimpanzee and gorilla, and very probably they are close to the human line as well. It is to be hoped that future discoveries may yield further and more adequate remains of these forms, so interesting because of their possible relation to our own phylogeny.

Australopithecus.—Another fossil anthropoid ape of considerable interest is *Australopithecus* (Fig. 356d), known by a nearly complete skull from a deposit probably of Pleistocene age in South Africa. Unfortunately, the individual was a "child"; and it is, of course, difficult to determine its relationships on that account (infant apes have a comparatively large braincase and a much more human aspect than adults). It was clearly not a chimpanzee or a gorilla, but a distinct type of higher anthropoid. The contours of the skull suggest that the adult would have had a shorter face and higher forehead than the living great apes, while its teeth, as well, are somewhat more human in type than is the case with the chimpanzee or gorilla. *Australopithecus*, however, is probably too late in time to have been a true human ancestor.

Human characters.—Man and his close fossil relatives are usually placed in a separate family; but, as a matter of fact, the anatomical features which distinguish men from apes are comparatively few, although, from our own point of view, important. Of great significance has been the growth of the brain. The average European male has a brain capacity of about 1,500 cubic centimeters—much more than twice that of any of the great apes. This increase is mainly in the neopallium, the "gray matter" of the cerebral hemispheres. Here new centers are developed, such as those having to do with speech; and especially prominent are areas, absent in the apes, which seem to be the seat of higher human faculties. This enlargement of the brain results in a much expanded braincase and the consequent disappearance of crests and supraorbital ridges. The canines are reduced. The tooth row (Figs. 353d, 354f) is shorter and the face less projecting, while the nose and nasal bones are more prominent. Still another sequel of tooth-row reduction is the retention, to some extent, of the originally long jaw, which now projects as the chin.

Other important differences are associated with the change in locomotor habits. Even among the higher apes we have seen a trend toward terrestrial life; man lives on the ground as a biped. Man's arms are short compared with those of the apes; his legs, long. It is highly improbable that we have descended from such a long-armed, short-legged form as the orang but rather that, starting from a common ancestor with arms of rather indifferent length, the apes during millions of years of tree-living have elongated their arms to varying degrees, while man has retained more of the original proportions. The human hand, except for somewhat greater breadth and flexibility, is of a type probably present in the ancestral apes; the living great apes have tended to elongate the fingers, except the thumb, for hooking over limbs. A greater difference is in the foot. The usual primate foot is similar to the hand. This, however, is an awkward structure for ground life. In man the toes have greatly shortened, the hallux has lost its primitive oposibility, and the calcaneum expands to form a prop at the back (the last is true of the higher anthropoid apes as well). In further adaptation to the bipedal gait, the back of man is much more sinuously curved than in the apes, with the effect of swinging the center of gravity up above the hips and raising the head.

The features listed above are among those which distinguish modern human types from the apes. Fossil human types tend to bridge this structural gap and exhibit intermediate conditions; but our knowledge of human ancestors is still a very imperfect one, and we know almost nothing of the evolution of the postcranial skeleton.

It is probable that the human line diverged from that of the great apes at about the *Dryopithecus* stage, in late Miocene times. There are, however, no certain skeletal remains of man in the Pliocene; it is not until the early Pleistocene that we find man present and already branching out into a number of types. There are three interesting finds from the Old World which seemingly date from the early part of the glacial period.

The Java "ape man."—*Pithecanthropus erectus* (Fig. 358a) was discovered some four decades ago on the banks of a Javanese river near the little village of Trinil, associated with an abundant mammal fauna which appears to be of early or Middle Pleistocene date (it was originally thought to be older). The remains consist merely of the skull cap, thigh bones, a few teeth, and perhaps a fragment of jaw. The femur is straight, as in man, suggesting (as the specific name implies) that erect posture had already been gained at this time. The teeth seem to be essentially human; and the jaw fragment (doubtfully assigned and from another locality), while lacking a projecting chin, seems otherwise to conform to the human pattern. The braincase was low, particularly in the brow region, and the supraorbital ridges prominent. The cranial capacity was about 940 cubic centimeters and was thus intermediate between that of the highest anthropoids and the lowest average in existing human races (1,200 cubic centimeters). The structure of the brain, as indicated by casts of the skull interior, was human in pattern, although extremely primitive; it is even possible that speech was developed. The Java man was thus definitely human, but primitive and ape-like in many features.

Piltdown man.—Differing in many features was *Eoanthropus* (Fig. 358c), the "dawn man" of Piltdown, Sussex. The type comes from a gravel bed which appears to have been laid down in the early Pleistocene but contains some redeposited Pliocene fossils. The whole skull and jaw were probably present originally in the gravel pit, but only broken pieces were recovered. There is, however, sufficient material to reconstruct everything except the facial region with considerable accuracy. The skull was highly vaulted, although thick-walled; the supraorbital ridges were nearly as weak as in a modern man; and the cranial capacity of 1,200 cubic centimeters brings it within the limits of our own species. In contrast with this, however, the jaw was very ape-like, with a retreating chin, a canine which

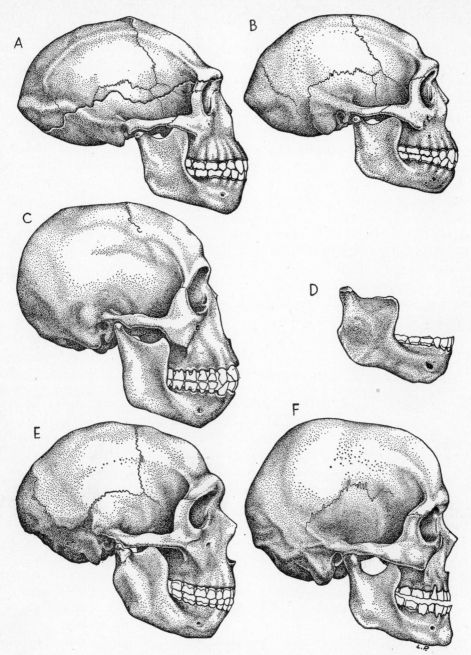

Fig. 358.—Skulls of fossil human types. *A, Pithecanthropus.* The face, braincase below the heavy line, and most of the jaw are restored. *B, Sinanthropus.* Face and back part of jaw restored. *C, Eoanthropus.* The face, some small areas of the braincase, and the tip of the jaw restored; the jaw doubtfully associated. *D,* The Heidelberg jaw. *E,* Neanderthal man. *F,* Cro-Magnon man from Grimaldi. (*A, E, F* after McGregor, *B* after Weinert, *Ursprung der Menschheit*, Ferdinand Enke, Stuttgart, *C* after Elliott Smith.)

projected above the other teeth, and other features which have led some writers to believe that the jaw really did not belong to the skull but was that of a chimpanzee. There are, however, no Pleistocene fossil chimpanzees in Europe; and strong evidence for the association of jaw and skull is afforded by the discovery nearby of a fragment of a second skull similar to the first, together with a tooth like those in the original jaw.

Peking man.—The most recent find of early Pleistocene man, and one which in some measure bridges the gap between the Trinil and Piltdown types, is that of *Sinanthropus* (Fig. 358*b*), of which a considerable amount of braincase and jaw material has been recovered from a cave deposit near Peking, China. Although there was no projecting chin, the jaw was of a more human type than that associated with the English find. The skull was thick walled, much as in *Eoanthropus;* but the vault was but little higher than that of *Pithecanthropus*, and there were well-developed supraorbital ridges. In bulk of brain the Chinese man was of an intermediate character, with a cranial capacity of from 1,000 to 1,100 cubic centimeters. Some fragmentary remains of the hand indicate that this was of a human, rather than an anthropoid-ape type.

The evidence of these finds shows us that at the beginning of the Pleistocene primitive men were already present in the Old World and were evolving along various lines. Of their postcranial skeletons we know almost nothing, and even the skulls are still imperfectly known. Fresh evidence will undoubtedly be forthcoming in the near future. In the meantime it is premature to form definite conclusions concerning the relationship of these early men to later human types.

Early human cultures.—Man is a maker and user of tools, and this trait may well have appeared early in his development. Flint is a material which appears to have found favor for tool-making because it is easily fractured and worked, although extremely hard. Flints, thought by some to have been used by man-like creatures, have been reported from Tertiary rocks. While such finds are of dubious nature, flints were certainly being worked in early Pleistocene times; and primitive implements have been found in the beds containing the Piltdown and Peking skulls. A whole series of culture stages constituting the Palaeolithic, or Old Stone Age, has been discovered in middle and late Pleistocene deposits in Europe. These were times when man was able to work flints and bone into useful tools and weapons but was not only ignorant of the use of metals but knew nothing of agriculture, pottery, or domestication of animals. The Middle Pleistocene stages of the Old Stone Age, the Chellean and Acheulean cultures, were characterized by the presence of a large and well-shaped tool, the *coup de poing*, or hand ax. Almost nothing is known of the makers of these implements, for they lived mainly in open-air camps rather than caves in which burials might be expected.

Heidelberg jaw.—Probably to these early times may be assigned the jaw (Fig. 358*d*) found in a gravel pit near the city of Heidelberg. The teeth and many other features of the specimen are typically human, so that the form is usually placed in the modern genus *Homo;* but the jaw was extraordinarily massive (more so than in any living race), and there was still no chin, the front edge descending steeply from the tooth row. The specimen is consequently considered as representing a different species from our own, *Homo heidelbergensis,* but except for its size, is fairly similar to the jaw of Neanderthal man.

Neanderthal man.—Dating from the last glaciation and from a warmer period preceding it is the
Mousterian culture, characterized by excellent
flake tools rather than hand axes. Definitely associated with this culture is Neanderthal man,
Homo neanderthalensis (Figs. 358e, 359). This
form is known not only from the original German
locality from which the name is derived but also
from many other regions of Europe. The brain
had as high a cranial capacity as most living men
(averaging about 1,550 cubic centimeters for
males). This was mostly accounted for by the
expansion in the occipital region of the brain, for
the forehead was low and the supraorbital ridges
greatly developed. These features, together with
a face more elongate than in modern men and the
undeveloped chin, must have given the creature
in life a very ape-like appearance. Here, for the
first time, complete skeletal remains are known.
The body was slightly stooped, the knees always
slightly bent, and in other details (despite the
relatively late date) there is still much suggestion
of the creature's ape ancestors. A Neanderthaloid type said to be somewhat closer to modern man in the development of the chin and other
features has recently been discovered in Palestine, but has not yet been described in detail.

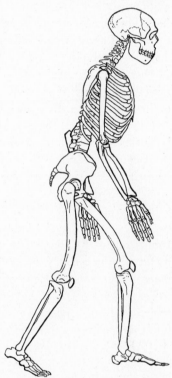

FIG. 359.—Skeleton of Neanderthal man. (After Weinert's *Ursprung der Menschheit,* Ferdinand Enke, Stuttgart.)

Modern man.—As the last glaciation drew to a close in Europe, there appeared a new series of cultures, the Upper Paleolithic—Aurignacian followed briefly by the Solutrean and Magdalenian. In these stages bone was used to a considerable extent; and the men of the time possessed a high degree of artistic talent, shown in the mural engravings and paintings of rock shelters.

At this comparatively late date (not more than 20,000 years ago at the outside) we find, for the first time in Europe, a modern type of man unquestionably to be assigned to our own species, *Homo sapiens.* In such a race as the Cro-Magnon type (Fig. 358f) associated with the Aurignacian culture the forehead was high, the cranial capacity about 1,500 cubic centimeters, the supraorbital ridges gone, the face short, the nose well developed, and the chin protruding.

These newcomers were not in all probability descendants of typical Neanderthal man. Probably the two were merely successive invaders of Europe, representing two waves of migration from an Asiatic (or African) center of human evolution and dispersion. It is not improbable, however, that the ancestor of modern man may have been a creature with many Neanderthaloid features, and the Palestine find mentioned above may perhaps be close to the common stock of these two forms.

With the coming of this truly modern type, our story may properly cease. The further story of racial differentiation and of the development by man of pottery, agriculture, weaving, domesticated animals, and metals belongs to the realm of the archeologist and anthropologist rather than to that of the paleontologist.

Extra-European types.—Our story of later human evolution has been told mainly on the basis of European discoveries. This is merely because this region has been more carefully studied than other sections of the Old World; the other portions of Eurasia and Africa have, as yet, been little explored but are beginning to yield many interesting finds.

The earlier Paleolithic cultures were widespread in Asia and Africa, although almost no skeletal remains have been found associated with them. In Africa a skull from Broken Hill, Rhodesia, seems to be of a very primitive type, presenting, in its heavy supraorbital ridges and massive face and jaws, analogies to Neanderthal man. Men similar to those of the European Aurignacian have been found in East Africa, associated with that culture at a date seemingly much earlier than that of their European appearance. The circumstances of the find appear to render it certain that they were contemporaries of makers of Mousterian flints. This suggests that Africa was the center of human evolution. There are, however, many who believe that Asia was the more probable center of dispersal.

Several skulls from Southern Africa may be related to the ancestry of the bushmen of that region, and types representing early races have been discovered in Australia and the East Indies.

The time of arrival of man in America has been a question of some interest. There is here no series of cultures comparable to those of the Old World, and no skeletons have been discovered which show marked differences from the modern Indian. Very probably man reached America only after the last retreat of the glaciers. But his arrival must have occurred at an early post-glacial date, for finds in the Southwestern United States and in South America show that he was present at a time when ground sloths, horses, camels, and other types now extinct were still in existence in the Western Hemisphere.

A SYNOPTIC CLASSIFICATION OF VERTEBRATES

In general the classification given below includes families as well as higher groups, except in certain cases (as the teleosts and birds) where families are exceedingly numerous and of comparatively little paleontological interest. A number of the more common or more familiar genera are listed. The geological and geographical range of each family (or higher group) is given. The portion of this range covered by the genera listed is specified, as far as necessary. If indication of either geographical or stratigraphic limits, or both, is omitted for a genus, its range is presumably that of the family (or higher group) to which it is assigned.

ABBREVIATIONS.—*Geological:* Carb., Carboniferous; Cret., Cretaceous; Dev., Devonian; Eoc., Eocene; Jur., Jurassic; L., Lower; M., Middle; Mioc., Miocene; Miss., Mississippian; Olig., Oligocene; Ord., Ordovician; Paleoc., Paleocene; Penn., Pennsylvanian; Perm., Permian; Pleist., Pleistocene; Plioc., Pliocene; R., Recent; Sil., Silurian; Tert., Tertiary; Trias., Triassic; U., Upper.

Geographical: Af., Africa; Ant., Antarctica; As., Asia; Aus., Australia; Cos., Cosmopolitan; EInd., East Indies; Eu., Europe; Gr., Greenland; Mad., Madagascar; NA., North America; NZ., New Zealand; Oc., oceans; SAf., South Africa; SA., South America; WInd., West Indies.

CLASS AGNATHA

ORDER HETEROSTRACI. **Family Pteraspidae,** U. Sil.–L. Dev. Eu., U. Sil. NA., *Palaeaspis* U. Sil., *Pteraspis Cyathaspis.* **Family Drepanaspidae.** Dev. Eu. NA. Aus., *Drepanaspis* L. Dev. Eu., *Phyllolepis* U. Dev. **Family Thelodontidae,** U. Sil.–Dev. Eu., Dev. NA., *Lanarkia* U. Sil., *Thelodus.*

ORDER OSTEOSTRACI. **Family Cephalaspidae,** U. Sil.–U. Dev. Eu., Dev. NA. Aus., *Cephalaspis* Eu. NA. **Family Tremataspidae,** U. Sil. Eu., *Tremataspis.* **Family Ateleaspidae,** U. Sil. Eu., *Ateleaspis.*
Of uncertain position: **Family Astraspidae,** M. Ord. NA., *Astraspis.*

ORDER ANASPIDA. **Family Birkeniidae,** U. Sil. Eu. NA., *Birkenia Pterolepis Pharyngolepis Rhyncholepis* Eu. **Family Lasaniidae,** U. Sil. Eu., *Lasanius.*

ORDER PALAEOSPONDYLOIDEA M. Dev. Eu., *Palaeospondylus.*

ORDER CYCLOSTOMATA. SUBORDER PETROMYZONTIA R., *Petromyzon.* SUBORDER MYXINOIDEA R. *Myxine Bdellostoma.*

CLASS PLACODERMI

ORDER ARTHRODIRA. SUBORDER ACANTHASPIDOIDIA, L.–M. Dev. Eu. NA., *Phlyctaenaspis Jaekelaspis* L. Dev., *Acanthaspis* M. Dev. SUBORDER COCCOSTEOIDIA, M.–U. Dev. Eu. NA. *Brachydirus Pachyosteus* U. Dev. Eu., *Dinichthys Titanichthys Mylostoma Dinomylostoma* U. Dev. NA., *Coccosteus.* SUBORDER HOMOSTEOIDIA M. Dev. Eu., *Homosteus Heterosteus.* SUBORDER PTYCTODONTOIDIA U. Dev.–L. Miss. NA., U. Dev. Eu., *Rhynchodus* U. Dev., *Ptyctodus.*

ORDER ANTIARCHI. **Family Asterolepidae.** M.–U. Dev. Eu., U. Dev. As. NA. Aus. Ant., *Pterich-thys Asterolepis* M. Dev., *Bothriolepis* U. Dev. **Family Remigolepidae,** U. Dev. Gr., *Remigolepis.*

CLASS CHONDRICHTHYES

ORDER ACANTHODII. **Family Diplacanthidae,** U. Sil.–L. Dev. Eu. NA., *Diplacanthus Parexus* Dev., Eu., *Climatius* Dev., *Onchus.* **Family Acanthodidae,** L. Dev.–L. Perm. Eu., U. Dev.–Perm. NA., U. Dev. Aus. Ant., *Cheiracanthus* Dev. Eu. Ant. *Acanthodes* Perm. **Family Ischnacanthidae,** L. Dev. Eu., *Ischnacanthus.*

Of uncertain position: **Family Gyracanthidae,** Dev. Carb. NA., Carb. Eu. Aus., *Gyracanthus* Carb. **Family Onychodontidae,** M. Dev. Eu. NA. Ant., *Onychodus.*

ORDER STEGOSELACHII, M. Dev. NA. Eu., Miss. Eu., *Macropetalichthys* M. Dev., *Cratoselache* Miss.

ORDER CLADOSELACHII. **Family Ctenacanthidae,** U. Dev.–L. Perm. NA., Carb. Eu., *Ctenacanthus.* **Family Cladoselachidae,** U. Dev. Carb. NA., Carb. Eu., *Cladoselache* U. Dev. **Family Symmoriidae,** Carb. NA. Eu., *Symmorium* NA., "*Cladodus*" Eu.

ORDER PLEURACANTHODII, U. Dev.–L. Perm. NA., Carb.–L. Perm. Eu., *Pleuracanthus* Carb.–Perm.

ORDER ELASMOBRANCHII

SUBORDER SELACHII

SUPERFAMILY HETERODONTOIDEA. **Family Heterodontidae,** Carb.–Cret. NA., Carb.–Eoc. Eu., Carb. As. Aus., Cret. NA., Trias.–Cret. Af., R. Pacific., *Orodus Edestus* Carb., *Helicoprion* Perm. Eu., *Hybodus* Trias.–L. Cret. Eu., *Acrodus* Trias.–U. Cret. Eu. Trias. Af. U. Cret. NA., *Heterodontus (Cestracion)* Jur.–Eoc. Eu. Cret. Af. R.

SUPERFAMILY NOTIDANOIDEA. **Family Chlamydoselachidae,** Plioc. Eu., R. Oc. *Chlamydoselachus.* **Family Notidanidae,** M. Jur.–Ter. Eu., Jur. NZ., R. Oc., *Notidanus.*

SUPERFAMILY LAMNOIDEA. **Family Scylliidae,** U. Jur.–Tert. Eu., Cret.–Tert. As., NA., Tert. Af., R. Oc., *Scyllium* Cret.–R. **Family Lamnidae,** M. Jur.–Tert. Eu., Cret. As., Cret.–Tert. NA. Af., R. Oc., *Lamna Oxyrhina* Cret.–R., *Odontaspis Carcharodon* Tert.–R. **Family Carchariidae,** Tert. Eu. NA. As. Af., R. Oc., *Carcharias Galeocerdo Sphyrna.*

SUPERFAMILY SQUALOIDEA. **Family Squalidae,** U. Jur.–Tert. Eu., Cret. As., Mioc. NZ., R. Oc., *Squalus* Cret.–R. **Family Pristiophoridae,** U. Jur. Eu., Cret. As., R. Oc., *Pristiophorus* Cret.–R.

SUBORDER BATOIDEA. **Family Squatinidae,** U. Jur.–Tert. Eu., U. Cret. As., R. Oc., *Squatina.* **Family Rhinobatidae,** U. Jur.–Tert. Eu., U. Cret. As., R. Oc., *Rhinobatis.* **Family Pristidae,** U. Cret. NA. As. Af., Eoc. Af., Tert. Eu. NA., R. Oc., *Sclerorhynchus* U. Cret. As., *Propristis* Af., *Pristis* Tert.–R. **Family Rajidae,** U. Jur.–Tert. Eu., U. Cret.–Tert. As., Tert. NA. SA., R. Oc., *Raja.* **Family Torpedinidae,** Tert. Eu., R. Oc., *Torpedo.* **Family Trygonidae,** U. Cret. Tert. As. Eu. NA., Tert. Af., R. Oc., *Ptychodus* Cret., *Xiphotrygon* Eoc. NA., *Trygon* Tert. Eu. R., *Myliobatis.*

ORDER RHENANIDA, L. Dev. Eu., *Gemundina.*

ORDER BRADYODONTI. **Family Petalodontidae,** U. Dev.–Carb. NA., Carb.–Perm. Eu., *Petalodus Dactylodus* Carb., *Janassa* Perm. **Family Cochliodontidae,** Carb.–U. Perm. Eu., U. Dev.–Carb. NA., *Cochliodus Deltodus* Carb., *Menaspis* Perm. **Family Psammodontidae,** Carb. Eu. NA., *Psammodus.* **Famiiy Copodontidae,** Carb. Eu. NA., *Copodus.*

ORDER HOLOCEPHALI. **Family Squalorajidae,** M. Trias.–L. Jur. Eu., *Squaloraja* L. Jur. **Family Myriacanthidae,** Jur.–Cret. Eu., *Myriacanthus Acanthostoma* Jur., *Ischyodus.* **Family**

Chimaeridae, M. Jur.–Tert. Eu., Cret. NA. NZ., R. Oc., *Ganodus Edaphodon* Cret.–
Tert., *Chimaera* Eoc.–R.

CLASS OSTEICHTHYES
SUBCLASS ACTINOPTERYGII

ORDER CHONDROSTEI

SUBORDER PALAEONISCOIDEA. **Family Palaeoniscidae,** M. Dev.–L. Cret. Eu., U. Dev.–L.
Perm. NA., M. Perm.–L. Trias. SAf., Trias. Aus., *Cheirolepis* Dev., *Eurynotus* Miss.,
Rhadinichthys Elonichthys Carb., *Amblypterus* L. Perm. Eu., *Palaeoniscus* U. Perm.
Eu., *Gyrolepis* Trias. Eu. **Family Platysomidae,** Miss.–U. Perm. Eu., Penn.–L. Perm.
NA., Perm. SAf. Mad., *Cheirodus* Penn. Eu., *Platysomus* Penn.–Perm. **Family Dorypte-
ridae,** U. Perm. Eu. *Dorypterus.* **Family Catopteridae,** Trias. NA. SA. Aus., *Catopterus*
NA. **Family Perleididae,** Trias. Eu. SAf. Aus. NA., *Helichthys* SAf., *Perliedus* Eu.

SUBORDER POLYPTERINI, Eoc.–R. Af., *Polypterus Calamoichthys* R.

SUBORDER BELONORHYNCHOIDEA, Trias.–L. Jur. Eu., Trias. Aus., *Saurichthys* Trias. Eu., *Belonorhynchus.*

SUBORDER ACIPENSEROIDEA. **Family Chondrosteidae,** L. Jur. Eu., *Chondrosteus.* **Family Aci-
penseridae,** Eoc.–R. Eu., R. As. NA., *Acipenser.* **Family Polyodontidae,** U. Cret. Eu.,
Eoc.–R. NA., R. As., *Crossopholis* Eoc., *Polyodon* R. NA.

ORDER HOLOSTEI

SUBORDER SEMIONOTOIDEA. **Family Semionotidae,** U. Perm.–L. Cret. Eu., Trias. NA., Trias.–
Jur. Aus., Trias.–Cret. Af., Cret. SA. As., *Acentrophorus* Perm., *Semionotus* Trias.,
Dapedius U. Trias.–L. Jur. Eu. U. Trias. As., *Lepidotus* Jur.–Cret. **Family Pycno-
dontidae,** Jur.–Eoc. Eu., Cret. NA. SA. As., *Gyrodus* Jur.–Cret. Eu., *Microdon* Jur.
Eu. L. Cret. NA., *Mesodon* Jur. Eu., *Pycnodus* U. Cret. Eoc. Eu. **Family Lepidos-
teidae,** Eoc.–Mioc. Eu., Eoc.–R. NA., Eoc. As., *Lepidosteus.*

SUBORDER AMIOIDEA. **Family Macrosemiidae,** U. Trias.–U. Cret. Eu., U. Cret. As., *Macro-
semius* Jur. **Family Eugnathidae,** M. Trias.–U. Cret. Eu., U. Trias.–L. Cret. NA., L.
Jur. As., *Caturus Eugnathus* Jur. **Family Amiidae,** U. Jur.–Mioc. Eu., Cret. SA., Eoc.–
R. NA., *Amiopsis Megalurus* Jur., *Amia* Eoc.–R. **Family Pachycormidae,** L. Jur.–
U. Cret. Eu., U. Cret. NA. SA., *Pachycormus Hypsocormus* Jur., *Protosphyraena* Cret.

SUBORDER PHOLIDOPHOROIDEA. **Family Pholidophoridae,** M. Trias.–L. Cret. Eu., Trias. Aus.,
Jur. NZ., *Pholidophorus* M. Trias.–L. Cret. Eu., *Pleuropholis* Jur. Eu. **Family Oligo-
pleuridae,** U. Jur.–L. Cret. Eu., U. Cret. As., *Oligopleurus* Jur.

Of uncertain position: **Family Aspidorhynchidae,** Jur.–Cret. Eu., Cret. As. Aus.
NA. SA., *Aspidorhynchus* Eu., *Belonostomus* Cret.

ORDER TELEOSTEI. SUBORDER ISOSPONDYLI, U. Trias.–R. Eu., Jur.–R. As., Cret.–R. NA. SA.
Aus., Eoc.–R. Af., R. Oc., *Leptolepis* U. Jur.–Cret. Eu., *Portheus* Cret. NA., *Osme-
roides* Cret. Eu., *Clupea* Tert. Eu. R. Oc., *Diplomystus* Eoc. NA., *Albula* Eoc. Eu. R.
Oc. SUBORDER OSTARIOPHYSI, Eoc.–R. Eu. NA., Tert.–R. SA., Plio.–R. As. Af., *Silurus*
Mioc.–R. Eu. R. As., *Leuciscus* Mioc.–R. Eu., *Arius* Eoc. Eu. Eoc.–R. Af., *Amiurus*
Eoc.–R. NA. R. As. SUBORDER APODES, U. Cret.–R. Eu. As., R. Oc., *Urenchelys* U.
Cret. As., *Anguilla* Eoc.–Mioc. Eu., R. SUBORDER PERCESOCES, Cret.–R. Eu. As. NA.,
R. Oc., *Sphyraena* Eoc.–Mioc. SUBORDER HEMIBRANCHII, Cret.–R. As., Eoc.–R. Eu.,
R. Oc., *Amphisyle* Olig. Eu. R. Oc., *Siphonostoma* Mioc. Eu. R. Oc. SUBORDER ANA-
CANTHINI, Eoc.–R. Eu. NA., R. Oc., *Gadus.* SUBORDER ACANTHOPTERYGII, Cret.–R.
Eu. As. NA., Eoc.–R. Af., R. SA. Oc., *Beryx* Cret.–R., *Trigla Serranus* Eoc.–Mioc.

Eu. R. *Labrodon.* Eoc.–Plioc. Eu., *Thynnus* Eoc.–R. Eu. *Semiophorus* Eoc. Eu., R., *Coelorhynchus* Eoc. Eu. Af., *Solea* Mioc. Eu. R.

SUBCLASS CROSSOPTERYGII

ORDER RHIPIDISTIA. **Family Osteolepidae,** ?L. Dev. M. Dev.–Carb. Eu., ?L. Dev. NA., Dev. Ant., *Osteolepis* M. Dev. Eu., *Megalichthys* Carb. **Family Holoptychiidae,** U. Dev. Eu. NA. Ant., *Glyptolepis Dendrodus* Eu., *Holoptychius.* **Family Rhizodontidae,** M. Dev.– Carb. Eu., U. Dev.–L. Perm. NA., *Sauripterus Eusthenopteron* U. Dev. NA., *Rhizodus* Carb.–L. Perm. NA.

ORDER COELACANTHINI, U. Dev.–Cret. Eu., Carb.–Trias. NA., L. Trias. SAf., *Diplocercides* Dev., *Coelacanthus* Carb.–Trias., *Wimania Alexia* Trias. Eu., *Undina* Jur., *Macropoma* Cret. Eu.

SUBCLASS DIPNOI

Family Dipteridae, M.–U. Dev. Eu. NA., *Dipterus.* **Family Ctenodontidae,** U. Dev.– Perm. Eu. NA., *Phaneropleuron* U. Dev. Eu., *Scaumanacia* U. Dev. NA., *Ctenodus Sagenodus* Carb.–L. Perm. **Family Ceratodontidae.** Trias.–Cret. Eu. As. Af. NA., Trias.–R. Aus., *Ceratodus* Trias.–Cret., *Neoceratodus* R. **Family Uronemidae,** Carb.– Perm. Eu. NA., *Uronemus* Carb. **Family Lepidosirenidae,** Tert.–R. Af., R. SA., *Lepidosiren* SA., *Protopterus* AF.

CLASS AMPHIBIA

ORDER LABYRINTHODONTIA

SUBORDER EMBOLOMERI. **Family Otocratiidae,** U. Miss. Eu., *Otocratia.* **Family Palaeogyrinidae,** Penn. Eu., *Paleogyrinus.* **Family Cricotidae,** Miss.–L. Perm. Eu., Penn.–L. Perm. NA., *Anthracosaurus* Miss., *Eogyrinus* Penn. Eu., *Cricotus* U. Penn.–L. Perm. NA., *Diplovertebron* U. Penn. Eu. **Family Pholidogasteridae,** U. Miss. Eu., *Pholidogaster.* **Family Loxommidae,** Miss.–Penn. Eu., Penn. NA., *Loxomma* Miss., *Orthosaurus Baphetes* Penn.

SUBORDER RHACHITOMI. **Family Eryopidae,** U. Penn.–L. Perm. Eu. NA., *Eryops* NA. **Family Rhinesuchidae,** M. Perm.–L. Trias. SAf., L. Trias. Eu., *Rhinesuchus* Perm. **Family Dissorhophidae,** L. Perm. NA., *Cacops Dissorhophus.* **Family Trematopsidae,** L. Perm. NA., *Trematops.* **Family Archegosauridae,** L. Perm. Eu. NA., *Archegosaurus* Eu. **Family Trimerorhachidae,** L. Perm. NA., *Trimerorhachis.* **Family Micropholidae,** L. Trias. SAf., *Micropholis.* **Family Cochleosauridae,** U. Penn. Eu., *Cochleosaurus.* **Family Dwinasauridae,** U. Perm. Eu., *Dwinasaurus.*

SUBORDER STEREOSPONDYLI. **Family Capitosauridae,** Trias. Eu. SAf. Aus., *Capitosaurus* Eu. SAf., *Cyclotosaurus.* **Family Trematosauridae,** Trias. Eu. SAf., *Trematosaurus* Eu. **Family Metoposauridae,** U. Trias. Eu., M.–U. Trias. NA., *Metoposaurus* Eu. *Anaschisma* NA. **Family Mastodonsauridae,** Trias. Eu., *Mastodonsaurus.* **Family Brachyopidae,** Trias. Eu. As. Aus. SAf., *Brachyops* As., *Plagiosternum Plagiosaurus* Eu.

ORDER LEPOSPONDYLI

SUBORDER MICRAMPHIBIA, Penn. Eu. NA., *Microbrachis* Eu.

SUBORDER LYSOROPHIA, U. Miss. Eu., Penn.–L. Perm. NA., *Adelogyrinus* U. Miss., *Lysorophus* L. Perm.

SUBORDER AISTOPODA, **Family Ophiderpetontidae,** ?U. Miss. Penn. Eu., Penn. NA., *Ophiderpeton* Penn. **Family Dolichosomidae,** Penn. Eu. NA., *Dolichosoma* Eu.

SUBORDER NECTRIDIA, **Family Urocordylidae,** Penn. Eu., Penn.–L. Perm. NA., *Urocordylus* Eu., *Sauropleura* Penn. NA. **Family Ceraterpetontidae,** Penn. Eu. NA., *Ceraterpeton* Eu. **Family Diplocaulidae,** L. Perm. NA., *Diplocaulus.*

ORDER PHYLLOSPONDYLI, **Family Ichthyostegidae,** U. Dev. Gr., *Ichthyostega Ichthyostegopsis.* **Family Colosteidae,** Penn. NA., *Colosteus Erpetosaurus.* **Family Peliontidae,** Penn. Eu. NA., *Eugyrinus* Eu., *Pelion* NA. **Family Branchiosauridae,** Penn.–L. Perm. Eu., *Branchiosaurus.* **Family Zatrachyidae,** Penn.–L. Perm. NA., L. Perm. Eu., *Stegops* Penn., *Zatrachys* Perm. NA.

ORDER URODELA (CAUDATA)

SUBORDER CRYPTOBRANCHOIDEA. **Family Hynobiidae,** R. As., *Hynobius.* **Family Cryptobran-chidae,** Olig.–Mioc. Eu., Plioc.–R. NA., R. As., *Megalobatrachus (Andrias)* Eu. As., *Cryptobranchus* R. NA.

Of uncertain position: *Hylaeobatrachus* L. Cret. Eu.

SUBORDER AMBLYSTOMOIDEA. **Family Amblystomidae,** R. NA., *Amblystoma*

SUBORDER SALAMANDROIDEA. **Family Salamandridae,** Olig.–R. Eu., R. As. Af. NA., *Sala-mandra* Eu., *Triturus* Mioc. Eu. R. **Family Amphiumidae,** R. NA., *Amphiuma.* **Family Plethodontidae,** R. NA. SA. Eu., *Plethodon* NA.

SUBORDER PROTEIDA. **Family Proteidae,** R. Eu. NA., *Proteus* Eu., *Necturus* NA.

SUBORDER MEANTES. **Family Sirenidae,** R. NA., *Siren.*

ORDER ANURA (SALIENTIA)

SUBORDER AMPHICOELA. **Family Lipelmidae,** R. NA. NZ.

Of uncertain position: *Montsechobatrachus* U. Jur. Eu., *Eobatrachus* U. Jur. NA.

SUBORDER OPISTHOCOELA. **Family Discoglossidae,** Olig.–R. Eu., R. As., *Discoglossus* ?Mioc. R. **Family Pipidae,** R. Af. SA., *Pipa* SA.

SUBORDER ANOMOCOELA. **Family Pelobatidae,** Olig.–R. As., Mioc.–R. Eu., R. NA., *Pelobates* Eu.

SUBORDER PROCOELA. **Family Palaeobatrachidae,** ?Jur.–Mioc. Eu., *Palaeobatrachus* Mioc. **Family Bufonidae,** Eoc.–R. As., Mioc.–R. Eu., Pleist.–R. SA., R. NA. Af. Aus., *Bufo* R. Eu. As. Af. NA. SA. **Family Brachycephalidae,** R. SA. **Family Hylidae,** Mioc.–R. Eu., R. Cos., *Hyla.*

SUBORDER DIPLASIOCOELA. **Family Ranidae,** Mioc.–R. Eu., R. Cos., *Rana.* **Family Polype-detidae,** R. As. Af. **Family Brevicipetidae,** R. As. Af. Aus. NA. SA.

ORDER APODA (GYMNOPHIONA), R. As. Af. SA., *Ichthyophis* As., *Typhlonectes* SA.

CLASS REPTILIA
SUBCLASS ANAPSIDA

ORDER COTYLOSAURIA

SUBORDER SEYMOURIAMORPHA. **Family Seymouriidae,** U. Penn. Eu., L. Perm. NA., *Sey-mouria* NA. **Family Kotlassiidae,** U. Perm. Eu., *Kotlassia.*

Of uncertain position: **Family Eosauravidae,** Penn. NA., *Eosauravus.*

SUBORDER DIADECTOMORPHA. **Family Diadectidae,** U. Penn.–L. Perm. NA., L. Perm. Eu., *Diadectes Diasparactus* NA. **Family Pareiasauridae,** M.–U. Perm. SAf., U. Perm. Eu., *Bradysaurus Embrithosaurus* M. Perm. SAf., *Pareiasaurus* U. Perm., *Elginia* Eu. **Family Procolophontidae,** L. Trias. SAf. Eu., Trias. NA., *Procolophon* SAf., *Telerpe-ton* Eu.

SUBORDER CAPTORHINOMORPHA. **Family Limnoscelidae,** U. Penn. or L. Perm. NA., *Limnos-celis.* **Family Captorhinidae,** L. Perm. NA., *Captorhinus Labidosaurus.* **Family Panty-lidae,** L. Perm. NA., *Pantylus.*

ORDER CHELONIA

SUBORDER EUNOTOSAURIA, M. Perm. SAf., *Eunotosaurus.*

SUBORDER AMPHICHELYDIA. **Family Triassochelyidae,** U. Trias. Eu., *Triassochelys Progano-chelys.* **Family Pleurosternidae,** U. Jur.–Cret. Eu., Cret.–L. Eoc. NA., *Pleurosternum* Jur., *Baëna* NA. **Family Thalassemyidae,** U. Jur.–Eoc. Eu., U. Cret. NA., *Thalassemys Eruysternum* U. Jur., *Desmatochelys* NA. **Family Plesiochelyidae,** U. Jur.–L. Cret. Eu., *Plesiochelys.*

SUBORDER PLEURODIRA. **Family Pelomedusidae,** U. Cret. NA., Eoc. Eu., Eoc.–R. Af., R. SA., *Podocnemis* Eoc.–R. **Family Chelydidae,** Eoc. As., Pleist.–R. Aus., R. SA., *Chelodina* Aus. **Family Miolaniidae,** ?U. Cret. SA., Pleist. Aus., *Miolania.*

SUBORDER CRYPTODIRA. **Family Dermatemydidae,** U. Cret.–R. NA. As., Olig. Eu., Eoc. Af., R. SA., *Dermatemys.* **Family Chelydridae,** Mioc. Eu., Mioc.–R. NA., R. EInd., *Chelydra* Eu. NA. **Family Testudinidae,** U. Cret.–R. NA. As., Eoc.–R. Eu., Olig.–R. SAf., R. SA., *Emys* Eoc.–R., *Stylemys* Olig. NA., *Testudo* Olig.–R. **Family Cheloniidae,** U. Cret.–Mioc. NA., U. Cret.–Olig. Eu., R. Oc., *Protostega Archelon Toxochelys* U. Cret. NA., *Chelone* Olig.–R. Eu. **Family Dermochelyidae,** Eoc. Af., Eoc.–Plioc. Eu., Mioc. NA., *Psephophorus* Eoc.–Plioc., *Dermochelys* R. **Family Trionychidae,** U. Cret.–R. NA. SA. As., Tert. Eu., Tert.–R. Af. As., *Plastomenus* U. Cret. NA., *Trionyx Amyda* Tert.–R.

SUBCLASS ICHTHYOPTERYGIA (validity doubtful)

ORDER MESOSAURIA, U. Penn. SAf. SA., *Stereosternum* SA., *Mesosaurus.*

ORDER ICHTHYOSAURIA. **Family Ichthyosauridae,** M. Trias.–L. Cret. Eu. NA., L. Cret. ?Cos., *Mixosaurus* Trias., *Eurypterygius Ichthyosaurus* Jur., *Ophthalmosaurus* U. Jur.–L. Cret. **Family Stenopterygiidae,** M. Trias.–L. Cret. Eu. NA., ?L. Cret. Cos., *Shastasaurus* Trias. NA., *Stenopterygius Lepteryoptgius Eurhinosaurus* Jur. **Family Omphalosauridae,** M. Trias. Eu. NA., *Omphalosaurus.*

SUBCLASS SYNAPTOSAURIA (validity doubtful)

ORDER PROTOROSAURIA (validity doubtful). **Family Araeoscelidae,** L. Perm. Eu. NA., *Araeoscelis* NA. **Family Broomiidae,** M. Perm. SAf., *Broomia.* **Family Protorosauridae,** U. Perm. Eu., *Protorosaurus.* **Family Pleurosauridae,** U. Jur. Eu., *Pleurosaurus.*

ORDER SAUROPTERYGIA

SUBORDER TRACHELOSAURIA, L. Trias. Eu., *Trachelosaurus.*

SUBORDER TANYSTROPHAEA, M. Trias. Eu., *Tanystrophaeus.*

SUBORDER NOTHOSAURIA. **Family Pachypleurosauridae,** M. Trias. Eu., *Simosaurus Neusticosaurus.* **Family Nothosauridae,** M. Trias. Eu., *Nothosaurus Lariosaurus Ceresiosaurus.*

SUBORDER PLESIOSAURIA. **Family Plesiosauridae,** U. Trias.–Jur. Eu., Jur.–Cret. NA., ?Cret. NZ., *Plesiosaurus* ?U. Trias. Jur. Eu., *Muraenosaurus* Jur. Eu., *Elasmosaurus* U. Cret. NA. **Family Pliosauridae,** Jur. Eu. As., U. Cret. NA. Aus., *Thaumatosaurus Peloneustes Pliosaurus* Jur. Eu., *Trinacromerum Brachauchenius* NA.

SUBORDER PLACODONTIA. **Family Placodontidae,** M.–U. Trias. Eu., *Placodus.* **Family Cyamodontidae,** M.–U. Trias. Eu., *Cyamodus Placochelys.*

SUBCLASS LEPIDOSAURIA (validity doubtful)

ORDER EOSUCHIA (validity doubtful). **Family Younginidae,** U. Perm. SAf., *Youngina.* **Family Proterosuchidae,** Trias. SAf., *Proterosuchus.* **Family Paliguanidae,** U. Perm.–L.Trias. SAf., *Palaeagama* U. Perm., *Paliguana* L. Trias. **Family Howesiidae,** L. Trias. SAf., *Howesia.* **Family Palaeochameleontidae,** U. Perm. Eu. Mad., *Palaeochameleo* Eu.

Family Saurosternidae, U. Perm. Af., *Saurosternum.* Family Thalattosauridae, Trias. NA., *Thalattosaurus.* Family Saphaeosauridae, U. Jur. Eu., *Saphaeosaurus.*

ORDER RHYNCHOCEPHALIA. Family Rhynchosauridae, M.–U. Trias. Eu. As., L. Trias. SAf. SA., *Rhynchosaurus* Eu., *Hyperodapedon* Eu. As., *Scaphonyx* SA. Family Sphenodontidae, Trias. Eu. SAf., U. Jur. Eu. NA., R. NZ., *Palacrodon* SAf., *Homaeosaurus* Jur. Eu., *Sphenodon* R. Family Champsosauridae, U. Cret.–L. Eoc. Eu. NA., *Champsosaurus.*

ORDER SQUAMATA

SUBORDER LACERTILIA

INFRAORDER KIONOCRANIA. Family Geckonidae, L. Cret. Eu., R. Cos., *Ardaeosaurus* L. Cret., *Gecko* R. Family Agamidae, Olig. Eu., Pleist.–R. Aus., R. Af., *Agama* Eu. As. Af. Family Iguanidae, Eoc.–R. NA., Eoc. Eu., R. SA., *Iguana.* Family Xantusiidae, R. NA., *Xantusia.* Family Lacertidae, Mioc.–R. Eu., R. As. Af., *Lacerta.* Family Tejidae, U. Cret.–R. NA., R. SA., *Tupinambis* R. Family Scincidae, Eoc.–R. Eu., R. Cos., *Scincus* As. Af. Family Helodermatidae, Eoc.–R. NA., Eoc. Eu., R. EInd., *Heloderma* R. NA. Family Anguinidae, U. Jur.–R. Eu., R. NA. SA. As. Af., *Euposaurus* U. Jur., *Anguis* Mioc.–R. Eu.

INFRAORDER PLATYNOTA. Family Varanidae, Eoc. Eu. NA., Pleist.–R. As. Aus., ?Mioc. R. Af., *Saniva* NA., *Megalania* Pleist. As. Aus., *Varanus* Pleist. As. R. Family Dolichosauridae, Cret. Eu., *Adriosaurus* L. Cret., *Dolichosaurus* U. Cret. Family Aigialosauridae, L. Cret. Eu., *Aigialosaurus Opetiosaurus.* Family Mosasauridae, U. Cret. Eu. NA. SAf. NZ., *Mosasaurus* Eu., *Platecarpus Clidastes Tylosaurus* NA., *Globidens* NA. Eu.

INFRAORDER AMPHISBAENIA. Family Amphisbaenidae, Olig.–R. NA., R. SA. Af. As. Eu. *Rhineura* Olig.

INFRAORDER RHIPTOGLOSSA. Family Chamaeleontidae, Eoc. NA. Eu., R. Af. As., *Prochameleo* Eoc., *Chameleo* R.

SUBORDER OPHIDIA. Family Typhlopidae, Mioc. NA., R. SA. Af. As. Aus., *Typhlops* R. Family Paleophidae, U. Cret.–Eoc. Eu., Eoc. NA. *Paleophis* Eoc. Family Boidae, U. Cret.–R. SA., Eoc.–R. NA., Eu., Plioc.–R. As., R. Af., *Python* Plioc. As. R. Af. As. Aus., *Boa* R. SA. Family Viperidae, U. Cret.–R. NA., Mioc.–R. Eu., R. As. Af. SA., *Crotalus* Pleist.–R. NA., *Vipera* Mioc.–R. Eu. R. As. Af. Family Elapidae, Tert. Eu., R. As. Af. Aus. NA. SA., *Naja* R. As. Af. Family Colubridae, Eoc.–R. Eu. NA., R. Cos., *Coluber* Pleist.–R. Eu. NA.

SUBCLASS ARCHOSAURIA

ORDER THECODONTIA

SUBORDER PSEUDOSUCHIA. Family Ornithosuchidae, Trias. Eu. SAf., *Euparkeria* L. Trias. SAf., *Ornithosuchus Scleromochlus* M. Trias. Eu., *Saltoposuchus* U. Trias. Eu. Family Aetosauridae, U. Trias. Eu. NA., *Aetosaurus* Eu., *Stegomus* NA. Family Herpetosuchidae, M. Trias. Eu., U. Trias. SAf. NA., *Herpetosuchus* Eu., *Sphenosuchus Notochampsa* SAf.

SUBORDER PHYTOSAURIA. Family Stagonolepidae, M. Trias. Eu., *Stagonolepis.* Family Phytosauridae, Trias. Eu. As. NA., *Phytosaurus* Eu., *Machaeroprosopus Rutiodon Mystriosuchus Palaeorhinus* NA. Family Desmatosuchidae, U. Trias. NA., *Desmatosuchus.* Family Erythrosuchidae, L. Trias. SAf., *Erythrosuchus.*

ORDER CROCODILIA. Family Teleosauridae, L.–M. Jur. Eu., Jur. Mad., ?Eoc. Af., *Teleosaurus* Eu., *Steneosaurus* Jur. Family Metriorhynchidae, M.–U. Jur. Eu., U. Jur. SA. NA.,

Metriorhynchus Eu. SA., *Geosaurus* Eu. **Family Atoposauridae**, U. Jur. Eu., *Atoposaurus Alligatorium Alligatorellus*. **Family Goniopholidae**, M. Jur.–Cret. Eu., Cret. NA. SA., *Pholidosaurus* U. Jur.–L. Cret. Eu., *Goniopholis* Cret. Eu. **Family Crocodilidae**, U. Cret.–R. NA., L. Cret.–Mioc. Eu., Tert.–R. SA. Af. As., *Hylaeochampsa* L. Cret. Eu., *Allognathosuchus* Paleoc.–Olig. NA., *Alligator* Mioc.–R. NA. R. As., *Crocodilus* Tert. Eu. Tert.–R. Af. As. Tert. NA. R. SA.

ORDER PTEROSAURIA

SUBORDER RHAMPHORHYNCHOIDEA, Jur. Eu., *Dimorphodon Rhamphorhynchus Campylognathus*.

SUBORDER PTERODACTYLOIDEA. **Family Pterodactylidae**, U. Jur. Eu. Af., *Pterodactylus Ornithodesmus Ctenochasma* Eu. **Family Ornithocheiridae**, L. Cret. Eu. *Ornithocheirus*. **Family Pteranodontidae**, U. Cret. Eu. NA., *Pteranodon Nyctosaurus* NA., *Ornithostoma* Eu.

ORDER SAURISCHIA

SUBORDER THEROPODA. **Family Hallopodidae**, U. Trias. NA. Eu., *Hallopus* NA., *Procompsognathus* Eu. **Family Podokesauridae**, Trias. Eu. NA., *Podokesaurus* NA., *Saltopus* Eu. **Family Coeluridae**, U. Jur.–L. Cret. Eu. NA., Cret. As. SA., *Compsognathus* U. Jur. Eu., *Ornitholestes* U. Jur. NA., *Velociraptor* As. **Family Ornithomimidae**, U. Jur. Af., Cret. NA. As., *Struthiomimus Ornithomimus* NA., *Oviraptor* As. **Family Zanclodontidae**, Trias. Eu., *Zanclodon*. **Family Megalosauridae**, Jur.–L. Cret. Eu. NA., Jur. Af., *Allosaurus Ceratosaurus* U. Jur. NA., *Megalosaurus* Eu. **Family Deinodontidae**, U. Cret. NA. Eu. As. SA., *Tyrannosaurus Deinodon* (*Gorgosaurus*) NA. **Family Spinosauridae**, U. Cret. Af., *Spinosaurus*. **Family Thecodontosauridae**, U. Trias. Eu. SAf. As. Aus. NA., *Anchisaurus* NA., *Thecodontosaurus*. **Family Plateosauridae**, U. Trias. Eu. SAf., *Plateosaurus* Eu., *Melanorosaurus* SAf.

SUBORDER SAUROPODA. **Family Cetiosauridae**, M. Jur.–L. Cret. Eu., L. Jur. Aus., M. Jur. Mad., U. Jur. Af., U. Jur.–L. Cret. NA., *Cetiosaurus* Eu., *Brachiosaurus* NA. Af. **Family Camarasauridae**, U. Jur. NA. Af., L. Cret. As., *Camarasaurus Brontosaurus Morosaurus* NA. **Family Diplodocidae**, U. Jur. NA., *Diplodocus*. **Family Titanosauridae**, Cret. Eu., U. Cret. As. Aus. Mad. SA. NA., *Titanosaurus* Eu. As. Aus. Mad. SA.

ORDER ORNITHISCHIA

SUBORDER ORNITHOPODA. **Family Hypsilophodontidae**, ?U. Trias. U. Jur.–U. Cret. NA., U. Trias. SAf., L. Cret. Eu., *Nannosaurus* U. Trias. NA., *Laosaurus* U. Jur. NA., *Hypsilophodon* L. Cret. Eu., *Thescelosaurus* U. Cret. NA. **Family Iguanodontidae**, U. Jur.–L. Cret. NA., U. Jur.–U. Cret. Eu., U. Jur. Af. SA., *Camptosaurus* U. Jur.–L. Cret. Eu. NA., *Iguanodon* L. Cret. Eu. **Family Trachodontidae**, U. Cret. NA. Eu. As. SA., *Trachodon Edmontosaurus Parasaurolophus Saurolophus Corythosaurus Lambeosaurus Hypacrosaurus*. NA. **Family Psittacosauridae**, Cret. As., *Psittacosaurus Protiguanodon*.

SUBORDER STEGOSAURIA. **Family Scelidosauridae**, L. Jur., Eu., *Scelidosaurus*. **Family Stegosauridae**, M. Jur.–L. Cret. Eu., U. Jur. NA. Af., *Stegosaurus* NA., *Omosaurus* Eu., *Kentrurosaurus* Af.

SUBORDER ANKYLOSAURIA. **Family Troödontidae**, U. Cret. NA., *Troödon*. **Family Acanthopholidae**, Cret. Eu. SA., *Acanthopholis Struthiosaurus* U. Cret. Eu. **Family Nodosauridae**, Cret. NA. Eu., *Polacanthus* L. Cret. Eu., *Ankylosaurus Nodosaurus Palaeoscincus* NA.

SUBORDER CERATOPSIA. **Family Protoceratopsidae,** U. Cret. As. NA., *Protoceratops* As. *Leptoceratops* NA. **Family Ceratopsidae,** U. Cret. NA., *Brachyceratops Triceratops Torosaurus Monoclonius.*

SUBCLASS SYNAPSIDA

ORDER PELYCOSAURIA. **Family Poliosauridae,** U. Penn.–L. Perm. NA., L. Perm. Eu., *Varanops Varanosaurus Mycterosaurus* L. Perm. NA., *Palaeohatteria* L. Perm. Eu. **Family Ophiacodontidae,** U. Penn.–L. Perm. NA., *Ophiacodon Theropleura.* **Family Sphenacodontidae,** U. Penn.–L. Perm. NA., L. Perm. Eu., *Sphenacodon Dimetrodon* NA., *Pantelosaurus* Eu. **Family Edaphosauridae,** U. Penn.–L. Perm. NA., L. Perm. Eu., *Edaphosaurus Naosaurus.* **Family Caseidae,** L. Perm. NA., *Casea.*

ORDER THERAPSIDA

SUBORDER ANNINGIAMORPHA, M. Perm. SAf., *Anningia.*

SUBORDER DROMASAURIA. **Family Galechiridae,** M. Perm. SAf., *Galechirus Galepus.* **Family Galeopidae,** M. Perm. SAf., *Galeops.*

SUBORDER DINOCEPHALIA. **Family Deuterosauridae,** M. Perm. Eu., *Deuterosaurus.* **Family Tapinocephalidae,** M. Perm. SAf., *Moschops Delphinognathus Tapinocephalus.* **Family Titanosuchidae,** M. Perm. SAf., *Jonkeria Titanosuchus Dinophoneus.* **Family Burnetiidae,** M.–U. Perm. SAf., *Burnetia* U. Perm.

SUBORDER DICYNODONTIA, M. Perm.–L. Trias. SAf., U. Perm. Eu., Trias. As. NA., *Dicynodon* Perm. SAf. Eu., *Cisticephalus Endothiodon Lystrosaurus* U. Perm. SAf., *Kannemeyeria* L. Trias. SAf.

SUBORDER THERIODONTIA. INFRAORDER GORGONOPSIA, M.–U. Perm. SAf., U. Perm. Eu., *Cynarioides Lycaenops Scymnognathus* SAf. INFRAORDER CYNODONTIA, U. Perm.–L. Trias. SAf., U. Perm. Eu., L. Trias. SA., *Thrinaxodon* U. Perm. SAf., *Gomphognathus Cynognathus Cynidiognathus Diademodon* L. Trias. SAf. INFRAORDER THEROCEPHALIA, M.–U. Perm. SAf., *Scymnosaurus Lycosuchus Scylacosaurus Scaloposaurus Whaitsia.* INFRAORDER BAURIAMORPHA, L. Trias. SAf., *Bauria Sesamodon Microgomphodon.*

SUBORDER ICTIDOSAURIA, U. Trias. SAf., *Karroomys.*

SUBORDER PROTODONTA, U. Trias. NA., *Dromatherium Microconodon.*

CLASS AVES
SUBCLASS PALAEORNITHES

ORDER ARCHAEOPTERYGIA, U. Jur. Eu., *Archaeopteryx Archaeornis*

SUBCLASS NEORNITHES

SUPERORDER ODONTOGNATHAE. ORDER ICHTHYORNITHIFORMES, U. Cret. NA., *Ichthyornis.* ORDER HESPERORNITHIFORMES, U. Cret. NA., *Hesperornis.*

SUPERORDER PALEOGNATHAE. ORDER CRYPTURIFORMES, Mioc.–R. SA., *Rhynchotus* R. ORDER STRUTHIOFORMES, Plioc.–Pleist. As., R. Af., *Struthio.* ORDER RHEIFORMES, Pleist.–R. SA., *Rhea.* ORDER CASUARIFORMES, Pleist.–R. Aus., ?Plioc. As., *Casuarius Dromaeus* Aus. ORDER AEPYORNITHIFORMES, ?Eoc. Af., Pleist. Mad., *Stromeria* Eoc., *Aepyornis* Mad. ORDER DINORNITHIFORMES, Pleist. NZ., *Dinornis.* ORDER APTERYGIFORMES, Pleist.–R. NZ., Pleist. Aus., *Apteryx* NZ.

SUPERORDER NEOGNATHAE. ORDER SPHENISCIFORMES, Olig. NZ. Seymour Is., Olig.–Mioc. SA., R. Oc., *Cladornis* Olig. SA. ORDER COLYMBIFORMES, Eoc.–R. Eu., Olig.–R. NA., R. Cos. ORDER PROCELARIIFORMES ?Eoc. Af., Olig.–R. Eu., Mioc.–R. NA. Pleist. Aus. NZ., R. Oc. ORDER PELICANIFORMES, Eoc.–R. Eu. NA., Mioc.–R. SA., Plioc.–R. As., Pleist. Aus., R. Cos., *Cyphornis* Eoc. NA., *Pelagornis* Mioc. Eu. ORDER CICONII-

FORMES ?U. Cret. Eu., Eoc.–R. Eu. NA., Mioc.–R. SA., Plioc.–R. As., R. Cos., *Odontopteryx* Eoc. Eu. ORDER ANSERIFORMES, Eoc.–R. Eu., Mioc.–R. NA. SA., Pleist. Aus. NZ., R. Cos., *?Gastornis* Eoc. Eu. ORDER FALCONIFORMES, Eoc.–R. Eu. NA., Mioc.–R. SA., Pleist. Aus. NZ., R. Cos. ORDER GALLIFORMES, Eoc.–R. Eu. NA., Mioc.– R. SA., Pleist. Aus., R. Cos., *Palaeortyx* Eoc.–Mioc. Eu., *Gallinuloides* Eoc. NA. OR- DER GRUIFORMES, ?U. Cret. NA., Eoc.–R. NA. Eu., Olig.–R. SA., Pleist. Aus. NZ., R. Cos., *Phororhachis Pelycornis* Mioc. SA., *Diatryma* Eoc. NA. ORDER CHARADRII- FORMES, ?Cret. NA., Eoc.–R. Eu. NA., Mioc.–R. SA., Pleist. Aus., R. Cos. ORDER COLUMBIFORMES, Eoc.–R. Eu., Pleist. Aus., R. Cos., *Didus* Pleist.–R. Mauritius. ORDER CUCULIFORMES, Olig.–R. Eu., R. Cos. ORDER PSITTACI, ?Olig. Eu., Pleist.–R. SA., Af. ORDER CORACIIFORMES, Eoc.–R. Eu. NA., R. Cos. ORDER PASSERIFORMES, Eoc.–R. Eu. NA., *Palaeospiza* Eoc. NA.

CLASS MAMMALIA

SUBCLASS PROTOTHERIA

ORDER MONOTREMETA. **Family Ornithorhynchidae,** Pleist.–R. Aus., *Ornithorhynchus.* **Family Echidnidae,** Pleist.–R. Aus., *Echidna.*

SUBCLASS ALLOTHERIA

ORDER MULTITUBERCULATA

SUBORDER TRITYLODONTOIDEA. **Family Tritylodontidae,** U. Trias.–M. Jur. Eu., U. Trias. SAf., *Tritylodon* SAf.

SUBORDER PLAGIAULACOIDEA. **Family Plagiaulacidae,** U. Jur.–L. Cret. Eu., U. Jur. NA., *Pla- giaulax.* **Family Ptilodontidae,** U. Cret.–Paleoc. Eu., U. Cret.–L. Eoc. NA., U. Cret. As., *Ptilodus* U. Cret.–Paleoc. NA., *Eucosmodon* Paleoc.–L. Eoc. NA. **Family Taenio- labidae,** Paleoc. NA. As., *Taeniolabis* (*Polymastodon*) NA.

SUBCLASS TRITUBERCULATA

ORDER PANTOTHERIA. **Family Amphitheriidae,** M. Jur. Eu., *Amphitherium.* **Family Pauro- dontidae,** U. Jur. Eu. NA. Af., *Paurodon.* **Family Dryolestiae,** U. Jur. Eu. NA., *Dryolestes, Melanodon* NA. **Family Docodontidae,** U. Jur. Eu. NA., *Docodon.*

ORDER SYMMETRODONTA. **Family Spalacotheriidae,** U. Jur. Eu. NA., *Spalacotherium* Eu. **Family Amphidontidae,** U. Jur. NA., *Amphidon Eurylambda.*

ORDER TRICONODONTA (subclass uncertain). **Family Triconodontidae,** M. Jur.–U. Jur. Eu., U. Jur. NA., *Priacodon* NA., *Triconodon.*

SUBCLASS DIDELPHIA (METATHERIA)

ORDER MARSUPIALIA

SUBORDER POLYPROTODONTIA. **Family Didelphiidae,** U. Cret.–Eoc. Mioc.–R. NA., Paleoc.– Mioc. Eu., Eoc.–R. SA., *Eodelphys* U. Cret., *Didelphys* Eoc.–R. **Family Borhyaenidae,** Eoc.–Plioc. SA., *Prothylacinus Borhyaena* Mioc. **Family Dasyuridae,** Pleist.–R. Aus., *Dasyurus Thylacynus.* **Family Notoryctidae,** R. Aus., *Notoryctes.* **Family Perameli- dae,** Pleist.–R. Aus., *Perameles.*

SUBORDER CAENOLESTOIDEA. **Family Caenolestidae,** Eoc.–R. SA., *Abderites* Mioc., *Caeno- lestes* R. **Family Polydolopidae,** Eoc. SA., *Polydolops.*

SUBORDER DIPROTODONTIA. **Family Phalangeridae,** Plioc.–R. Aus., *Wynyardia* Plioc., *Phal- anger* Pleist.–R. **Family Phascolomiidae,** Pleist.–R. Aus. *Thylacoleo* Pleist., *Phasco- lomys.* **Family Macropodidae,** Pleist.–R. Aus., *Macropus.* **Family Diprotodontidae,** Pleist. Aus., *Diprotodon Nototherium.*

SUBCLASS MONODELPHIA (PLACENTALIA)

ORDER INSECTIVORA

SUBORDER DELTATHERIDIOIDEA. **Family Deltatheridiidae,** U. Cret. As., L. Eoc. NA., *Deltatheridium* Cret., *Didelphodus* Eoc.,

SUBORDER ZALAMBDODONTA. **Family Centetidae,** Paleoc.–Olig. NA., Pleist.–R. Mad., R. Af., *Palaeoryctes* Paleoc., *Apternodus* Olig., *Centetes* R. Mad., *Potomogale* Af. **Family Solenodontidae,** Pleist.–R. WInd., *Solenodon.* **Family Chrysochloridae,** R. Af., *Chrysochloris.*

SUBORDER ERINACEOMORPHA. **Family Zalambdalestidae,** U. Cret. As., *Zalambdalestes.* **Family Leptictidae,** U. Cret.–Olig. NA.. Paleoc.–Olig. As., *Diacodon* Eoc. NA., *Leptictis* Olig. NA. **Family Erinacedae,** Eoc.–R. Eu., Olig.–Plioc. NA., Olig.–R. As., R. Af., *Erinaceus* Olig.–R. Eu. Plioc.–R. As., R. Af., *Gymnura* R. As. **Family Dimylidae,** Olig.–Mioc. Eu.. *Dimylus.*

SUBORDER SORICOMORPHA. **Family Soricidae,** Olig.–R. Eu. NA., R. As. Af., *Protosorex* Olig. NA., *Sorex* Olig.–R. Eu. Pleist.–R. NA. **Family Talpidae,** Eoc.–R. Eu., Olig.–R. NA., R. As., *Talpa* Olig.–R. Eu., *Proscalops* Olig. NA. **Family Nyctitheriidae,** Paleoc.–Eoc. NA., Eoc. Eu., *Nyctitherium* Eoc. NA.

SUBORDER MENOTYPHLA. **Family Anagalidae,** Olig. As., *Anagale.* **Family Tupaiidae,** ?Eoc. NA., R. EInd., *Tupaia* R. **Family Macroscelididae,** R. Af., *Macroscelides.*

SUBORDER UNCERTAIN: **Family Mixodectidae,** Paleoc.–Eoc. NA., *Mixodectes* Paleoc. **Family Pantolestidae,** Paleoc.–Eoc. NA., L. Eoc. Eu., *Pantolestes* Eoc. NA. **Family Apheliscidae,** L. Eoc. NA., *Apheliscus.*

ORDER DERMOPTERA. **Family Galeopithecidae,** R. As., *Galeopithecus.* **Family Plagiomenidae,** Paleoc.–Eoc. NA., *Plagiomene.*

ORDER CHIROPTERA

SUBORDER MEGACHIROPTERA. **Family Pteropodidae,** Olig. Eu., R. SA. Af. As. Aus., *Archaeopteropus* Olig.

SUBORDER MICROCHIROPTERA. **Family Emballonuridae,** Olig. Eu., R. SA. Af. As. Aus., *Vespertiliavus* Olig. **Family Rhinolophidae,** Eoc.–R. Eu., Pleist.–R. As., R. SA. Af. Aus., *Pseudorhinolophus* Eoc.–Mioc. Eu., *Rhinolophus* Eoc.–R. Eu. R., *Palaenycteris* Mioc. Eu. **Family Phyllostomatidae,** Paleoc. NA., Olig. Af., Pleist.–R. SA., *Zanycteris* Paleoc. **Family Vespertiliontidae,** Olig.–R. Eu., Pleist.–R. NA. SA., R. As. Af. Aus., *Nyctinomus* Mioc.–R. Eu. R. Cos. **Family Natalidae,** R. SA. Mad. **Family Archaeonycteridae,** M. Eoc. Eu., *Archaeonycteris.* **Family Palaeochiropterygidae,** M. Eoc. Eu., *Palaeochiropteryx.*

ORDER TILLODONTIA. **Family Esthonychidae,** L. Eoc. Eu. NA., *Esthonyx.* **Family Tillotheriidae,** M.–U. Eoc. NA., *Tillotherium.*

ORDER TAENIODONTA. **Family Stylinodontidae,** Paleoc.–Eoc. NA., *Conoryctes Onychodectes Psittacotherium* Paleoc., *Camalodon* L. Eoc., *Stylinodon* M. Eoc.

ORDER CARNIVORA

SUBORDER CREODONTA

INFRAORDER PROCREODI. **Family Arctocyonidae,** Paleoc.–L. Eoc. NA. Eu., Paleoc. As., *Oxyclaenus Claenodon* Paleoc. NA., *Arctocyon* Paleoc. Eu.

INFRAORDER ACREODI. **Family Mesonychidae,** Paleoc.–Eoc. NA. Eu., Eoc.–Olig. As., *Triisodon* Paleoc. NA., *Dissacus* U. Paleoc.–L. Eoc., *Pachyaena* L. Eoc. NA., *Mesonyx* M. Eoc. NA., *Synoplotherium* U. Eoc. NA., *Andrewsarchus* L. Olig. As.

INFRAORDER PSEUDOCREODI. **Family Oxyaenidae**, Eoc. NA. Eu., *Oxyaena Palaeonictis* L. Eoc. NA. Eu., *Patriofelis Thinocyon* M. Eoc. NA., *Limnocyon* M.–U. Eoc. NA. **Family Hyaenodontidae**, Eoc.–Olig. Eu. NA., ?Paleoc. Eoc.–L. Mioc. As., Olig.–L. Mioc. Af., *Sinopa* L.–M. Eoc. NA. M. Eoc., Eu., *Tritemnodon* M. Eoc. NA., *Pterodon Apterodon* U. Eoc.–Olig. Eu. Olig.–?Mioc. Af., *Hyaenodon* Olig. NA. Eu.

INFRAORDER EUCREODI. **Family Miacidae**, Eoc. Eu. NA., *Didymictis Viverravus* L. Eoc. NA., *Miacis Uintacyon Vulpavus* NA.

SUBORDER FISSIPEDIA

INFRAORDER ARCTOIDEA. **Family Canidae**, U. Eoc.–R. NA. Eu., Olig.–R. As., Pleist.–R. Af. As. Aus., R. SA., *Procynodictis* U. Eoc. NA., *Cynodictis* Olig. Eu. NA., *Daphoenus* Olig. NA., *Temnocyon Cynodesmus Daphoenodon* L. Mioc. NA., *Amphicyon* U. Olig.–Mioc. Eu. Mioc. NA., *Tomarctus (Tephrocyon)* Mioc.–Plioc. NA., *Borophagus Pliocyon* Plioc. NA., *Dinocyon* Plioc. Eu., *Hyaenognathus* Pleist. NA., *Canis* Pleist.–R. Cos., *Vulpes* Pleist.–R. Eu. R. As. Af. NA., *Cuon* Pleist. Eu. R. As., *Otocyon* R. Af. **Family Procyonidae**, Mioc.–R. NA., Plioc. Eu., Plioc.–R. SA., Pleist.–R. As., *Phlaocyon Alletocyon* Mioc. NA., *Procyon* Pleist.–R. NA. SA., *Ailurus* R. As. **Family Ursidae**, Plioc.–R. Eu. As. NA., Pleist.–R. SA., *Ursavus* Mioc. Eu.. *Hemicyon* Mioc. Eu. NA., *Hyaenarctus* U. Mioc.–Plioc. Eu. As., *Ailuropus* Pleist.–R. As., *Arctotherium* Pleist. NA. SA., *Ursus* Pleist.–R. Eu. As. Af. NA., *Tremarctos* R. SA. **Family Mustelidae**, Olig.–R. Eu. As. NA., Plioc.–R. Af., Pleist.–R. SA., *Bunaelurus Oligobunis* Olig. NA., *Plesictis* Olig. Eu., *Potamotherium* Olig.–Mioc. Eu., *Megalictis* Mioc. NA., *Gulo* Pleist. Eu. R. NA. As., *Mellivora* Plioc.–R. As. R. Af., *Mustela* Mioc.–R. Eu. As. NA., *Taxidea* Pleist.–R. NA., *Mephitis* Pleist.–R. NA., *Lutra* Mioc.–R. Eu. NA. Plioc.–R. As. R. SA. Af.

INFRAORDER AELUROIDEA. **Family Viverridae**, ?Olig. Mioc.–R. Eu., Plioc.–R. As., R. Af., *Progenetta* Mioc. Eu., *Viverra* Mioc. Eu. R. As. Af., *Herpestes* Mioc.–R. Eu. Plioc.–R. Af. R. As., *Cryptoprocta* R. Mad., *Proteles* R. Af. **Family Hyaenidae**, Plioc.–Pleist. Eu., Plioc.–R. As. Af., *Ictitherium* Plioc. As., *Hyaena* Plioc.–R. Af. As. Pleist. Eu. **Family Felidae**, Olig.–R. Eu. NA., Mioc.–R. Af. As., Pleist.–R. SA., *Dinictis Hoplophoneus* Olig. NA., *Pseudaelurus* Mioc. Eu. Af. NA., *Metailurus* Plioc. Eu. As., *Machairodus* Plioc.–Pleist. Eu. Plioc. As., *Smilodon* Pleist. NA. SA., *Felis* Plioc.–R. Eu. As. NA. Pleist.–R. SA. Af.

SUBORDER PINNIPEDIA. **Family Otariidae**, Mioc.–R. NA. SA., Pleist.–R. Aus., *Allodesmus* Mioc. NA., *Otaria* Pleist.–R. SA. **Family Odobaenidae**, Plioc.–R. Eu., Pleist.–R. NA., *Prorosmarus* Plioc. NA., *Odobaenus* Plioc. Eu. Pleist.–R. NA. **Family Phocidae**, Mioc.–R. Eu. NA., Plioc. Af., R. Oc., *Phoca*.

ORDER CONDYLARTHRA. **Family Meniscotheriidae**, Paleoc.–L. Eoc. NA., Paleoc. Eu., *Meniscotherium* NA., *Pleuraspidotherium* Eu. **Family Phenacodontidae**, Paleoc.–L. Eoc. NA., L. Eoc. Eu., *Tetraclaenodon (Euprotogonia)* Paleoc., *Ectocion Phenacodus* L. Eoc. **Family Hyopsodontidae**, Paleoc.–Eoc. NA., *Mioclaenus* Paleoc., *Hyopsodus* Eoc.

ORDER LITOPTERNA. **Family Didolodontidae**, Eoc.–Olig. SA., *Didolodus* Eoc. **Family Proterotheriidae**, Olig.–Plioc. SA., *Thoatherium* Mioc., *Diadiaphorus* Mioc. **Family Macraucheniidae**, Olig.–Pleist. SA., *Protheosodon* Olig., *Theosodon* Mioc., *Macrauchenia* Pleist.

ORDER AMBLYPODA. **Family Pantolambdidae**, Paleoc. NA., *Pantolambda*. **Family Periptychidae**, Paleoc. NA., *Periptychus*. **Family Coryphodontidae**, Paleoc.–L. Eoc. NA., Eoc. Eu. As., *Coryphodon* L. Eoc. NA. Eu., *Eudinoceras* U. Eoc. As. **Family Uintatheriidae**, U. Paleoc.–Eoc. NA., Eoc. Eu. As., *Uintatherium Loxolophodon* Eoc. NA.

ORDER NOTOUNGULATA

SUBORDER ENTELONYCHIA. **Family Arctostylopidae,** Paleoc. As., L. Eoc. NA., *Palaeostylops* As., *Arctostylops* NA. **Family Notostylopidae,** Eoc. SA., *Notostylops.* **Family Isotemnidae,** Eoc.–Olig. SA., *Isotemnus Pleurostylodon* Eoc. **Family Homalodontotheriidae,** Eoc.–Mioc. SA., *Homalodontotherium* Mioc.

SUBORDER TYPOTHERIA. **Family Notopithecidae,** Eoc.–Olig. SA., *Notopithecus Oldfieldthomasia* Eoc. **Family Archaeopithecidae,** Eoc. SA., *Archaeopithecus.* **Family Archaeohyracidae,** Olig. SA., *Archaeohyrax.* **Family Typotheriidae,** Olig.–Pleist. SA., *Typotherium* Pleist. **Family Hegetotheriidae,** Olig.–Mioc. SA. *Hegetotherium* Mioc., *Pachyrukhos* Pleist. **Family Interatheriidae,** Olig.–Pleist. SA., *Protypotherium* Mioc., *Interatherium* Mioc.–Plioc.

SUBORDER TOXODONTIA. **Family Toxodontidae,** Olig.–Pleist. SA., *Proadinotherium* Olig., *Adinotherium Nesodon* Mioc., *Toxodon* Plioc.–Pleist. **Family Notohippidae,** Olig.–Mioc. SA., *Notohippus* Olig. **Family Leontiniidae,** Olig.–Mioc. SA., *Leontinia* Olig.

ORDER ASTRAPOTHERIA. **Family Trigonostylopidae,** Eoc.–Olig. SA., *Trigonostylops* Eoc. **Family Astrapotheriidae,** Eoc.–Mioc. SA., *Albertogaudrya* Eoc., *Astrapotherium* Mioc.

ORDER PYROTHERIA. **Family Pyrotheriidae,** Eoc.–Olig. SA., *Carolozittelia* Eoc., *Pyrotherium* Olig.

ORDER PERISSODACTYLA

SUBORDER EQUOIDEA. **Family Equidae,** Eoc.–Pleist. NA., Eoc. Mioc.–R. Eu., Plioc.–R. As. Af., Pleist SA., *Hyracotherium* L. Eoc. Eu., *Eohippus* L. Eoc. NA., *Orohippus* M. Eoc. NA., *Epihippus* U. Eoc. NA., *Mesohippus* Olig. NA., *Anchitherium* Mioc. NA. Eu., *Parahippus* Mioc. NA., *Hypohippus* U. Mioc.–Plioc. NA. As., *Merychippus* U. Mioc.–Plioc. NA., *Hipparion* U. Mioc.–Plioc. NA. U. Mioc.–L. Pleist. Eu. As., *Pliohippus Plesippus* Plioc. NA., *Hippidium Onohippidium* Pleist. SA., *Equus* Pleist.–R. **Family Palaeotheriidae,** Eoc.–Olig. Eu.. Eoc. As., *Propalaeotherium Paloplotherium* Eoc. Eu., *Palaeotherium* Eoc.–Olig. Eu.

SUBORDER TAPIROIDEA. **Family Tapiridae,** Eoc.–Pleist. NA., Olig.–Plioc. Eu., Pleist.–R. SA. As., *Homogalax (Systemodon)* Eoc., *Tapirus* Olig.–R. **Family Lophiodontidae,** Eoc. NA. As. Eu., *Lophiodon* Eu. **Family Helatelidae,** Eoc.–Olig. Eu. NA. As., *Heptodon Helateles* Eoc. NA., *Colodon* Olig. NA.

SUBORDER RHINOCEROTOIDEA. **Family Hyracodontidae,** Eoc.–Olig. NA. As., *Hyrachyus* Eoc. NA., *Hyracodon* Olig. NA. **Family Amynodontidae,** Eoc.–Olig. NA. As., Olig. Eu., *Amynodon* U. Eoc. NA., *Metamynodon* Olig. NA., *Cadurcotherium* Olig. Eu. **Family Rhinocerotidae,** Olig.–R. As., Olig.–Plioc. NA., Eoc.–Pleist. Eu., Mioc.–R. Af., *Prothyracodon* Eoc. Eu. NA., *Trigonias Caenopus* Olig. NA. Eu., *Diceratherium* U. Olig.–Mioc. NA. Mioc. Eu. Plioc. As. *Baluchitherium* Olig. As., *Aceratherium* Mioc. Eu. Plioc. As., *Aphelops* Mioc.–Plioc. NA., *Teleoceras* Mioc. Eu. Mioc.–Plioc. NA., *Chilotherium* Plioc. Eu. As., *Rhinoceros* Plioc.–R. As., *Coelodonta* Pleist. Eu. As., *Diceros* Plioc.–Pleist. As. Plioc. Eu. Pleist.–R. Af., *Ceratotherium* R. Af., *Dicerorhinus* U. Mioc.–Pleist. Eu. Pleist.–R. As., *Elasmotherium* Pleist. As.

SUBORDER BRONTOTHERIOIDEA. **Family Brontotheriidae,** Eoc.–L. Olig. NA. Eu. As., *Lambdotherium Eotitanops* L. Eoc. NA., *Palaeosyops* M. Eoc. NA., *Dolichorhinus Limnohyops* U. Eoc. NA., *Brontops* Olig. NA. As., *Brontotherium Megacerops* Olig. NA., *Embolotherium* Olig. As. **Family Chalicotheriidae,** Eoc.–Mioc. NA., Olig.–Plioc. Eu., U. Eoc.–Pleist. As., Plioc.–?Pleist. Af., *Eomoropus* Eoc. NA., *Schizotherium* Olig. Eu. As., *Moropus* L. Mioc. NA., *Macrotherium* Mioc. Eu., *Chalicotherium* Plioc.–Pleist.

ORDER ARTIODACTYLA

SUBORDER RUMINANTIA

INFRAORDER PROTOSELENODONTIA (provisional group). **Family Homacodontidae,** Eoc. NA. ?Eu., *Diacodexis* (*Trigonolestes*) L. Eoc. NA., *Homacodon* M. Eoc. NA. **Family Dichobunidae,** Eoc.–Olig. Eu., *Dichobune.* **Family Anoplotheriidae,** Eoc.–Olig. Eu., Eoc. ?As., *Dacrytherium* Eoc. Eu., *Diplobune Anoplotherium* Eoc.–Olig. Eu. **Family Caenotheriidae,** U. Eoc.–Mioc. Eu., *Caenotherium* Olig.–Mioc. **Family Oreodontidae,** U. Eoc.–Plioc. NA., *Protoreodon* U. Eoc., *Oreodon* (*Merycoidodon*) Olig., *Promerycochoerus Merycochoerus Merychyus* Mioc., *Pronomotherium* Plioc. **Family Agriochoeridae,** U. Eoc.–Olig. NA., *Protagriochoerus* U. Eoc., *Agriochoerus* Olig.

INFRAORDER TYLOPODA. **Family Camelidae,** U. Eoc.–Pleist. NA., Plioc.–R. As., Pleist. Eu., Pleist.–R. SA. Af., *Protylopus* U. Eoc. *Poëbrotherium* Olig., *Oxydactylus Stenomylus* Mioc., *Alticamelus Pliauchenia* Mioc.–Plioc. NA., *Camelops* Pleist. NA., *Camelus* Plioc.–R. As. Pleist.–R. Af., *Auchenia* Pleist.–R. SA. **Family Xiphodontidae,** Eoc.–Olig. Eu., *Xiphodon.*

INFRAORDER PECORA. **Family Amphimerycidae,** Eoc.–Olig. Eu., Eoc. As., *Amphimeryx* Eu., *Archaeomeryx* As., **Family Tragulidae** (incl. **Hypertragulidae**), U. Eoc.–Plioc. NA., Olig.–Plioc. Eu., Mioc.–R. As. Af., *Leptomeryx Hypisodus Protoceras* Olig. NA., *Hypertragulus* Olig.–Mioc. NA., *Synthetoceras* Plioc. NA., *Gelocus* Olig. Eu., *Dorcatherium* (*Hyaemoschus*) Mioc.–Plioc. Eu. As. Mioc.–R. Af., *Tragulus* Plioc.–R. As. **Family Cervidae,** Mioc.–R. As. Eu. NA., Pleist.–R. SA. Af., *Blastomeryx Dromomeryx* U. Mioc. NA., *Dicrocerus* U. Mioc. Eu., *Cervus* Plioc.–R. Eu. Pleist.–R. NA. R. As., *Cervulus* Plioc. Eu. R. As., *Capreolus* Plioc.–R. Eu. As., *Megaceros* Pleist. Eu., *Cervalces* Pleist. NA., *Alces* Plioc.–R. Eu. Pleist.–R. As. NA., *Rangifer* Pleist.–R. Eu. As. NA., *Odocoileus* Pleist.–R. NA., *Mazama* SA. **Family Giraffidae,** Mioc.–Plioc. Eu. As., Plioc.–R. Af., *Palaeomeryx* Mioc. Eu., *Samotherium* Plioc., *Sivatherium* Plioc. As., *Giraffa* Plioc.–R., *Okapia* R. Af. **Family Antilocapridae,** Mioc.–R. NA., *Merycodus* Mioc.–Plioc., *Aletomeryx* Plioc., *Capromeryx Tetrameryx* Pleist., *Antilocapra* Pleist.–R. **Family Bovidae,** Mioc.–R. Eu. As. Af., Pleist.–R. NA., *Tragocerus* Mioc.–Plioc. Eu. As., *Gazella* Plioc. Eu. Plioc.–R. As. Pleist.–R. Af., *Oreamnos* Pleist.–R. NA., *Capra* Plioc.–R. As. Pleist.–R. Eu. R. Af., *Ovis Ovibos* Pleist.–R. Eu. As. NA., *Symbos* Pleist. NA., *Bos* Plioc.–R. As. Pleist.–R. Eu. Af., *Bison* Pleist.–R. Eu. As. NA.

SUBORDER SUINA. **Family Cebochoeridae,** Eoc. Eu., *Cebochoerus.* **Family Achaenodontidae,** U. Eoc. NA., *Achaenodon.* **Family Entelodontidae,** Olig.–L. Mioc. NA., Olig. Eu. As., *Archaeotherium* Olig. NA., *Entelodon* Olig. Eu., *Dinohyus* L. Mioc. **Family Anthracotheriidae,** U. Eoc.–Mioc. Eu. As., Olig. NA., Mioc. Af., *Anthracotherium* Eoc.–Olig., *Ancodus* (*Hyopotamus*) Olig., *Brachyodus* Olig.–Mioc. Eu. Mioc. As. Af. **Family Hippopotamidae,** Plioc.–R. Af., Plioc.–Pleist. As., Pleist. Eu., *Hippopotamus.* **Family Suidae,** Olig.–R. NA. Eu., Mioc.–R. As. Af., Pleist.–R. SA., *Choerotherium* Mioc. Eu., *Lystriodon Hyotherium* Mioc. Eu. As., *Sus* Mioc.–R. Eu. As. Plioc.–R. Af., *Cheleuastochoerus* Plioc. As., *Perchoerus* (*Thinohyus*) Olig. NA., *Prosthenops* Mioc.–Plioc. NA., *Mylohyus Platygonus* Pleist. NA., *Dicotyles* Pleist.–R. NA. SA

ORDER HYRACOIDEA. **Family Saghatheriidae,** Olig. Af., Plioc. Eu., *Megalohyrax Saghatherium* Olig., *Pliohyrax* Plioc. **Family Myohyracidae,** L. Mioc. Af., *Myohyrax.* **Family Hyracidae,** Mioc.–R. Af., R. As., *Hyrax.*

ORDER EMBRITHOPODA. **Family Arsinoitheriidae,** Olig. Af., *Arsinoitherium.*

ORDER BARYTHERIA. **Family Barytheriidae,** Eoc. Af., *Barytherium.*

ORDER PROBOSCIDEA. **Family Moeritheriidae,** U. Eoc.–Olig. Af., ?Olig. As., *Moeritherium.* **Family Dinotheriidae,** Mioc.–Pleist. Af., Mioc.–Plioc. Eu. As., *Dinotherium.* **Family Trilophodontidae,** Olig.–Pleist. Af., Olig.–Plioc. As., Mioc.–Plioc. Eu., Mioc.–L. Pleist. NA., Pleist. SA., *Phiomia* Olig. Af., *Trilophodon* Mioc., *Tetralophodon* Plioc., *Rhynchotherium Amebelodon* Plioc. NA., *Platybelodon* Plioc. As. **Family Mastodontidae,** Olig. Af., Mioc.–Plioc. Eu., Mioc.–Pleist. NA., *Palaeomastodon* Olig., *Mastodon* Mioc.–Pleist. **Family Elephantidae,** Plioc.–R. As., Plioc.–Pleist. Eu., Pleist. NA. SA., Pleist.–R. Af., *Stegodon* Plioc.–Pleist. As., *Archidiskodon* Plioc.–Pleist., *Parelephas* Pleist. NA., *Elephas* Pleist.–R. As., *Mammonteus* Pleist. Eu. As. NA. *Palaeloxodon* Pleist. Eu. Af., *Loxodonta* Pleist.–R. Af.

ORDER SIRENIA. **Family Prorastomidae,** M. Eoc. Af., Eoc. WInd., *Prorastomus* WInd., *Eotheroides* (*Eotherium*) Af. **Family Halicoridae,** Eoc. Af., Eoc.–Plioc. Eu., Olig.–Plioc. NA., Olig. Mad., R. Indian Ocean, Pacific, *Eosiren* U. Eoc. Af., *Halitherium* Olig. Eu., *Metaxytherium* Plioc. Eu., *Felsinotherium* Plioc. Eu., *Halicore* R. Indian Ocean, *Rhytina* Pleist.–R. (extinct) Pacific. **Family Manatidae,** Pleist.–R. Atlantic Ocean, *Manatus.* **Family Desmostylidae,** Mioc. Pacific., *Desmostylus.*

ORDER EDENTATA (XENARTHRA)

SUBORDER PALAEANODONTA. **Family Metacheiromyidae,** U. Paleoc.–Eoc. NA., *Palaeanodon* Paleoc.–L. Eoc., *Metacheiromys* M. Eoc. **Family Epoicotheriidae,** Olig. NA., *Epoicotherium.*

SUBORDER PILOSA

INFRAORDER GRAVIGRADA. **Family Megatheriidae,** Olig.–Pleist. SA., Plioc.–Pleist. NA., *Hapalops* Mioc., *Megalonyx* Plioc.–Pleist. NA., *Megatherium Nothrotherium* Pleist. **Family Mylodontidae,** Mioc.–Pleist. SA., Pleist. NA., *Mylodon* Pleist., *Scelidotherium Glossotherium* Pleist. SA.

INFRAORDER VERMILINGUA. **Family Myrmecophagidae,** Pleist.–R. SA., *Myrmecophaga.*

INFRAORDER TARDIGRADA. **Family Bradypodidae,** Pleist.–R. SA., *Bradypus.*

SUBORDER LORICATA. **Family Dasypodidae,** Eoc.–R. SA., Pleist.–R. NA., *Proeutatus Stegotherium Peltephilus* Mioc., *Chlamydotherium* Plioc., *Tatu* Pleist.–R., *Dasypus* R. SA. **Family Glyptodontidae,** Olig.–Pleist. SA., Plioc.–Pleist. NA., *Propalaeoplophorus* Mioc., *Glyptodon* Plioc.–Pleist. SA., *Panochthus* Pleist. SA.

ORDER PHOLIDOTA. **Family Manidae,** ?Olig.–Mioc. Eu., Pleist.–R. As., R. Af., *Manis* Pleist.–R.

ORDER TUBULIDENTATA. **Family Tubulodontidae,** L. Eoc. NA., *Tubulodon.* **Family Orycteropodidae,** ?Olig.–Mioc. Plioc. Eu., Plioc. As., R. Af., *Orycteropus* Plioc.–R.

ORDER RODENTIA

SUBORDER SIMPLICIDENTATA

INFRAORDER SCIUROMORPHA

SUPERFAMILY APLODONTOIDEA. **Family Ischyromyidae,** Ecc.–Olig. NA., Eoc. Eu., Olig. As., *Paramys* Eoc., *Ichyromys* Olig. NA. **Family Mylagaulidae,** Mioc.–Plioc. NA., *Mylagaulus Ceratogaulus.* **Family Aplodontiidae,** Mioc.–R. NA., *Mylagaulodon* Mioc., *Aplodontia* R.

SUPERFAMILY SCIUROIDEA. **Family Sciuridae,** Olig.–R. Eu. NA., R. As. AF., *Sciurus.*

SUPERFAMILY CASTOROIDEA. **Family Castoridae,** Olig.–R. NA., Mioc.–R. Eu., R. As., *Palaeocastor* Mioc. NA., *Steneofiber* Mioc. Eu., *Castor* Plioc.–R. Eu. Pleist.–R. NA. R. As., *Trogontherium* Pleist. Eu., *Castoroides* Pleist. NA.

SUPERFAMILY GEOMYOIDEA. **Family Heteromyidae,** Olig.–R. NA., *Adjidaumo* Olig. **Family Geomyidae,** Olig.–R. NA., *Entoptychus* Mioc., *Geomys* Mioc. R.

SUPERFAMILY ANOMALUROIDEA. **Family Anomaluridae,** R. Af., *Anomalurus.* **Family Pseudosciuridae,** Eoc.–Olig. Eu., Olig.–Mioc. Af., *Sciuroides* Eoc., *Pseudosciurus* Olig. Eu. **Family Theridomyidae,** Eoc.–Mioc. Eu., *Theridomys.* **Family Pedetidae,** Mioc.– R. Af., *Pedetes.*

INFRAORDER MYOMORPHA

SUPERFAMILY MYOXOIDEA. **Family Myoxidae,** ?U. Eoc. Mioc.–R. Eu., R. As. Af., *Myoxus* Eu. As.

SUPERFAMILY DIPODOIDEA. **Family Dipodidae,** Mioc.–R. Af., Plioc.–R. As., Pleist.–R. Eu. NA., *Zapus* Pleist.–R. NA., *Dipus* R. Af. As.

SUPERFAMILY MYOIDEA. **Family Spalacidae,** Mioc.–R. Eu., R. As. Af., *Spalax.* **Family Muridae,** Eoc.–R. NA. As., Olig.–R. Eu., Pleist.–R. SA., R. Af. Aus., *Eumys* Olig. NA., *Cricetodon* Olig.–Mioc. Eu., *Mus* Plioc.–R. Eu. R. Cos., *Microtus* Plioc.–R. Eu. Pleist.–R. As. NA., *Fiber* Pleist.–R. NA., *Peromyscus* Plioc.–R. NA. **Family Criceto- pidae,** Olig. As., *Cricetops.*

INFRAORDER HYSTRICOMORPHA

SUPERFAMILY BATHYERGOIDEA. **Family Bathyergidae,** Olig. As., ?Mioc. R. Af., *Bathyer- gus* R.

SUPERFAMILY HYSTRICOIDEA. **Family Hystricidae,** Olig.–R. Eu., Plioc.–R. As., R. Af., *Hystrix.* **Family Erethizontidae,** Olig.–R. SA., Pleist.–R. NA., *Eosteiromys* Olig., *Steiromys Sciamys* Mioc., *Erethizon* NA. **Family Dinomyidae,** Pleist. WInd., R. SA., *Dinomys* SA. **Family Dasyproctidae,** Pleist.–R. SA., *Dasyprocta.* **Family Caviidae,** Olig.–R. SA., Pleist. NA., *Cavia* Plioc.–R. SA., *Hydrochoerus* Plioc.–R. SA. Pleist. NA. **Family Chinchillidae,** Olig.–R. SA., *Megamys* Pleist. **Family Capromyidae,** Mioc.–R. SA., R. WInd., *Neoromys* Mioc., *Myopotamus* Pleist.–R. SA. **Family Octo- dontidae,** Mioc.–R. SA., *Ctenomys.* **Family Ctenodactylidae,** R. Af., *Ctenodactylus.* **Family Petromyidae,** R. Af., *Petromys.* **Family Thryonomyidae,** ?Mioc. Pleist.–R. Af., *Thryonomys.* **Family Heptaxodontidae,** Pleist. WInd., *Heptaxodon.*

INFRAORDER UNCERTAIN: **Family Eurymylidae,** Paleoc. As., *Eurymylus.*

SUBORDER DUPLICIDENTATA. **Family Leporidae,** Olig.–R. NA. As., Plioc.–R. Eu., R. SA. Af., *Palaeolagus* Olig. NA., *Desmolagus* Olig. As., *Lepus* Mioc.–R., *Oryctolagus* Pleist.–R. Eu. Af. **Family Ochotonidae,** Olig.–R. Eu., Pleist.–R. NA., Mioc. Af., R. As., *Ti- tanomys* Olig.–Mioc. Eu., *Prolagus* Mioc.–Pleist. Eu., *Ochotona* Plioc.–R.

ORDER CETACEA

SUBORDER ARCHAEOCETI. **Family Protocetidae,** M.–U. Eoc. Af., *Protocetus Prozeuglodon.* **Family Dorudontidae,** U. Eoc. NA., Olig. Eu. NZ., *Dorudon* Eoc. **Family Zeuglodon- tidae,** M. Eoc. Af., U. Eoc. Eu. NA., *Zeuglodon.*

SUBORDER ODONTOCETI. **Family Agorophiidae,** U. Eoc. NA., *Agorophius.* **Family Squalo- dontidae,** Mioc. Eu. NA. Aus. NZ., Mioc.–Plioc. SA., *Squalodon Prosqualodon.* **Family Iniidae,** Mioc. NA., Plioc.–R. SA., R. As., *Inia* R. SA. **Family Ziphiidae,** Mioc.–Plioc. Eu., Mioc. NA. SA., R. Oc., *Mesoplodon* Mioc. Eu., *Ziphius* R. **Family Delphinidae,** Mioc.–Pleist. Eu. NA. SA. As., Mioc. Af., Pleist. NA., R. Oc., *Kentriodon* Mioc. NA., *Delphinus.* **Family Platanistidae,** Mioc.–Pleist. NA., R. As., *Platanista* R. **Family Physeteridae,** Mioc.–Pleist. Eu. Aus. NA. As., Mioc. SA., R. Oc., *Physodon* Mioc., *Aulophyseter* Mioc. NA., *Physeter* R.

SUBORDER MYSTICETI. **Family Cetotheriidae,** Olig.–Plioc. Eu., Mioc. NA. SA., *Cetotherium.* **Family Balaeonopteridae,** Mioc.–Pleist. NA., Plioc.–Pleist. Eu., R. Oc., *Plesiocetus* Mioc., *Balaeonoptera* Mioc.–R. **Family Balaenidae,** Mioc.–Pleist. SA., Plioc.–Pleist. Eu., R. Oc., *Balaena* R.

SUBORDER uncertain: **Family Patriocetidae,** Olig. Eu., *Patriocetus.*

ORDER PRIMATES

SUBORDER LEMUROIDEA. **Family Adapidae,** Eoc. Eu. NA., *Adapis Pronycticebus* Eu., *Pelycodus Notharctus* NA. **Family Lemuridae,** Pleist.–R. Mad., *Megaladapis Archaeolemur* Pleist., *Lemur Indris Chiromys.* **Family Lorisidae,** R. Af. As., *Loris* As., *Galago* Af. **Family Plesiadapidae,** Paleoc.–Eoc. Eu. NA., *Plesiadapis (Nothodectes).*

SUBORDER TARSIOIDEA. **Family Tarsiidae,** Paleoc.–Eoc. Eu. NA., R. EInd., *Tetonius (Anaptomorphus) Omomys* Eoc. NA., *Necrolemur* Eoc. Eu., *Tarsius* R.

SUBORDER ANTHROPOIDEA

INFRAORDER PLATYRRHINI. **Family Cebidae,** Mioc.–R. SA., *Homunculus* Mioc., *Cebus* R. **Family Hapalidae,** Pleist.–R. SA., *Hapale.*

INFRAORDER CATARRHINI. **Family Cercopithecidae,** Olig.–R. Af., Plioc.–R. As., Plioc.–Pleist. Eu., *Parapithecus* Olig., *Macacus* Plioc.–Pleist. Eu. Plioc.–R. As. R. Af., *Papio* Plioc.–Pleist. As. Pleist.–R. Af., *Libypithecus* Plioc. Af., *Mesopithecus* Plioc. Eu., *Semnopithecus* Plioc. Eu. Plioc.–R. As. **Family Simiidae,** Olig.–R. Af., Mioc.–R. As., Mioc.–Plioc. Eu., *Propliopithecus* Olig. Af., *Pliopithecus* Mioc.–Plioc. Eu. Mioc. Af., *Dryopithecus* Mioc.–Plioc. As. Eu. Mioc. Af., *Hylobates* R. As. EInd., *Simia* Plioc.–R. As., *Anthropopithecus Gorilla* R. Af., *Australopithecus* ?Pleist. Af. **Family Hominidae,** Pleist. Eu. As. Af. EInd., R. Cos., *Pithecanthropus* Pleist. Java, *Sinanthropus* Pleist. China, *Eoanthropus* Pleist. England., *Homo* Pleist.–R.

BIBLIOGRAPHY

The books and papers listed below include but a small proportion of even the more fundamental and important works dealing with fossil vertebrates. Special emphasis has been given to comprehensive monographs, bibliographic sources, and well-illustrated descriptions of typical forms. Some notes regarding workers in the field have been included.

Vertebrate paleontology was essentially founded by Cuvier somewhat over a century ago. As a comparative anatomist he studied petrefactions in the light of his knowledge of modern types. Much of his work is summarized in his *Ossemens fossiles* (No. 5). Sir Richard Owen, working somewhat later in the nineteenth century, was, again, a comparative anatomist and the first English paleontologist of importance. Von Meyer, his contemporary, published many fine works on German fossils, and Agassiz's important work on fossil fishes (No. 21) also dates from the first half of the century. Neither Cuvier, Owen, nor Agassiz believed in evolution. Darwin did no original work in paleontology, but the acceptance of his theories gave a new point to the study of fossils and led to a wide expansion of the field.

In America little work was done until exploration had opened up the great western fossil country. Joseph Leidy, the anatomist, whose active career in the field of paleontology was mainly between 1850 and 1875, was the first American worker of importance. In the late sixties Cope of Philadelphia and Marsh of New Haven entered the field and dominated it until the closing years of the century; Osborn, Scott and Williston began work in the '70s.

GENERAL WORKS

1. ZITTEL, K. A. VON. *Gründzüge der Paläontologie.* Munich and Berlin.

    This useful work covers both invertebrates and vertebrates. The last German edition of Volume 2 (*Vertebrata*), revised by Broili and Schlosser, was published in 1923. In an English translation edited by Eastman, Volume 2 (*Fishes, Amphibians, Reptiles and Birds*) was published in 1902 and is thus out of date; Volume 3 (*Mammals*), published in 1925, dates in the main from the same period, but a few of the more important connections and additions have been made by Sir A. Smith Woodward. [An English revision of Volume 2 has just appeared—March, 1933.]

2. ABEL, O. 1919. *Die Stämme der Wirbeltiere.* Berlin and Leipzig. Pp. 914.

    Contains numerous useful illustrations, particularly of fishes and reptiles.

3. WOODWARD, A. SMITH. 1898. *Outlines of Vertebrate Paleontology for Students of Zoölogy.* Cambridge. Pp. 494.

    Excellent, but out of date in many respects because of more recent discoveries.

4. LULL, R. S. 1929. *Organic Evolution.* 2d ed. New York. Pp. 762, 31 pls.

    Good elementary accounts of a number of vertebrate groups, including dinosaurs and several mammalian orders.

5. CUVIER, G. 1834–36. *Recherches sur les ossemens fossiles, où l'on rétablit les caractères de plusieurs animaux dont les révolutions du globe ont détruit les espèces.* 4th ed. 4°. Paris. 10 vols., 2 vols. pls.

    The first great paleontological work. First issued in 1812.

6. ABEL, O. 1912. *Grundzüge der Palaeobiologie der Wirbeltiere.* Stuttgart. Pp. 703.

    A stimulating study of adaptations in living and fossil vertebrates.

7. ABEL, O. 1927. *Lebensbilder aus der Tierwelt der Vorzeit.* 2d ed. Jena. Pp. 714.

    Interesting discussion of a number of representative faunas from Permian to Pleistocene.

BIBLIOGRAPHIES

A few general sources are noted here; other more restricted bibliographies are cited under the various groups.

8. *Neues Jahrbuch für Mineralogie, Geologie und Palaeontologie.* 1883——. Stuttgart.

Contains abstracts of practically all the paleontological literature of the past century. Index volumes have been published at irregular intervals.

9. *The Zoölogical Record.* 1864——. London.

A year-by-year bibliography of all zoölogical papers, arranged taxonomically. The literature on fossils is well covered in the more recent volumes, less so in the earlier issues.

10. *Biological Abstracts.* 1926——. Philadelphia.

Covers all biological literature including paleontology.

11. HAY, O. P. 1902. "Bibliography and Catalogue of the Fossil Vertebrata of North America," *Bull. U.S. Geol. Surv. No. 179.* Pp. 868. 1929. "Second Bibliography, etc.," *Publ. Carnegie Inst. Washington, No. 390.* 2 vols. Pp. 2003.

These works list every citation of every American fossil form, together with the general literature on every group ever present in North America.

EVOLUTION

12. WELLS, H. G.; HUXLEY, J. S.; and WELLS, G. P. 1931. *The Science of Life.* London and New York. Pp. 1514.

Includes an excellent presentation of evolutionary theories.

VERTEBRATE STRUCTURE

13. BEER, G. R. DE. 1928. *Vertebrate Zoölogy: an Introduction to the Comparative Anatomy, Embryology, and Evolution of Chordate Animals.* London. Pp. 505.

Brief but good account of vertebrate anatomy.

14. VERSLUYS, J., and OTHERS. 1927. *Vergleichende Anatomie der Wirbeltiere.* Berlin. Pp. 906.

A sound, comprehensive, and up-to-date work. The chapter on the skeleton (by Versluys) takes the fossil forms into account.

15. GOODRICH, E. S. 1930. *Studies on the Structure and Development of Vertebrates.* London. Pp. 907.

Excellent discussion of many problems dealing with the skull, backbone, fins, etc., in lower vertebrates.

16. REYNOLDS, S. H. 1913. *The Vertebrate Skeleton.* 2d ed. Pp. 535.

A standard work, prepared from the paleontologist's point of view, although dealing primarily with living forms.

17. EDINGER, T. 1929. "Die fossilen Gehirne," *Ergeb. Anat. u. Entwickl.* Vol. 28. Pp. 249.

Endocranial structure in all vertebrate classes.

18. GREGORY, W. K. 1929. *Our Face from Fish to Man.* New York. Pp. 295.

Evolution of cranial structure in fossil and recent forms from fish through primitive tetrapods to mammals.

LOWER CHORDATES AND VERTEBRATE ORIGINS

19. DELAGE, V., and HÉROUARD, E. 1898. *Traité de Zoologie concrète.* Tome 8, *Les Procordés.* Paris. Pp. 379; 54 pls.

Detailed and well-illustrated description of structure and development of lower chordates.

De Beer (13) also gives a concise account.

20. PATTEN, W. 1912. *The Evolution of the Vertebrates and Their Kin.* Philadelphia. Pp. 486; 309 figs.

An elaborate presentation of the arachnid theory, with much of the argument based on fossil types.

FISHES, GENERAL

The first comprehensive study of fossil fishes was that of Louis Agassiz nearly a century ago (21). A more recent thorough survey of the field is that of Smith Woodward (22). With these two workers should be ranked Traquair, who published many important papers on Scotch Paleozoic fishes during the latter decades of the nineteenth century; and no mention of fossil fishes could be made without reference to Hugh Miller, the Scottish stonemason, who collected much of the Old Red Sandstone material studied by Agassiz and published several volumes compounded of paleontology, theology, and homely philosophy. Among the comparatively few American workers who have devoted themselves mainly to fishes may be mentioned Newberry, Dean, Eastman, and Patten. Among later European workers may be mentioned Pander and Rohon, older Russian workers on Paleozoic material; Leriche, Priem, and Sauvage in France; Hennig and the erratic but brilliant Jaekel in Germany; Watson in England; and Stensiö of Stockholm, whose thorough work on cranial structure has profoundly modified our concepts of fish history.

21. Agassiz, L. 1833–44. *Récherches sur les poissons fossiles.* 5 vols. Pp. 1420; 369 pls. With supplement, *Monographie des poissons fossiles du vieux grès rouge on système Dévonien (Old Red Sandstone); des Iles Britanniques et de Russie.* Neuchatel. Pp. 207; 42 pls.

An account of all forms known at that time. While the text is antiquated, the numerous colored plates are still very valuable.

22. Woodward, A. Smith. 1889–1901. *Catalogue of the Fossil Fishes in the British Museum.* London. 4 vols. Pp. 2493; 70 pls.

Not merely a catalogue; in reality a summary of our knowledge of fossil fishes to the date of publication. It is still extremely useful, especially for Mesozoic and Tertiary forms.

23. Dean, B. 1916–23. *A Bibliography of Fishes.* New York. 3 vols. Pp. 2160.

A complete bibliography of all works on fishes, recent and fossil. An author list, with comprehensive indices.

24. Goodrich, E. S. 1909. *A Treatise on Zoölogy* (ed. E. Ray Lankester), Part IX, *Vertebrata Craniata,* First Fascicle, "Cyclostomes and Fishes," London. Pp. 534.

An excellent account of fishes, living and fossil, with particular attention to morphology. Still good except for some Paleozoic groups.

25. Gregory, W. K. 1928. "Studies on the Body Forms of Fishes," *Zoologica* (New York), 8:325–421.

Observations on probable habits and relations of fossil types.

AGNATHA

Our older knowledge of ostracoderms is due in great measure to Lankester and particularly Traquair. Of recent work, that of Stensiö and Kiaer is the most important.

26. Stensiö, E. A. 1927. "The Downtonian and Devonian Vertebrates of Spitzbergen. Part I; Family Cephalaspidae," *Skrifter om Svalbard og Nordishavet, No. 12* (Norske Videnskaps-Akademi i Oslo). 2 vols. Pp. 391; 112 pls.

An exhaustive study of the cranial structure of the Osteostraci, with an account of previous work and a discussion of the structure and relationships of all the agnathous types.

27. Kiaer, J. 1924. "The Downtonian Fauna of Norway. I, Anaspida," *Videnskapsselskapets-Skrifter, 1924,* Part 1, *Mat.-Naturv. Klasse No. 6.* Pp. 139; 14 pls.

First discovered by Traquair in the late nineties, the anaspids became adequately known only as a result of Kiaer's work. A thorough description of the morphology and evolutionary significance of these forms.

28. KIAER, J. 1927. "The Structure of the Mouth of the Oldest Known Vertebrates, Pteraspids and Cephalaspids," *Palaeobiologica*, 1:117–34; 2 pls.

   Description of the *Pteraspis* shield. An important posthumous monograph on this group is in press.

29. SOLLAS, W. J., and SOLLAS, I. B. J. 1903. "An Account of the Devonian Fish *Palaeospondylus gunni* Traquair," *Philos. Trans. Roy. Soc. London*, Ser. B, 196:267–94; 2 pls.

   First described by Traquair, the nature of this little fish has been hotly debated. Sollas gives a résumé of this discussion and an account of the result of serial sectioning.

30. BULMAN, O. M. B. 1931. "Note on *Palaeospondylus gunni* Traquair," *Ann. and Mag. Nat. Hist. London*, Ser. 10, 8:179–90; 1 pl.

   A new restoration.

31. TRAQUAIR, R. H. 1899. "Report on Fossil Fishes Collected by the Geological Survey of Scotland in the Silurian Rocks of the South of Scotland," *Trans. Roy. Soc. Edin.*, 39:827–64; 5 pls. *Supplement*, 1905. 40:879–88; 3 pls.

   Thelodus and *Lanarkia*, *Birkenia* and *Lasanius*.

32. LANKESTER, E. R. 1867–69. *A Monograph of the Fishes of the Old Red Sandstone of Britain.* Part I, *The Cephalaspidae.* Monogr. Palaeontogr. Soc. London. Pp. 62; 14 pls.

   Many figures of specimens of cephalaspids and pteraspids. The text is antiquated.

33. HOLMES, G. B. 1928. "A Bibliography of the Conodonts, with Descriptions of Early Mississippian Species," *Proc. U.S. Nat. Mus.*, Vol. 72. Pp. 38; 11 pls.

CHONDRICHTHYES, GENERAL

34. DEAN, B. 1909. "Studies on Fossil Fishes (Sharks, Chimaeroids, and Arthrodires)," *Mem. Amer. Mus. Nat. Hist.*, 9:211–87; 16 pls.

   Good illustrations of *Cladoselache* and late Devonian arthrodires.

35. WOODWARD, A. SMITH. 1921. "Observations on Some Extinct Elasmobranch Fishes," *Proc. Linnean Soc. London, Session 133*, pp. 29–39.

   Summary of the more recent work on lower gnathostomes and suggestions as to relationships.

ARTHRODIRES

The earlier work on this group was mainly done by Pander and Traquair in Europe, and by Newberry, Dean, and Hussakof in America. Heinz of Oslo and Gross are the most recent workers in this field.

36. HEINZ, A. 1931. "Untersuchungen über den Bau der Arthrodira," *Acta Zoologica*, 12:225–39; 2 pls.

   General account of the group.

37. HEINZ, A. 1930. "Revision of the Structure of *Coccosteus decipiens*," *Ag. Norsk. geol. tidsskr.*, 12:291–313; 2 pls.

38. HEINZ, A. 1932. *The Structure of Dinichthys; a Contribution to Our Knowledge of the Arthrodira.* Bashford Dean Memorial Volume. New York. Pp. 115–224; 9 pls.

39. GROSS, W. 1932. "Die Arthrodira Wildungens," *Geol. und Pal. Abh.*, Vol. 19. Heft 1. Pp. 61; 2 pls.

   Describes a large number of interesting forms from the early Upper Devonian.

40. HEINZ, A. 1929. "Die downtonischen und devonischen Vertebrata von Spitzbergen. II. Acanthaspiden," *Skrifter om Svalbard og Ishavet, No. 22* (Oslo). Pp. 81; 24 pls. *Nachtrag.* Pp. 20; 3 pls.

   Primitive early Devonian forms.

—See also Dean, No. 34.

ANTIARCHA

41. TRAQUAIR, R. H. 1894–1906. *The Asterolepidae.* Mon. Palaeontogr. Soc. London. Pp. 134; 31 pls.

42. PATTEN, W. 1904. "New Facts Concerning *Bothriolepis*," *Biol. Bull.*, **7**:113–24.
    See also No. 20.

43. STENSIÖ, E. A. 1931. "Upper Devonian Vertebrates from East Greenland," *Meddel. om Grönland* (Copenhagen), Vol. **86**, No. 1. Pp. 207; 36 pls.
    A thorough description of *Bothriolepis* and *Remigolepis* and a general consideration of the position of the group.

44. GROSS, W. 1931. "*Asterolepis ornata.* Eichw. und das Antiarchi-Problem," *Palaeontogr.*, **75**:1–62; 12 pls.

ACANTHODII

45. DEAN, B. 1907. "Notes on Acanthodian Sharks," *Amer. Jour. Anat.*, **7**:209–26.

46. REIS, O. M. 1896. "Ueber *Acanthodes Bronni* Ag." *Morphol., Arbeiten*, **6**:143–218; 2 pls.

ARMORED SHARKS

47. STENSIÖ, E. A. 1925. *On the Head of the Macropetalichthyids, with Certain Remarks on the Head of the Other Arthrodires.* Field Mus. Nat. Hist. Chicago, Geol. Ser., No. 4, pp. 91–197; 13 pls.
    Description of braincase structure and bearing of this form on evolution of lower gnathostomes.

48. WOODWARD, A. SMITH. 1924. "Un nouvel Elasmobranche (*Cratoselache Pruvosti* gen. et. sp. nov.) du calcaire carbonifère inférieur de Denée." *Livre Jubil. Cinquant. fond. Soc. Géol. Belgique* 1924, pp. 59–62, 1 pl.

CLADOSELACHII

Cladoselache has been studied especially by Dean (see No. 34, Part I, and reference there to earlier papers).

PLEURACANTHS

49. REIS, O. M. 1897. "Das Skelett der Pleuracanthiden und ihre systematische Bedeutung," *Abh. Senchant. naturf. Ges. Frankfurt*, **20**:57–155; 1 pl.
—Good figures in Fritsch, No. 79, Vols. **2** and **3**.

ELASMOBRANCHS

A general account in Goodrich, No. 24.

50. JAEKEL, O. 1894. *Die Selachier von Bolca, ein Beitrag zur Morphogenie der Wirbeltiere.* Berlin. Pp. 176; 8 pls.
    Figures a number of Eocene forms.

51. FOWLER, A. W. 1911. "A Description of the Fossil Fish Remains of the Cretaceous Eocene and Miocene Formations of New Jersey," *Bull. Geol. Surv. N.J.*, **4**:22–182.
    One of numerous illustrated accounts of shark teeth.
On *Hybodus* and allied types, see Woodward, No. 62.

GEMUNDINA

52. BROILI, F. 1930. "Ueber *Gemündina Stürtzi*," *Abhandl. bavar. Akad. Wiss., Math.-naturw. Abt.*, N.S., **6**:1–24; 4 pls.
    First described by Traquair; redescribed and restored in this recent paper.

BRADYODONTS

The grouping of the Paleozoic pavement-toothed types as bradyodonts was suggested by Smith Woodward (No. 36). For teeth of these forms see the following:

53. DAVIS, J. W. 1883. "On the Fossil Fishes of the Carboniferous Limestone Series of Great Britain," *Trans. Roy. Dublin Soc.*, 2d ser., **1**:327–548; 3 pls.

HOLOCEPHALI

54. DEAN, B. 1906. "Chimaeroid Fishes and Their Development," *Publ. Carnegie Inst. Washington, No. 32.* Pp. 195; 144 figs.

Includes a résumé of fossils. See also Dean, No. 34.

ACTINOPTERYGIANS

The papers listed below deal mainly with Paleozoic and Mesozoic forms. The literature on teleosts is vast and widely scattered. Most of the fossil types, however, are summed up in Woodward, No. 22, Vols. **3** and **4**, and Goodrich, No. 24.

55. TRAQUAIR, R. H. 1875. "On the Structure and Systematic Position of the Genus *Cheirolepis*," *Ann. and Mag. Nat. Hist.*, 4th ser., **15**:237–49; 1 pl.

Restoration of the oldest actinopterygian.

56. TRAQUAIR, R. H. 1877–1914. *The Ganoid Fishes of the British Carboniferous Formations.* Mon. Palaeontogr. Soc. London. Pp. 186; 40 pls.

Good descriptions of palaeoniscids. Figures also in Fritsch, No. 79.

57. WATSON, D. M. S. 1925. "The Structure of Certain Palaeoniscids and the Relationships of That Group with Other Bony Fish," *Proc. Zoöl. Soc. London*, 1925, pp. 815–70; 2 pls.

58. WATSON, D. M. S. 1928. "On Some Points in the Structure of Palaeoniscid and Allied Fish," *Proc. Zoöl. Soc. London*, 1928, pp. 48–70.

This and No. 57 are important morphological papers, particularly for skull structure.

59. BROUGH, J. 1931. "On Fossil Fishes from the Karroo-System and Some General Considerations on the Bony Fishes of the Triassic Period," *Proc. Zoöl. Soc. London*, *1931*, pp. 235–96; 4 pls.

Good figures of Triassic chondrosteans and general discussion of Triassic bony-fish faunas.

60. TRAQUAIR, R. S. 1879. "On the Structure and Affinities of the Platysomidae," *Trans. Roy. Soc. Edinburgh*, **29**:343–91; 4 pls.

61. GOODRICH, E. S. 1927. "*Polypterus* a Palaeoniscid?" *Palaeobiologica*, **1**:87–92.

Advocates placing this living type in Actinopterygii rather than Crossopterygii.

62. WOODWARD, A. SMITH. 1902–12. *The Fishes of the English Chalk*, Mon. Palaeontogr. Soc. London. Pp. 264; 54 pls.

Mainly early teleosts, with many good figures.

63. WOODWARD, A. SMITH. 1916–19. *The Fossil Fishes of the English Wealden and Purbeck Formations.* Mon. Palaeontogr. Soc. London. Pp. 148; 26 pls.

Mainly holosteans, also *Leptolepis* and *Hybodus*.

CROSSOPTERYGIANS AND LUNGFISH

The classic figures of these forms are the plates of Agassiz (No. 21) and Pander (No. 66). The relationship of this group to tetrapods has been stressed by Gregory (No. 64) and Watson (No. 74). A study of cranial structure by Stensiö is in preparation.

64. GREGORY, W. K. 1915. "Present Status of the Problem of the Origin of the Tetrapoda, with Special Reference to the Skull and Paired Limbs," *Ann. N.Y. Acad. Sci.*, **26**:317–83; 1 pl.

Relations of crossopterygians and lungfish to tetrapod ancestry.

65. BRYANT, W. L. 1919. "On the Structure of *Eusthenopteron*," *Bull. Buffalo Soc. Nat. Sci.*, **13**:1–23; 18 pls.

See also Watson, No. 74.

66. PANDER, C. H. 1860. *Ueber die Saurodipterinen, Dendrodonten und Glyptolepiden des Devonischen Systems.* St. Petersburg. 4°.

Good figures of Devonian specimens.

67. GOODRICH, E. S. 1919. "Restoration of the Head of *Osteolepis*," *Jour. Linn. Soc. London Zoöl.*, **34**:181–88.

68. WATSON, D. M. S. 1921. "On the Coelacanth Fish," *Ann. Mag. Nat. Hist.*, 9th ser., **8**:320–37.

Skull structure. See also Woodward, No. 62.

69. STENSIÖ, E. A. 1921. *Triassic Fishes from Spitzbergen.* Teil I. Wien. Pp. 307; 35 pls.

Especially coelacanths, but also a general discussion of bony-fish relationships.

70. DOLLO, L. 1895. "Sur la phylogénie des Dipneustes," *Bull. Soc. Belge Géol. Paléont. et Hydrol.*, **9**:79–128.

A brilliant essay in which the evolutionary trend of the lungfish series was first clearly demonstrated.

71. WATSON, D. M. S., and GILL, E. L. 1923. "The Structure of Certain Palaeozoic Dipnoi," *Jour. Linn. Soc. London Zoöl.*, **35**:163–216.

Skull restorations.

AMPHIBIA

The earlier finds of amphibians were principally described by Huxley (British material), Fric and Credner (continental Europe), and Cope (America). Among more recent workers may be mentioned Broili, Broom, Case, Moodie, Watson, and Williston. Particularly important in pointing out the evolutionary trends in the Amphibia are Nos. 73 and 74. For a bibliography see No. 89.

DEVONIAN FORMS

72. SÄVE-SÖDERBERGH, G. 1932. "Preliminary Note on Devonian Stegocephalians from East Greenland," *Meddelelser om Grönland* (Copenhagen), **94**, No. 7. Pp. 107; 22 pls.

A more detailed account is to be published in 1933.

LABYRINTHODONTS

73. WATSON, D. M. S. 1919. "The Structure, Evolution and Origin of the Amphibia—The 'Orders' Rachitomi and Stereospondyli," *Philos. Trans. Roy. Soc. London*, Ser. B, **209**:1–73; 2 pls.

74. WATSON, D. M. S. 1926. "The Evolution and Origin of the Amphibia," *Philos. Trans. Roy. Soc. London*, Ser. B, **214**:189–257.

Treats of the Embolomeri.

—On the origin of the Amphibia see also Gregory, No. 64.

75. WATSON, D. M. S. 1930. "The Carboniferous Amphibia of Scotland," *Palaeontologia Hungarica*, **1**:221–52; 3 pls.

Skulls of some of the oldest and most primitive tetrapods.

76. CASE, E. C. 1911. "Revision of the Amphibia and Pisces of the Permian of North America," *Publ. Carnegie Inst. Wash., No. 146.* Pp. 148; 25 pls.

—The two following references treat of stereospondyls:

77. FRAAS, E. 1889. "Die Labyrinthodonten der schwäbischen Trias," *Palaeontogr.*, **36**:1–158; 17 pls.

78. WIMAN, E. 1915. "Ueber die Stegocephalen aus der Trias Spitzbergens," *Bull. Geol. Inst. Upsala*, **13**:1–34; 9 pls. (see also *ibid.*, **14**:229–40; 3 pls.).

—Nos. 79, 81, and 83 also treat somewhat of labyrinthodonts.

SMALLER AMPHIBIANS

79. FRITSCH, A. 1879–1901. *Fauna der Gaskohle und der Kalkstein der Permformation Böhmens.* Prague. 4 vols., 4°. Pp. 492; 154 pls.

Many colored plates of amphibians, particularly branchiosaurs and lepospondyls.

80. COPE, E. D. 1875. "Synopsis of the Extinct Batrachia from the Coal Measures," *Rept. Geol. Surv. Ohio, Palaeontology,* 2:350–411; 20 pls.

Figures much of the American Carboniferous material (mainly branchiosaurs and lepospondyls). This is revised in the two following papers:

81. ROMER, A. S. 1930. "The Pennsylvanian Tetrapods of Linton, Ohio," *Bull. Amer. Mus. Nat. Hist.,* 59:77–147.

82. STEEN, M. 1930. "The British Museum Collection of Amphibia from the Middle Coal Measures of Linton, Ohio," *Proc. Zoöl. Soc. London, 1930,* pp. 849–91; 6 pls.

83. CREDNER, H. 1881–93. "Die Stegocephalen und Saurier aus dem Rothliegenden des Plauen'schen Grundes bei Dresden, Part I–X." *Zeitschr. deutsch. Geol. Ges.,* Vols. 33–35, 37–38, 42. Pp. 345; 45 pls., branchiosaurs described in Parts I–V, IX.

Permian branchiosaurs.

84. BULMAN, O. M. B., and WHITTARD, W. F. 1926. "On *Branchiosaurus* and Allied Genera (Amphibia)," *Proc. Zoöl. Soc. London, 1926,* pp. 535–97; 4 pls.

A restudy of typical branchiosaurs.

85. SOLLAS, W. J. 1920. "On the Structure of *Lysorophus* as Exposed by Serial Sections," *Phil. Trans. Roy. Soc. London,* Ser. B, 212:1–47; 1 pl.

86. DOUTHITT, H. 1917. *The Structure and Relationships of Diplocaulus.* "Contrib. Walker Mus.," Vol. 2. Pp. 1–40; 2 pls.

REPTILES

Owen in England and Leidy and Cope in America were the most prominent of earlier writers. Among later workers in the field may be mentioned Williston, Baur, Broili, Nopcsa, Broom (especially therapsids), Case (Permian and Triassic), Watson (especially therapsids), Seeley (pterosaurs and therapsids), Brown, Gilmore, and von Huene (especially dinosaurs).

87. WILLISTON, S. W. 1925. *The Osteology of Reptiles,* ed. W. K. Gregory. Cambridge. Pp. 300.

A valuable account of the skeleton of fossil reptiles, followed by a systematic section.

88. WATSON, D. M. S. 1928. Article "Reptiles," in *Encyclopaedia Brittanica,* 14th ed., 19: 180–200.

A concise and up-to-date account with much emphasis on fossils.

89. NOPCSA, F. VON. 1926. "Osteologia reptilium fossilium et recentium," *Fossilium catalogus,* Pars 27. Berlin. Pp. 391. Also "Supplement," *ibid.,* Pars 50 (1931). Pp. 62.

Lists (with comments as to content) every paper of importance dealing with fossil reptiles and amphibians.

90. WILLISTON, W. S. 1914. *Water Reptiles of the Past and Present.* Chicago. Pp. 258.

Semipopular account of aquatic groups.

91. OWEN, R. 1849–1884. *A History of British Fossil Reptilia.* Reprinted from publications of the Palaeontographical Society, etc., London.

Many excellent figures of Mesozoic reptiles—turtles, dinosaurs, marine reptiles, etc.

92. WILLISTON, S. W. 1911. *American Permian Vertebrates.* Chicago. Pp. 183; 38 pls.

Seymouria, Varanops, etc.

93. ANDREWS, C. W. 1910–13. *A Descriptive Catalogue of the Marine Reptiles of the Oxford Clay.* London. 2 vols., 4°. Pp. 411; 18 pls.

Plesiosaurs, crocodilians, ichthyosaurs. Good figures.

COTYLOSAURIA

The American forms have been mainly described by Cope, Broili, Case, and Williston. Pareiasaurs were first adequately described by Seeley; the South African forms are now being revised by Haughton and Boonstra (No. 97).

94. CASE, E. C. 1911. "A Revision of the Cotylosauria of North America," *Publ. Carnegie Inst. Wash., No. 145.* Pp. 122; 14 pls.

Particularly *Diadectes*.

95. WATSON, D. M. S. 1919. "On *Seymouria*, the Most Primitive Known Reptile," *Proc. Zoöl. Soc. London, 1918*, pp. 267–301.

See also Williston, No. 92. This important form was first described by Broili.

96. ROMER, A. S. 1928. "A Skeletal Model of the Primitive Reptile *Seymouria*, and the Phylogenetic Position of That Type," *Jour. Geol.*, **36**:248–60.

97. HAUGHTON, S. H., and BOONSTRA, L. D. 1929–30. "Pareiasaurian Studies," *Ann. S. Af. Mus.*, **28**:79–122, 261–89, 297–367, 429–503; 3 pls.

98. WILLISTON, S. W. 1912. "Restoration of *Limnoscelis*, a Cotylosaur Reptile from New Mexico," *Amer. Jour. Sci.*, 4th ser., **34**:457–68.

99. WILLISTON, S. W. 1917. "*Labidosaurus* Cope, a Lower Permian Cotylosaur Reptile from Texas," *Jour. Geol.*, **25**:309, 321.

100. SUSHKIN, P. P. 1928. "Contributions to the Cranial Morphology of *Captorhinus* Cope," *Palaeobiologica*, **1**:263–80.

101. WATSON, D. M. S. 1914. "*Procolophon trigoniceps*, a Cotylosaurian Reptile from South Africa," *Proc. Zoöl. Soc. London*, 1914, pp. 735–47; 3 pls.

CHELONIA

Turtles are the commonest of fossils in many late Mesozoic and Tertiary deposits, and more papers have been published on this group than on any other reptilian order; most, however, are routine descriptions of remains of the shell. For a brief general account, see Williston, No. 90.

102. HAY, O. P. 1908. "The Fossil Turtles of North America," *Publ. Carnegie Inst. Wash., No. 75.* Pp. 568; 113 pls.

103. WIELAND, G. R. 1909. "Revision of the Protostegidae," *Amer. Jour. Sci.*, 4th ser., **27**:101–30; 3 pls.

Structure of *Archelon*, a Cretaceous marine turtle.

104. JAEKEL, O. 1914–16. "Die Wirbeltierfunde aus dem Keuper von Halberstadt," *Palaeont. Zeitschr.*, **1**:155–215, 2 pls.; **2**:88–214, 7 pls.

Describes *Triassochelys*, a primitive Triassic form.

105. NOPCSA, F. 1923. "*Kallokibotium*, a Primitive Amphichelydean Tortoise from the Uppermost Cretaceous of Hungary," *Palaeont. Hungarica*, **1**:1–34; 4 pls.

106. WATSON, D. M. S. 1914. "*Eunotosaurus africanus* Seeley and the Ancestry of the Chelonia," *Proc. Zoöl. Soc. London*, 1914, pp. 1011–20; 1 pl.

MESOSAURS

107. McGREGOR, J. H. 1908. *On Mesosaurus brasiliensis, n. sp. from the Permian of Brazil.* Commisão dos Estudos das Minas de Carvão de Pedra do Brazil. Pp. 302–36; 4 pls.

ICHTHYOSAURS

Ichthyosaurs were among the first of fossil reptiles to be discovered and described by early writers such as Conybeare and Mantell. The typical Jurassic forms have been comprehensively reviewed by von Huene (No. 108). Triassic types have been studied by Merriam and Wiman. A brief account is given by Williston (No. 90).

108. HUENE, F. VON. 1922. *Die Ichthyosauria des Lias und ihre Zusammenhänge.* Berlin. Pp. 114; 22 pls.

With a general discussion of ichthyosaur evolution and a bibliography.

109. GILMORE, C. W. 1905. "Osteology of *Baptanodon* Marsh," *Mem. Carnegie Mus.*, 2:77–129, 6 pls.; 325–37, 3 pls.

A good account of the same form (*Ophthalmosaurus*) in Andrews, No. 93.

110. MERRIAM, J. C. 1908. "Triassic Ichthyosauria with Special Reference to the American Forms," *Mem. Univ. Calif.*, 1:1–196; 18 pls.

111. WIMAN, C. 1910. "Ichthyosaurier aus der Trias Spitzbergens," *Bull. Geol. Inst. Upsala*, 10:124–48; 6 pls. (see also *ibid.*, 11:230–41; 1 pl. [1912]).

PROTOROSAURIA

This group was established by Williston and may be regarded as merely a provisional assemblage.

See also Williston, No. 90.

112. WILLISTON, S. W. 1914. "The Osteology of Some American Permian Vertebrates," *Jour. Geol.*, 22:364–419.

On *Araeoscelis*, with an argument for its relationship to the lizards.

113. HUENE, F. VON. 1926. "Zur Beurteilung von *Protorosaurus*," *Centralbl. Min. Geol. Pal. 1926*, Abt. B., pp. 469–75.

SAUROPTERYGIANS

A good description of many of the European Jurassic forms will be found in Andrews, No. 93; see also Fraas, No. 115. Williston has been the main worker on the American Cretaceous plesiosaurs. A brief account in Williston, No. 90.

114. WILLISTON, S. W. 1903. "North American Plesiosaurs. Part I," *Publ. Field Mus. Dept. Geol.*, 2:1–77; 29 pls. (continued in *Amer. Jour. Sci.*, 21:221–36, 6 pls. [1906]; *Proc. U.S. Nat. Mus.*, 32: 477–89, 4 pls. [1907]; and *Jour. Geol.*, 16:715–36 [1908]).

115. FRAAS, E. 1910. "Plesiosaurier aus dem oberen Lias von Holzmaden," *Palaeontographica*, 57:105–40; 5 pls.

Figures two fine skeletons.

116. PEYER, B. 1923. "*Ceresiosaurus calcagnii* nov. gen. nov. spec." *Abh. Schweiz. Paläont. Ges.*, 51:1–68; 7 pls.

A nothosaur, with a discussion of other members of the group.

117. BROILI, F. 1912. "Zur Osteologie des Schädels von *Placodus*," *Palaeontogr.*, 59:147–55; 1 pl.

Good figures.

118. PEYER, B. 1931. "*Tanystropheus langobardicus*," *Abh. Schweiz. Pal. Gesellsch.*, Vol. 50. Pp. 110; 14 pls.

Excellent account of this curious sauropterygian.

EOSUCHIA

119. BROOM, R. 1914. "A New Thecodont Reptile," *Proc. Zoöl. Soc. London, 1914*, pp. 1072–77. (see also *Bull. Amer. Mus. Nat. Hist.*, 51:67–76).

On *Youngina*.

RHYNCHOCEPHALIANS

120. HUENE, F. VON. 1929. "Ueber Rhynchosaurier und andere Reptilien aus den Gondwana-Ablagerungen Südamerikas," *Geol. u. Paleont. Abhandl.*, Vol. 31. Pp. 62; 8 pls.

Scaphonyx, a rhynchosaur, with a résumé of the Triassic rhynchocephalians.

121. BROWN, B. 1905. "The Osteology of *Champsosaurus* Cope," *Mem. Amer. Mus. Nat. Hist.*, 9:1–26; 4 pls.
     See also Williston, No. 90.

SQUAMATA

     See Williston, No. 90.
     —On lizards:
122. FEJÉRVÁRY, G. J. DE. 1918. "Contributions to a monograph on Fossil Varanidae and on Megalanidae," *Ann. Mus. Hungar.*, 16:341–467; 2 pls.
123. GILMORE, C. W. 1928. "Fossil Lizards of North America," *Mem. Nat. Acad. Sci.*, 22:1–201; 27 pls.
     —On mosasaurs:
124. WILLISTON, S. W. 1898. "Mosasaurs," *Univ. Geol. Surv. Kansas*, 4:83–221; 63 pls.
125. OSBORN, H. F. 1899. "A Complete Mosasaur Skeleton, Osseous and Cartilaginous," *Mem. Amer. Mus. Nat. Hist.*, 1:167–88; 3 pls.
     —On snakes:
126. NOPCSA, F. 1923. "*Eidolosaurus* und *Pachyophis* zwei neue neocom-Reptilien," *Palaeontogr.*, 65:96–154.
127. NOPCSA, F. 1925. "Wirbeltier-Reste der Baharije-Stufe (unterstes Cenoman) 5. Die *Symoliophis*-Reste." *Abh. Bayer. Akad. 30*, Part 4. Pp. 1–27; 1 pl.

THECODONTIA

     Von Huene has worked most extensively on European forms; Broom and Haughton, on those of South Africa; Camp, Case, and Mehl are the most active workers on the American phytosaurs.
128. BROOM, R. 1913. "On the South African Pseudosuchian Euparkeria and Allied Genera," *Proc. Zoöl. Soc. London, 1913*, pp. 613–33; 5 pls.
     Skulls, etc., of some generalized thecodonts.
129. HUENE, F. VON. 1921. "Neue Pseudosuchier und Coelurosaurier aus dem württembergischen Keuper," *Acta Zoologica*, 2:329–403; 4 pls.
130. HUENE, F. VON. 1911. "Ueber *Erythrosuchus* Vertreter der neuen Reptil-Ordnung Pelycosimia," *Geol. u. Pal. Abh. Jena*, 10:1–60; 12 pls.
131. HAUGHTON, S. H. 1924. "The Fauna and Stratigraphy of the Stormberg Series," *Ann. S. Af. Mus.*, 12:323–497.
     Particularly *Sphenosuchus* and *Notochampsa*.
132. HUENE, F. VON. 1920. "Osteologie von *Aetosaurus ferratus*," *Acta Zoologica*, 1:465–91.
133. McGREGOR, J. H. 1906. "The Phytosauria, with Especial Reference to *Mystriosuchus* and *Rhytidodon*," *Mem. Amer. Mus. Nat. Hist.*, 9:29–101; 6 pls.
134. CAMP, C. L. 1930. "A Study of the Phytosaurs with Description of New Material from Western North America," *Mem. Univ. Calif.*, 10:1–161; 6 pls.
135. CASE, E. C. 1922. "New Stegocephalians and Reptiles from the Upper Triassic of Western Texas," *Publ. Carnegie Inst. Washington, No. 321.* Pp. 84; 14 pls.
     Desmatosuchus, phytosaurs, stereospondyls.

CROCODILIA

     A general account in Williston, No. 90.
136. MOOK, C. C. 1925. "A Revision of the Mesozoic Crocodilia of North America," *Bull. Amer. Mus. Nat. Hist.*, 51:319–432; 2 pls.
137. FRAAS, E. 1902. "Die Meer-krokodilier (Thalattosuchia) des oberen Jura unter specieller Berücksichtigung von *Dacosaurus* und *Geosaurus*," *Palaeontogr.*, 49:1–72; 8 pls.

PTEROSAURIA

Seeley in England and Pleininger in Germany are among the more important workers on European Jurassic pterosaurs. The American Cretaceous forms were described mainly by Marsh and Williston.

138. PLEININGER, F. 1930. "Pterosauria," *Fossilium catalogus*, Pars 45. Berlin. Pp. 84.
    Bibliography.

139. SEELEY, H. G. 1901. *Dragons of the Air*. London. Pp. 240.
    A good summary of older work, but illustrations none too good.

140. PLEININGER, F. 1901. "Beiträge zur Kenntniss der Flugsaurier," *Palaeontogr.*, **48**:65–90;
    2 pls.
    Pterodactylus, etc.

141. EATON, G. F. 1910. "Osteology of *Pteranodon*," *Mem. Conn. Acad. Sci.*, **2**:1–38; 31 pls.
    A good account of this large form.

142. STROMER, E. 1913. "Rekonstruktion des Flugsauriers *Rhamphorhynchus*," *Neues Jahrb. f. Mineral., Geol. u. Palaeont.*, pp. 49–68; 3 pls.

DINOSAURS, GENERAL

Many of the older European remains were described by Owen. In America Marsh was the principal student of dinosaurs during the latter part of the nineteenth century. More recent workers on dinosaurs include von Huene (particularly saurischians) and Nopcsa (especially ornithischians) in Europe, and Brown, Gilmore, Lull, Lambe, Holland, and Parks in North America. East African (Tendaguru) types are being described by Janensch and Hennig; von Huene has discussed South American forms. For an elementary account of dinosaurs, see Lull, No. 4. Restorations of a number of forms in Heilman, No. 177.

143. MATTHEW, W. D. 1915. *Dinosaurs*. New York: Amer. Mus. Nat. Hist. Pp. 117.
    A popular account.

144. MARSH, O. C. 1896. "The Dinosaurs of North America," *Sixteenth Ann. Rept. U.S. Geol. Surv.*, pp. 133–244; 84 pls.
    Summarizes all known of American types to that date. Still valuable.

SAURISCHIA—BIPEDS

145. HUENE, F. VON. 1932. *Die fossile Reptil-Ordnung Saurischia, ihre Entwicklung und Geschichte*. Berlin. 2 vols. 4°. Pp. 368; 56 pls.
    A modern summary of our knowledge of saurischian dinosaurs, with special reference to Triassic forms.

146. LULL, R. S. 1915. "Triassic Life of the Connecticut Valley," *Bull. Geol. and Nat. Hist. Surv. Conn.*, **24**:1–285; 12 pls.
    Footprints of early dinosaurs, etc.

147. MATTHEW, W. D., and BROWN, B. 1922. "The Family Deinodontidae," *Bull. Amer. Mus. Nat. History*, **46**:367–75.
    Discussion of theropod relationships.

148. HUENE, F. VON. 1926. "The Carnivorous Saurischia in the Jurassic and Cretaceous Formations, Principally in Europe," *Revista del Museo de La Plata*, **29**:35–167.
    Review of knowledge of theropods (in broad sense) to 1921; particularly discusses "*Megalosaurus*" of European Jurassic and Lower Cretaceous and *Compsognathus*.

149. GILMORE, C. W. 1920. "Osteology of the Carnivorous Dinosauria," *U.S. Nat. Mus. Bull. No. 110*. Pp. 159; 36 pls.
    Jurassic and Cretaceous types in North America, especially *Antrodemus* (*Allosaurus*) and *Ceratosaurus*.

150. OSBORN, H. F. 1917. "Skeletal Adaptations of *Ornitholestes, Struthiomimus, Tyrannosaurus*," *Bull. Amer. Mus. Nat. Hist.*, **35**:733–71; 4 pls.

   A well-illustrated account of these forms.

151. LAMBE, L. W. 1917. "The Cretaceous Theropod Dinosaur *Gorgosaurus*," *Geol. Surv. Canada. Mem. 100.* Pp. 84.

   Osteology of a large Cretaceous carnivore.

152. HUENE, F. VON. 1926. "Vollständige Osteologie eines Plateosauriden aus dem Schwäbischen Keuper," *Geol. u. Pal. Abh.*, **16**:139–79; 7 pls.

   Good description of the "pro-sauropod" *Plateosaurus*.

SAUROPODS

153. HUENE, F. VON. 1927. "Short Review of the Present Knowledge of the Sauropoda," *Mem. Queensland Museum*, **9**:121–26 (also in *Eclog. Geol. Helvet.*, Vol. **20** [1927]).

154. MOOK, C. C. 1918. "The Habitat of the Sauropodous Dinosaurs," *Jour. Geol.*, **26**:459–70.

155. GILMORE, C. W. 1925. "A Nearly Complete Articulated Skeleton of *Camarasaurus*, a Saurischian Dinosaur from the Dinosaur National Monument, Utah," *Mem. Carnegie Mus.*, **10**:347–84; 5 pls.

156. HATCHER, J. B. 1901. "*Diplodocus* (Marsh). Its Osteology, Taxonomy and Probable Habits, with a Restoration of the Skeleton," *Mem. Carnegie Mus.*, **1**:1–63; 13 pls.

   See also Holland, *Mem. Carnegie Mus.*, **2**:225–64, 8 pls. (1906); and **9**:379–403, 4 pls. (1924).

157. OSBORN, H. F., and MOOK, C. C. 1921. "*Camarasaurus, Amphicoelias*, and Other Sauropods of Cope," *Mem. Amer. Mus. Nat. Hist.*, N.S., **3**:247–87; 25 pls.

ORNITHOPODS

There is no comprehensive account of these interesting bipeds; papers describing some of the more interesting types are cited below.

158. HULKE, J. W. 1883. "An Attempt at a Complete Osteology of Hypsilophodon Foxii," *Philos. Trans. Roy. Soc. London*, **173**:1035–62; 12 pls.

   See also the following:

159. NOPCSA, F. 1905. "Notes on British Dinosaurs. Part I, *Hypsilophodon*." *Geol. Mag.*, 5th ser., **2**:203–8.

160. GILMORE, C. W. 1909. "Osteology of the Jurassic Reptile *Camptosaurus*," *Proc. U.S. Nat. Mus.*, **36**:197–332; 15 pls.

161. DOLLO, L. 1923. "Le centenaire des Iguanodons (1822–1922)," *Philos. Trans. Roy. Soc. London*, Ser. B, **213**:67–78; 1 pl.

   See also earlier articles by the same author in *Bull. Mus. Roy. Hist. Nat. Belgique*, Vols. **1–4** (1882–84).

162. BROWN, B. 1916. "*Corythosaurus casuarius*: Skeleton, Musculature and Epidermis," *Bull. Amer. Mus. Nat. Hist.*, **35**:709–16; 10 pls. (also *ibid.*, **33**:559–65; 1 pl.).

163. LAMBE, L. M. 1920. "The Hadrosaur *Edmontosaurus* from the Upper Cretaceous of Alberta," *Mem. Geol. Surv. Canada*, Vol. **120.** Pp. 79.

164. PARKS, W. A. 1922. "*Parasaurolophus walkeri*, a New Genus and Species of Crested Trachodont Dinosaur," *Mem. Geol. Surv. Canada*, Vol. **13.** Pp. 32; 9 pls.

165. GILMORE, C. W. 1924. "On the Genus *Stephanosaurus*, with a Description of the Type Specimen of *Lambeosaurus lambei* Parks," *Can. Geol. Surv. Bull.*, **38**:29–48; 5 pls.

STEGOSAURS

166. GILMORE, C. W. 1914. "Osteology of the Armored Dinosauria in the United States National Museum, with Special Reference to the Genus *Stegosaurus*," *U.S. Nat. Mus. Bull.*, Vol. **89.** Pp. 136; 37 pls.

167. HENNIG, E. 1924. "*Kentrurosaurus aethipicus*, die Stegosaurier-Funde von Tendaguru, Deutsch-Ostafrika"; and JANENSCH, W., "Ein aufgestelltes Skelett, etc.," *Palaeontogr. Suppl.*, **7**:101–276, 6 pls.
　　Description of an East African form related to *Stegosaurus*.

ANKYLOSAURS

168. LULL, R. S. 1921. "The Cretaceous Armored Dinosaur *Nodosaurus textilis* Marsh," *Amer. Jour. Sci.*, 5th ser., **1**:97–126; 4 pls.
169. NOPCSA, F. 1929. "Dinosaurierreste aus Siebenbürgen," *Geologica Hungarica, Ser. Palaeontologia Fasc.*, **4**:1–72, 6 pls.
　　Osteology and reconstruction of *Struthiosaurus*, a small Upper Cretaceous armored type.

HORNED DINOSAURS

170. HATCHER, J. B., MARSH, O. C., and LULL, R. S. "The Ceratopsia," *Mon. U.S. Geol. Surv.*, Vol. **49**. Pp. 157; 51 pls.
　　Includes all the earlier work.
171. BROWN, B. 1917. "A Complete Skeleton of the Horned Dinosaur *Monoclonius*," *Bull. Amer. Mus. Nat. Hist.*, **37**:281–306; 4 pls.
　　Good figures.
172. GREGORY, W. K., and MOOK, C. C. 1925. "On *Protoceratops*, a Primitive Ceratopsian Dinosaur from the Lower Cretaceous of Mongolia," *Amer. Mus. Novitates*, Vol. **156**. Pp. 9.

BIRDS

　　The literature on fossil birds is widely scattered. Schufelt and Wetmore in America and Lambrecht of Budapest are the more active recent workers. A comprehensive work on fossil birds by the last is in press.

173. LAMBRECHT, K. 1921. *Fossilium catalogus*. **1**, *Animalia*, Pars 12, "Aves." Berlin. Pp. 108.
　　Good bibliography.
174. LAMBRECHT, K. 1930. "Fortschritte der Palaeo-Ornithologie," *Proc. VIIth Internat. Ornith. Congr. Amsterdam*, pp. 73–99.
175. PYCRAFT, W. P. 1910. *A History of Birds*. London. Pp. 489; 37 pls.
　　A general account, with some mention of fossil forms.
176. WETMORE, A. 1929. "Birds of the Past in North America," *Smithson. Inst. Wash. Rept.*, *1928*, pp. 377–89; 11 pls.
177. HEILMAN, G. 1926. *The Origin of Birds*. London. Pp. 208; 2 pls.
　　A well-illustrated and readable discussion of bird origins, with an account of Jurassic and Cretaceous birds, the reconstruction of a hypothetical "Proavis" and a résumé of the archosaurian reptile groups.
178. MARSH, O. C. 1880. "Odontornithes: a Monograph of the Extinct Toothed Birds of North America," *Rept. Geol. Expl. 40th Parallel*. Washington. Pp. 216; 34 pls.
179. MILNE-EDWARDS, Ä. 1867–71. *Recherches anatomiques et paléontologiques pour servir à l'histoire des oiseaux fossiles de la France*. Paris. 2 vols. text; 2 vols. pls.
　　Tertiary fossil types, and numerous illustrations of skeletons of modern forms as well.
180. MATTHEW, W. D., and GRANGER, W. 1917. "The Skeleton of *Diatryma*, a Gigantic Bird from the Eocene of Wyoming," *Bull. Amer. Mus. Nat. Hist.*, **37**:307, 326, 4 pls.
181. OWEN, R. 1879. *Memoirs on the Extinct Wingless Birds of New Zealand*. London.
　　Moas, etc. Mainly a reprint of the author's previous separate papers on these forms.

PELYCOSAURS

　　American synapsids have been mainly studied by Cope, Case, and Williston. The earlier work was summarized by Case in 1907 (No. 182). Much information on the group is contained in Williston's *Osteology* (No. 87). For *Varanops*, a primitive form, and *Casea* see Williston, No. 92.

182. CASE, E. C. 1907. "Revision of the Pelycosauria of North America," *Publ. Carnegie Inst. Wash., No. 55.* Pp. 176; 35 pls.

183. WILLISTON, S. W., and CASE, E. C.. 1913. "Description of a Nearly Complete Skeleton of *Ophiacodon* Marsh," *Publ. Carnegie Inst. Wash., No. 181*, pp. 37–59; 1 pl.

184. ROMER, A. S. 1927. "Notes on the Permo-Carboniferous Reptile *Dimetrodon*," *Jour. Geol.*, 35:673, 679.
    Reconstruction.

THERAPSIDA

The South African mammal-like forms were first studied by Owen, later by Seeley. Work by Broom during the past three decades has been instrumental in showing the importance and diversity of these forms. Watson has contributed a number of important papers on morphology, and Haughton has described a number of interesting types.

185. BROOM, R. 1932. *The Mammal-like Reptiles of South Africa and the Origin of Mammals.* London. Pp. 376.
    An important comprehensive account.

186. GREGORY, W. K. 1926. "The Skeleton of *Moschops capensis* Broom, a Dinocephalian Reptile from the Permian of South Africa." *Bull. Amer. Mus. Nat. Hist.*, 56:179–251; 21 pls.

187. WATSON, D. M. S. 1921. "The Bases of Classification of the Theriodontia," *Proc. Zoöl. Soc. London, 1921*, pp. 35–98.
    Skull morphology, particularly gorgonopsians.

188. WATSON, D. M. S. 1931. "On the Skeleton of a Bauriamorph Reptile," *Proc. Zoöl. Soc. London, 1931*, pp. 1163–1205.

189. PEARSON, H. S. 1924. "A Dicynodont Reptile Reconstructed," *Proc. Zoöl. Soc. London, 1924*, pp. 827–55.

190. SIMPSON, G. G. 1926. "*Dromatherium* and *Microconodon*," *Amer. Jour. Sci.*, 5th ser., 12: 89–108.

MAMMALS, GENERAL

Cuvier and Owen were early European students of fossil mammals, followed later by such workers as Gaudry, Gervais, and Filhol in France, Forsyth Major, and Lydekker in England, Kowalevsky and Rütimeyer in Central Europe. Among recent or active European students of mammals may be cited Andrews, Forster Cooper, Hopwood, and Reynolds in England; Boule, Déperet, and Teilhard de Chardin in France; Schlosser, Stehlin, Dietrich, Helbing, Schaub, and Zdanksy in Central Europe. Indian material was described in earlier times by Falconer and Lydekker, more recently by Pilgrim and Forster Cooper. Much Chinese mammal material has been described by a series of writers in *Palaeontologia sinica* on the basis of material collected by Swedish expeditions. Mongolian mammals have been collected by the American Museum (New York), and numerous preliminary papers have been published by Matthew and Granger. The important Fayum, Egypt, fauna has been described mainly by Andrews, Schlosser, and Stromer; and Hopwood and Andrews are among those who have described scattered finds from other regions of Africa.

In America all of the three principal early workers—Leidy, Cope, and Marsh—published voluminously on mammals. Leidy's and Cope's major works are cited below (Nos. 201–3), while Cope published numerous smaller papers in the *American Naturalist* and Marsh's many publications are scattered through the *American Journal of Science*. Osborn, Scott, Wortman, Matthew, and Gregory were later entrants into the field; while additional workers now active include Granger, Loomis, Merriam, Peterson, Simpson, Sinclair, Stock, Thorpe, Troxell, and Wood among others. Some South American workers are noted elsewhere.

191. WEBER, M.; BURLET, H. M. DE; and ABEL, O. 1927. *Die Säugetiere.* 2d ed. Jena. 2 vols.
    The standard work of reference on mammalian anatomy and classification. Fossil types treated, as appendices in most instances by Abel.

192. FLOWER, W. H., and LYDEKKER, R. 1891. *An Introduction to the Study of Mammals, Living and Extinct.* London. Pp. 763.

Still a good account of living forms, although much of the paleontology is out of date.

193. GREGORY, W. K. 1910. "The Orders of Mammals," *Bull. Amer. Mus. Nat. Hist.*, **27**:1–524.

Discussion of classification and relationships of groups.

194. SIMPSON, G. G. 1931. "A New Classification of Mammals," *Bull. Amer. Mus. Nat. Hist.*, **59**:259–93.

195. FLOWER, W. H. 1891. *An Introduction to the Osteology of the Mammalia.* 3d ed. London. Pp. 383.

An old, but very useful, little book.

196. TROUESSART, E. L. 1897–99. *Catalogus mammalium tam viventium quam fossilium.* Nova editio. Berlin. Pp. 1469. Also *Supplement* (1904–5). Pp. 929.

197. MATTHEW, W. D. 1915. "Climate and Evolution," *Ann. N.Y. Acad. Sci.*, **24**:171–318.

Particularly evolution of mammal groups in time and space.

198. OSBORN, H. F. 1910. *The Age of Mammals in Europe, Asia and North America.* New York. Pp. 652.

A faunal treatment. A new edition is in preparation.

199. SCOTT, W. B. 1913. *Land Mammals of the Western Hemisphere.* New York. Pp. 707; 32 pls.

A good semi-technical account of the more prominent groups of American fossils.

200. GREGORY, W. K. 1921. *The Origin and Evolution of the Human Dentition.* Baltimore. Pp. 566; 15 pls.

Includes a discussion of molar evolution in mammals.

201. LEIDY, J. 1854. "The Ancient Fauna of Nebraska," *Smithsonia Contrib. Knowl.*, Vol. **6**, Art. 7. Pp. 126; 24 pls.

This and the following contain the original descriptions of many American fossil types.

202. LEIDY, J. 1869. "The Extinct Mammalian Fauna of Dakota and Nebraska, Including an Account of Some Allied Forms from Other Localities, Together with a Synopsis of the Mammalian Remains of North America," *Jour. Acad. Nat. Sci. Phila.*, Vol. **7**. Pp. 272; 30 pls.

203. COPE, E. D. 1884. "Vertebrata of the Tertiary Formations of the West," *Rept. U.S. Geol. Surv. Territ.*, Vol. **3**. Pp. 1044; 76 pls.

"Cope's Bible," a huge tome, which figures and describes a great number of Tertiary mammals. A basic work of importance, although many of the forms included have been described later from more complete material.

204. SCHLOSSER, M. 1887–90. "Die Affen, Lemuren, Chiroptern, Insectivoren, Marsupialier, Creodonten and Carnivoren des Europäischen Tertiärs," *Beitr. Paläont. Oesterr.-Ungarns.* **6**:1–227, 9 pls.; **7**:1–162; **8**:1–107.

Valuable summary and index to the older material on smaller mammal types of Europe. Unfortunately, few illustrations.

205. MATTHEW, W. D. 1927. "The Evolution of the Mammals in the Eocene," *Proc. Zoöl. Soc. London, 1927*, pp. 947–85.

Important summary of probable relationships of placental groups and their early evolution.

206. MATTHEW, W. D. 1897. "A Revision of the Puerco Fauna," *Bull. Amer. Mus. Nat. Hist.*, **9**:259–323.

This is now far out of date; a comprehensive revision of the Paleocene faunas by this author is in press.

207. STEHLIN, H. G. 1903–16. "Die Säugetiere des schweizerischen Eocaens, Critischer Catalog der Materialien." *Abh. Schw. Pal. Ges.*, **30**:1–153, 3 pls.; **31**:155–455, 8 pls.; **32**:447–595, 2 pls.; **33**:597–690, 1 pl.; **35**:691–837, 2 pls.; **36**:839–1164, 6 pls.; **38**:1165–1298; **41**:1297–1552, 2 pls.

Mainly a detailed discussion of the dentition and its bearing on the relationships of European Eocene forms.

208. MATTHEW, W. D. 1930. "Critical Observations upon Siwalik Mammals," *Bull. Amer. Mus. Nat. Hist.*, **56**:437–560.

Includes discussion of evolution of bears, cats, chalicotheres, and giraffes.

209. MATTHEW, W. D. 1924. "Third Contribution to the Snake Creek Fauna," *Bull. Amer. Mus. Nat. Hist.*, **50**:59–210.

Includes discussion of evolution of a number of mammal groups.

MESOZOIC ORDERS

210. SIMPSON, G. G. 1928. *A Catalogue of the Mesozoic Mammalia in the Geological Department of the British Museum.* London. 4°. Pp. 225; 12 pls.

211. SIMPSON, G. G. 1929. "American Mesozoic Mammalia," *Mem. Peabody Mus. Yale Univ.*, Vol. **3**, Part I. Pp. 235; 32 pls.

MARSUPIALS

212. SIMPSON, G. G. 1930. "Postmesozoic Marsupialia." *Fossilium catalogus.* I, *Animalia.* Pars 47. Pp. 87. Berlin.

Literature and a general discussion of marsupial evolution.

213. SINCLAIR, W. J. 1906. "Mammalia of the Santa Cruz Beds: Marsupialia," *Rept. Princeton Univ. Exped. Patagonia*, **4**:333–460; 26 pls.

South American carnivores.

214. OWEN, R. 1878. *Researches on the Fossil Remains of the Extinct Mammals of Australia.* London.

Reprints of papers previously published separately in *Phil. Trans. Roy. Soc. London, 1859–1872; Diprotodon, Thylacoleo*, and other Pleistocene forms.

INSECTIVORES

For a general discussion of the group, see Gregory, No. 193, and Matthew, No. 205.

215. GREGORY, W. K., and SIMPSON, G. G. 1926. "Cretaceous Mammals from Mongolia," *Amer. Mus. Novitates, No. 225.* Pp. 20.

Description of the oldest known placentals. Popular account by Gregory in *Scientific Monthly*, March, 1927, pp. 225–35. See also Simpson in *Amer. Mus. Nov.*, Nos. 329 and 330 (1928).

216. MATTHEW, W. D. 1915–18. "A Revision of the Lower Eocene Wasatch and Wind River Faunas. Part IV: Entylonychia, Primates, Insectivora [part]," *Bull. Amer. Mus. Nat. Hist.*, **34**:429–83; 1 pl. Part V: Insectivora [continued], Glires, Edentata," *ibid.*, **38**:565–657.

217. MATTHEW, W. D. 1913. "A Zalambdodont Insectivore from the Basal Eocene," *Bull. Amer. Mus. Nat. Hist.*, **33**:307–14; 2 pls.

BATS

218. REVILLOD, P. 1917–22. "Contributions à l'étude des Chiroptères des terrains tertiaires," *Mém. Soc. paléont. Suisse*, **43**:63–132, 2 pls.; **44**:63–128, 2 pls.; **45**:133–95, 1 pl.

219. MATTHEW, W. D. 1917. "A Paleocene Bat," *Bull. Amer. Mus. Nat. Hist.*, **37**:569–71.

TAENIODONTS

220. WORTMAN, J. L. 1897. "The Ganodonta and Their Relationship to the Edentata," *Bull. Amer. Mus. Nat. Hist.*, **9**:59–110.
—See also Cope, No. 203.

TILLODONTS

221. MARSH, O. C. 1876. "Principal Characters of the Tillodontia," *Amer. Jour. Sci.*, 3d ser., **11**:249–52; 2 pls.
—See also Cope, No. 203.

CARNIVORES

Cope and Matthew have been the most influential of workers on the evolution of carnivores.

CREODONTS

222. MATTHEW, W. D. 1915. "A Revision of the Lower Eocene Wasatch and Wind River Faunas. Part I: Order Ferae (Carnivora). Suborder Creodonta," *Bull. Amer. Mus. Nat. Hist.*, **34**:1–103.
223. MATTHEW, W. D. 1909. "The Carnivora and Insectivora of the Bridger Basin, Middle Eocene," *Mem. Amer. Mus. Nat. Hist.*, **9**:291–567; 11 pls.
This and other papers by this author discuss the phylogeny of the early carnivores.
224. WORTMAN, J. L. 1901–2. "Studies of Eocene Mammalia in the Marsh Collection, Peabody Museum. Part I: Carnivora," *Amer. Jour. Sci.*, 4th ser., **11**:333–48, 437–50; **12**:143–54, 193–206, 281–96, 377–82, 421–32; **13**:39–46, 115–28, 197–206, 433–48; **14**:17–23; 10 pls.
Partially superseded by No. 223.
—See also Matthew, No. 205.

HYAENIDS

225. ZDANSKY, O. 1924. "Jungtertiäre carnivoren Chinas," *Palaeontologia sinica*, Ser. C. Vol. **2**. No. 1. Pp. 149; 33 pls.
Many figures of Pliocene carnivores, particularly *Hyaena, Ictitherium*, felids, and mustelids.
226. REYNOLDS, S. H. 1902. *A Monograph of the British Pleistocene Mammalia. The Cave Hyaena.* Mon. Palaeontogr. Soc. London. Pp. 25; 14 pls.

FELIDS

227. MATTHEW, W. D. 1910. "The Phylogeny of the Felidae," *Bull. Amer. Mus. Nat. Hist.*, **28**:289–316.
See also No. 208.

MUSTELIDS

Evolution discussed by Matthew (No. 209). The literature is scattered.

CANIDS

228. MATTHEW, W. D. 1930. "The Phylogeny of Dogs," *Jour. Mammalogy*, **11**:117–38.
See also No. 209.
229. HATCHER, J. B. 1902. "Oligocene Canidae," *Mem. Carnegie Mus.*, **1**:65–108; 7 pls.
Particularly *Daphoenus*.
230. PETERSON, O. A. 1910. "Description of New Carnivores from the Miocene of Western Nebraska," *Mem. Carnegie Mus.*, **4**:205–78; 2 pls.
Particularly *Daphoenodon*.

PROCYONIDS

231. WORTMAN, J. L., and MATTHEW, W. D. 1899. "The Ancestry of Certain Members of the Canidae, the Vivenidae and Procyonidae," *Bull. Amer. Mus. Nat. Hist.*, **12**:109–39; 1 pl.
Phlaocyon.

BEARS

232. FRICK, C. 1926. "The Hemicyoninae, and an American Tertiary Bear," *Bull. Amer. Mus. Nat. Hist.*, **56**:1–119.

Figures primitive bear-like types but denies their relationship. See Matthew, No. 208, for probable phylogeny.

233. MERRIAM, J. C., and STOCK, C. 1925. "Relationships and Structure of the Short Faced Bear *Arctotherium* from the Pleistocene of California," *Publ. Carnegie Inst. Wash., No. 347*, pp. 1–35; 10 pls.
—See also No. 208.

PINNPEDS

234. KELLOGG, R. 1922. "Pinnipeds from Miocene and Pleistocene Deposits of California . . . . and a Résumé of Current Theories Regarding the Origin of the Pinnipedia," *Univ. Calif. Publ. Bull. Dept. Geol. Sci.*, **13**:23–132.

Includes a summary of all known pinnipeds.

CONDYLARTHS

Cope was the describer of *Phenacodus*, central type of the order, and responsible for emphasizing its primitive nature.

235. OSBORN, H. F. 1898. "Remounted Skeleton of *Phenacodus primaevus*. Comparison with *Euprotogonia*," *Bull. Amer. Mus. Nat. Hist.*, **10**:159–64; 1 pl.

236. GRANGER, W. 1915. "A Revision of the Lower Eocene Wasatch and Wind River Faunas. Part III: Order Condylarthra. Families Phenacodontidae and Meniscotheriidae," *Bull. Amer. Mus. Nat. Hist.*, **34**:329–61.

237. MATTHEW, W. D. 1915. "A Revision of the Lower Eocene Wasatch and Wind River Faunas. Part II: Order Condylarthra, Family Hyopsodontidae," *Bull. Amer. Mus. Nat. Hist.*, **34**:311–28.

AMBLYPODS

Both Marsh and Cope were early workers on these forms; dispute over priority of description of uintatheres was a major cause of the bitter feud between the two which lasted until the end of their careers.

238. OSBORN, H. F. 1898. "Evolution of the Amblypoda. Part I: Taligrado and Pantodonta," *Bull. Amer. Mus. Nat. Hist.*, **10**:169–218.

Paleocene forms and *Coryphodon*.

239. MARSH, O. C. 1884. "Dinocerata, a Monograph of an Extinct Order of Gigantic Mammals," *Mon. U.S. Geol. Surv.*, Vol. **10**. Pp. 255; 56 pls.

Excellent plates of uintatheres.

240. SIMPSON, H. G. 1929. "A New Paleocene Uintathere and Molar Evolution in the Amblypoda," *Amer. Mus. Novit.*, No. **387**. Pp. 9.

PERISSODACTYLS
HORSES

241. LOOMIS, F. B. 1926. *The Evolution of the Horse*. Boston. Pp. 249; 25 pls.

242. MATTHEW, W. D. 1926. "The Evolution of the Horse; a Record and Its Interpretation," *Quar. Rev. Biol.*, **1**:139–85; 1 pl.

TAPIRS

243. HATCHER, J. B. 1896. "Recent and Fossil Tapirs," *Amer. Jour. Sci.*, 4th ser., **1**:161–80; 4 pls.

244. SCHAUB, S. 1928. "Der Tapirschädel von Haslen. Ein Beitrag zur Revision der oligocänen Tapiriden Europas," *Abh. Schweiz. Pal. Ges.*, **47**:1–28; 1 pl.

LOPHIODONTS

245. DÉPÉRET, C. 1904. "Etudes paléontologiques sur les *Lophiodon* du Minervois," *Arch. Mus. Hist. Nat. Lyon,* Vol. **9.** Pp. 49; 4 pls.

RHINOCEROTIDAE

There is no comprehensive modern work on this group. Brief summaries of rhinoceros evolution are contained in the two following papers:

246. MATTHEW, W. D. 1931. "Critical Observations on the Phylogeny of the Rhinoceroses," *Univ. Calif. Publ. Bull. Dept. Geol. Sci.,* Vol. **20,** No. 1. Pp. 9.

247. OSBORN, H. F. 1923. "The Extinct Giant Rhinoceros *Baluchitherium* of Western and Central Asia," *Nat. Hist.,* **23**:209–28.

248. OSBORN, H. F. 1898. "The Extinct Rhinoceroses," *Mem. Amer. Mus. Nat. Hist.,* **1**:75–164; 9 pls.

    Particularly Eocene and Oligocene forms.

249. PETERSON, O. A. 1920. "The American Diceratheres," *Mem. Carnegie Mus.,* **7**:399–456; 10 pls.

    Good figures.

250. RINGSTROM, T. 1924. "Nashörner der *Hipparion*-Fauna Nordchinas," *Palaeontogr. sinica,* Ser. C, Vol. **1,** Part 4. Pp. 150; 12 pls.

    Pliocene rhinoceroses of Asia, with many good figures.

    Particularly *Chilotherium.*

TITANOTHERES

251. OSBORN, H. F. 1929. "The Titanotheres of Ancient Wyoming, Dakota and Nebraska," *U.S. Geol. Surv. Monogr. 55.* 2 vols. Pp. 953; 236 pls.

    Complete account of all known forms.

CHALICOTHERIIDAE

252. HOLLAND, W. J., and PETERSON, O. A. 1913. "The Osteology of the Chalicothereoidea; with Special Reference to a Mounted Skeleton of *Moropus elatus* Marsh, Now Installed in the Carnegie Museum," *Mem. Carnegie Mus.,* **3**:189–406; 30 pls.

    Good figures.

—See also Matthew, No. 208.

ARTIODACTYLS, GENERAL, AND EARLY FORMS

The literature on artiodactyls is vast, and there are few comprehensive treatments even of families. There is little agreement on classification, or even on the bases of classification. For various suggestions as to groupings, see Stehlin, No. 207, based on molar construction; Matthew, No. 253, teeth and feet; Loomis, No. 254, premolars; Pearson, No. 256, mastoid region.

253. MATTHEW, W. D. 1929. "Reclassification of the Artiodactyl Families," *Bull. Geol. Soc. Amer.,* **40**:403–8.

254. LOOMIS, F. B. 1925. "Dentition of Artiodactyls," *Bull. Geol. Soc. Amer.,* **36**:583–604.

255. SINCLAIR, W. J. 1914. "A Revision of the Bunodont Artiodactyla of the Middle and Lower Eocene of North America," *Bull. Amer. Mus. Nat. Hist.,* **33**:267–95.

—On European Eocene artiodactyls, see Stehlin, No. 207.

PIG-LIKE FORMS

256. PEARSON, H. S. 1927. "On the Skulls of Early Tertiary Suidae," *Philos. Trans. Roy. Soc. London,* Ser. B, Vol. **215.** Pp. 72.

    The braincase of primitive European artiodactyls, with suggestions as to classification based on the presence or absence of the mastoid.

257. KOWALEVSKY, W. 1873. "Monographie der Gattung *Anthracotherium* Cuv. und Versuch einer natürlichen Classification der fossilen Hufthiere," *Palaeontogr.*, **22**:131–346; 11 pls.

258. SCOTT, W. B. 1894. "The Structure and Relationships of *Ancodus*," *Jour. Acad. Nat. Sci. Phila.*, **9**:461–97; 2 pls.

259. PEARSON, H. S. 1928. "Chinese Fossil Suidae," *Palaeontographica sinica*, Ser. C, Vol. **5**, Part 5. Pp. 75; 4 pls.

260. GIDLEY, J. W. 1921. "Pleistocene Peccaries from the Cumberland Cave Deposit," *Proc. U.S. Nat. Mus.*, **57**:651–78.

261. REYNOLDS, S. H. 1920. *A Monograph on the British Pleistocene Mammals. Hippopotamus.* Mon. Paleontogr. Soc. Pp. 38; 6 pls.

PRIMITIVE SELENODONTS

262. SCOTT, W. B. 1899. "The Selenodont Artiodactyls of the Uinta Eocene," *Trans. Wagner Free Inst. Sci. Phila.*, **6**:1–121; 4 pls.
    Various primitive selenodont types.

263. LOOMIS, F. B. 1924. "Miocene Oreodonts in the American Museum," *Bull. Amer. Mus. Nat. Hist., New York*, **51**:1–37.

264. THORPE, M. R. 1925. "The Geological History of the Oreodonts," *Jour. Mammalogy*, **6**: 69–82.
    A monograph of the group by this writer is in course of preparation.

265. WORTMAN, J. L. 1895. "On the Osteology of *Agriochoerus*," *Bull. Amer. Mus. Nat. Hist.*, **7**:145–78; 1 pl.

266. SCOTT, W. B. 1895. "The Osteology and Relations of *Protoceras*," *Jour. Morphol.*, **11**:303–74; 3 pls.

CAMELS

267. WORTMAN, J. L. 1898. "The Extinct Camelidae of North America and Some Associated Forms," *Bull. Amer. Mus. Nat. Hist.*, **10**:93–142, 1 pl.

268. LOOMIS, F. B. 1928. "*Poëbrotherium*," *Amer. Jour. Sci.*, **16**:137–42.

269. LOOMIS, F. B. 1910. "Osteology and Affinities of the Genus *Stenomylus*," *Amer. Jour. Sci.*, 4th ser., **29**:297–323.

GIRAFFIDS

270. BOHLIN, B. 1926. "Die Familie Giraffidae mit besonderer Berücksichtigung der fossilen Formen aus China," *Palaeontogr. sinica*, Ser. C, Vol. **4**, No. 1. Pp. 179; 12 pls.
    —See also Matthew, No. 208.

CERVIDS

271. MATTHEW, W. D. 1908. "Osteology of *Blastomeryx* and Phylogeny of the American Cervidae," *Bull. Amer. Mus. Nat. Hist.*, **24**:535–62.

272. LOOMIS, F. B. 1928. "Phylogeny of the Deer," *Amer. Jour. Sci.*, **16**:531–42.

ANTILOCAPRIDAE

273. MATTHEW, W. D. 1904. "A Complete Skeleton of *Merycodus*," *Bull. Amer. Mus. Nat. Hist.*, **20**:101–29; 1 pl.
    —See also Matthew, No. 209.

BOVIDS

274. PILGRIM, G. E., and HOPWOOD, A. T. 1928. *Catalogue of the Pontian Bovidae of Europe in the Department of Geology of the British Museum.* London. 4°. Pp. 144; 9 pls.
    Figures many Pliocene types.

SUBUNGULATES

275. ANDREWS, C. W. 1906. *A Descriptive Catalogue of the Tertiary Vertebrates of the Fayum, Egypt.* London. Pp. 324; 26 pls.

Describes the earliest known subungulate faunas—*Moeritherium, Palaeomastodon* (and *Phiomia*), *Arsinoetherium*, early hyracoids, and sirenians.

HYRACOIDS

276. SCHLOSSER, M. 1911. "Beiträge zur Kenntnis der oligozänen Landsäugetiere aus dem Fayum, Ägypten," *Beitr. Geol. Pal. Oesterr.-Ung.*, **24**:51–167; 7 pls.

277. MATSUMOTO, H. 1926. "Contribution to the Knowledge of the Fossil Hyracoidea of the Fayum, Egypt," *Bull. Amer. Mus. Nat. Hist.*, **56**:253–350.

PROBOSCIDIANS

The literature, particularly on Pleistocene forms, is vast. A monograph of the group by Osborn is in course of publication. The author's conclusions are summarized in the following paper:

278. OSBORN, H. F. 1925. "Final Conclusions on the Evolution, Phylogeny and Classification of the Proboscidea," *Proc. Amer. Philos. Soc.*, **44**:17–35.

—For the Fayum forms, see Andrews, No. 275, and the following:

279. MATSUMOTO, H. 1924. "A Revision of *Palaeomastodon* Dividing It into Two Genera with Descriptions of Two New Species," *Bull. Amer. Mus. Nat. Hist.*, **50**:1–58.

280. OSBORN, H. F. 1925. "The Elephants and Mastodons Arrive in America," *Nat. Hist.*, **25**: 3–23.

A popular account of American forms.

281. POHLIG, H. 1889–92. "Dentition und Kranologie des *Elephas antiquus* Falc. mit Beiträgen über *Elephas primigenius* Blum und *Elephas meridionalis* Nestr.," *Nova Acta Akad. Caes. Leop.-Car.*, **53**:1–259, 10 pls., and **57**:267–466, 5 pls.

282. DÉPÉRET, C.; MAYET, L.; and ROMAN, F. 1923. "Les Éléphants fossiles," *Ann. Univ. Lyon*, N.S., Vol. **42**. Pp. 225; 10 pls.

A summary of European fossil types.

SIRENIANS

283. SIMPSON, G. G. 1932. "Fossil Sirenia of Florida and the Evolution of the Sirenia," *Bull. Amer. Mus. Nat. Hist.*, **59**:419–503.

284. DÉPÉRET, C., and ROMAN, F. 1920. "Le *Felsinotherium Serresi* des sables pliocènes de Montpellier et les rameaux phylétiques des Siréniens fossiles de l'ancien Monde," *Arch. Mus. Hist. Nat. Lyon*, *1920*. Pp. 55; 7 pls.

285. ABEL, O. 1904. "Die Sirenen der mediterranen Tertiärbildungen Oesterreichs," *Abh. Geol. Reichsanst. Wien*, Bd. **19**, Heft 2. Pp. 223; 7 pls.

SOUTH AMERICAN UNGULATE GROUPS

Much of the important South American fossil mammal material was described by Florentino Ameghino on the basis of material collected by his brother Carlos; much of the importance of this work, however, was obscured by the erection by Ameghino of an impossible phylogenetic hypothesis in which, patriotically, South America was made a great center of general mammalian evolution. A number of types, particularly from the Pleistocene, were described by Owen, Burmeister, Gaudry, Roth, Lydekker, and other early writers. The Santa Cruz (Miocene) forms have been monographed by Scott and Sinclair on the basis of material collected for Princeton by Hatcher, and Loomis has revised the *Pyrotherium* beds fauna. Much material from the later periods, collected by Riggs for the Field Museum, Chicago, is in process of description, as are Eocene and Oligocene forms collected by Simpson.

286. SCOTT, W. B. 1912. "Mammalia of the Santa Cruz Beds. Part 3. Entylonychia," *Rept. Princeton Univ. Exped. Patagonia*, **6**:238–86; 3 pls.

287. SINCLAIR, W. J. 1909. "Mammalia of the Santa Cruz Beds. Typotheria." *Rept. Princeton Univ. Exped. Patagonia*, **6**:1–110; 11 pls.

288. SCOTT, W. B. 1912. "Mammalia of the Santa Cruz Beds. Order Toxodontia," *Rept. Princeton Univ. Exped. Patagonia*, **6**:287–300.

289. SCOTT, W. B. 1928. "Astrapotheria of the Santa Cruz Beds," *Rept. Princeton Univ. Exped. Patagonia*, **6**, Part 4, 301–42, 6 pls.

290. SCOTT, W. B. 1910. "Litopterna of the Santa Cruz Beds," *Rept. Princeton Exped. Patagonia*, **7**, Part 1, 1–156; 20 pls.

291. SEFVE, J. 1923. "*Machrauchenia patagonica*," *Bull. Geol. Inst. Univ. Upsala*, **19**:1–21. Osteology, restoration, habits.

292. LOOMIS, F. B. 1914. *The Deseado Formation of Patagonia.* Amherst. Pp. 237. Oligocene forms.

EDENTATES

293. SIMPSON, G. G. 1931. "*Metacheiromys* and the Edentata," *Bull. Amer. Mus. Nat. Hist.*, **49**:295–381.

294. BURMEISTER, H. 1874. "Monografía de los Glyptodontes en el Museo Público de Buenos Aires," *Anales Mus. Púb. Buenos Aires*, **1**:1–412; 43 pls.

295. SCOTT, W. B. 1904. "Mammalia of the Santa Cruz Beds. Edentata," *Rept. Princeton Univ. Exped. Patagonia*, **5**:161–364; 34 pls.

296. STOCK, C. 1925. "Cenozoic Gravigrade Edentates of Western North America," *Publ. Carnegie Inst. Wash., No. 331.* Pp. 206; 47 pls.

Detailed description of *Nothrotherium* and *Mylodon* and general discussion of occurrence and relationships of ground sloths.

297. ANDREWS, C. W. 1896. "On a Skull of *Orycteropus gaudryi*, Forsyth Major, from Samos," *Proc. Zoöl. Soc.*, 1896, pp. 290–99.

WHALES

Van Beneden, Abel, and Kellogg have been, successively, the most active students of fossil cetaceans. A brief account is given in Lull, No. 4.

298. KELLOGG, R. 1928. "The History of Whales. Their Adptation to Life in the Water," *Quar. Rev. Biol.*, **3**:29–76, 174–208.

A recent summary of the field with full references to all work.

299. VAN BENEDEN, P. J., and GERVAIS, P. 1880. *Ostéographie des cétacés vivants et fossiles.* Paris. Pp. 642; atlas of 64 pls.

300. STROMER, E. 1908. "Die Archaeoceti des ägyptischen Eozäns," *Beitr. Pal. Geol. Oesterr.-Ung.*, **21**:106–78; 4 pls.

RODENTS

301. MATTHEW, W. D. 1910. "On the Osteology and Relationships of *Paramys*, and the Affinities of the Ischyromyidae," *Bull. Amer. Mus. Nat. Hist.*, **28**:43–72; 5 pls.

302. SCHLOSSER, M. 1885. "Die Nager der europäischen Tertiärs," *Palaeontogr.*, **31**:9–162; 8 pls.

303. SCOTT, W. B. 1905. "Mammalia of the Santa Cruz Beds. Glires." *Rept. Princeton Exped. Patagonia*, **5**:1–160; 29 pls.

304. TROXELL, E. L. 1921. "*Palaeolagus*, an Extinct Hare," *Amer. Jour. Sci.*, 5th ser., **1**:340–48.

PRIMATES

Fossils are few, but the literature is vast. Gregory has been the most thorough student of the lower primates. Among students of fossil human specimens may be mentioned Du Bois (*Pithe-*

canthropus), Smith Woodward (*Eoanthropus*), Black (*Sinanthropus*), Boule (late Pleistocene types), Keith, and Elliot Smith.

—On dental evolution, see Gregory, No. 200.

305. SMITH, G. ELLIOT. 1927. *The Evolution of Man.* 2d ed. London. Pp. 207.

306. GREGORY, W. K. 1928. "The Upright Posture of Man. A Review of Its Origin and Evolution," *Proc. Amer. Philos. Soc.,* **67**:339–74.

307. ABEL, O. 1931. *Die Stellung des Menschen im Rahmen der Wirbeltiere.* Jena. Pp. 398.
    Résumé of primate evolution.

308. GREGORY, W. K. 1921. "On the Structure and Relationships of *Notharctus*, an American Eocene Primate," *Mem. Amer. Mus. Nat. Hist.,* N.S., **3**:49–243; 37 pls.
    Includes much general material on primate evolution.

—On Eocene tarsioids, see Matthew and Granger, No. 216, and Stehlin, No. 207.

309. GREGORY, W. K. 1916. "Studies on the Evolution of the Primates," *Bull. Amer. Mus. Nat. Hist.,* **35**:239–355.
    Particularly anthropoid apes.

310. GREGORY, W. K., and HELLMAN, M. 1926. "The Dentition of *Dryopithecus* and the Origin of Man," *Anthrop. Papers Amer. Mus. Nat. Hist.,* **28**:1–123; 25 pls.

Fossil human remains are reviewed in the following four works:

311. OSBORN, H. F. 1916. *Men of the Old Stone Age.* 2d ed. New York. Pp. 545.

312. BOULE, M. 1923. *Les hommes fossiles.* 2d ed. Paris. Pp. 505. (English translation by Ritchie. 1923. Pp. 504.)

313. McCURDY, G. G. 1924. *Human Origins.* New York. 2 vols. Pp. 956.

314. WEINERT, H. 1930. *Menschen der Vorzeit.* Stuttgart. Pp. 145.

INDEX

INDEX

The index is mainly taxonomic. Complete references are given to all genera, together with the scientific names of higher groups and the more common popular names. Families, however, are not, in general, listed, but may be located by consulting the type genus.

A few of the more general accounts of major skeletal features have been indexed, and references are given to the place where various structures are first described or defined. For the details of anatomy in the various types, consult the name of the genus or group.

[References to classification in boldface; to figures in italics; bibliographic references are preceded by the letter "B."]

Aard vark, 381, 391, B473
Aard wolf, 292
Abderites, 266, **442**, *241b*
Acanthaspidoidea, **433**
Acanthaspis, 42–43, **433**
Acanthodes, 47, **434**, *36*, *52a*
Acanthodii, 46–48, 60, 71, 73, **434**, B455
Acanthopholis, 203, **440**
Acanthopterygii, 85, **435**
Acanthorhina, *50*
Acanthostoma, **434**
Acentrophorus, 77, **435**
Aceratherium, 334, **445**
Acetabulum, 100
Achaenodon, 360–61, **446**, *318b*
Acipenser, 75, **435**
Acipenseroidea, **435**
Acorn worms, 9, 18
Acreodi, **443**
Acrodus, 53–54, **434**
Actinopterygii, 62, 69, 71–85, 104, **435**, B456
Adapis, 415, 416, **449**
Adaptive radiation, 5
Adelogyrinus, **436**
Adinotherium, 312, **445**
Adjidaumo, **447**
Adriosaurus, 160, **439**, *143*
Aeluroidea, 288, 291–95, **444**
Aepyornis, 214, **441**
Aepyornithiformes, 214, **441**
Aëtosaurus, 168, **439**, *146a*
Agnatha, 20–21, 22–32, **434**, B453–54
Agorophius, 395, **448**
Agriochoerus, 348, **446**, *307e*
Aigialosaurus, 160, **439**
Ailuropus, 290, **444**

Ailurus, 290, **444**
Air bladder; *see* Lung
Aistopoda, 112–13, **436**
Albatross, 217
Albertogaudrya, 316, **445**
Albula, **435**
Alces, **446**
Aletomeryx, **446**
Alexia, **436**
Alisphenoid, 243
Alletocyon, **444**
Alligator, **440**
Alligatorellus, 173, **440**, *156a, b*
Alligatorium, **440**
Allodesmus, 296, **444**
Allognathosuchus, **440**
Allosaurus, 187–88, **440**, *163a, 168c, 169c, 171a*
Allotheria, 257–58, **442**
Alouatta, 421
Alticamelus, 350, **446**, *305l*
Amblypoda, 301, 304–7, **444**, B469
Amblypterus, **435**
Amblystoma, **437**
Amblystomoidea, **437**
Amebelodon, 374, **447**, *325g*
Amia, 77, 79, 80, 81, **435**
Amioidea, **435**
Amiopsis, 79, **435**, *67*
Amiurus, **435**
Amniote egg, 120
Amphibia, 20–21, 86, 93–119, **436**, B457; embryology of, 93–94; primitive forms of, 94–103; ancestry of, 104–5; classification of, 105–6; oldest forms of, 106
Amphibious dinosaurs, 190–95
Amphichelydia, 135–37, **438**

Amphicoela, **437**
Amphicyon, **444**
Amphidon, **442**
Amphilestes, 260, **442**
Amphimeryx, **446**
Amphioxus, 16, 18, 19, *10*
Amphisbaenia, 160, **439**
Amphisyle, **435**
Amphitherium, 260, **442**, *257c*
Amphitragulus, 355
Amphiuma, **437**
Amyda, 139, **438**, *117a–c*
Amynodon, **445**
Amynodont rhinoceroses, 332
Anacanthini, 84, **435**
Anagale, 274, **443**, *246d*
Anapsid temporal region, 128
Anapsida, 128, **437**
Anaptomorphus, **449**
Anaspida, 27, **433**, *18, 19*
Ancestry of vertebrates, 18–19, *11*
Anchisaurus, 189–90, **440**, *168a, 169a*
Anchitherium, 326, 327, **445**
Ancodus, 362–63, **446**, *307a, 318c, 320*
Andrewsarchus, 283, **443**
Andrias, 119, **437**
Angius, **439**
Angular: in bony fishes, 67; in amphibian, 99; becomes tympanic, 244
Angular processes of jaw in marsupials, 262
Ankle; *see* Tarsus
Ankylosauria, 196, 202–3, **440**, B464
Ankylosaurus, 202, **440**, *164c*
Anningia, 231, 232, **441**, *215a*

Anningiamorpha, 441
Anomaluroidea, 406, 448
Anomalurus, 406, 448
Anomocoela, 437
Anoplotherium, 346, 446, *305h, 306b*
Anseriformes, 217, 442
Anteaters, 381; South American, 381, 382, 387
Antelopes, 351, 357-59; American "antelope," 351, 357
Anthracosaurus, 436
Anthracotherium, 362-63, 446, *305c*
Anthropoidea, 411, 419-32, 449
Anthropopithecus, 426, 449
Antiarchi, 43-45, 60, 434, B455
Antilocapra, 357, 446
Antlers, of deer, 353, 355
Anura, 117-19, 437
Aotus, 421
Apes, man-like, 425-27
Apheliscus, 443
Aphelops, 334, 445
Aplodontia, 402, 447
Aplodontoidea, 402-4, 447
Apoda, 119, 437
Apodes, 84, 435
Apternodus, 443
Apterodon, 444
Apterygiformes, 215, 441
Apteryx, 441
Arachnids, 19
Araeoscelis, 146-48, 154, 159, 438, *123e-f, 127, 128*
Archaeoceti, 394, 448
Archaeohyrax, 445
Archaeolemur, 417, 449
Archaeomeryx, 351-52, 446, *304c, e*
Archaeonycteris, 443
Archaeopithecus, 445
Archaeopteropus, 443
Archaeopterygia, 441
Archaeopteryx, 210-11, 441
Archaeornis, 210-11, 441, *190, 191, 192*
Archaeotherium, 362, 446, *305d, 318b*
Archegosaurus, 436
Archelon, 138, 438, *117d, 119*
Arches, branchial, 11, *6;* in sharks, 35; in land animals, 99
Archidiskodon, 376, 447
Archosauria, 154, 163-66, 439, *162*

Arctocyon, 443
Arctoidea, 288-91, 444
Arctostylops, 311, 445, *280*
Arctotherium, 290, 444, *254k, 258d*
Ardaeosaurus, 439
Arius, 435
Armadillos, 381, 382, 384, B473
Armor: in ostracoderms, 22, 33-34; degeneration of, in fishes, 32, 45, 48, 49; *see also* Ankylosauria, Chelonia, Edentata Stegosauria
Armored dinosaurs; *see* Stegosauria, Ankylosauria
Arsinoëtherium, 366, 368, 370, 446, *322b, f, 324*
Arthrodira, 39-43, 60, 433, B454
Arthropods, 19
Articular: in bony fishes, 69; in amphibians, 99; becomes malleus, 245-46
Artiodactyla, 339-65, 446, B470-71
Aspidorhynchus, 81, 435, *69*
Asterolepis, 44, 434
Astragalus, 253
Astrapotheria, 315-16, 445, B473
Astrapotherium, 315-16, 445, *277d*
Astraspis, 433
Ateleaspis, 433
Ateles, 421
Atlas, 251
Atoposaurus, 440
Auchenia, 350, 446
Auks, 215, 219
Aulophyseter, 397, 448, *342c*
Auditory apparatus; *see* Ear
Auditory ossicles, 244, 245-46; *see also* Stapes
Australopithecus, 427, 449, *356d*
Aves, 20-21, 206-19, 441, B464
Axial skeleton; *see* Vertebrae, Ribs
Axis, 251
Aye-Aye, 417

Baboons, 422-24
Backbone; *see* Vertebrae
Baëna, 438
Balaena, 399, 448
Balenoptera, 399, 448
Baluchitherium, 334, 445, *291d*
Bandicoots, 265
Baphetes, 436, *89a*

Barracudas, 84
Barytheria, 446
Barytherium, 372, 446
Basioccipital: in bony fishes, 68; in amphibians, 99; in mammals, 243
Basisphenoid: in bony fishes, 68; in amphibians, 99; in mammals, 243
Bathyergoidea, 409, 448
Bathyergus, 409, 448
Batoidea, 434
Bats, 275-77, B461
Bauria, 235, 441, *218b*
Bauriamorpha, 234, 235-36, 441
Bdellostoma, 22, 433
Bear dogs, 289
Bears, 290, B469
Beavers, 405; mountain "beaver," 402
Belonorhynchoidea, 435
Belonorhynchus, 70, 435, *62*
Belonostomus, 435
Beryx, 435
Bibliography, 451-74; general works, 451; bibliographies, 452
Bipedalism, in archosaurs, 163-65
Birds, 206-19, 441-42, B464; structure of, 206-9; Jurassic forms of, 209-11; Cretaceous, 211-13; Tertiary, 213-14; flightless types of, 214-16; higher bird groups, 216-19
Birkenia, 27, 433, *18*
Bison, 359, 446, *317*
Blastomeryx, 355, 357, 446, *312b, 313d, 315*
Boa, 439
Bone, 9-10; dermal and replacement, 9; bones of skull in bony fishes, 64, 66-67; replacement bones of skull in same, 66-67; *see also* Skull, Limbs, etc.
Borhyaena, 264, 442, *241c*
Borophagus, 289, 444
Bos, 359, 446
Bothriolepis, 44-45, 434, *33*
Bowfin, 79
Brachauchenius, 151, 438
Brachiosaurus, 194-95, 440
Brachycephalidae, 437
Brachyceratops, 441
Brachydirus, 433
Brachyodont, 247, 298

Brachyodus, 363, **446**

Brachyops, **436**

Bradyodonti, 58–59, 60, **434**, B455

Bradypus, **447**

Bradysaurus, 130, **437**, *112*

Brain, 13–14, *18;* Osteostraci, 25, *17;* amphibians, 103; ptero-saurs, 176; sauropod dino-saurs, 192–93; mammals, 239–40

Braincase, 11, 12, *5, 26;* in bony fishes, 64–68; in amphibians, 99; in mammals, 241, 243, 244; *see also* Skull, Head structure

Branchial arches; *see* Arches, branchial

Branchiosaurus, 115–16, **437**, *100e, 103, 104*

Bream, 85

Brevicipetidae, **437**

Brontops, 335, **445**, *301*

Brontosaurus, 190, 194, **440**

Brontotherioidea, 337–38, **445**

Brontotherium, 335, **445**

Broomia, **438**

Bufo, **437**

Bunaelurus, **444**

Bunodont teeth, 248, 297

Burnetia, **441**

Bustards, 217

Cacops, 109–10, **436**, *99*

Cadurcotherium, **445**

Caenolestes, 266, 267, **442**

Caenolestoidea, 266–67, **442**

Caenopus, 333, 334, **445**, *288d, 300*

Caenotherium, 346, **446**, *305i, 306d*

Calamoichthys, 76, **435**

Calcaneum, 253

Camalodon, 277, **443**

Camarasaurus, 190, 194, **440**, *168d, 175, 177*

Camelops, 350, **446**, *304b, 310b*

Camels, 348–50, B471

Camelus, 350, **446**

Camptosaurus, 196–97, 198, 199, **440**, *179, 180*

Campylognathus, **440**

Canals in mammalian skull, 245

Canine teeth, 247

Canis, 6, 288, **444**, *224*

Capitosaurus, 111, **436**, *98*

Capra, 359, **446**

Capreolus, **446**

Capromeryx, **446**

Captorhinomorpha, 131–32, 437

Captorhinus, 131, **437**, *114*

Capuchin monkey, 421

Carapace, turtle, 133–34

Carcharias, 55, **434**

Carcharodon, 55, **434**

Cariamas, 217

Carnassial teeth, 279

Carnivora, 279–96, **443**, B468–69

Carnivorous dinosaurs, 181–90

Carp, 83, 84

Carolozittelia, **445**

Carpus, 101; mammals, 252–53; *see also* Limbs

Cartilage, 9

Casea, 225, **441**, *206*

Cassowary, 213–14

Castor, 405, **447**

Castoroidea, 405, **447**

Castoroides, 405, **447**, 352

Casuariiformes, 214, **441**

Casuarius, **441**

Catarrhini, 421–32, **449**

Catfish, 82, 83

Catopterus, 75, **435**, *60*

Caturus, 79, 81, **435**, *66*

Cats, 292–95, B468

Cattle, 351, 357–59, B471

Caudata; *see* Urodela

Cavia, 408, **448**

Cebochoerus, 361, **446**

Cebus, 421, **449**

Cenozoic, subdivisions of, 254

Centetes, 271, **443**

Central elements: of carpus, 101, of tarsus, 102; *see* Limbs

Centrum of vertebra, 10, 96

Cephalaspis, 24–28, 56, **433**, *16, 17*

Cephalochorda, 16

Ceraterpeton, **436**

Ceratodus, 91, **436**, *56a*

Ceratogaulus, 405, **447**

Ceratopsia, 196, 203–5, **441**, B464

Ceratopsidae, **441**

Ceratosaurus, 187, 188, **440**

Ceratotherium, 335, **445**

Cercopithecidae, **449**

Cercopithecus, 423

Ceresiosaurus, 151, **438**, *134*

Cervalces, **446**

Cervical region and vertebrae, mammals, 250, 251

Cervulus, **446**

Cervus, **446**

Cestracion; *see* Heterodontus

Cetacea, 392–99, **448**, B473

Cetiosaurus, 194, **440**

Cetotherium, 398, **448**, *342d*

Chalicotheres, 337–38, B470

Chalicotherium, 338, **445**

Chamaeleons, 160

Chameleo, **439**

Champsosaurus, 156–57, **439**, *141b*

Chardriiformes, 218, **442**

Cheiracanthus, **434**

Cheirodus, 74, **435**, *59*

Cheirolepis, 66, 73, **435**, *52b, 54*

Cheleuastochoerus, **446**, *304d, 318e*

Chelodina, **438**

Chelone, 139, **438**

Chelonia, 132–40, **437**, B459

Chelydra, 138, **438**

Chevrotains, 351, 352–53

Chilotherium, 334, **445**

Chimaera, 59, **435**

Chimaeras; *see* Holocephali

Chimpanzee, 426

Chinchilla, 408

Chinese man, 430

Chiromys, 417, **449**

Chiroptera, 275–77, **443**

Chlamydoselachus, 54, **434**

Chlamydotherium, **447**

Choeritherium, **446**

Chondrichthyes, 20–21, 34, 35, 45–61, 63, B454

Chondrostei, 72, 73–77, 85, **435**

Chondrosteus, 75, **435**, *61*

Choneziphius, 396

Chordata, 16

Chordates, primitive, 16–18, B452

Chrysochloris, **443**

Ciconiiformes, 217, **441**

Circulatory system, 15

Cisticephalus, **441**

Civets, 291–92

Cladodus, 49, 51, 52, 53, **434**, *27b, 38*

Cladornis, **441**

Cladoselache, 50–51, **434**, *27a, 39, 40*

Cladoselachii, 49–51, **434**, B455
Claenodon, **443**
Clasping organ, sharks, 37
Classification, 6–7; of vertebrates, *12*, 20–21, 433–49
Clavicle, 99
Cleithrum, 99
Clidastes, **439**, *124e, 142b, d*
Climatius, 46, **434**, *35*
Clupea, **435**
Coati, 290
Coccosteoidea, **433**
Coccosteus, 39–42, **433**, *29*
Cochliodus, 58, **434**
Cochliosaurus, **436**
Codfishes, 84
Coelacanthini, 88, **436**
Coelacanthus, 88, **436**
Coelenterates, 18
Coelodonta, 335, **445**
Coelorhynchus, **436**
Colodon, 330, **445**
Colosteus, 116–17, **437**
Coluber, **439**
Columbiformes, 218, **442**
Columnella; *see* Stapes
Colymbiformes, 216, **441**
Compsognathus, 181–82, 185, **440**
Condylarthra, 301–4, **444**, B469
Conies, 366–68
Coniophis, *123g–i*
Conodonts, 23, *15*
Conoryctes, 277, **443**
Coronoids: in bony fishes, 67; in amphibians, 99
Coots, 217
Copodus, **434**
Coprolites, 2
Coraciiformes, 219, **442**
Coracoid, 100, 122, 252
Cormorants, 217
Coryphodon, 306, 307, **444**, *271b, 272b, d, 275*
Corythosaurus, 199, **440**
Cosmoid scale, 60–61
Cotylosauria, 128–32, **437**, B459
Cratoselache, 49, **434**
Creodonta, 280–87, **443**, B468
Crested dinosaurs, 199–200
Cricetodon, **448**
Cricetops, *348d*
Cricotus, 108, **436**, *85a, b*
Crocodilia, 163, 170–73, **439**, B461

Crocodilus, **440**, *155c*
Cro-Magnon man, 431
Crossopholis, **435**
Crossopterygii, 62, 69, 85–88, **436**, B456–57; relation of, to amphibia, 104
Crossotelos, *100c, d*
Crotalus, **439**
Cryptobranchoidea, **437**
Cryptobranchus, **437**
Cryptocleidus, *123c–d*
Cryptodira, 137–39, **438**
Cryptoprocta, **444**
Crypturiformes, 214, **441**
Ctenacanthus, 51, 53, **434**
Ctenodactylus, 408, **448**
Ctenodus, 91, **436**
Ctenomys, **448**
Cuckoos, 219
Cuculiformes, 219, **442**
Cultures, early human, 430, 431
Cuneiform bones, 252, 253
Cuon, **444**
Cyamodus, **438**
Cyathaspis, **433**
Cyclostomata, 22–24, **433**
Cyclotosaurus, **436**
Cynarioides, **441**, *209b*
Cynodesmus, 288, **444**, *258b*
Cynodictis, 287, **444**, *254f, 258a, 259*
Cynodontia, 234, 235, **441**
Cynognathus, 226–31, 234, 235, **441**, *207, 208, 209c, 211c*
Cyphornis, **441**
Dacrytherium, **446**
Dactylodus, 58, **434**
Dapedius, 78, **435**, *64*
Daphoenodon, 286, **444**, *260*
Daphoenus, 289, **444**, *210d, 211f, 212c, 231b, 256c*
Darwin, 4
Dasyprocta, **448**
Dasypus, **447**
Dasyurus, 265, **442**
Dawn man of Piltdown, 428–30
Deciduous teeth, 247
Deer, 351, 353–56, B471
Deinodon, 188–89, **440**, *172*
Delphinognathus, 232, **441**, *217c*
Deltatheridioidea, 270, 271, **443**
Deltatheridium, 270, 271, 272, **443**, *246a, 247a, f*
Deltodus, 58, **434**, *49c*

Dendrodonts, 87
Dendrodus, **436**
Dentary: in bony fishes, 67; in amphibians, 99; in mammals, 245
Denticles, dermal, 16, 39, 63, *9*
Dentine, 16
Dermal supraoccipital: in bony fishes, 67; in amphibians, 98; equals interparietal, 243
Dermatemys, 138, **438**
Dermochelys, 139, **438**
Dermoptera, 274–75, **443**
Desmatochelys, **438**
Desmatosuchus, 159–60, **439**, *154*
Desmolagus, **448**, *349d*
Desmostylus, 379, **447**, *334*
Deuterosaurus, **441**
Devil's corkscrews, 405
Diacodexis, 343, **446**, *305a*
Diacodon, 273, **443**, *247d, g*
Diadectes, 129, **437**, *107a–c, 111*
Diadectomorpha, 129–31, **437**
Diademodon, **441**, *210c*
Diadiaphorus 316, **444**, *268g, h, 283b*
Diapsid temporal region, 128, 154
Diasparactus, **437**
Diastema, 247, 299
Diatryma, 217–18, **442**, *195a*
Diceratherium, 333, **445**, *289c. 296c, 297b*
Dicerorhinus, 335, **445**
Diceros, 335, **445**, *291e*
Dichobune, 346, **446**, *305b*
Dicotyles, 365, **446**, *303b*
Dicrocerus, 355, **446**, *305n, 313e*
Dicynodon, 234, **441**, *218c*
Dicynodontia, 233, **441**
Didelphia, 255, **442**
Didelphodus, **443**, *228*
Didelphys, 264, **442**, *196d, 211e, 241d, f, 242*
Didolodus, 316, **444**, *268f*
Didus, **442**
Didymictis, 285, **444**, *256b*
Digitigrade gait, 253
Digits, 101
Dimetrodon, 224–25, **441**, *200, 203, 209a, 210a, 211a*
Dimorphodon, **440**
Dimylus, **443**
Dingo, 288
Dinichthys, 39–42, **433**, *30*

Dinictis, 294, 295, **444**, *254n*, *261c*, *262*

Dinocephalia, 232, **441**

Dinocyon, **444**

Dinohyus, 362, 446, *307c*, *319*

Dinomylostoma, **433**

Dinomys, **448**

Dinophoneus, 232, **441**, *217b*

Dinornis, **441**, *194*

Dinornithiformes, 214–15, **441**

Dinosaurs, 179–205, B462

Dinotherium, 372, **447**, *327*

Diochotichus, 396

Diphycercal tail fin, 8, *3*

Diplacanthus, **434**

Displasiocoela, **437**

Diplobune, 346, **446**, *303a*, *307d*

Diplocaulus, 113–14, **436**, *102a*

Diplocercides, 88, **436**

Diplodocus, 190, 194, **440**, *169e*, *174*, *176*, *178*

Diplomystus, **435**

Diplovertebron, 94, 101, 107, 108, **436**, *84*, *92a*

Dipnoi, 62, 69, 89–92, 104, **436** B457

Dipodoidea, 407, **448**

Diprotodon 266, **442**, *241d*

Diprotodonta, 263, 265–66, **442**

Dipterus, 89, **436**, *79*, *80*

Dipus, 407, **448**

Discoglossus, **437**

Dissacus, **443**

Dissorhophus, **436**

Docodon, **442**

Dodo, 215, 219

Dogs, 288–89, B468

Dolichorhinus, 336, **445**

Dolichosaurus, 160, **439**

Dolichosoma, 113, **436**

Dolphins, 395, 396, 397

Doormice, 407

Dorsal vertebrae, mammals, 250

Dorudon, 394, **448**

Dorypterus, **435**

Doves, 219

Drepanaspis, 31, **433**, *23*

Dromaeus, **441**

Dromasauria, 231–32, **441**

Dromatherium, 237, **441**, *221b*

Dryolestes, 260, **442**, *239c*

Dromomeryx, **446**

Dryopithecus, 426–27, 428, **449** *353c*, *354e*

Duck-billed dinosaurs, 198–200

Ducks, 217

Dugong, 376, 377, 378–79, *331b*

Duplicidentata, 409–10, **448**

Dwinasaurus, **436**

Eagles, 217

Ear: primitive, 14; osteostraci, 25; amphibians, 103; mammals, 244, 245–46; *see also* Otic capsule

Ear drum, 103

Echidna, 256, **442**

Echinoderms, 18, 19

Ectepicondylar foramen, 126

Ectocion, 303, **444**

Ectoloph, 249

Ectopterygoid: in bony fishes, 67; in amphibians, 98

Edaphodon, **435**

Edaphosaurus, 225, **441**, *204*, *205*, *210b*

Edentata, 381–89, **447**, B473

Edestus, 53, **434**, *42c*

Edmontosaurus, 199, **440**, *182a*

Eels, 82, 84

Eggs, 15; chondrichthyes, 37; amphibians, 93; reptiles, 120

Elapidae, **439**

Elasmosaurus, 151, **438**, *124c*

Elasmotherium, 335, **445**

Electric organs, Osteostraci, 25–27

Elephants, 301, 370–71, 375–76

Elephas, 376, **447**

Elginia, **437**

Elonichthys, **435**

Emballonuridae, **443**

Embolomeri, 108–9, **436**

Embolotherium, 336, **445**

Embrithopoda, 368, 370, **446**

Embrithosaurus, **437**

Emu, 213, 214

Emys, 137, **438**

Endothiodon, **441**

Entelodon, 362, **446**

Entelonychia, 309, 311–12, **445**

Entepicondylar foramen, 124, 252

Entoconid, 248

Entotympanic, 244

Eoanthropus, 428, 430, **449**, *358c*

Eobatrachus, **437**

Eodidelphys, **442**

Eogyrinus, 94, 107, 108, **436**, *83*, *88a*

Eohippus, 323, 330, 331, **445**, *287a*, *288a*, *298a*, *290a*, *291a*, *292*

Eomoropus, 338, **445**

Eosauravus, **437**

Eosiren, 378, **447**

Eosuchia, 154, 166, **438**, B460

Eosteiromys, **448**

Eotheroides, 378, **447**, *331a*, *332*

Eotherium, **447**

Eotitanops, 337, **445**

Epihippus, 325, **445**

Epimys, 407

Epiphyses, 241

Epipterygoid: in bony fishes, 68; in amphibians, 99; becomes alisphenoid, 243

Epoicotherium, **447**

Equoidea, 322–28, **445**, B469

Equus, 322–23, 327–28, **445**, *287d*, *288b*, *289b*, *290f*, *291b*

Erethizon, 408, **448**

Ericiolacerta, *213c*

Erinoceamorpha, 273, **443**

Erinaceus, 273, **443**

Erpetosaurus, 116, **437**

Eryops, 109, 123, 124, **436**, *85c*, *88b–d*, *89b*, *90*, *92b*, *97*, *98*

Erythrosuchus, 170, **439**

Esthonyx, 278, **443**, *252a*

Ethmoid ossifications, 68, 99, 243

Eucosmodon, **442**

Eucreodi, **444**

Eudinoceras, **444**

Euganthus, **435**

Eugyrinus, **437**

Eumys, **448**, *349b*

Eunotosauria, 139–40, **437**

Eunotosaurus, 139–40, **437**, *120*

Euparkeria, 166, 182, **439**, *148:*, *150a, b*

Euposaurus, **439**

Euprotogonia, **444**

Eurhinosaurus, 146, **438**

Eurhinodelphis, 396

Eurylambda, 260, **442**, *258b*

Eurylepis, **435**, *54*

Eurymylus, **448**

Eurypterids, 19; influence of, on vertebrates, 33–34

Eurypterygius, 146, **438**

Eurysternum, **438**

Eusthenopteron, 66, 87, **436**, *53a,b,*
56b, 77
Eustachian tube, 245
Eutheria, 255, **443**
Evolution, theories of, 3–5
Exoccipital: in bony fishes, 68;
in amphibians, 99; in mam-
mals, 243
Eyes, 13, 14

Falconiformes, 217, **442**
Feathers, 206
Feet: *see* Digits, Limbs
Felis, 292, **444**
Felsinotherium, 379, **447**
Femur, 102, 252
Fenestra ovale, 244
Fiber, 407, **448**
Fibula, 102
Fibulare, 102, 253
Fins, 8, 11, 12, *3;* shark-like
fishes, 37–38; bony fishes, 69;
crossopterygians cf. amphib-
ians, 104
Fisher, 291
Fishes, 22–92; structure of, 7–16;
classification of, 20–21, 35,
B453
Fissipedia, 287–95, **444**
Flamingos, 217
Flight: in pterosaurs, 176; in
birds, 206–7, 211; in bats, 275
Flightless birds, 213–16
Flounder, 85
Flying fish, 84
Flying lemur, 274–75
Flying reptiles; *see* Pterosauria
Foramen magnum, 68
Foramina in skull of mammals,
244–45
Fossils, nature of, 1–2
Fowls, 217
Foxes, 288
Frogs, 93, 94, 117–19
Frontal: in bony fishes, 67; in
amphibians, 98; in mammals,
241

Gadus, 435
Galago, 417, 418, **449**
Galeocerdo, 434
Galechirus, 441
Galeopithecus, 274–75, **443**
Galeops, 441
Galepus, 231, **441**, *215b*
Galliformes, 217, **442**

Gallinuloides, **442**
Ganodus, **435**
Ganoid scale, 63, 64
Gar pike, 78–79
Gastornis, **442**
Gazella, 358, **446**, *313h*
Gecko, 160, **439**
Geese, 217
Gelocus, 353, **446**
Gemundina, 48, 57–58, 59, 60,
434, B455, *48*
Gemoyoidea, 405–6, **447**
Geomys, 405, **448**
Geosaurus, 173, **440**, *155d, 156c, d*
Gibbons, 425–26
Gila monster (Heloderma), 160
Gill arches; *see* Arches, branchial
Gills, 15; in lower chordates, 16,
17, 18; cyclostomes, 23; ostra-
coderms, 25, 28, 30; gnatho-
stomes, 35, 37; bony fishes,
69–70; amphibians, 101; ex-
ternal, 116; *see also* Spiracle
Giraffa, **446**
Giraffes, 351, 356–57
Girdles, pectoral and pelvic, 12;
see also Limbs, Fins
Glass "snake," 160
Glenoid cavity: in shoulder
girdle, 101; for jaw, 243
Globidens, 161, **439**
Glyptolepis, **436**
Glossotherium, 389, **447**
Glyptodon, 384, 386, **447**, *337c,*
339
Glyptodonts, 381, 382, 384–87,
B473
Gnathostomes, 35
Goats, 351, 357–59
Gomphognathus, **441**
Goniopholis, 173, **440**
Gophers, 405
Gorgonops, **441**
Gorgonopsia, 234–35, **441**
Gorgosaurus, 188, **440**, *169d*
Gorilla, 426, *449*
Gravigrada, 388–90, **447**, B473
Graviportal mammals, 254, 301
Grebes, 216
Ground sloths, 381–82, 388–90,
B473
Grouse, 217
Gruiformes, 217–18, **442**
Gryposaurus, 199
Guinea pig, 408

Gular plates, 67
Gulls, 219
Gulo, 291, **444**
Gymnophiona; *see* Apoda
Gymnura, 273, **443**
Gyracanthus, 47, **434**
Gyrodus, **435**
Gyrolepis, **435**

Haemal arches, 11
Hag-fishes, 22–24, 32, *13*
Halicore, 378, **447**
Halitherium, 378, **447**, *333*
Hallopus, 440
Hallux, 250
Hapale, 420, **449**
Hapalops, 388, 389, **447**, *338c*
Hares, 409–10
Hawks, 217
Head, structure of: Osteostraci,
25–27; arthrodires, 40–41;
see also Skull, Braincase, Jaws
Hedgehog, 273
Hegetotherium, 314, **445**
Heidelberg jaw, 430–31
Helaletes, 330, **445**
Helichthys, **435**
Helicoprion, **434**
Heloderma, **439**
Helodus, *49b*
Hemibranchii, 84, **435**
Hemichorda, 9, 18, *10*
Hemicyon, 290, **444**, *254i, 258c*
Heptaxodon, **448**
Heptodon, **445**, *264a*
Herons, 217
Herpestes, **444**
Herpetosuchus, **439**
Herrings, 83
Hesperornis, 209, 212–13, 215,
441, *188, 193*
Hesperornithiformes, **441**
Heterocercal tail fin, 8, *3*
Heterodontoidea, **434**
Heterodontus, 52, 53, **434**
Heteromyidae, **447**
Heteromys, 405
Heterosteus, **433**
Heterostraci, 29–32, **433**
Hipparion, 327, **445**
Hippidium, 327, **445**, *294*
Hippopotamus, 363–64, **446**,
305g, 318d
Hoactzin, 217

Hogs, giant, 361–62
Holocephali, 59–60, 434, B456
Holoptychius, 87, 89, 436, *75, 76*
Holostei, 77–81, 85, 435
Homacodon, 343, 446, *264c, 306a*
Homaeosaurus, 155, 439, *140*
Homalodontotherium, 309, 445, *276, 277a*
Homo, 449; *heidelbergensis*, 430–31, *358d*; *neanderthalensis*, 431, *353d, 354f*; *sapiens*, 431–32
Homocercal tail fin, 72, 82, *3*
Homogalax, 330, 445, *288f*
Homosteoidea, 433
Homosteus, 43, 433
Homunculus, 421, 449
Hoplophoneus, 294, 295, 444, *356d, 261a*
Hoploplteryx, *73*
Horned dinosaurs; *see* Ceratopsia
Horns: dinosaurs, 204; amblypods, 306; toxodonts, 312; rhinoceroses, 330; titanotheres, 336; pecorans, 351; tragulids, 353; giraffes, 356; prongbucks, 357; bovids, 358
Horses, 322–28; modern forms of, 322–23, 327–28, B469
Howesia, 438
Howling monkeys, 421
Humerus, 101, 252
Humming birds, 219
Hyaemoschus, 352, 446
Hyaena, 292, 444, *254m, 258f*
Hyaenarctos, 290, 444, *254j*
Hyaenas, 291, 292, B468
Hyaenodon, 284, 444
Hyaenognathus, 289, 444
Hybodus, 53–54, 434, *6, 27e, 42d, 43*
Hydrochoerus, 408, 448
Hyla, 437
Hylaeobatrachus, 437
Hylaeochampsa, 440
Hylobates, 425, 449
Hynobius, 437
Hyoid arch, 35
Hyomandibular, 35, 36; in bony fishes, 68–69; becomes stapes, 103
Hyopotamus, 446
Hyopsodus, 303–4, 444, *268c, d*
Hypacrosaurus, 440
Hyperdactyly, 144
Hyperodapedon, 156, 439, *141a*
Hyperphalangy, 144

Hypertragulus, 353, **446**
Hypisodus, 353, **446**
Hypocone, 248
Hypoconid, 248
Hypoconulid, 248
Hypohippus, 326, **445**
Hypophysis, 13; in cylostomes, 23
Hypsilophodon, 198, **440**, *181a, d*
Hypsiprimnodon, 266
Hypsocormus, **435**
Hypsodont, 247, 299
Hypural bones, 82, *3*
Hyrachyus, 331, **445**, *288c, 291c*
Hyracodon, 331–32, **445**, *296a, 297a, 298*
Hyracoidea, 366–68, **446**, B472
Hyracotherium, 323, **445**, *227b*
Hyrax, 366, **446**
Hystricoidea, 408–9, **448**
Hystricomorpha, 408–9, **448**
Hystrix, 408, **448**

Ichthyodorulites, 59
Ichthyophis, **437**
Ichthyopterygia, 146, **438**
Ichthyornis, 212–13, 215, **441**, *192*
Ichthyornithiformes, **441**
Ichthyosauria, 142–46, **438**, B459–60
Ichthyosaurus, 146, **438**
Ichthyostega, 117, **437**, *95*
Ichthyostegopsis, 117, **437**
Ictidosauria, 237, **441**
Ictitherium, 292, **444**
Iguana, **439**
Iguanodon, 198, **440**, *181b*
Ilium, 100
Inia, 396, **448**
Incisors, 247
Indris, 417, **449**
Insectivora, 269–74, **443**, B467; primitive forms, 270–71
Interatherium, 314, **445**
Intercentrum, 96, 123
Interclavicle, 99
Intermedium, 101, 102, 252, 253
Interparietal, 243
Intertemporal: in bony fishes, 67; in amphibians, 98
Invertebrates, relation of, to vertebrates, 18–19
Ischium, 100

Ischnacanthus, 47, **434**
Ischyodus, **434**
Ischyromys, 403, **447**, *349a*
Isospondyli, 83, **435**
Isotemnus, **445**
Jaekelaspis, 42–43, **433**, *31*
Janassa, **434**
Java man, 428
Jaws, 12, 13; origin of, 11; primitive absence of, 22; sharks, 35–36; bony fishes, 67, 68–69; amphibians, 99; mammals, 245–46
Jerboas, 407
Jonkeria, 232, **441**, *216, 217a*
Jugal: in bony fishes, 67; in amphibians, 98; in mammals, 243

Kangaroo rats, 405
Kangaroos, 266
Kannemeyeria, 234, **441**, *196b, 219*
Karroomys, **441**
Kentriodon, 396, **448**, *344*
Kentrurosaurus, 202, **440**
Kiaeraspis, 17
Kingfishers, 219
Kinkajou, 289
Kogia, 397
Kionocrania, 160, **439**
Kiwi, 213–15
Kotlassia, **437**

Labial cartilages, *6*
Labidosaurus, 131–32, **437**, *113*
Labrodon, **436**
Labyrinthodontia, 105–12, **436**, B457
Lacerta, **439**
Lacertilia, 159–62, **439**
Lacrimal: in bony fishes, 67; in amphibians, 98; in mammals, 242
Lacrimal duct, 245
Lamarck, 4
Lambdoidal crest, 243
Lambdotherium, 337, **445**
Lambeosaurus, 199, **440**, *182b*
Lamnoidea, **434**
Lamna, 55, **434**, *44b*
Lampreys, 22–24, 27, *13, 14*
Lanarkia, 31–32, 33, **433**
Laosaurus, **440**
Lariosaurus, **438**, *124d*
Lasanius, 27, 28, **433**

Lateral line organs, 14–15; in amphibians, 103

Legs; see Limbs

Lemur, 417, **449**

Lemuroidea, 411, 415–18, **449**

Leontinia, 313, **435**

Lepidosauria, 154, **438**

Lepidosiren, 91, **436**

Lepidosteus, 77, 78, **435**

Lepidotus, 78, **435**, *63*

Lepospondyli, 112–14, **436**, B458

Leptictis, **443**

Leptobos, 359

Leptoceratops, **441**

Leptolepis, 83, **435**, *70, 71*

Leptomeryx, 353, 355, **446**, *312a, 313a, 314*

Leptopterygius, **438**

Lepus, 410, **448**

Leuciscus, **435**

Limbs: paired, primitive absence of, 22; fishes, 35; primitive land forms, 94, 99–102; primitive reptile, 123–24; reptiles, general, 126; archosaurs, 163–65; birds, 207–8; mammal-like reptiles, 229–30; mammals, 251–54; ungulates, 299–301; see also Wing, Fin

Limnoscelis, **437**

Limnocyon, 285, **444**

Limnohyops, 337, **445**, *289e, 291g*

Lion, 292

Lipelmidae, **437**

Lipotes, 396

Litopterna, 316–17, **444**, B473

Lizards, 147, 158, 159–62; origin, 159; marine, 160–62

Llama, 348, 350

Locomotion in mammals, 253–54

Loons, 216

Lophiodon, 330, **445**

Lophiodonts, B470

Lophodont teeth, 248, 297–98

Loricata, 384–87, **447**

Loris, 417, **449**

Loxodonta, 376, **447**

Loxolophodon, **444**

Loxomma, 108, **436**

Lumbar vertebrae, mammals, 250, 251

Lunar, 252

Lung, 62, 69–70

Lungfish; see Dipnoi

Lutra, 291, **444**

Lycaenops, **441**, *211b, 213b, 214b*

Lychosuchus, **441**, *218a*

Lysorophia, 114, **436**

Lysorophus, 114, 119, **436**, *100a, b, 102b*

Lystrosaurus, 234, **441**

Macacus, 423, **449**

Machaeroprosopus, 169, **439**, *152*

Machairodus, **444**

Mackerel, 85

Macrauchenia, 317, **444**, *283a, 284a, b*

Macropetalichthys, 48–49, **434**, *8, 37*

Macropoma, 88, **436**, *78*

Macropus, 266, **442**

Macroscelides, 274, **443**

Macrosemius, **435**

Macrotherium, **445**

Magnum, 253

Mammal-like reptiles, 220–38

Mammalia, 21, 239–432, **442**; see also Mammals

Mammals: synapsid ancestry of, 237–38; structure of, 239–54; primitive forms of, 255–67; placentals, 268–432; bibliography, general, 465–67

Mammonteus, 376, **447**, *325d, 326d*

Mammoths, 376

Man: characters of, 427–28; fossil types of, 428–32

Man-o'war birds, 217

Manatee, 376, 379

Manatus, **447**

Manis, 390, **447**

Marmosets, 420

Marsupial bones, 256, 261

Marsupialia, 215, 261–67, 269, **442**, B467; compared with multituberculates, 258

Marsupium, 261

Marten, 291

Mastodon, 374–75, **447**, *326a, 329, 330*

Mastodons, 372–75

Mastodonsaurus, 111, **436**, *85d*

Mastoid, 244; in artiodactyls, 342–44

Maxilla: in bony fishes, 67; in amphibia, 98; in mammals, 243

Mazama, **446**

Meantes, **437**

Megacerops, 335, **445**

Megaceros, 354, **446**, *313f, 316*

Megachiroptera, 275–76, **443**

Megaladapis, 417, **449**

Megalania, 160, **439**

Megalichthys, 88, **436**, *52c, 55c*

Megalictis, **444**

Megalobatrachus, **437**

Megalohyrax, 367, **446**, *323*

Megalonyx, 389, **447**

Megalosaurus, 187, **440**

Megalurus, **435**

Megamys, **448**

Megatherium, 389, **447**

Melanodon, 260, **442**, *238c*

Melanorosaurus, **440**

Mellivora, **444**

Menaspis, **434**

Meniscotherium, 304, **444**, *268e*

Menodus, 335, *296f, 297d*

Menotyphla, 273–74, **443**

Mephitis, 291, **444**

Merriamia, 124a

Merychippus, 326–27, **445**, *287c, 290d*

Merychyus, 347, **446**

Merycochoerus, **446**, *304a*

Merycodus, 357, **446**, *312c, 313g*

Mesaxonic toe reduction, 300

Mesodon, 78, **435**

Mesohippus, 325, **445**, *290b, 293*

Mesonyx, 283, **443**, *254b*

Mesoplodon, 396, **448**

Mesopithecus, 424, **449**, *356a, 357*

Mesosauria, 141–42, **438**, B459

Mesosaurus, 141–42, **438**, *121*

Metacarpals, 101

Metacheiromys, 383, **447**, *336*

Metacone, 248

Metaconid, 248

Metaconule, 248

Metailurus, **444**, *254d, 261d*

Metaloph, 249

Metamynodon, 332, **445**, *299*

Metatarsals, 102

Metatheria, 255, **442**

Metaxytherium, 378, **447**

Metoposaurus, **436**

Metriorhynchus, 173, **440**

Miacis, 287, **444**

Mice, 407–8

Micramphibia, 112, **436**

Microbrachis, 112, **436**

Microchiroptera, 276, **443**

Microcleidus, 132a
Microconodon, 237, **441**
Microdon, 78, **435**, *65*
Microgomphodon, **441**
Micropholis, **436**
Microtus, **448**
Mioclaenus, **444**
Miohippus, 325, *287b*
Miolania, **438**
Miosiren, 378, *322c*
Mixodectes, **443**
Mixosaurus, 145, *126*
Moas, 214–15
Moeritherium, 371–72, 373, **447**, *322d, g, 325a*
Molar teeth: structure and evolution of, 247–49; in ungulates, 297–99
Moles, 273; golden mole, 272
Monitors, 160
Monkeys, 420–24
Monoclonius, 203, 204, **441**, *164d, 181c, f, 185*
Monodelphia, 255
Monotremata, 256–57, 258, **442**
Montsechobatrachus, **437**
Moropus, 337–38, **445**, *288h, 289f, 291h, 296g, 297e*
Morosaurus, **440**, *148c, 163b*
Mosasaurs, 160–62
Mosasaurus, **439**
Moschops, 232, **441**, *231a*
Moschus, 355
Mouth: cyclostomes, 23; ostracoderms, 25, 28, 31
Multituberculata, 257–58, 269, **442**
Muraenosaurus, 151, **438**, *129, 131a–b, 132b*
Mus, 407, **448**
Muscular system, 15
Musk-ox, 357, 359
Mustela, 291, **444**, *254l, 255b, 258e*
Mustelids, 290–91, B468
Mutations, 5
Mycterosaurus, 222, **441**, *199*
Mylagaulodon, **447**
Mylagaulus, 405, **447**
Myliobatis, 56, **434**, *45a, 46d*
Mylodon, 389, **447**, *335, 337b, 338d*
Mylohyus, **446**, *307b*
Mylostoma, 42, **433**
Myohyrax, **446**

Myoidea, 407–8, **448**
Myomorpha, 406–8, **448**
Myoxoidea, 407, **448**
Myoxus, 407, **448**
Myriacanthus, **434**, *50*
Myrmecophagus, 387, **447**
Mysticeti, 397–400, **448**
Mystriosuchus, 169, **439**, *153*
Myxine, 22, **433**, *13*
Myxinoidea, **433**

Naja, **439**
Nannosaurus, **440**
Naosaurus, **441**
Nares: external, in amphibians, 98; mammals, external, 241; mammals, internal, 243; *see also* Nostrils.
Narwhal, 397
Nasal: in bony fishes, 67; in amphibia, 98; in mammals, 242–43
Nasal capsule, 11
Natalidae, **443**
Neanderthal man, 431
Necrolemur, 419, **449**
Nectridia, 113–14, **436**
Necturus, **437**
Nematoptychius, 55a
Neoceratodus, 91, **436**, *82*
Neognathae, 216, **441**
Neoreomys, **448**, *348e*
Neornithes, **441**
Nerve cord, 13; lower chordates, 16–18; invertebrates, 18–19
Nerves, cranial, 13; in mammals, 244–45
Nervous system, 13–14
Nesodon, 312, **445**, *277c, 278b, d, 297a, b*
Neural arch and spine, 11
Neusticosaurus, **438**
Newts, 94
Nighthawks, 219
Nodosaurus, 202, **440**, *184*
Nostrils: primitive, 14; jawless vertebrates, 23, 28, 29, 30, 31, 32; gnathostomes, 35; internal, 117; *see also* Nares
Notharctus, 415–16, **449**, *234, 353a, 354a, 355*
Nothodectes, **449**
Nothosauria, 151–52, **438**
Nothosaurus, 151, **438**
Nothrotherium, 389, **447**, *338d, 340*

Notidanoidea, **434**
Notidanus, 54, **434**, *44a*
Notochampsa, **439**
Notochord, 8–9, 10–11; lower chordates, 16, 17, 18; cylostomes, 23
Notohippus, 313, **445**
Notopithecus, **445**
Notoryctes, **442**
Notostylops, 311, **445**
Nototherium, **442**
Notoungulata, 301, 308–15, **445**, B473
Nyctinomus, **443**, *249a–c*
Nyctipithecus, 421
Nyctitherium, **443**
Nyctosaurus, **440**

Occipital condyle: amphibians, 99; reptiles, 121, 125; therapsids, 227; mammals, 243
Ochotona, 410, **448**
Octodontidae, **448**
Odobaenus, 296, **444**
Odocoileus, **446**
Odontaspis, 55, **434**
Odontoceti, 395–97, **448**
Odontognathae, **441**
Odontopteryx, 217, **442**
Okapia, 351, 356, **446**
Olecranon, 101
Oldfieldthomasia, 314, **445**, *297e, f*
Oligobunis, **444**
Oligopleurus, 80–81, **435**
Omomys, *227a*
Omosaurus, **440**
Omphalosaurus, 145, **438**
Onchus, **434**
Onohippidium, 327, **445**
Onychodectes, **443**, *252b*
Onychodus, 47, **434**
Operculum, 37, 67
Opetiosaurus, **439**
Ophiacodon, 222, 224, **441**, *196a, 198, 201, 212a, 213a, 214a*
Ophiderpeton, 112, **436**
Ophidia, 160, 162, **439**
Ophthalmosaurus, **438**, *123a–b, 124b, 125a–b*
Opisthocoela, **437**
Opisthocomus, 217
Opisthotic: in bony fishes, 68; in amphibians, 99; in mammals, 244
Opossum, 261, 263, 267

Orang-utan, 426
Orbitosphenoid, 243
Ordovician vertebrates, 24
Oreamnos, 359, 446
Oreodon, 347, 446, *305j*, *306c*,
    307f
Ornithischia, 180, 195–205, 440,
    B463–64
Ornithocheirus, 440
Ornithodelphia, 255
Ornithodesmus, 440
Ornitholestes, 181, 185, 440, *165*,
    166
Ornithomimus, 185, 440
Ornithopoda, 195–200, 440, B463
Ornithorhynchus, 256, 442, *196c*,
    211d
Ornithostoma, 440
Ornithosuchus, 166, 182, 439,
    150c
Orodus, 53, 434, *42a, b*
Orohippus, 325, 445
Orthogenesis, 5
Orthosaurus, 94, 108, 436, *87*
Orycteropus, 391, 447, *341*
Oryctolagus, 410, *448*
Osmeroides, 435
Ostariophysi, 83–84, 85, 435
Osteichthyes, 20–21, 35, 45, 62–
    92, 435
Osteolepis, 66, 87, 436, *53c–f, 74*
Osteostraci, 24–27, 433
Ostracoderms, 22, 24–32
Ostrich, 213, 214, 215
Otaria, 444
Otic capsule, 11
Otic notch: in amphibians, 98;
    in primitive reptiles, 122; re-
    duced or modified in reptiles,
    124, 129, 130, 131
Otocratia, 436
Otocyon, 288, 444
Otter, 291
Ovibos, 359, 446
Oviraptor, 440
Ovis, 359, 446
Owl monkey, 421
Owls, 219
Oxyaena, 283, 444, *254d*, *255a*,
    257
Oxyclaenus, 281, 443
Oxydactylus, 350, 446, *311*
Oxyrhina, 55, 434

Pachyaena, 443
Pachyrukhos, 314, 445

Pachycormus, 79–80. 435
Pachyosteus, 433
Paddle fishes, 75
Palacrodon, 439
Palaeagama, 438
Palaeanodon, 383, 447
Palaeanodonta, 382, 383, 447,
    B473
Palaeaspis, 433
Palaenycteris, 443
Palaeobatrachus, 437
Palaeocastor, 405, 447, *348b*
Palaeochameleo, 438
Palaeochiropteryx, 443, *250*
Palaeognathae, 213–16, 441
Palaeogyrinus, 94, 96–99, 108,
    436, *86*
Palaeohatteria, 441
Palaeolagus, 410, 448, *348f*
Palaeoloxodon, 376, 447
Palaeomastodon, 373, 374, 447,
    328a
Palaeomeryx, 446
Palaeonictis, 285, 444
Palaeoniscids, 73–75, 76
Palaeoniscoidea, 435
Palaeoniscus, 73–74, 435, *58*
Palaeophis, 162, 439
Palaeorhinus, 439
Palaeornithes, 211, 441
Palaeortyx, 442
Palaeoryctes, 272, 443
Palaeoscincus, 202, 440
Palaeosimia, 426
Palaeospiza, 442
Palaeospondyloidea, 28–29, 433
Palaeospondylus, 28–29, 32, 33,
    433, *20, 21*
Palaeostylops, 312, 445
Palaeosyops, 337, 445, *288g*
Palaeotherium, 328, 445, *295*
Palate: crocodiles, 170–71; birds,
    209, 213, 215; mammal-like
    reptiles, 226–27; mammals,
    243; *see also* Skull
Palatine: in bony fishes, 67; in
    amphibians, 98
Paliguana, 438
Pantelosaurus, 441
Pantolambda, 304–6, 444, *270*,
    271a, 272a, 273a, b
Pantolestes, 274, 443
Pantylus, 437
Paracone, 248
Paraconid, 248

Paloplotherium, 445
Pan, 426
Panda, 290
Pangolins, 381, 390
Panochthus, 384, 386, 447, *338b*
Pantotheria, 249, 260, 261, 442
Papio, 423, 449
Parahippus, 326, 445, *290c*
Parallelism, 5; in archosaurs, 163
Paramys, 403, 405, 406, 447,
    348a, 350, 351
Parapithecus, 421, 449, *354c, 356b*
Parasaurolophus, 199, 440
Parasphenoid: in bony fishes,
    67; in amphibians, 99; be-
    comes vomer, 243
Paraxonic toe reduction, 300, 339
Pareiasaurs, 129–31
Pareiasaurus, 437
Parelephas, 376, 447
Parexus, 46, 434
Parietal: in bony fishes, 67; in
    amphibians, 98; in mammals,
    242
Paroccipital; *see* Opisthotic
Paroccipital process of exoccipi-
    tal, 243
Parrots, 219
Passeriformes, 219, 442
Patriocetus, 398, 449
Patriofelis, 285, 444
Paurodon, 442
Pavement-toothed sharks, 58–59
Pea fowl, 217
Peccaries, 360, 364, 365
Pecora, 340, 351–59, 446
Pectoral girdle, amphibians, 99–
    100
Peleon, 437
Pedetes, 406, 448
Peking man, 430
Pelagornis, 441
Pelicaniformes, 217, 441
Pelicans, 217
Pelobates, 437
Peloneustes, 438
Peltephilus, 447
Pelycodus, 449
Pelycornis, 442
Pelycosauria, 158, 221–25, 441,
    B464–65
Penguins, 216–17
Perameles, 265, 442
Percesoces, 84, 435
Perch, 85

Perching birds, 219
Perchoerus, 365, **446**, *318f*
Periods, geologic, 3
Periotic, 244
Periptychus, 304–5, **444**, *274*
Perissodactyla, 319–38, **445**, B469–70
Perleidus, **435**
Peromyscus, **448**
Petalodus, 58, **434**, *49a*
Petrels, 217
Petromyzon, 22, 23, **433**, *13*, *14*
Petromyzontia, **433**
Petrosal, 244
Phalangeal formula, 102; in reptiles, 124; in therapsids, 230, 232, 235; in mammals, 253
Phalanger, 266, **442**
Phalanges, 101
Phaneropleuron, 91, **436**
Pharyngolepis, 27, **433**, *19*
Phascolarctos, 266
Phascolomys, 266, **442**
Pheasants, 217
Phenacodus, 301–3, 304, **444**, *264b*, *265*, *266*, *268a*, *b*, *269*
Phiomia, 373, 374, **447**, *325b*, *328b*
Phlaocyon, 290, **444**, *254h*
Phlyctaenaspis, **433**
Phoca, **444**
Pholidogaster, **436**
Pholidophoroidea, **435**
Pholidophorus, 80–81, **435**, *68*
Pholidosaurus, **440**
Pholidota, 390, **447**, B473
Phororhachos, 218–19, **442**, *189*, *195b*
Phyllolepis, 31, **433**
Phyllospondyli, 114–17, **437**, B458
Phyllostomatidae, **443**
Physeter, 397, **448**
Physodon, **448**
Phytosauria, 168–69, **439**
Phytosaurus, 169, **439**
Pigeons, 219
Pigs, 360, 364–65, B470–71
Pika, 410
Pilosa, 384, 387–90, **447**
Piltdown man, 428–30
Pineal body; *see* Eye
Pinnipedia, 295–96, **444**, B469
Pipa, **437**
Pipefish, 85

Pisces, 21; *see also* Fishes
Pisiform, 252
Pithecanthropus, 428, **449**, *358a*
Pituitary, 13
Placental mammals, 268; family tree of, *245;* primitive types, structure of, 268–69
Placentalia, **443**
Placochelys, 152, **438**, *136*
Placodermi, 20–21, 35, 39–45, 63, **433**, *28*
Placodontia, 152–53, **438**
Placodus, 152–53, **438**, *135*
Plagiaulacoidea, **442**
Plagiaulax, 258, **442**
Plagiomene, 275, **443**, *248*
Plagiosaurus, **436**
Plagiosternum, **436**
Plantigrade gait, 254
Plastomenus, **438**
Plastron, turtle, 134
Platanista, **448**
Platecarpus, 161, **439**, *158c*
Plateosaurus, 189–90, **440**, *167*, *173*
Platybelodon, 374, **447**, *325f*
Platygonus, 365, **446**, *305e*, *321*
Platynota, 160, **439**
Platyrrhini, 420–21, **449**
Platysomus, 74, **435**
Plesiadapis, 416, **449**
Plesictis, **444**
Plesiocetus, **448**
Plesiochelys, **438**
Plesiosauria, 148–51, **438**
Plesiosaurus, 151, **438**
Plesippus, 327, **445**
Plethodon, **437**
Pleuracanthodii, 51–52, **434**, B455
Pleuracanthus, 51–52, **434**, *26*, *41*
Pleuraspidotherium, **444**
Pleurocentrum, 96
Pleurodira, 137, **438**
Pleuropholis, **435**
Pleurosaurus, **438**
Pleurosternum, **438**
Pleurostylodon, 311, **445**, *279c*, *d*
Pliauchenia, 349, **446**
Pliocyon, **444**
Pliohippus, 327, **445**, *290e*
Pliohyrax, **446**
Pliopithecus, 426, **449**
Pliosaurus, 151, **438**

Plovers, 219
Podocnemis, **438**
Podokesaurus, 181–82, 184, **440**
Poëbrotherium, 348–49, **446**, *309a*, *310a*
Polacanthus, 203, **440**
Poliosauridae, **441**
Pollex, 250
Polydolops, 266, **442**
Polymastodon; see Taeniolabis
Polyodon, 75, **435**
Polypedetidae, **437**
Polyprotodonta, 263–65, **442**
Polypterus, 70, 76–77, **435**, *56c*, *e*, *57*
Polypterini, **435**
Porcupines, 408, 409
Porpoises, 395, 397
Portheus, 83, **435**, *72*
Postorbital: in bony fishes, 67; in amphibians, 98; absence of, in mammals, 241
Potomogale, 271, 272, **443**
Potamotherium, **444**
Prairie dog, 405
Prearticular: in bony fishes, 67; in amphibians, 99; in mammals, 245
Predentary, 195
Prefrontal: in bony fishes, 67; in amphibians, 98; absence of, in mammals, 242
Premaxilla: in bony fishes, 67; in amphibians, 98; in mammals, 241, 243
Premolars, 247; molarization of, 298
Preopercular, in bony fishes, 67
Presphenoid, 243
Prevomer: in bony fishes, 67; in amphibians, 98; reduced in mammals, 243–44
Priacodon, 259, **442**, *237a*, *238a*, *239a*
Primates, 411–32, **449**, B473–74; adaptations of, to arboreal life, 411–12, 413–14; dentition of, 412–13; brain of, 414; skull of, 414–15
Prioniodus, *15*
Pristiophorus, **434**
Pristis, 55, **434**
Proadinotherium, 312, **445**, *279g*, *h*
"Proavis," 211
Proboscidea, 370–76, **447**, B472
Procamelus, 349, **446**, *309b*
Procellariiformes, 217, **441**

Prochameleo, **439**
Procoela, **437**
Procolophon, 131, **437**, *III*
Procompsognathus, 181, 184, **440**
Procreodi, **443**
Procynodictis, **444**
Procyon, 289, **444**
Proeutatus, 384, **447**, *337a, 338a*
Proganochelys, **438**
Progenetta, **444**
Prolagus, **448**
Promerycochoerus, 347, **446**, *308*
Prongbuck, 357, B471
Pronomotherium, 347, **446**
Proötic: in bony fishes, 68; in amphibians, 99; in mammals, 244
Propalaeoplophorus, **447**
Propalaeotherium, **445**
Propliopithecus, 424–25, 426, **449**, *354d, 356c*
Pronycticebus, 415, 416, **449**, *353b, 354b*
Propristis, **434**
Prorastomus, **447**
Prorosmarus, 296, **444**
Proscalops, 273, **443**, *246c, 247e*
Prosqualodon, 395, **448**, *342b*
Prosthenops, **446**
Protagriochoerus, **446**
Proteida, **437**
Proteles, 292, **444**
Proterosuchus, **438**
Proteus, **437**
Protheosodon, **444**
Prothylacinus, 264, **442**, *244*
Prothyracodon, **445**
Protiguanodon, **440**
Protoceras, 353, **446**
Protoceratops, 204–5, **441**, *186*
Protocone, 248
Protoconid, 248
Protoconule, 248
Protocetus, 394, **448**
Protodonta, **441**
Protohippus, 327
Protoloph, 249
Protopterus, 91, **436**
Protoreodon, 347, **446**
Protorosauria, 146–48, **438**, B460
Protorosaurus, 147, 148, **438**
Protoselenodontia, 343–48, **446**, B471
Protosorex, **443**

Protosphyraena, **435**
Protospinax, 55
Protostega, 138, **438**
Prototheria, 255, **442**
Protylopus, 349, **446**
Protypotherium, 314, **445**, *277b, 278c, e, 282*
Prozeuglodon, 394, **448**, *342a*
Psammodus, 58, **434**, *49d*
Psephophorus, **438**
Pseudailurus, **444**
Pseudocreodi, **444**
Pseudorhinclophus, **443**
Pseudosciurus, 406, **448**, *348c*
Pseudosuchia; *see* Thecodontia
Psittaciformes, 219, **442**
Psittacosaurus, 205, **440**
Psittacotherium, 277, **443**, *251b*
Pteranodon, 177–78, **440**, *146c, 161*
Pteraspis, 30–31, **433**, *22*
Pterichthys, 44–45, **434**, *32, 34*
Pterodactyloidea, 177–78, **440**
Pterodactylus, 177, **440**, *159b, 160*
Pterodon, **444**
Pterolepis, **433**
Pteropodidae, **443**
Pterosauria, 173–78, **440**, B462
Pterygoid: bony fishes, 67; amphibians, 99; mammals, 243
Ptilodus, 258, **442**, *23c, d*
Ptychodus, **434**, *45b*
Ptyctodontoidea, **433**
Ptyctodus, 43, **433**
Pubis, 100
Pycnodus, 78, **435**
Pygostyle, 208
Pyrotheria, 317–18, **445**, B473
Pyrotherium, 317–18, **445**, *285*
Python, **439**

Quadrate: in bony fishes, 68; in bony fishes, 99; becomes incus, 243, 245–46
Quadratojugal: in bony fishes, 67; in amphibians, 98; absence of, in mammals, 243
Quail, 217

Rabbits, 409–10
Raccoons, 289–90, B468
Radiale, 101, 252
Radius, 101
Rails, 217
Raia, 55, **434**, *46b*

Rana, **437**
Rangifer, **446**
Ratites, 214–16
Rats and related types, 406–°
Rays, 55–56; fins of, 11, 38
Remigolepis, **434**
Reptilia, 20–21, 120–205, 220–39, **437**, B458; characters of, 120–21; primitive forms, structure of, 121–26; radiation of, 126–28; classification of, 128–29, 141
Respiratory system, 15
Rhachitomi, 109–11, **436**
Rhadinichthys, **435**
Rhamphorhynchoidea, 177, **440**
Rhamphorhynchus, 173–77, **440**, *157, 158, 159a*
Rhea, 213–14, 215, **441**
Rheiformes, 214, **441**
Rhenanida, 57, **434**, B455
Rhinesuchus, **436**
Rhineura, **439**
Rhinobatis, 55, **434**
Rhinoceros, 334–35, **445**
Rhinocerotoidea, 330–35, **445**, B470
Rhinolophus, **443**
Rhipidistia, 86–88, **436**
Rhiptoglossa, 160, **439**
Rhizodonts, 87
Rhizodus, **436**
Rhodesian man, 432
Rhynchocephalia, 154–57, 163, **439**, B460–61
Rhyncholepis, 27, **433**
Rhynchosaurus, 156, **439**
Rhynchotherium, 374, **447**
Rhynchotus, **441**
Rhytina, **447**
Ribs, 11; in amphibians, 96; sacral, 96, 100; abdominal, 134; mammals, 250–51
Road runners, 219
Rodentia, 400–410, **447**, B473
Rostral bone: in bony fishes, 67; in horned dinosaurs, 204
Ruling reptiles; *see* Archosauria
Ruminantia, 340–59, **446**
Rupicapra, 359
Rutiodon, **439**

Sabre-toothed cats, 294–95
Sagenodus, 91, **436**, *55c*
Saghatherium, 367, **446**, *322a, e*
Sagittal crest, 241

Sailfish, 85
Salamanders, 93, 117, 118, 119
Salamandra, 437
Salamandroidea, 437
Salientia; *see* Anura
Saniwa, 439
Salmon, 82, 83
Saltoposuchus, 166, 439, *151*
Saltopus, 440
Samotherium, 354, 446, *305m, 313c*
Sandpipers, 219
Saphaeosaurus, 439
Sarcophilus, 265
Saurichthys, 435
Sauripterus, 436, *94a*
Saurischia, 180–95, 440, B462–63
Saurolophus, 440
Sauropleura, 113, 436, *101*
Sauropoda, 181, 190–95, 440; ancestors of, 189–90
Sauropterygia, 148–53, 438, B460
Saurosternum, 439
Scales: bony, 10; fulcral, 38, 72; in bony fishes, 63–64; in land forms, 95
Scaloposaurus, 441
Scaphoid, 252
Scaphonyx, 439
Scaphyrhynchus, *56d*
Scapula, 100, 252; *see also* Limbs
Scaumenacia, 91, 436, *81*
Scelidosaurus, 202, 440
Scelidotherium, 447
Schizotherium, 445
Sciamys, 448, *349c*
Scincus, 439
Sciuroides, 448
Sciuroidea, 405, 447
Sciuromorpha, 402–6, 447
Scleromochlus, 439
Sclerorhynchus, 434, *47*
Scolopodus, *15*
Scylacosaurus, 441
Scyllium, 55, 434
Scymnognathus, 234, 441, 220
Scymnosaurus, 441
Sea-cows, 376–80
Sea horse, 82, 84
Seals, 295–96
Selenodont teeth, 248, 297
Seminotoidea, 435
Semionotus, 78, 81, 435, *63*
Semiophorus, 436

Semnopithecus, 424, 449
Sense organs, 14–15
Serranus, 435
Sesamodon, 441
Sewellel, 402
Seymouria, 120–24, 125, 127, 128–29, 437, *105, 106, 108*
Seymouriamorpha, 129, 437
Shagreen, 39
Shark-like fishes; *see* Chondrichthyes
Sharks, 35, 45, 52–56
Shastasaurus, 438
Sheep, 351, 357–59
Shoulder girdle; *see* Girdle, pectoral; Limbs
Shrews, 273; jumping shrews and tree shrews, 273–74
Shell of turtle, 133–34
Silurus, 435
Simia, 426, 449
Simosaurus, 153, 438, *133*
Simplicidentata, 401–9, 447
Sinanthropus, 430, 449, *358b*
Sinopa, 284, 444, *254c, 255c*
Siphonostoma, 435
Siren, 437
Sirenia, 376–80, 447
Sivatherium, 354, 446
Skates, 55–56
Skeleton, general, 9–13
Skin derivatives, 16
Skinks, 160
Skull: origin of, 12, 13; bony fishes, 64–69; amphibians, 96–99; primitive reptiles, 121–22; reptiles, general, 124–25; birds, 208–9; therapsids, 226–29; mammals, 241–46
Skunk, 291
Sloths, 381, 387–90
Smilodon, 294, 295, 444, *254p, 261b*
Snakes, 158, 160, 162
Snipe, 219
Solea, 436
Solenodon, 271, 443
Sorex, 273, 443
Soricomorpha, 273, 443
Spalacotherium, 260, 442, *257b, 259b*
Spalax, 448
Sperm whales, 397
Sphenacodon, 224, 441, *202*
Sphenisciformes, 216–17, 441

Sphenodon, 127, 155–57, 159, 439, *139*
Sphenosuchus, 439
Sphyraena, 435
Sphyrna, 434
Spider monkeys, 421
Spinal cord; *see* Nerve cord
Spinosaurus, 188, 440
Spiny finned fishes, 85
Spiracle, 15, 37; in bony fishes, 67, 70; in amphibians, 98, 103
Splenial, in bony fishes, 67, in amphibians, 99
Squalodon, 395, 448
Squaloraja, 434
Squaloidea, 434
Squalus, 55, 434, *54c*
Squamata, 158–62, 439, B461
Squamosal: in bony fishes, 67; in amphibians, 98; in mammals, 243
Squatina, 55, 434, *46a*
Squirrels, 405
Stagonolepis, 439
Stapes, 103, 245–46
Stegodon, 375, 447, *326c*
Stegomus, 439
Stegops, 437
Stegosauria, 195, 200–202, 440, B463–64
Stegosaurus, 201–2, 440, *164b, 182c, 183*
Stegoselachii, 49, 434, B455
Stegotherium, 384, 447
Steiromys, 448
Stem reptiles, 128
Steneofiber, 405, 447
Steneosaurus, 173, 439, *146b, 148b, 149, 155a, b*
Stenopterygius, 146, 438, *125c*
Stereospondyli, 111–12, *436*
Stereosternum, 438
Sternum, 251
Stromeria, 441
Structure of vertebrates, 7–16, B452
Sticklebacks, 84
Storks, 217
Struthio 441
Struthiomimus, 185–86, 440, *168b, 169b, 170*
Struthioniformes, 214, 441
Struthiosaurus, 203, 440
Sturgeon, 75
Stylemys, 438

Styles, in molar teeth, 249
Stylinodon, 277, **443**
Subungulates, 366–80, B472
Suina, 340, 349–65, **446**, B470–71
Supraoccipital: in bony fishes, 68; in amphibians, 99; in mammals, 243
Supratemporal: in bony fishes, 67; in amphibians, 98
Surangular: in bony fishes, 67; in amphibians, 99
Sus, 364, **446**, *305f*
Swans, 217
Swifts, 219
Swine; *see* Suina
Symbos, **446**
Symmetrodonta, 249, 260, 261, **442**
Symmetry, 7–8
Symmorium, **434**
Synapsid temporal region, 128
Synapsida, 220–38, **441**
Synaptosauria, 153, **438**
Syndactylous foot, marsupials, 263
Syndyoceras, 353
Synoplotherium **443**, *256a*
Synsacrum, 208
Synthetoceras, 353, **446**, *313b*
Systemodon; see Homogalax

Tabular: in bony fishes, 67; in amphibians, 98
Taeniodonta, 277–78; **443**, B468
Taeniolabis, 258, **442**, *236a*
Talpa, 273, **443**
Tanystrophaea, 153, **438**
Tanystrophaeus, 153, **438**, *137*
Tapinocephalus, 232, **441**
Tapiroidea, 329–30, **445**, B469
Tapirus, 330, **445**, *288e, 289d, 291f, 296d, 297c*
Tardigrada, 387–88, **447**
Tarpon, 83
Tarsioidea, 411, 418–19, **449**
Tarsius, 411, 413, 418–19, 421, **449**
Tarsus, 102, in mammals; 252–53; *see also* Limbs
Tasmanian devil, 265
Tasmanian wolf, 265
Tatu, **447**
Taxidea, 291, 44
Taxonomy, 6–7
Teeth, 16; in sharks, 36–37; labyrinthine, in crossoptery-

gains, 86–87; lungfish, 90; amphibians, 96–97, 104; mammals, 246–49; carnivores, 297; ungulates, 297–99
Teleosaurus, 173, **439**
Teleoceras, 334, **445**
Teleostei, 81–85, **435**
Telerpeton, **437**
Temnocyon, 288, **444**, *254g*
Temporal arches: reptiles, 128; mammals, 241, 243
Temporal bone, 244
Tenrec, 271
Tephrocyon, **444**
Teratornis, 217
Terns, 219
Testudo, 137–38, **438**, *115, 116c*
Tetonius, 419, **449**, *355b*
Tetraclaenodon, 303, **444**
Tetralophodon, 374, **447**, *326b*
Tetrameryx, **446**, *305*
Tetrapoda, 21, 92, 93; ancestry of, 104; origin of, 104–5
Thalassemys, **438**
Thallatosaurus, 157–58, **439**
Thaumatosaurus, 152, **438**, *130, 131c*
Thecodontia, 166–70, **439**, B461
Thecodontosaurus, **440**
Thelodus, 31–32, 33, **433**, *24*
Theosodon, 317, **444**
Therapsida, 221, 225–38, **441**, B465
Theridomys, 406, **448**
Theriodontia, 234–36, **441**
Therocephalia, 234, 235, **441**
Theromorpha, 221
Theropleura, **441**
Theropoda, 181–90, **440**
Thescelosaurus, **440**, *164a*
Thinocyon, **444**
Thinohyus; see Perchoerus
Third trochanter of femur, 252
Thoatherium, 316, **444**, *283c, 284a*
Thrinaxodon, **441**
Thryonomys, 408, **448**
Thylacinus, 265, **442**
Thylacoleo, 266, **442**, *241e*
Thynnus, **436**
Tibia, 102; *see* Limbs
Tibiale, 102; *see* Limbs
Tiger, 292
Tillodontia, 278, **443**, B468
Tillotherium, 278, **443**, *251a*
Time scale, geologic, 2–3

Tinamous, 214
Titanichthys, 42, **433**
Titanomys, 448
Titanosaurus, 195, **440**
Titanosuchus, 232, **441**
Titanotheres, 335–37, B470
Toads, 117–19
Toes; *see* Digits, Limbs
Tomarctus, **444**
Tongue, so-called, in cyclostomes, 22–23
Torosaurus, **441**
Torpedo, 56, **434**
Tortoises, 137–38
Toxochelys, **438**, *116b*
Toxodon, 312, **445**, *281*
Toxodontia, 312–13, **445**
Trachelosauria, 153, **438**
Trachelosaurus, 154, **438**
Trachodon, 199, **440**, *181e*
Trachodonts, 198–200
Tragoceras, 358, **446**, *305p*
Tragulina, 340
Tragulus, 352, **446**
Trapezium, 253
Trapezoid, 253
Tree shrews, 273–74, 416
Tree sloths, 381, 382, 387
Tremarctos, 290, **444**
Tremataspis, **433**
Trematops, **436**, *92c*
Trematosaurus, 111, **436**
Triassochelys, 135–36, 139, **438**, *116a, 118*
Tricentes, 281, *254a*
Triceratops, 203, 204, **441**, *182d*
Triconodon, 260, **442**
Triconodonta, 249, 259–60, 261, **442**
Trigla, **435**
Trigonias, 333, **445**, *296b*
Trigonolestes, **446**
Trigonostylops, 316, **445**
Triisodon, 283, **443**
Trilophodon, 373, 374, **447**, *325c*
Trimerorachis, 111, **436**
Trinacromerum, **438**
Trinil man, 428
Trionyx, 139, **438**
Tritemnodon, **444**
Tritubercular theory of origin of molar teeth, 247
Trituberculata, **442**
Triturus, **437**